Canadian Shield
Adirondack Mtns.
New England Highlands
Appalachian Plateau
Valley and Ridge
Interior Lowlands
Blue Ridge
Ozark Dome
Interior Plateau
Piedmont
Ouachita Mtns.
Coastal Plain

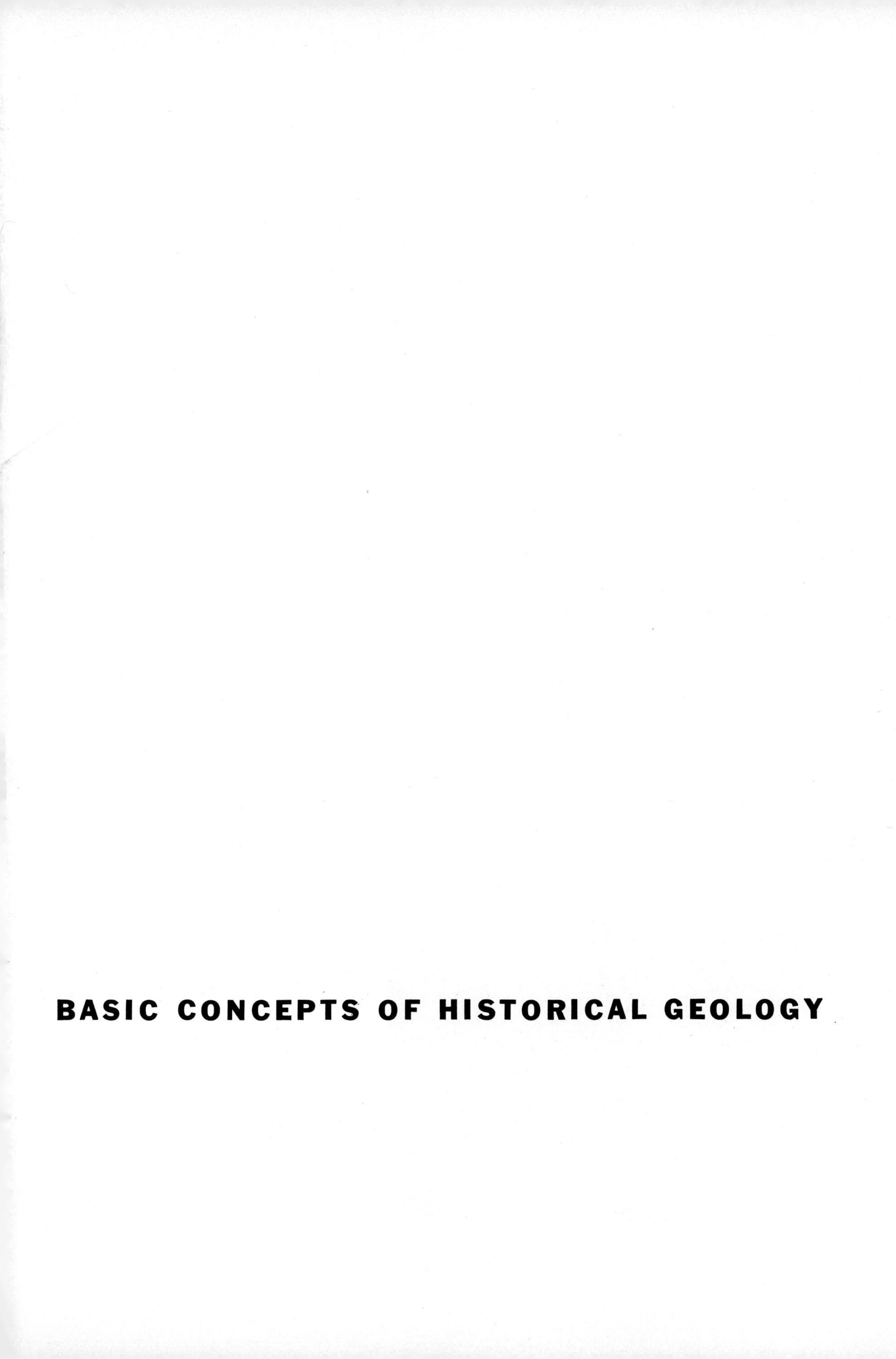

BASIC CONCEPTS OF HISTORICAL GEOLOGY

Basic Concepts of Geology

Basic Concepts of Physical Geology

Basic Concepts of Historical Geology

Basic Concepts of

EDGAR WINSTON SPENCER

Chairman, Department of Geology

Washington and Lee University

Historical Geology

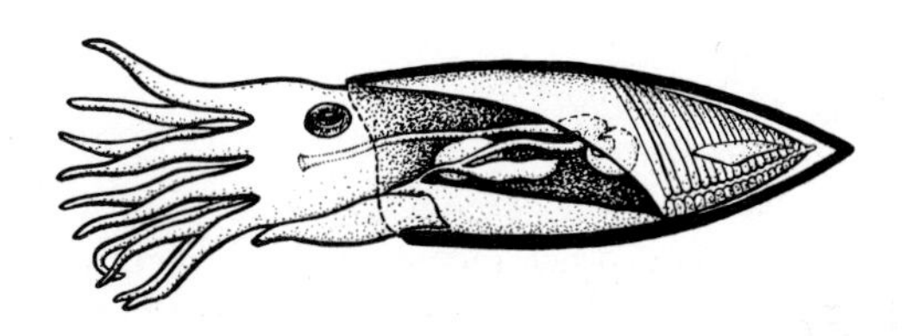

with drawings by

Elizabeth Humphris Spencer

THOMAS Y. CROWELL COMPANY, NEW YORK, ESTABLISHED 1834

First Printing, January, 1962
Second Printing, June, 1962
Third Printing, June, 1963
Fourth Printing, July 1964
Fifth Printing, July, 1965
Sixth Printing, March, 1966
Seventh Printing, June, 1967

Designed by Laurel Wagner

Library of Congress Catalog Card Number: 62-7081

Manufactured in the United States of America
by Rand McNally & Company, Book Mfg. Division, Chicago, Ill.

To my father TERREL FORD SPENCER *in sincere gratitude*

Preface

Basic Concepts of Physical Geology and *Basic Concepts of Historical Geology* were written as a single integrated book for a one year course in Physical and Historical Geology. The text is designed for students who are taking geology as a liberal arts subject as well as for students whc plan to major in geology. It has been published in two volumes, each presenting the material traditionally covered in one semester courses in Physical and Historical Geology. The two volumes complement one another, but they may be used separately without difficulty. Because the concepts of geologic time and the place of the earth in the universe are so important, a brief treatment of these topics has been included in the volume on Physical Geology for those students who will not take a full year course. A more comprehensive treatment is given in the volume on Historical Geology.

This text has been written in the full recognition that there are a number of fine textbooks available which cover the principles and processes of geology. However, this book is written from a different point of view and with a somewhat different purpose in mind. It is assumed that the student comes to this first course in geology without a background in natural science, but with a curiosity about the earth on which he lives, an open mind, and a willingness to learn. It is hoped that he will carry away from the course a grasp of the fundamental ideas of geology, a knowledge of the scientific methods used by geologists, their limitations, and an awareness of the broad scope of the field and its major contributions to human knowledge. The material selected, its organization, and the manner of presentation are designed to accomplish these purposes rather than to stress terminology, processes, or detailed factual data. However, it is recognized that many of the basic and most important ideas cannot be grasped without a working knowledge of certain scientific terms and processes. These are defined as they are introduced.

Treatment has been highly selective. Some topics are developed fully in order to give the student an appreciation for the thoroughness characteristic of scientific investigations. Other advanced, even controversial, ideas are discussed briefly to give the student a glimpse of the research problems faced in the earth sciences, and the scientist's need for imagination as well as factual information in seeking the solutions. The interdependence of the natural sciences is emphasized throughout.

Outlines are employed where they will be most useful to the student as a means of quick summary. Data which are often presented in appendices are incorporated in the chapters to which they are most pertinent. Each volume has a set of eight pages of color maps at the end of the book. These are intended to illustrate various types of geologic and topographic maps, and to provide the teacher with a valuable tool for map study.

Both volumes have a number of new features. The Physical Geology text presents:

1. An introductory section about the profession of geology, what geologists do, how the field is applied, the means of communication, and the methods used by geologists.
2. A chapter on the sources of energy for processes acting in and on the earth.
3. A chapter dealing with the major divisions of the crust of the earth.
4. A chapter on the concept of sequential development of land forms by various geomorphic agents. The limitations of this idea are also clearly explained.

The text on Historical Geology presents:

1. An expanded discussion of the methods used to unravel the history of the earth.
2. Discussions of the origin of the atmosphere and hydrosphere.
3. A chapter on the origin of life on earth.
4. A short chapter dealing with the controversy over the nature of the continental borders of North America during the Paleozoic. Both the borderland hypothesis and the island arc hypothesis are explained.
5. A chapter devoted to the description of the most important groups of invertebrates is presented before the history of North America. Thus the student is supplied with information about the morphology and ecology of each group before he is confronted with data about the time of its first appearance or its evolution.
6. The physical history of North America is taken up starting with the Precambrian and continuing to the present. These chapters are brief; each contains a summary of the life of the period, a summary of the physical history of the United States for the period, and a discussion of several of the most important aspects of the physical history. These are selected to illustrate particular concepts or methods.
7. The theory of evolution of life is treated separately from the physical history of the continent.
8. A chapter explaining the main trends of the evolutionary processes with examples from the invertebrates precedes the story of the development of fishes, amphibians, reptiles, and mammals.

This text is designed and written for the elementary college level student.

EDGAR WINSTON SPENCER

Washington and Lee University
Lexington, Virginia

Acknowledgments

It should be recognized by all who read this text that our knowledge of the world is based on the work of many individuals. The findings of some of these individuals are so often used and widely recognized that they become a part of our general knowledge. After a time the source may be forgotten. The efforts of others may never become widely recognized even though they provide the basis for important discoveries of later workers. Scientific methods lead to a pyramiding of knowledge. We owe a debt of gratitude to all who have contributed. In a text the findings of only a few individuals can be selected for discussion. Direct acknowledgment to these persons has been made in the text where it seems most appropriate. Likewise, acknowledgments for illustrations and photographs have been made in the headings for these.

I am especially indebted to the late Professor Marcellus Stow of Washington and Lee University whose teachings and personal friendship led me into the field of geology. To my teachers at Columbia University, Professors Arie Poldervaart, Walter Bucher, Maurice Ewing, Marshall Kay, Charles Behre, Sidney Paige, John Imbrie, and Arthur Strahler, I am most grateful for the inspiration of their teaching and their dedication to the study of the earth. The research and teachings of these men have greatly influenced my thinking and approach to earth science; however, I alone am responsible for any errors which may appear in this book.

My sincere thanks go to those friends, colleagues, and students who have given me the benefit of their ideas about teaching elementary geology, and to those who have helped directly in the preparation of the manuscript and illustrations in this book. For his patience and thoroughness throughout the work in editing this text I wish to thank my friend, Philip Winsor.

I appreciate the many helpful suggestions of Miss Agnes Creagh who assisted in editing the manuscript.

I am most grateful to my wife not only for her encouragement, but for drawing many of the illustrations and for reading and making suggestions about the preparation of the manuscript.

E. W. S.

Contents

II THE PRESENT IS A KEY TO THE PAST

III THE DAWN OF EARTH HISTORY

IV THE LIVING AND THE DEAD

I TIME AND THE ROCK RECORD

1 Geologic Time

THE NATURE OF THE RECORD OF THE ROCKS

It is not clear whether the earth was in a molten or solid state at its creation, but molten rocks are being formed within the earth today, and they are intruded and extruded through the solid crystalline rocks of the earth's crust. We may assume that it has not been substantially different in the past. As soon as the earth developed an atmosphere the solid rocks on the earth's surface were weathered and eroded by processes similar to those acting today. This disintegrated and dissolved rock material was then transported by water, ice, or air and eventually settled out to form layers. The type of sediment formed in each layer depends to a large extent on the environment in which it was deposited. Life began, and the remains of the dead became incorporated in the rocks being formed. Another impression, created by the great movements of the earth's unstable crust, is also left as a dynamic record in the rocks. The earth has been gently warped upward in some places exposing areas that were sea bottoms. In other areas, downwarping has submerged parts of the continents below the waters of the ocean. Occasionally the crust has been intensely folded into long chains of high mountains. The discovery and explanation of all this await investigation and interpretation of the rock layers. Their composition, structure, variations in thickness, distribution—all these furnish part of the details of this story. With painstaking care geologists are able to piece this information together and decipher the long record. If they are lucky, they will be able to reconstruct a large part of the earth's story. They may be able to describe the evolution of life and the changing form of the continents during much of the earth's history. At the present time a relatively accurate and complete record is available for the past half billion years.

The story is not without flaw, and obviously it is incomplete in places, but it is known in far greater detail than most people realize. The imperfections in our knowledge result largely from the almost unbelievable complexity of the rock record. First we must learn to interpret the rocks that are being formed today. This gives us a clue as to how the environment of deposition leaves its imprint in the rocks and provides the basis for interpretation of similar impressions in older rocks. Trouble arises as soon as we first attempt to apply this simple procedure. First we note that rock outcrops are almost lacking over large areas. Then when we find several outcrops we are confronted with the problem of determining the ages of the rocks relative to one another, for it is necessary to study a number of outcrops of the same age if we are to obtain a fairly good idea of what the ancient history of the region is.

The problem might be likened to one of piecing together the history of the earth from a library of books written in a language unknown to the student. Each book describes the history of individual localities throughout the world. Each initially contained a day-by-day account of almost everything that happened at that locality. Unfortunately the library is not complete—pages are lost from some of the books, other pages are mutilated, and some books are missing. Like most library collections, some of the books are complete and detailed with definitive data, others lack clarity, and there are often several that are ambiguous.

In this course on historical geology you will learn how we go about formulating questions to ask the earth, how the answers to the questions are revealed to us, and what major and often far-reaching conclusions can be drawn from these answers.

GEOLOGIC CONCEPT OF TIME

The geologic concept of time is one of the most difficult ideas for the beginning student to grasp. We must learn to think in terms of lengths of time that so far exceed our common experience that we tend to lose their significance. It is a simple matter to be aware of the fact that the earth is thousands of millions of years old, and to know the approximate time of many events in the earth's history. It is not so easy to comprehend or appreciate fully the implications that these great spans of time hold for the processes acting on the surface of the earth and within it. For example, rises in sea level too small to be detected within the span of recorded history might flood most of the continents of the world if continued over a period of a few million years. Although this example is purely hypothetical there is positive, undeniable evidence that seas have invaded the continents in the past and have, in fact, covered almost all the land surface of the world. Some areas are being slowly submerged today, while others are emerging perhaps to rise eventually as mountains in the future. As a second example we may cite the Grand Canyon. How could a canyon several miles wide and as much as a mile deep have been formed? Without an understanding of the time involved it is a perplexing problem. But to those who know how streams erode and transport rock debris it is not at all difficult to visualize the formation of the canyon over a period of millions of years as the rocks exposed in the walls of the canyon gradually crumble, break away, and fall into the Colorado River which transports them to the sea. In other words the canyon is being enlarged today, right now, in just about the same way and perhaps as fast as it ever has been in the past. The face of the earth has never before looked exactly the way it does right now. It will never be the same again. It is not even the same from day to day, but the changes are so slow that we generally fail to perceive them at all. In the short term these changes seem insignificant; in the long term they may convert seas into mountains and mountains into plains. The examples cited above serve to emphasize that it is the cumulative effects of natural processes over periods of geologic time that have brought about the record of change that is the history of the earth.

"The most amazing movie ever made"

What is a long time? Sometimes we think of things that happened a few years ago as being far removed in time. Most of us think of the Revolutionary War or the arrival of Columbus in North America as events that took place a "long time ago." Beyond that our thinking is so vague that when we start to deal with geologic time we can hardly perceive the difference in 1 million and 100 million years. James C. Rettie (1950) devised one of the most interesting schemes to help us grasp the meaning of geologic time, his concept of "the most amazing movie ever made." Imagine that an inhabitant of some other planet made a time-lapse movie of the earth, taking one frame each year. When the picture is shown it is run at the normal speed of 24 frames per second. Thus it is possible to show 24 years of earth history every second. The film is run continuously night and day for a year starting

Fig. 1-1. The Grand Canyon of the Colorado River. The Colorado River and many of its tributaries are deeply entrenched in nearly flat-lying strata. These strata provide a record of the history of this region for a period of more than a billion years of earth history. Some of the rock units exposed near the rim of the canyon contain fossils of marine invertebrate animals. That the rim is now about a mile above sea level indicates that the region has been uplifted in relation to the sea. In the distance the extinct volcanoes of the San Francisco Mountains of central Arizona are visible. (Photo by Union Pacific Railroad.)

at midnight on New Year's Eve. It is possible in this length of time to show about one-sixth of the earth's history or the last 757 million years.

For the first 3 months the movie runs without showing any signs of life upon the earth. By April, the first single-celled amoeba-like animals appear in the seas, and these are soon followed by multicellular animals like the corals and sponges. Late in the month of May we see the first vertebrates, fishes. The year is half gone before the first signs of land plants appear. Up to that time the lands have been bare of grasses, trees, and shrubs, and certainly would have been a hostile environment for most animals. Toward the end of summer the first vertebrate animals, the amphibians, begin to crawl out on the land to spend part of their time. Almost a month later the film is showing the first reptiles. Soon these are dominated by a particular group, the dinosaurs. Among the reptiles there were not only many land giants, but others that lived a fish-like existence in the seas, and still others that dominated life in the air. Thus the reptiles dominated life over most of the face of the earth. Their dominance ends when we see the Rocky Mountains begin to rise from a shallow sea late in November. By December birds appear, and the mammals start to dominate the life of the continents. By Christmas the Colorado River is beginning to form and to cut a great canyon in the southwestern part of North America. All over the United States the shape of the landscape starts to become more familiar. Sometime in the morning of December 31 we get our first glimpse of man. During the afternoon ice caps form and begin to expand across the lands of the northern hemisphere. They advance and retreat four times during the afternoon and evening. About 11 o'clock at night man begins to be more in evidence, and by 11:45 men have appeared who can make stone implements to cultivate the soil. At 11:45 we see the dawn of civilization, and when there is 1 minute and 22 seconds left the Christian era begins. Columbus discovers America 20 seconds before midnight, and the Declaration of Independence is signed only 8 seconds before the end of the film. The First and Second World Wars, the Korean War, and the Atomic or Space Age occupy the last two seconds of this year-long movie.

HISTORY OF THE GEOLOGIC TIME SCALE

The geologic time scale is a system used by geologists to subdivide the great span of time since the origin of the earth. The system was started before anyone even thought of radioactive dating, so the units of geologic time are not familiar units, such as years or centuries. Of necessity the system relates rock units to time. Thus the Cambrian Time or Period is the span of time during which a particular sequence of rock units was formed. Long after the name was applied we came to learn that the number of years in the Cambrian Period was about 80 million. Now as each year passes we are obtaining an increasing number of absolute dates to show us just how many years are represented in various parts of our geologic time scale. Like many other scientific ideas the geologic time scale has undergone a number of changes since the first efforts were made to divide the rock record. In order to better understand the structure and use of the modern time scale you should know something of the fascinating history of its development.

Johann Lehmann. One of the first attempts to classify the rocks of the earth's crust was made by Johann Lehmann in 1756. Lehmann, teacher of mineralogy and mining in Berlin, divided the various types of rock units he observed into three groups:

1. Crystalline rocks containing no fossils were called primary rocks—"formed at the beginning of the earth."
2. The consolidated and stratified rocks in which fossils could be found were called secondary rocks—"formed during the flood."
3. Unconsolidated sediments and loosely consolidated material were called alluvial rocks—"formed since the time of Noah's Flood."

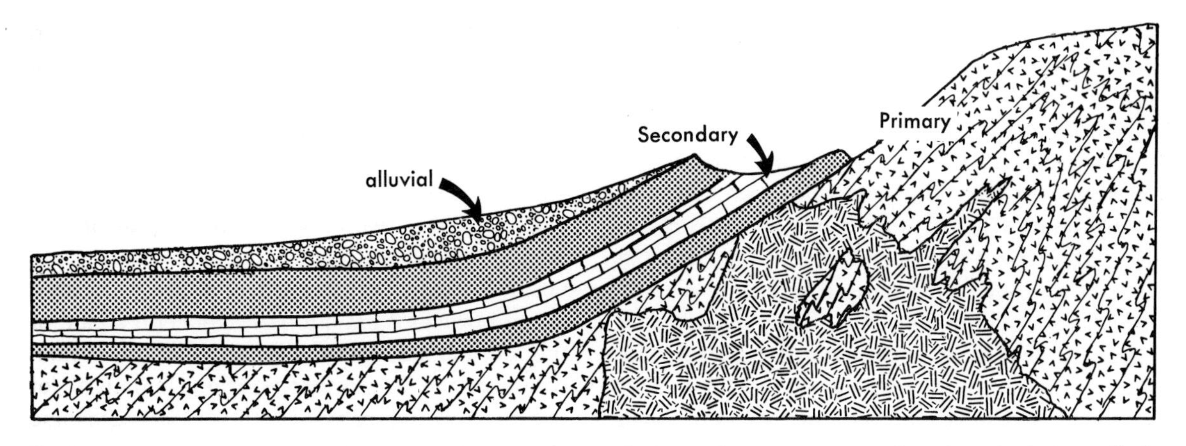

Fig. 1-2. Lehmann's three rock groups. Lehmann observed three distinct groups of rocks which he called "primary rocks," "secondary rocks," and "alluvial rocks." The primary rocks are crystalline igneous and metamorphic rocks; the secondary rocks are stratified fossiliferous units such as limestone and sandstones; the alluvial rocks are unconsolidated sediments that are found covering the older types. Lehmann thought that the alluvial rocks were formed since the flood in the time of Noah. We now recognize these as recent glacial deposits and stream and shallow sea sediments.

Giovanni Arduino. Soon after Lehmann formulated his classification Giovanni Arduino proposed another one. Arduino was a prominent geologist in Venice where he served as professor of mineralogy and metallurgy. He is credited with being the first to recognize that the crystalline rocks are of volcanic origin, and that paleontology and chemistry can be applied to the chronology of the formations. He recognized a fourfold classification of the earth's crust:

1. Primary mountains – those containing metallic ores and crystalline rocks.
2. Secondary mountains–those built up of marble and limestone.
3. Low mountains and hills–those generally composed of gravels, sand, clay, and volcanic materials.
4. Earthy and rocky materials which rest upon all the preceding. He called these loose unconsolidated sediments alluvial material.

In both the Lehmann and the Arduino systems there is an implied relationship between rock units and time. Because the fourth unit described by Arduino lies upon the other three, it must be younger than they are.

George Füshsel. Füshsel, a French physician who was a contemporary of Lehmann, described and subdivided a large stratigraphic sequence near Paris into nine units and subunits. He went so far as to propose time units for the series of rocks, assuming that each rock unit was formed during a different time. Among Füshsel's outstanding accomplishments was the construction of a geologic map and cross sections. These cross sections show that he recognized the true implications of tilted strata. The greatest contribution made by George Füshsel to the young science of geology was the first statement of the principle of uniformitarianism: "Indeed, the manner in which nature at the present time is still acting and producing things must be assumed as the rule in our explanation; we know no other." In order to make sure that his work would be available to educated men of all nations he wrote it in Latin. As a result the work was ignored not only by scientists of other nations, but by those of his native country as well. This was a most unfortunate circumstance because it set back our understanding of the nature of the stratigraphic record of time for many years.

Abraham G. Werner. An even more influential factor in Füshsel's oblivion was the teaching of Abraham G. Werner. Werner was born in Prussian Silesia in 1749. He became interested in earth science as a child while playing around the mines near his home. When studying at the University of Leipzig, he wrote his first important work, a new method of mineral description. At the age of 25 he became an instructor at the university and soon initiated many new ideas on techniques of instruction. He introduced practical demonstrations as a part of training in the natural sciences. Werner asked his students questions continuously, took them on field trips, and invited them into his home. Undoubtedly he was one of the most effective teachers in the history of earth science. So popular and brilliant a man was he that his teachings dominated geologic thought for almost 40 years. His ideas were rigidly based on fact at a time when most of what was written and taught was based on pure speculation. Unfortunately Werner misunderstood what he observed in a number of instances, and his persuasive ability made it difficult for others to correct the misinterpretations that became so firmly entrenched in the minds of his followers. Werner's basic concept was that the ocean had gradually receded from the continents to its present position, and that the oceans had deposited all the rocks visible in the crust. Hence the name "Neptunists" was

Fig. 1-3. Law of superposition. This view of the Carmen Mountains of Mexico illustrates the typical layering or stratification of consolidated sedimentary rock units. In a sequence such as this the strata on top is the youngest. Successively older units appear below. This relationship holds only if the sequence has not been deformed so intensively that it is upside down. (Courtesy of Jack Ammann, Inc.)

applied to Werner and his followers. In 1790 he modified Lehmann's classification to:

1. Primitive series—chemical precipitates from the ocean deposited before emergence of the land. We now recognize these as igneous and metamorphic rocks.
2. Transition series—consolidated sedimentary rocks deposited in layers which extend without interruption around the world. These we now know to be nonexistent.
3. Stratified series (Secondary)—these are the stratified fossiliferous rocks. Werner thought these were products of the erosion of mountains which emerged as the seas receded.
4. Alluvial (Tertiary)—poorly consolidated rocks formed after the oceans had withdrawn.
5. Volcanic series—Werner thought these were of minor importance representing nothing more than the local effects of burning coal beds.

Werner taught that the ages of rocks could be recognized everywhere by the nature—lithology—of the rocks. He failed to observe that a great variety of rocks were being formed even in his own lifetime.

James Hutton. This Scotsman was a contemporary of Werner. He lacked the general personal appeal of Werner and found it a difficult task to convince the geologists of the day that many of Werner's ideas were wrong. Hutton proved that most of the primary rocks of Werner's classification were, in fact, rocks that had been in a molten state (igneous rocks). He also recognized that many of the characteristic structures and other features of old sedimentary rocks are identical with sediments being deposited at the present. His observations led to the establishment of the principle of uniformitarianism, "the present is the key to the past," although this idea had been expressed earlier by Füshsel. He also clearly stated his observation that younger rocks are above older rocks in a stratigraphic sequence. This is known as the principle of superposition. These are two of the most significant principles in geology.

William "Strata" Smith. Smith (1769–1839) is known as the "Father of Historical Geology." He was a man who never had any formal education beyond that of a village school. During most of his lifetime he was not considered a geologist, and he did not even belong to the London Geological Society. These formalities didn't stand in his way, however; he was a man with an insatiable curiosity and a knack of taking notes on nearly everything he observed. His life's work was engineering, and to it he brought an immense amount of imagination and skill. He was employed to drain swamps, locate canals, and restore springs. He realized that an understanding of rock units was of great value in accomplishing these tasks. His success in these projects put him in such great demand that he was called to all parts of England. Often he traveled as much as 10,000 miles a year, and on all these trips he kept careful notes of the types of rocks he saw on the way. Probably his most important contribution was the observation that certain rock units can be identified by the particular assemblages of fossils they contain. This led to the formulation of the "law of faunal succession." These important findings of Smith first appeared in a paper written by his friend Rev. Joseph Townsend. Oddly enough the paper was entitled "The Character of Moses established for Veracity as an Historian, recording events from Creation to the Deluge." Later Smith published three volumes describing the fossil content of the strata that outcrop in England. In 1815 he published a geologic map of the entire country at the scale of 5 miles to an inch which has not been substantially changed since then except in details. It is not surprising that Smith is also known as the "Father of Civil Engineering."

Baron George Cuvier. Another outstanding figure of the late 1700's and early 1800's is Baron George Cuvier. He was Counsellor of State for Napoleon and for many periods of his life had the responsibility for defending all bills brought before either house in the government. He was Perpetual Secretary of the National Institute and in his "spare" time maintained a museum and produced some of the most truly remarkable work in the field of comparative anatomy. It was the application of this work that makes him significant in the field of historical geology. He constantly surprised people by being able to identify fossil vertebrates from a few fragments of bone. He made studies of the assemblages of fossils found in sedimentary rocks of different units and noted that in faunas collected from a series of rocks very striking differences occurred in adjacent rock units. This he interpreted as an indication of a sudden and widespread catastrophic event in the earth's past that had caused many of the animals of the time to die. These assemblages, he noted, were followed by newer assemblages which contained a few of the older animals and a considerable number of new ones.

Chevalier de Lamarck. About the same time Cuvier was doing his work in comparative anatomy another Frenchman, Chevalier de Lamarck, was engaged in the study of fossils and zoology. Lamarck concentrated his work on the invertebrate fossils which are so abundant in the stratigraphic record. One of the most significant contributions to come from his studies of fossils was a book dealing with the theory of organic evolution. Darwin studied the works of Lamarck and based a large part of his theory of evolution on results from these studies of invertebrate fossils. These works have caused geologists to bestow upon Lamarck the title of the "Father of Invertebrate Paleontology."

The works of Hutton, Cuvier, Lamarck, and finally Smith compelled Werner's followers to admit that the Neptunists' concept of the formation of all deposits in a retreating sea was inadequate to explain the facts. All this had to be accomplished before our present time scale could be devised.

Fig. 1-4. Law of faunal succession. William "Strata" Smith learned to recognize various rock units by the particular assemblages of fossils which they contained. In this case it would be possible to recognize the angular unconformity by the difference in the inclination of the beds above and below the break in the record. If the assemblages in these units were known it would be possible to recognize the break by the fact that the assemblage in the concealed unit is missing in the exposure. This would be particularly applicable in discovering a break in a well when there are no surface exposures.

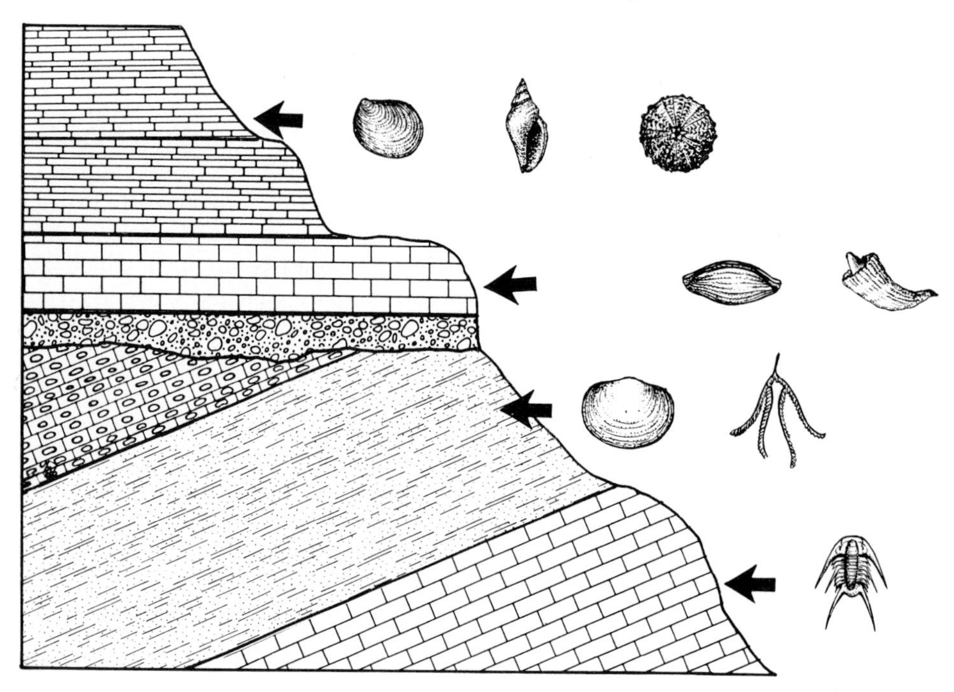

Charles Lyell. The first appearance of a geologic time scale similar to that used today was in 1833 in a textbook by Charles Lyell, *Principles of Geology.* Lyell's classification has a threefold subdivision of the series of rocks, Primary, Secondary, and Tertiary. But these were given completely different meanings from those initially assigned to those names by Lehmann. The system was devised to include both the rock units identified by William Smith and some others that had been identified in Europe. Within each of the major divisions of the scale there are "groups" of strata of similar lithology. Not all of the strata recognized by Smith outcrop at the surface in any single locality; therefore, it was some time before the correct positions of some units could be established within the sequence. Studies of the fossil fauna and flora parallel the studies of rock lithologies. William "Strata" Smith recognized that different rock groups contain different fossil assemblages. The observed differences were so great in some cases that Cuvier's idea that there had been a number of catastrophes in the past which destroyed most forms of life became accepted and used as a basis for subdividing the rock record. It was noted that these marked changes in the forms of life often occurred where the rocks of one group or series were deposited on those of an earlier sequence which had been folded or warped, a condition giving rise to an angular unconformity between the strata of the two groups.

It was soon discovered that it is possible to correlate groups of strata by their position relative to these unconformities. The same rock units containing almost identical fossils were found immediately above an angular unconformity in many localities in Europe and England. Eventually it was shown that similar units and fossils had identical relations to unconformities in North America. The evidence suggested that there had been a number of periods in the geologic past when the entire earth's crust was strongly deformed. As a result of these periods of deformation, mountains formed, climates changed, seas withdrew from the continents, and whole populations of animals died out.

Fig. 1-5. Angular unconformity. The vertical beds are of Precambrian age. They are overlain by sedimentary rocks of Devonian age. The gap represented by this break is at least two hundred million years. At some time in this interval the older rocks were folded, uplifted, and eroded. Following these events the Devonian strata were laid down nearly flat over the beveled edges of the Precambrian units. Still later the entire sequence was uplifted and eroded to expose this unconformity. It is found in southwestern Colorado near the Box Canyon at Ouray. (Photo by Edgar W. Spencer.)

Many geologists consider that such widespread deformations of the crust are the ultimate basis for correlation of geologic events throughout the world. But the question of whether there are periodic earth movements affecting large parts of the earth's crust almost simultaneously is still subject to debate. We do know that world-wide correlation on this basis is not a simple process. Complications are found as stratigraphic study is pursued in greater detail. At the present time thousands of stratigraphers, paleontologists, and other geologists are working on problems that are related to this question. They are making more exact correlations between rock units, fossil assemblages, and geologic time and their relation to deformation of the crust. In general the trend of their findings seems to point to major errors in the earlier idea that all of geologic

CENOZOIC ERA	*Quaternary Period (1M)*	Last 10,000 years (Recent) Pleistocene Epoch	*Neogene Period (28M)*
	Tertiary Period (59M)	Pliocene Epoch Miocene Epoch	
		Oligocene Epoch Eocene Epoch Paleocene Epoch	*Paleogene Period (32M)*
MESOZOIC ERA		*Cretaceous Period (70M)* *Jurassic Period (25M)* *Triassic Period (30M)*	
PALEOZOIC ERA		*Permian Period (30M)* *Carboniferous Period* { *Pennsylvanian Period (25M)* / *Mississippian Period (30M)* } *Devonian Period (55M)* *Silurian Period (40M)* *Ordovician Period (80M)* *Cambrian Period (80M)*	
Precambrian		Approximately 4.5 Billion years	

Fig. 1-6. Chart of Geologic Time Scale. The Precambrian is often known as the Cryptozoic Eon and is subdivided into the Archean (older) and Algonkian Eras. The Paleozoic, Mesozoic, and Cenozoic Eras are known collectively as the Phanerozoic Eon. Note the divisions of the Cenozoic Era. It is often divided into Tertiary and Quaternary Periods. The preferred usage in this book is Paleogene and Neogene Periods.

time may be divided into several major eras separated by almost catastrophic periods of deformation. Instead it is found that the entire crust of the earth is not generally deformed throughout the world at the same time. Mountains are found to develop slowly over periods of millions of years. Even the changes in forms of life characteristic of different eras seem to be much less drastic than formerly thought. In fact we appear to be approaching a time when the concept of the era will be accorded less significance.

With this background on the history of the formulation of our time scale let us examine the scale and its subdivisions.

THE MODERN TIME SCALE

Eras

Unusually prominent unconformities are found separating the Primary, Secondary, and Tertiary groups of Lyell's classification in many places. From the abundance of paleontologic data on the rocks of the various groups, paleontologists learned that certain groups of animals dominated each group. The Primary rocks of Lyell were found to consist of two parts—unfossiliferous crystalline rocks and sedimentary rocks characterized by fossils of invertebrates and fishes. The Secondary groups were characterized by the remains of certain cephalopods, the ammonites, and reptiles including the dinosaurs; the Tertiary group by mollusk and mammal remains. The prominence of the unconformities and the impressive changes in faunas in these divisions led to their acceptance as "eras" of geologic time. They were given names which reflect the stages of the development of life in each: Paleozoic (old life), Mesozoic (middle life), and Cenozoic (modern life).

Periods

Within the rock units of each era other unconformities and noteworthy changes in faunas and floras are observed. Many of these breaks can be recognized in different parts of the world and therefore have come to be generally accepted. Each of these units of time is called a period. The rock units formed within periods are called systems. The systems and periods are usually given the same names. These are the names of the locality in which the system was first recognized and described. This locality is often called the "classic locality or type section" for rocks of that period, and the ages of other rocks which are to be classified in the same period must either be correlated with the rocks of that type section or be shown to have formed during a time when no deposits were formed in the type section.

At the present time the Paleozoic Era is divided into either six or seven periods. The different numbers arise from differences in the rock sections in Europe and in North America. In North America seven periods are recognized: Cambrian, Ordovician, Silurian, Devonian, Mississippian, Pennsylvanian, and Permian. In Europe the Pennsylvanian and Mississippian are combined into what is known as the Carboniferous Period. The Mesozoic Era is divided into three periods: Triassic, Jurassic, and Cretaceous. The Cenozoic Era, the one in which we live, is divided into two parts, the Paleogene and Neogene. It should be noted that this usage is relatively new, and intended to replace the use of an older division, Tertiary and Quaternary. The reason for preferring the new terms is that the terms Tertiary, meaning third part, and Quaternary, meaning fourth part, have no basis in fact. They are a hangover from Lyell's classification. The exact equivalence of the terms is shown in Fig. 1-6. It is not surprising that we find increasing numbers of subdivisions of the time scale in the upper or younger parts. The younger rock units overlie older strata and tend to cover them up. The younger units are more widespread, are better exposed, and can be studied in greater detail than the older units.

So far no mention has been made of the lower part of the Primary series in the classification of Lyell. These are in large part igneous and metamorphic rocks that contain few if any fossils that can be exactly identified. These rocks contain more than three-quarters of the earth's history. It is probable that they include as much as seven-eighths of the record, yet the division is unclear. The reason for this is that they are more complicated than the younger rocks. They are poorly exposed, and where they are exposed they yield very little information in return for a great deal of hard work. Undoubtedly one important reason for the disregard of these rocks is the fact that very little oil and gas is found in rocks older than the lowest part of the Paleozoic Era, the Cambrian Period. Nevertheless these rocks, the Precambrian units, are receiving considerable attention at the present time. They will become increasingly important in the future as we are forced to search more intensively for new mineral resources to maintain the industries of the world.

Nomenclature summary

A summary of the nomenclature is useful to help keep the various terms distinguished. A rather rigid system of terminology is used to differentiate rock units from time units.

The *era* is the largest grouping of periods of geologic time. Each era covers many millions of years, and each is characterized by the existence of certain major groups or forms of life, the remains of which are found in the rocks formed during the era.

Periods are the fundamental units of the standard geologic time scale. They are sep-

Time Units	Time-Stratigraphic Units
Era	
Period	System (rock units formed during a period)
Epoch	Series (units formed during an epoch)
Age	Stage (units formed during an age)

Fig. 1-7. Equivalence of time and time-stratigraphic units.

arated on the basis of unconformities at the classic localities or "type sections." The rock units formed during a period are called *systems.*

The periods are subdivided into *epochs,* and the rock units formed during the time represented by an epoch are called *series.* Like periods the epochs are named for localities where they are first identified.

Epochs are in turn subdivided into *ages* when it is felt that the chronology is sufficiently detailed to justify a time unit this small. The rocks formed during an age are called a *stage.*

TIME UNITS AND MEASUREMENT OF GEOLOGIC TIME

The geologist's vital interest in time arises from one of the primary objectives of geology —to decipher the history of the earth from its beginning to the present. The geologist studies the rocks of the crust of the earth, determines when and how they were formed, then correlates the results of detailed local studies in such a way as to show what the earth as a whole was like at some given time in the past. He wants to show where the oceans were, where mountain ranges stood, what the climates were like, and what forms of life inhabited the earth. In other words he wishes to reconstruct the earth as it was and see how it has changed through time.

What is a time unit?

We think of time as a period during which an action, process, or event continues. It is an abstract continuum which man has arbitrarily divided into units to serve his purposes of relating the sequence and length of events. We break up this time continuum into terms of the period of certain events within the solar system. One day, for instance, is the time required for the earth to complete one rotation about its axis, and a year is the duration of one complete revolution of the earth around the sun. To complete this process 365 days, 5 hours, 48 minutes, and 45.51 seconds are required. Unfortunately geologists are not nearly as successful in measuring the duration of events in the geologic past as the astronomers are in measuring time units today. Of course the problems are not really comparable. The record of events left for the geologists to unravel lacks evidence of perfectly periodic events from beginning to end. Only a few parts of the rock record contain time markers, and these are often difficult to interpret.

MEASUREMENT OF GEOLOGIC TIME

Very few students actually seem to enjoy learning historical dates just for the fun of knowing them. Often they are even looked upon as stumbling blocks to learning the "interesting" parts of history. You can never appreciate the value of dates until you try to unravel history without knowing them. Imagine attempting to reconstruct the history of some part of the world you have never seen, nor even heard of, from an accumulation of undated newspapers, and you will understand something of the problem confronting the student of the earth's history. Eventually you would be able to piece together the history by establishing sequences of events and by finding an occasional date recorded within the papers. While this technique is time consuming and sometimes difficult, it does offer a definite challenge and often leads to fascinating solutions.

There are essentially two techniques by which geologic time can be measured. The first is by observing some feature of a rock or rock unit that gives evidence of the existence in the past of a process that was unidirectional and nonreversible. The movement of the hands of a clock is such a process, although it can hardly be used for the geologic past. The clock would be of no use if you could not depend on the hands to move in one direction all the time. It has the added advantage of moving at a constant rate in that one direction. Some "geologic clocks" do not proceed at constant rates; therefore, they cannot be used to tell absolute time. Nevertheless they are useful in fixing the time of one event in relation to the time of some second event. Some of the unidirectional, nonreversible processes that are indicated in rocks are:

1. Decay of radioactive substances. This is the best possible "geologic clock" because the rate of decay is constant and the dates we obtain are absolute dates that can be stated in terms of years.
2. Evolution of life. This evolution has proceeded since the first forms of life appeared on earth. Evidence of the process is found in the form of fossils, preserved parts of animals and impressions of plants and animals. Many of the same phyla or types of animals are represented through long periods of time, but, as a group, the fossils of any one time are a unique assemblage. There is nothing about these assemblages that automatically tells us how old they are, but they provide a reference system for determining the order of succession of geologic events as will be explained. Fossils are by far the most widely used means of determining sequences of events.
3. Accumulation of sediments.
4. Erosion of the land surface.
5. Decay of minerals exposed at the earth's surface.
6. Increase of the salinity of the oceans.

The first technique by which geologic time is measured is, as we have seen, the interpretation of unidirectional processes. The second is analysis of the record of events that have resulted from processes which recur with a fixed periodicity. Such processes are not uncommon within small areas, but there is disagreement among geologists on the question of the existence of such processes on a worldwide scale. Locally, seasonal variations in climate influence the rate and types of sediments formed in lakes. This results in the formation of finely banded or varved deposits. Some geologists believe there is evidence to support the existence of periodic changes of great extent. Some of these pulsations may include:

1. Periodic changes in the world climate bringing periods of glaciation in the high latitudes.
2. Periodic movements within the earth's crust causing deformation and the formation of mountain ranges.

Because of the uncertainty about the validity of these periodic changes they are of little value in working out the history of the earth.

Radioactive dating

This method of obtaining absolute dates for geologic events evolved from the discovery of X rays by Roentgen in 1895. A year later Becquerel found that uranium produces effects similar to those of the X rays. Two years later Mme. Curie isolated radium from the uranium mineral pitchblende, at that time a rare and relatively unknown mineral for which there was no use. Radium exhibits the phenomenon of spontaneous emission of rays, a process called radioactivity. Shortly thereafter Lord Rutherford found that the radiation produced by radioactive elements consists of three kinds of rays which are now called alpha, beta, and gamma rays. The alpha rays are small particles ejected at a very high speed. They carry a

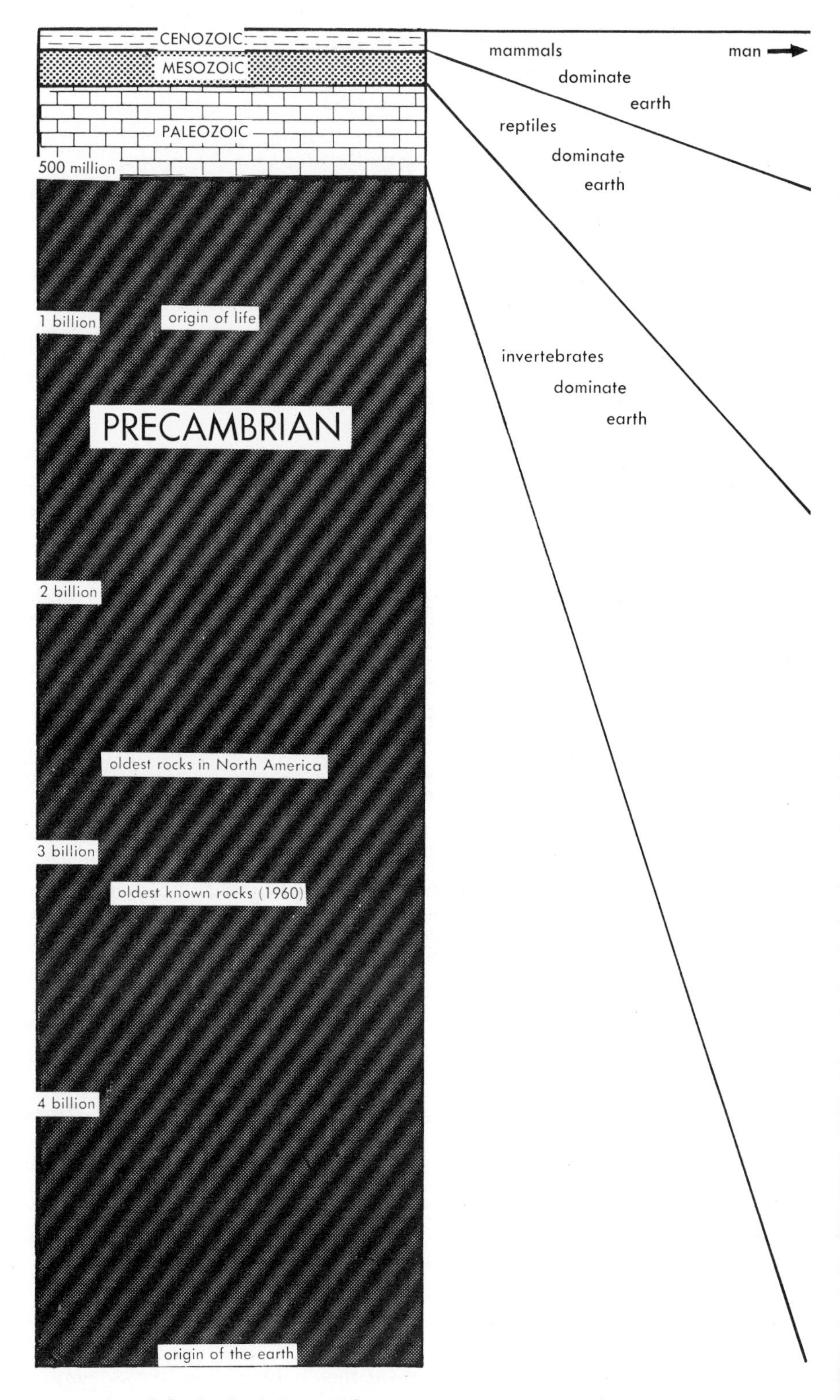

Fig. 1-8. Diagrammatic representation of the Geologic Time scale.

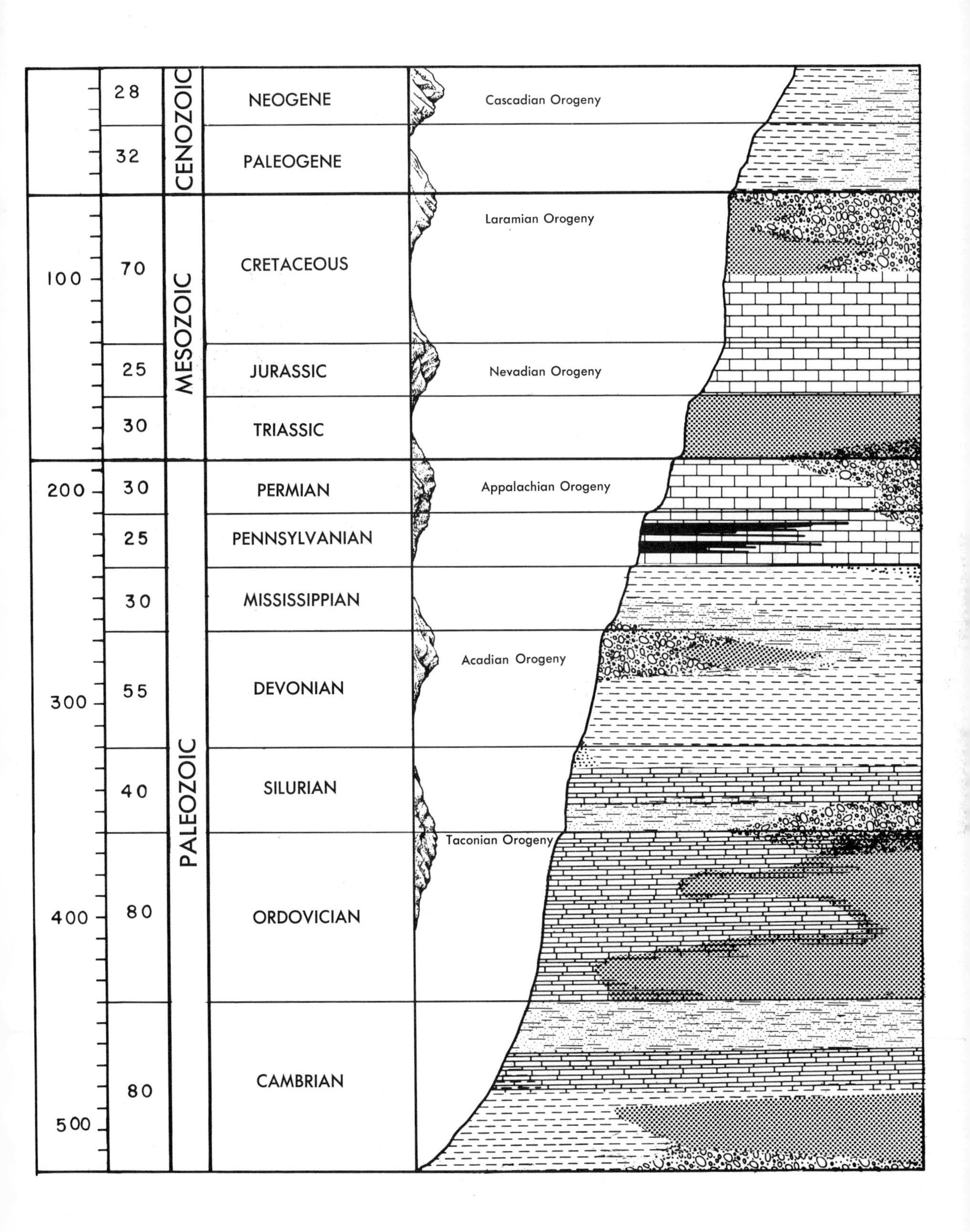
28
NEOGENE
Cascadian Orogeny
32
PALEOGENE
CENOZOIC
100
70
CRETACEOUS
Laramian Orogeny
25
JURASSIC
Nevadian Orogeny
30
TRIASSIC
MESOZOIC
200
30
PERMIAN
Appalachian Orogeny
25
PENNSYLVANIAN
30
MISSISSIPPIAN
300
55
DEVONIAN
Acadian Orogeny
40
SILURIAN
Taconian Orogeny
400
80
ORDOVICIAN
80
CAMBRIAN
500
PALEOZOIC

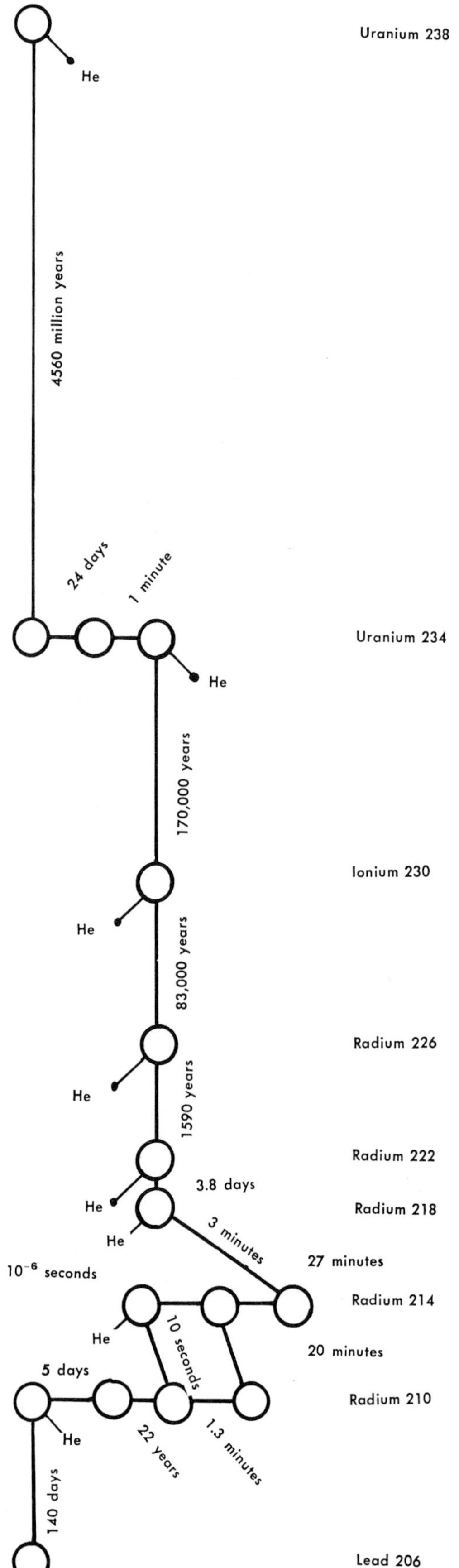

positive electrical charge. They cannot penetrate far through matter and have a tendency to pick up two negatively charged particles, electrons, with the resulting neutralization of their charge. The atoms formed from this combination make up a gas called helium. Thus it was found that atoms of one element can be formed by the decomposition of atoms of another element. The beta rays are composed of electrons moving at much higher velocities and with much greater penetrating power than the alpha particles. The third kind, gamma rays, are quanta of energy corresponding to X rays and are very much like visible light except that their wave length is shorter.

You will remember from physical geology that elements are substances which cannot be broken down by ordinary chemical means. They have the same number of protons in the nucleus as they have electrons in orbits about the nucleus. They may, however, have different numbers of neutrons in the nucleus in which case they are called isotopes of the element. Some isotopes are stable; others are radioactive and will spontaneously break down to form (1) a stable isotope of the same element, (2) another radioactive isotope of the same element, or (3) a different element or a stable or radioactive isotope of that different element. Uranium-238 is an example of a radioactive isotope of the element uranium.

Decay of uranium to lead. Uranium-238 like most other radioactive substances is transformed into a stable substance, lead-206, only after passing through a number of other radioactive isotopes. Radioactive decay occurs in such a way that half of the radioactive substance decays in a given period of time; that period, called the half life, is a constant for a given isotope. The disintegration of uranium is diagrammatically sketched in Fig. 1-9. The half life of uranium-238 is 4.56 x 10^9 years. One million grams of uranium-238 will pro-

Fig. 1-9. Radioactive dating. This is a schematic representation of the decay of uranium-238 to form lead-206 and helium gas. Note the great number of intermediate steps. The half life of each phase of the decay is indicated as is the release of helium. (After Zeuner.)

duce 1/7600 gram of uranium lead per year.

During a period of deformation in the earth's crust a molten mass of rock matter, magma, may be intruded into the deformed rocks from great depth. After the deformation has subsided the magma cools and crystallizes into a solid rock composed of several minerals. Let us suppose that one of those minerals contains uranium-238. As soon as it has crystallized the nuclei of the atoms of uranium-238 begin to disintegrate. A certain percentage of the atoms disintegrate every minute. After 4560 million years, half of them will have disintegrated. As the uranium-238 disintegrates, helium and lead-206 are formed as end products of the decay. Both of these materials are stable and undergo no further change. Thus the ratio of helium and lead-206 to the amount of uranium-238 bears a definite relationship to the age of the mineral or rock in which it is found and, therefore, to the time of its formation. In our example the rock was formed during a period of deformation, so the age of the rock is the age of the deformation.

A number of other radioactive substances have proved useful in determining the age of geologic events. Noteworthy among them are the decay of rubidium to strontium by the emission of a beta particle, and the decay of potassium to argon.

Carbon-14. This method of dating is well known for its use in dating archaeological findings. Professor W. F. Libby at the University of Chicago developed the method which depends on the presence of radioactive carbon in organic matter. Carbon-14 is formed in the upper atmosphere when nitrogen-14/7 is bombarded by neutrons in the form of cosmic rays. The nitrogen, when hit by a neutron, emits a proton, a positive particle, and becomes carbon-14/6. The carbon-14 combines with oxygen to form carbon dioxide which is absorbed by all living matter. When the plant or animal dies it stops absorbing the carbon-14, and the carbon-14 present in the organism begins to decay, forming nitrogen-14/7 again. The half life of carbon-14 is about 5600 years. In order to date the remains of the plant or animal the amount of carbon-14 in the organic matter is measured and compared with the amount

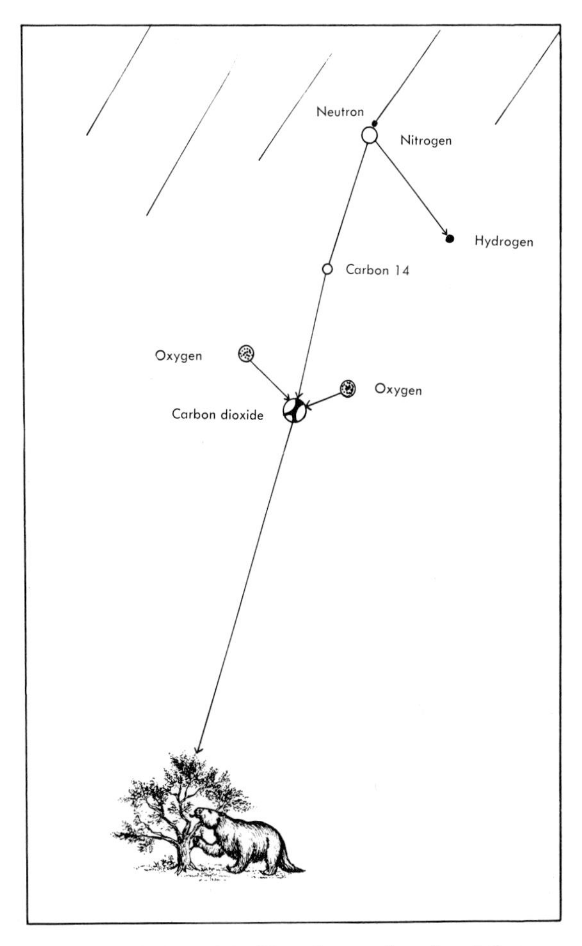

Fig. 1-10. Carbon-14. Cosmic rays bombard the upper atmosphere producing neutrons. When these neutrons collide with nitrogen in the atmosphere small amounts of carbon-14 and hydrogen are produced. The carbon-14 combines with oxygen to form carbon dioxide. The carbon dioxide containing carbon-14 is absorbed by plants and eventually animals feeding on the plants add carbon-14 to their bodies. When the plant or animal dies it ceases to absorb additional carbon-14, and that in the dead remains begins to decay. Half of the remaining carbon-14 decays every 5568 years.

found in living matter today. The ratio is a measure of the length of time the carbon-14 in the dead matter has been decaying, and therefore its age. For example if we find exactly half as much carbon-14 in a piece of wood that has been buried in an old river deposit as we find in living trees then the age of the old wood can be estimated as follows: assuming that the old wood had the same concentration of carbon-14 in it when it was living as the present-day trees, then one half has decayed. Thus the age is equal to the half life of carbon-14 or 5600 years.

Limitations of the radioactive methods. Although the radioactive methods of dating are the best we have for obtaining absolute ages of rocks, there are certain limitations to their usefulness. The initial development of the radioactive dating method was followed by certain refinements of technique. Some of the first dates obtained by the method were not properly corrected, but the techniques have now been perfected to such an extent that they yield very reliable results. Besides this initial drawback there are limitations implicit in the mode of occurrence and nature of the radioactive isotopes.

1. The half life of carbon-14, 5600 years, is so short that most of it decays after about 50,000 years. Therefore, it is of no value in dating older forms of organic matter. Nevertheless it is most useful in work pertaining to the relatively recent history of the earth.
2. Carbon-14 is confined to organic matter and provides no means of dating rocks that do not contain organic matter.
3. Uranium-238 is largely confined to igneous rocks and particularly pegmatites. Potassium-argon dating is useful in dating the micas of metamorphic rocks. But the occurrence of uranium is not sufficiently widespread to solve more than a small fraction of all dating problems. Micas are largely confined to igneous and metamorphic rocks, so there is little opportunity to date by these means the most commonly found rocks, those of sedimentary origin.
4. Where uranium is found in an igneous rock and dated, we learn the age of the igneous rock. If that igneous body has intruded a sedimentary rock unit

Fig. 1-11. Dating by means of an intrusion. If one of the dikes from the stock (lower right) contains minerals which can be dated, the absolute age of the intrusion can be determined. Because the magma intruded the overlying sandstones and limestones they must be older than the intrusion. The dike (left center) cuts across folded strata; thus the folding must have preceded the intrusion. There is an angular unconformity in the upper right. The dikes there are truncated; thus the dolostone and cherty limestone above the unconformity must be younger than the intrusion. The sequence of events represented is: first, deposition of the sandstones and limestone; second, folding of these strata; third, intrusion of the magma; fourth, uplift and erosion; fifth, deposition of dolostone and cherty limestone; and sixth, tilting of the region and erosion.

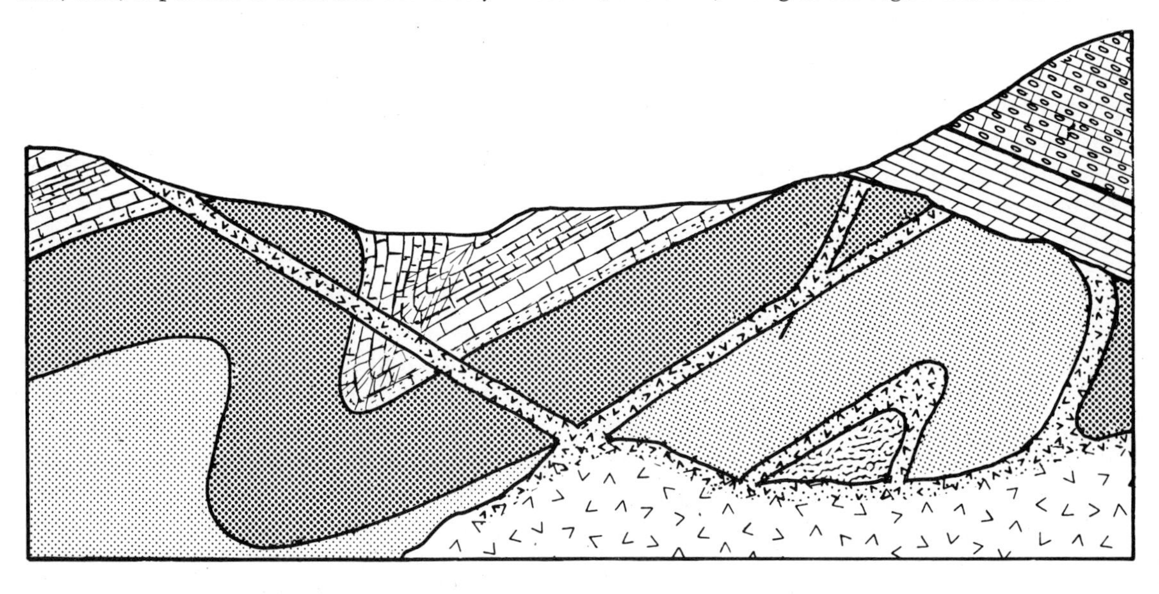

it proves only the minimum age for the unit and leaves us with no maximum age.

5. The dates are accurate to within about .10 per cent, but even this is a long time when you are dating rocks that are billions of years old.
6. Finally, all of the methods used in radioactive dating are time consuming, difficult, and expensive. They require special laboratory equipment and cannot be used to obtain dates in the field.

Age of the earth

The uranium-lead, rubidium-strontium, and potassium-argon series of radioactive decay offer the best means of estimating the age of the earth. The dates obtained by these methods are the minimum ages for the earth, and they provide no idea of the maximum age. Only a few years ago the oldest rocks were dated as 2 billion years old. As this book goes to press the oldest date is 3.3 billion years for a conglomerate in Southern Rhodesia. It is likely that this date will not continue to be the oldest for very long. For reasons we will explore in the chapter on the origin of the earth, it is thought that the earth is about 4 to 4 1/2 billion years old and that the universe is nearly 5 billion years old.

Rates of sedimentation

If accurate rates of sedimentation could be determined for various types of sedimentary rocks, it would be possible to estimate the time required for the formation of each unit of stratified rock by measuring its thickness. This knowledge would be extremely valuable because it could be easily applied. Unfortunately, our understanding of the processes of sedimentation throw serious doubt on this method of dating. We know that sedimentation is rarely a continuous process. Thick layers may be formed in short periods of time followed by many years of slow deposition, nondeposition, or even removal of some of the material. Average annual rates can be estimated and do provide a general idea of the time involved for the formation of thick layers, but, for any particular locality, the figures might produce very misleading results. Three direct methods have been used to estimate rates of sedimentation:

1. Thicknesses of annual deposits. If each laminated unit of sediments such as a section of varves is known to be an annual deposit the thickness of the section can be divided by the number of layers to arrive at a value for the average thickness deposited each year. A second procedure is to count the varves. The problem is to prove that the layers are annual. Even among Pleistocene varves the annual thicknesses sometimes vary from 1 mm to as much as 40 cm. The variation is even greater for nonglacial deposits. These data indicate that it may take from 8 years to 14,000 years for 1 foot of sediment to accumulate. Obviously then this is not a very satisfactory method for more than crude estimates of time.

The first method of dating geological events by means of annual layers of sediments is credited to Baron Gerard de Geer of Stockholm. His work on varves started as early as 1878 and has been the most popular method of dating deposits laid down during the last ice age, the Pleistocene. In general these deposits are thinly laminated layers of alternating color and texture. They are formed where meltwaters from an ice cap flow into quiet water in a glacial lake, a bay, or the sea. In the summer the rate of melting is accelerated, and large quantities of water, carrying fine rock debris in suspension, flow into the lake. The material in suspension is of the general consistency of flour; it is white and is produced as a result of abrasion of the rocks under the ice cap as it moves. The heavier particles in the rock "flour" settle out rapidly, forming a layer on the bottom of the lake. Finer materials remain in suspension until winter comes. Then the lake freezes over, cutting off the supply of coarse sediment. The finer material that remained in suspension slowly settles to the bottom, forming a thin, generally darker, and finer-textured layer. The process is repeated season after season, leaving a record of each passing year. In some years the summers are longer and warmer than others, leaving a thicker varve as a record.

During periods of glaciation the ice fronts advance and retreat over large areas. Lakes form when the margin of the ice is in one position and disappear when the ice front moves or when the lake is drained. However, the varve counts can be extended from one area to another if the varves formed near the top or bottom of one lake can be correlated with those in another lake. At first, correlation was done on the basis of thickness of the varves. Then it was discovered that individual varves may vary in thickness in different parts of the same lake. This led to correlation by means of similarity of sequences of varves.

Varve analysis has been extremely useful in dating the advances and retreats of ice caps and in mapping their positions and durations. However, varves are not restricted to glacial deposits or to the Pleistocene. Varved deposits may result from any seasonal conditions capable of influencing the nature of the deposits. Some examples are:

a. Extreme changes in temperature or moisture will influence the texture and quantity of sediments produced.
b. Alternate carbonate-rich and carbonate-poor layers may form varves.
c. Seasonal variation in the quantity of organic matter available may result in varves. The quantity of plankton (free-swimming and floating marine organisms) produced varies with the seasons.

2. When the deposits are not varved it is possible to estimate the rate of sedimentation if the ages of the overlying and underlying units can be determined. For example if the top and bottom of a sequence can be dated by radioactive means then the thickness of the intervening layers can be measured and divided by the age differences between the top and bottom to yield the average rate of sedimentation. The value is reliable only if the sequence is unbroken. This type of analysis has been made on rocks of Cambrian age. It is found that it required about 2000 years to produce each foot of sediment in one locality. A similar study made on rocks of Pliocene age revealed a rate of 1 foot every 600 years. Such values cannot be considered as having significance for more than the restricted area in which they were measured. We can observe that the rates of sedimentation are highly variable in different parts of the world today.

3. Present rates of sedimentation. Even these are not entirely reliable as a means of estimating the rates of deposition of past deposits. We observe that present rates are variable even for the same rock types. In lakes, for example, rates of deposition have varied as much as 0.05 mm to 1 mm per year.

What generalizations can be made about rates of sedimentation? At best, measurements of rates of sedimentation are not reliable enough to be used to determine age of rock units with the accuracy ordinarily required. The rates are of some value in that they provide a crude estimate of the time required for deposition of sections of sediment in which there are no breaks or intervals of lost time. Sometimes sedimentary rates are the best means available for estimating ages, but they should be applied with some caution. You can get an idea of the order of magnitude of these rates from the average rate of 600 to 700 years required to build up a foot of black shale. Somewhat less time is ordinarily required for a silt or sandstone.

Rates of weathering

The beginnings of the development of a soil from the rubble of several old Roman buildings and in a number of ancient gravel pits have provided a clue to the length of time necessary for rocks to weather. Of course the rates vary considerably in different types of climates, but it can be estimated that at least a few thousand years are necessary for a soil profile to develop in temperate climates. This knowledge is most valuable in work with deposits laid down on the land surface, and where the ages are known in some detail. It finds application in work with the glacial deposits that form a veneer over the land surfaces in the northern hemisphere.

Rates of denudation and erosion

Here again the problem is complex, and the rates vary considerably from one climate to another. By confining attention to the rates of downcutting by streams and the rates of retreat of waterfalls it is possible to get at least a qualitative estimate of the rate at which the continents are worn away. Running water is only one of the means by which land surfaces are lowered and removed, but it is probably responsible for the removal of most materials from the continents. Rates of downcutting range from extremely slow rates for old streams near sea level to several feet per day in some extreme instances. Lake Ragunda drained suddenly in 1796. The stream issuing from it cut down several meters in a couple of days. Niagara Falls is receding at rates between 3 and 5 feet per year; St. Anthony Falls on the Mississippi recedes a little more than 2 feet per year. The escarpment at Bryce Canyon, Utah, is estimated to recede about one-fiftieth of a foot per year. These values do not seem large at first, but over millions of years they could produce astonishing results. It has been estimated that between 20 and 25 million years would suffice to lower all the continents to sea level if uplift and volcanism ceased.

REFERENCES

ADAMS, F. D., 1938, *The Birth and Development of the Geological Sciences*: Dover Publications, New York, 506 p.

BOWEN, R. N. C., 1958, *The Exploration of Time:* George Newnes Limited, London, 143 p.

ZEUNER, F. E., 1950, *Dating The Past:* Methuen & Co., London, 474 p.

GENERAL REFERENCES

COLBERT, E. H., 1955, *Evolution of the Vertebrates:* John Wiley and Sons, New York, 479 p.

DUNBAR, C. O., and RODGERS, JOHN, 1957, *Principles of Stratigraphy:* John Wiley and Sons, New York, 356 p.

DUNBAR, C. O., 1960, *Historical Geology:* John Wiley and Sons, New York, 567 p.

FENTON, C. L., and FENTON, M. A., 1958, *The Fossil Book:* Doubleday and Company, Garden City, 482 p.

GILLULY, JAMES, WATERS, A. C., and WOODFORD, A. O., 1959, *Principles of Geology:* W. H. Freeman and Company, San Francisco, 534 p.

KAY, MARSHALL, 1951, North American Geosynclines: Geol. Soc. America Mem. 48, 143 p.

KING, P. B., 1951, *The Tectonics of Middle North America:* Princeton University Press, Princeton, 203 p.

———, 1959, *The Evolution of North America:* Princeton University Press, Princeton, 190 p.

MOORE, R. C., 1958, *Introduction to Historical Geology:* McGraw-Hill Book Company, New York, 656 p.

POLDERVAART, ARIE, Editor, 1955, *Crust of the Earth:* Geol. Soc. America Sp. Paper 62, 762 p.

ROMER, A. S., 1959, *The Vertebrate Story:* The University of Chicago Press, Chicago, 437 p.

SIMPSON, G. G., PITTENDRIGH, C. S., and TIFFANY, L. H., 1957, *Life, an Introduction to Biology:* Harcourt, Brace and Company, New York, 845 p.

STIRTON, R. A., 1959, *Time, Life, and Man:* John Wiley and Sons, New York, 558 p.

STOVALL, J. W., and BROWN, H. E., 1954, *The Principles of Historical Geology:* Ginn and Company, Boston, 471 p.

2 The Rock Record

ROCK UNITS

The story of the past is told by the units of rock. Because continents are continually undergoing erosion and removal of material, most of the record is contained in rocks formed in the seas. Occasionally continental deposits are covered by the advance of a sea over the land mass, but the greatest part of the record consists of sands, silts, clays, and limy muds deposited in the oceans. The original site of deposition of most of the strata now exposed on the continents was much like the shallow continental shelf and continental slopes which border the land masses today.

The sediments are sensitive to the environment in which they are deposited, and they bear the impression left by some of the environmental factors, such as the depth of the water, the size and type of materials brought into the environment, and other physical, chemical, and biological characteristics of the environment. The details of the environmental factors and their impression on the deposits are left for a later discussion.

In general, marine sediments form through the settling of matter through the water to the bottom where a layer is built up. If the material being supplied or the physical, chemical, or biological factors influencing the environment change, the nature of the layers being formed also changes. This brings into existence a feature known as stratification, a structure produced by deposition of sediments in beds, layers, laminae, lenses, wedges, and other essentially tabular units. The sediments may be fragmental or crystalline, formed from settling of solid insoluble debris, or the product of chemical precipitation, or they may be composed of organic remains. The resulting layers can be traced and identified. The layers or stratification results from variations in such features of the sediment as:

a. Color.
b. Texture (size, shape, and fabric).
c. Density.
d. Composition.
e. Fossil content.

The rock units resulting from stratification can be subdivided and recognized on the basis of objective criteria. They can be identified in the field and mapped as units.

The differentiation and recognition of rock units are so important that much attention has been given to the formulation of a system of nomenclature to be used in describing them. A commission of stratigraphers has established the following procedures for the subdivision of rock units:

Groups
  Formations
    Members
      lentils—tongues—beds

The basic unit is the formation, a lithologically distinctive product of essentially continuous sedimentation selected from a local succession of strata as a convenient unit for purposes of mapping, description, and reference (American Commission on Stratigraphic Nomenclature). In general the composition is dominated by one or two constituents such as massive layers of sandstone or thick units of alternating shale and sandstone layers.

Formations. Formations are usually given two names. The first of these is geographic, the name of the locality where the unit was first described or of a place where it is exceptionally well exposed, usually called the type section. The second name, when it is used, gives the rock type if the formation is composed of a single type of sediment such as the Martinsburg shale and the Tuscarora sandstone. In some cases the lithology is not so distinctive that a single type name can be used. Then the geographic name is used followed by the word "formation."

Groups. When a number of formations are related to one another by their lithologic characteristics or by their position relative to breaks

Fig. 2-1. Unconformities. Four types of breaks in the rock record are depicted below. In *A* there is an angular discordance between the strata above and below the unconformity. The older folded strata have been subjected to erosion and were planed off before the younger strata above the erosion surface were deposited. Note the basal conglomerate unit directly above the break. *B* and *C* are similar types of breaks except that part of the topography was buried in *B* while the contacts between the units in *C* are almost perfectly parallel. The nonconformity at the bottom is the break between the older igneous mass and the overlying strata which have been tilted. The igneous mass was intruded, solidified, uplifted, and eroded before the deposition of the sandstone unit over it.

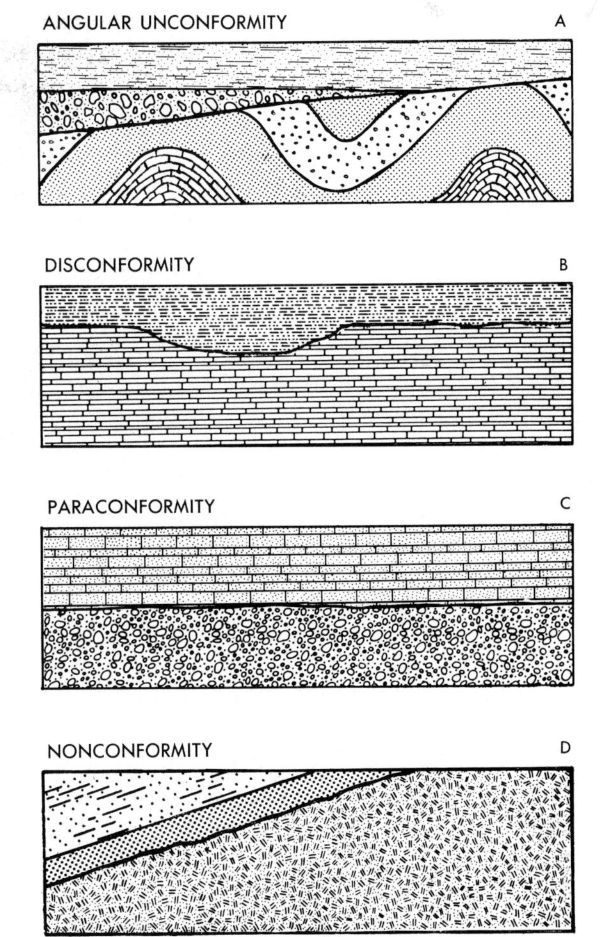

such as unconformities, the entire sequence of formations may be given a name. They are called a group. The term group always follows the name of the group—i.e., Clinton Group and Medina Group. The breaks used to separate groups may be any of the types of unconformities:

a. Interruptions in deposition or nondeposition.
b. Deformation and erosion.
c. Erosion without deformation.

Unconformities are by no means the only basis for recognition of groups. Most groups are formations that may be related to one another lithologically or genetically.

Members, beds, lentils. Imagine for the moment that you are faced with the problem of making subdivisions of the rock units exposed near your school. Because you probably do not already know the names and character of the units you would not be biased as you start the task. Your first job would be to decide which breaks you would recognize as boundaries between rock units. In a few regions this would be quite simple, but in many areas there are a great number of units exposed. Now if you had to map an area the size of your state you would probably start by selecting rather large groups of units, whereas if you had to map a quarry you might select the smallest changes you could find. This is essentially what has happened regarding the subdivision of formations. Where mapping is done in detail it is possible to make many subdivisions of the existing formations. These small subdivisions are called members if they extend over a large area, lentils or lenses if they are only locally distributed, and tongues or wedges if they wedge out in one direction between sediments of different lithology. The terms "beds" and "laminae" are also used for these smallest subdivisions.

Do not become confused by this array of terminology because at best the terms are loosely defined. The subdivision of any particular unit of rock depends on the interpretation of the person who first described it, and on what that unit was like at the type section. Some units are restudied after many years, and the subdivisions are changed. If necessary, new names are applied in order to remove or reduce confusion. Not infrequently two units outcropping in different places are given the same name and later prove to be entirely different units, or one may be found to be a thickened part of the other.

Biostratigraphic units

A biostratigraphic unit is a unit of rock which can be distinguished by the assemblage of fossil fauna (animals) or flora (plants) which it contains. A designation different from that applied to rock units based on lithology is required for these units because the boundaries of units containing certain assemblages of fossils do not always conform with the physically distinguishable characteristics of formations, members, or even the small beds, lenses, etc. The fundamental biostratigraphic unit is the zone (sometimes called a faunizone or florizone). This unit is named for one of the fossils found in it.

One of the most recent reviews of the zone concept has been made by Dr. Curt Teichert of the U. S. Geological Survey. He points out four popular misconceptions about zones. These misconceptions are:

a. That the name fossil is restricted to the zone that is named after it.
b. That only the name fossil and no others occur in the zone.
c. That all rocks in which the name fossil occurs belong to the zone.
d. That rocks in which the name fossil does not occur may not be included in the zone.

The exact significance of the zones is still subject to some debate arising from the various uses of the term. Two usages are given here:

1. Many stratigraphers use the term "zone" for time units in which case the presence of a zone would serve as a marker

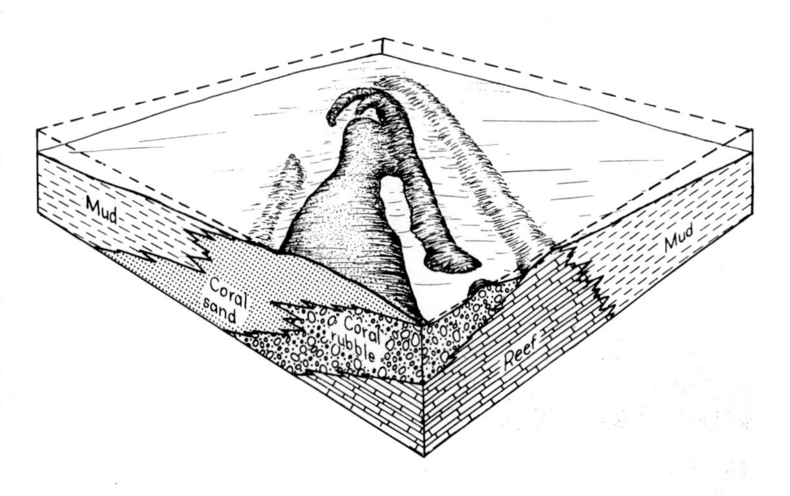

Fig. 2-2. Reef facies. The sediments associated with the reef are surrounded by muds which are being formed contemporaneously. It is apparent that a number of different types of sediment are being produced and deposited simultaneously. The reef, coral sand, and coral rubble make up facies of the mud unit. They reflect particular environments of deposition. This reef is at Batavia Bay, Java. (Modified after R. C. Moore.)

of a particular time in the geologic past. When the zone is used as a time unit it does not necessarily conform to the boundaries of rock units.

2. The zone is a rock unit which is characterized by a distinct fossil assemblage. (Note that it is a particular assemblage of fossils, not a particular fossil, that distinguishes the zone.)

Facies (sedimentary)

Sedimentary facies is another term about which there has been considerable debate. The concepts of sedimentary facies have become so important that a conference on the importance of facies in geologic history was held in 1949 at the meetings of The Geological Society of America. The resulting volume (Memoir 39 of The Geological Society of America) is one of the best and most comprehensive statements of the meanings, problems, and interpretations of facies.

Facies as a part of a stratigraphic unit. This meaning of facies is best understood through careful examination of an area in which sediments are now accumulating. The reef complex, Fig. 2-2, serves this purpose because here we find that within relatively short distances very different types of sediments are being formed. At the time illustrated, mud, coral sand on the beach and sand under the water, coral rubble, and coral rubble with algal remains in it are all being deposited. From the cross section it is obvious that this situation has continued for some time. Contemporaneous deposition of a number of different sediments undoubtedly occurred in the past. These deposits vary in thickness and interfinger with one another. Imagine that this reef exists in a sea which throughout most of its extent is slowly accumulating mud. After many years the mud encroaches on the reef and finally covers it. The living organisms on the reef are dead, and the reef becomes a part of the mud-rock unit. Some millions of years later the compacted mud-rock unit, a shale, is uplifted, eroded, and exposed at the earth's surface. The extensive layer of mud is given a formation name. It reflects the environment in which it was deposited, but within this shale formation there exist the rocks of the coral reef. They are a complex group of rocks which interfinger with the shale and with one another. Each of them reflects something of the very localized environment in which it was formed, and each is genetically related to those about it. Each may be called a sedimentary facies of the shale formation.

Facies defined. The most common usage of the term facies is this: "any recognizable rock record of a depositional or organic environment is considered a facies irrespective of stratigraphic position" (Krumbein and Sloss, *Stratigraphy and Sedimentation*).

This definition means that the occurrence of a certain type of sedimentary unit may be interpreted as evidence of the existence of a

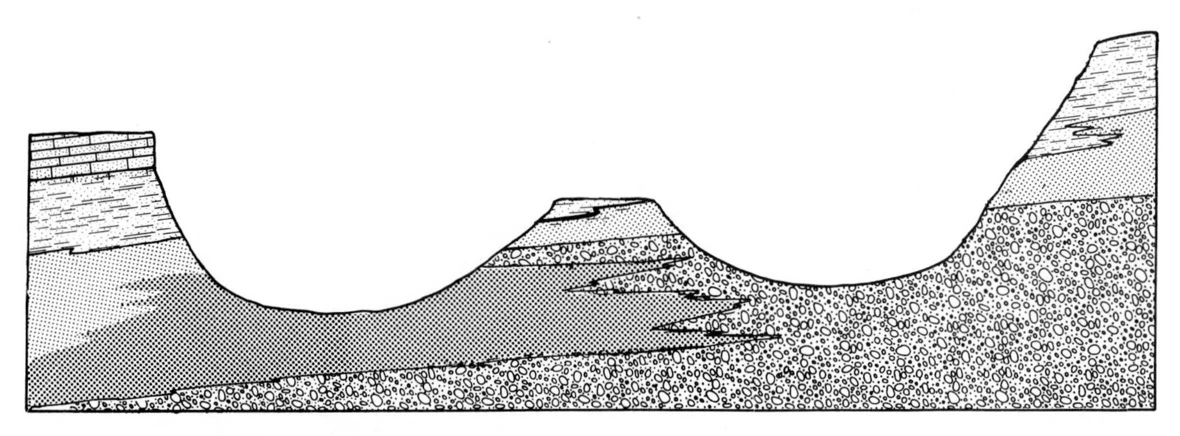

Fig. 2-3. Facies changes. A cross-sectional view of a sedimentary sequence in which the lithologies of the units change laterally. These changes reflect differences in environment such as distance from source of coarse sediment, water temperature, current and wave action. This section might be interpreted as having formed when a land mass stood to the east (right). Coarse conglomerates were deposited near the land and extensively around it when it was highest and subject to most rapid erosion. Later the conglomerates and gravels graded westward into coarse sands and then into fine sand. Toward the top of the section sands and sandy shales are deposited in the east, indicating that the land mass has been worn low. In the west at the top of the section limestone containing sand is exposed. Conditions there must have been favorable to lime-secreting organisms or to direct precipitation of $CaCO_3$.

particular environmental condition at the time of deposition. Every time a closely similar type of sedimentary unit is found, it also may be interpreted as evidence of that particular depositional environment. The definition implies that this interpretation can be made, to a large extent, independently of the relation that this unit bears to the other units with which it is closely associated, i.e., with which it interfingers.

An alternative use of the facies concept is favored by many geologists. The alternative is to think of the facies as a part of a definite stratigraphic unit (a rock unit). The facies is still considered the result of a particular set of environmental factors, but it is restricted to lateral changes within a particular stratigraphic unit, caused by variation of environments during deposition.

Those who prefer the second definition do not object to the first one in theory, but point out that it is not always practical, because similar rock deposits differing in only minor aspects may originate under very different types of conditions. They believe that it is safer to consider each variation within a stratigraphic unit as an integral part of that unit.

TIME-STRATIGRAPHIC UNITS

Time is an abstract continuum which can be broken up into arbitrary units of absolute length, i.e., years. The absolute age of rocks can often be determined by analysis of radioactive minerals. The passage of time brings about another unidirectional, nonreversible process which leaves its record in rocks—evolution. The products of evolution make it possible to recognize sequences of strata in their correct order, but provide no measure of the time involved in the evolutionary process (in absolute units). Rock units are deposits of sediments which can be easily recognized by their physical, chemical, or biological characteristics. They can be mapped on the basis of these objective criteria. Why, we may ask, is it now necessary to add still another type of unit to this already rather complex system of classification? The answer is simple: we find that the boundaries of rock units do not always correspond to any single time. To clarify this problem let us consider two situations.

First take the case of a sequence of rock units in which the boundaries of the rock units parallel time lines. A varve, which approaches this condition about as closely as anything can, may extend over the entire area of a large lake. During the course of a winter a thin layer of dark sediment may settle over the entire lake bottom. For an earth that is 4 billion years old the period of one winter is such a small portion of time that for all intents and purposes we may consider that the dark layer formed in an instant. Every point on the layer formed contemporaneously, and we can say that the boundary between two varves thus corresponds to a particular time in the earth's history. A similar situation holds for large parts of the deep-ocean basins where sedimentation consists essentially of the remains of the protozoans (animals of microscopic size) which slowly settle to the bottom and build up layers of calcareous and siliceous oozes.

In the second case, the points on the contact between two units do not represent a surface that was formed at one time. In this instance we may say that the time lines cut across the rock-unit boundaries. A number of factors determine what the sedimentary deposit in a given locality will be like. These factors include all the conditions of the environment which can leave an imprint on the sediments as well as the nature of the materials supplied to the area. The salinity, depth, and temperature of the water can all influence the nature of the deposit as can the distance of the area from the shore line and the type of shore line. Thus the blanket of sediments being deposited at any one time on the bottom of a shallow sea at the margin of a continent is not of a uniform nature.

Even within recorded history the positions of the seas have changed locally. Fluctuations in sea level caused by the storing of vast quantities of water in ice caps have figured prominently in the determination of shore lines over the past million years. At other times fluctuations have resulted from warping of the crust of the earth.

As these fluctuations occur the shore line extends farther inland or retreats toward the ocean basins. As it moves, the environments of deposition may shift also. Let us assume that the sea level is rising along a shore line of moderate relief. Waves pounding at the shore break up the rocks exposed along a sea cliff. These rock materials are washed back and

Fig. 2-4. Map and cross-sectional view of rugged coast. Coarse sediments derived from the wave-cut cliff cover the sea bottom near the shore line. Farther out successively finer sediments are laid down. The hypothetical case illustrated here in which gravels grade into coarse sand, finer sand, sandy mud, mud and finally limestone is not always duplicated in nature. Coarse sediments are often found on the edge of the continental shelf. They apparently were carried out there during storms, and the finer factions of sediment are removed by slight currents and agitation of the water near the bottom when large waves come in.

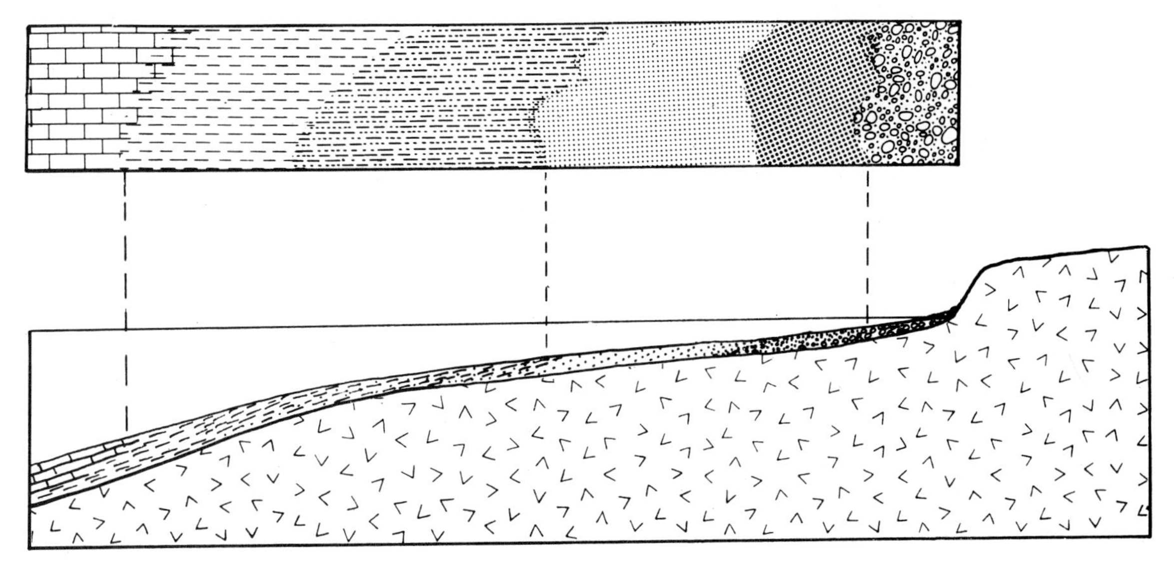

forth in the wave motion and gradually are broken into finer and finer sizes. The finer sizes may be washed out toward the sea or carried along parallel to the shore by the "longshore" currents. Several miles out from this coast line the deposits may be predominantly mud or limy muds containing the remains of small animals, such as the protozoans. As the sea level rises and the coast line moves inland the environments are shifted toward the continent until the limy muds are being deposited above the coarse fragments broken from the sea cliff earlier. If the transgression of the sea across the continent continues for a long period of time the gravels, sands, and muds deposited off the shore will constitute extensive deposits. If there are no reversals during the transgression the layer of gravel formed may appear to have a uniform sharp contact against the overlying sand, and similarly the sand may appear in sharp contact with the muds. Except for that section near the shore line, the mud will appear to overlie the sand, and the sand will appear to overlie the gravel throughout their extent. There may be no immediately obvious evidence to suggest that all three were formed at the same time. The time lines actually cut across the rock-unit boundaries in this case. Fig. 2-5 shows similar situations in which seas have both advanced and retreated from the land.

The time-stratigraphic unit is necessary because the time lines do not always parallel rock-unit boundaries. Frequent mistakes are made if we say that a particular formation was deposited at a certain time in the geologic past. The time-stratigraphic unit is a name which applies to those rock units or parts of rock units which were actually deposited within a given time interval. The names applied to time-stratigraphic units are given in Fig. 2-6.

CORRELATION

What it is and why it is necessary

Webster tells us that correlation is the process of showing the connection between two related things, but it is more specifically

Fig. 2-5. Advancing and retreating sea. In Figs. 2-4 and 2-5 a number of different lithologies are being deposited at any one time. In the lower half of this diagram seas were advancing (transgressing) across the crystalline land mass. Gravels, sands, sandy shales, and sandy limestones were deposited at successively greater distances from shore. Note that as the seas transgressed the position of the zone in which each type of rock was deposited also shifted. Thus it appears that a conglomerate layer was formed, followed by sandstone, then sandy shale, and finally sandy limestone. The horizontal dashed line approximates a time line. When the sea began to retreat from the land, finer sediments replaced the coarse conglomerates near shore as features of the shore line of emergence replaced those of submergence.

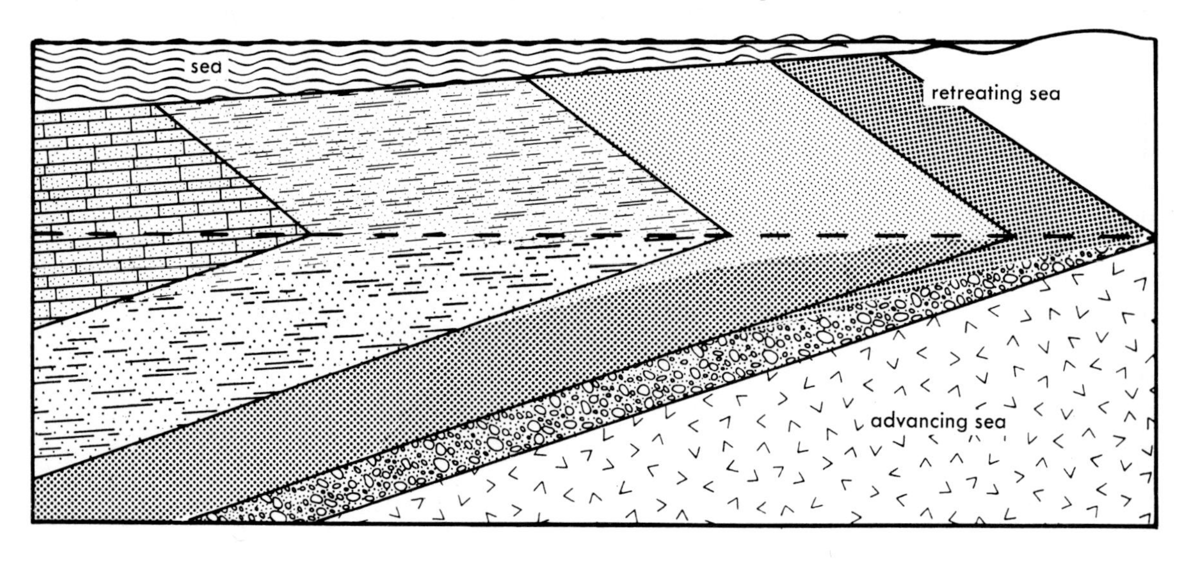

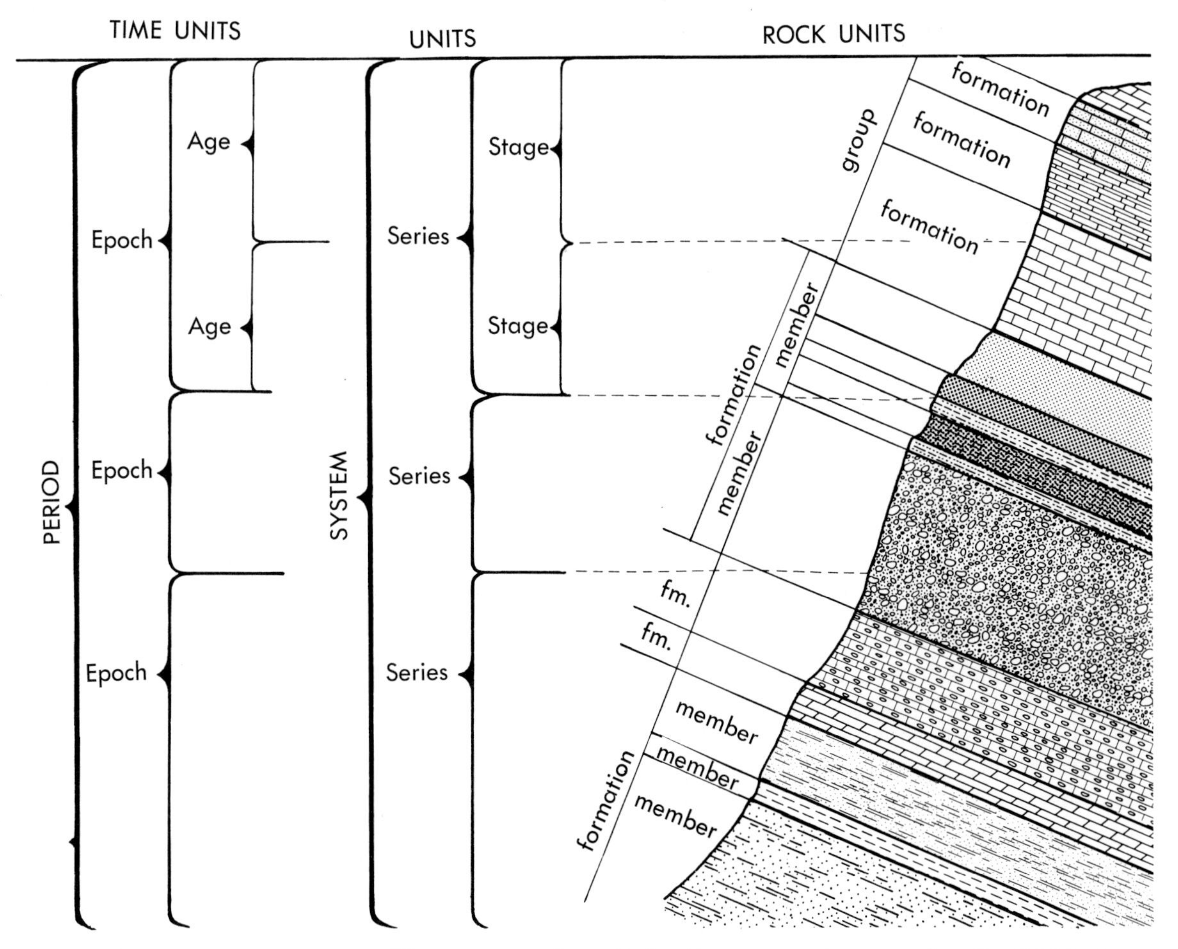

Fig. 2-6. Subdividing a sequence. The sequence of stratified sedimentary rocks exposed on the right is shown broken down as it might be for the purposes of mapping. Note the relationships of the various types of subdivisions. A group may be composed of a number of formations. They may be divided into members, and each member may be subdivided into beds, lentils, wedges, or smaller units. Notice that the series boundaries do not all conform to formation or group boundaries. A series is composed of the rock units formed during an epoch.

defined as it is used in geology to mean "the determination of the equivalence in geologic age and stratigraphic position of two formations or other stratigraphic units in separated areas; or, more broadly, the determination of the contemporaneity of events in the geologic histories of two areas" (*Glossary of Geology and Related Sciences,* American Geological Institute). The broad definition implies the real reason for the importance of the methods of correlation in geology. It is necessary to be able to relate widely separated and dissimilar bodies of rock in order to establish the connection between the sequences of events in different places. The significance of a local sequence of events is often lost if we do not know its relation to the surrounding areas. Ideally we would like to be able to reconstruct what was happening over the entire face of the world during each of the major periods of geologic time.

Correlation, like most other phases of geologic study, has a different significance for various groups of people. It is used for a variety of purposes. One person may be interested in the light it throws on the development of continents, movements of seas, or evolution of life. Others may find it primarily useful because this knowledge is of vital importance in locating rich mineral deposits. The formation of coal was widespread in rocks of certain ages, particularly in the Carboniferous Period in the Paleozoic. For the person or government looking for coal, this knowledge is of great importance in directing the search in unexplored regions. Efforts can be concentrated in areas where rocks of Carboniferous age occur.

An interesting example of the use of a knowledge of age relations is found in the occurrence of gold as placer deposits (along streams) in California. The gold was deposited in stream valleys during the Eocene Epoch of the Cenozoic Era. Following the Eocene, volcanic activity in the region filled the old valleys with dust, ash, and lava, and new valleys formed on the surface of these volcanic rocks. The rivers formed new valleys during the volcanic activity but changed their courses as new ash deposits dammed or filled some of the valleys. The present stream patterns were not established until the volcanism had subsided. These modern streams have cut down through the volcanic rocks and in places exposed the gravel deposits formed in the older valleys. An estimated $600,000,000 worth of gold is to be found in the Eocene stream valleys, but only a minute amount of gold occurs in the valleys formed during the volcanic activity. Obviously it is extremely important to know the age of the gravels before you start digging in one of the old, partially exposed stream deposits. A lot of time, money, and effort has been lost digging in gravels of the wrong age.

Correlation is particularly important in exploration for petroleum. Oil and gas occur in the pore spaces around sand grains or in solution pockets in limestone. Once a rock unit is known to contain oil in several places, it is highly probable that the same unit will contain oil in other nearby areas which have a similar history. Thus it becomes important to be able to recognize the same rock units. Of course the occurrence of oil in numerous places in one unit does not insure its occurrence throughout the unit.

From what has been said the student should note that the process of correlation is not confined to one category of geologic units. It may be desirable to correlate rock units, time-stratigraphic units, or biostratigraphic units depending on the purpose of the correlation.

Methods of correlation

When correlation of stratigraphic sections in one area with those in another was first started, it was generally believed that the divisions or boundaries between rock units were all "time lines," indicating that the whole unit had been formed during one period in time. Consequently, correlation came to be looked

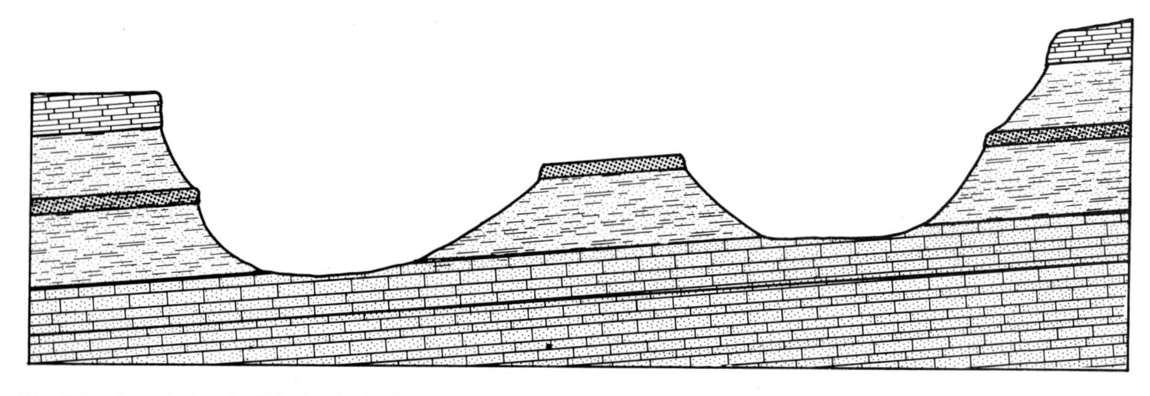

Fig. 2-7. Correlation by lithologic similarity and position in a sequence. In the region depicted above lithologies are constant enough to make correlation of units possible both by similarities of the units (texture, color, composition, etc.) and by their position in an established sequence.

on primarily as a means of correlating events in time. As the true nature of the differences in rock units, time units, biostratigraphic units, facies, and time-stratigraphic units became clarified, the need for different types of correlation became obvious.

The following is a brief summary of the methods used in correlation of rock units, biostratigraphic units, and time-stratigraphic units.

1. ROCK UNITS
   a. Continuity of contacts between units.
   b. Lithologic similarity.
   c. Stratigraphic position of a unit in a sequence of strata.
   d. Well logs.
   e. Structural characteristics.

2. BIOSTRATIGRAPHIC UNITS
   a. Stage of evolution of the fauna.
   b. Guide fossils.
   c. Faunal resemblance (assemblages of fossils).
   d. Position in a biostratigraphic sequence.

3. TIME-STRATIGRAPHIC UNITS
   a. Quantitative chronology—radioactive dating methods.
   b. Eustatic changes in sea level.
   c. Paleontology.

I. Methods of correlating rock units

A. *Lateral continuity.* The simplest and most straightforward method of correlation is to find the contact between two distinct lithologic units and trace out that contact in the field. In some cases this can be done for many miles. The contact may be mapped using a plane table and alidade. Aerial photographs of the region will often show the contact because of visible differences in the way the two units weather: one may be more resistant and stand up as a cliff, while the other is lower; or different types of soils may develop on the two types of rock. Units of differing resistance to erosion and weathering are particularly prominent in arid and semiarid regions. Where more rainfall occurs or when the action of erosion has continued for millions of years without interruption, the contacts may not be prominent. In these areas deep soils are likely to cover the rock units, and the geologists may have to rely on the type of soil and the presence of certain plants that are restricted to the soils of particular rock types. This method is frequently used in the swampy areas of the Gulf Coast of the United States. In making use of these indirect indicators of the unit, it must be remembered that the soil and plants are characteristic of a particular rock type, not necessarily a particular rock unit.

B. *Position in a stratigraphic sequence.* This method involves the recognition of strata with distinctive lithologic characteristics arranged in a systematic order. If the sequence is found to be the same over a large area then it may be possible at other localities within and near the area to recognize a particular unit by its relation to the others in the sequence.

C. *Structural relations.* If a sea transgresses or advances over an area composed of rock units that have been previously folded and contorted in a period of deformation of the earth's crust, the new sediments will not be parallel to the boundaries of the older units. They will bear an angular relation to one another, called an angular unconformity. A new sequence of sediments may be deposited on the former land mass. Later, after the sea has retreated from the land, and erosion again cuts valleys into the new sediments, it may be possible to identify the younger rock units by the relation they bear to the older folded strata.

D. *Lithologic similarity.* In a rock unit the nature or character of the rock, including the texture, composition, and fabric, is referred to as lithology. These features may be partially determined with hand specimens, but more often a binocular or petrographic microscope or some accurate means of mechanical or chemical analysis is used. In short, any method that employs physical and chemical criteria for identification of the rock unit may be used for the purposes of correlation. Here again it is necessary that the unit have some unique characteristics or at least a certain group of characteristics which make it possible to distinguish it from others.

Correlation by lithologic similarity is extensively used in petroleum exploration. In drilling wells, it is necessary to recognize the rock units being penetrated in order to calculate the depth of the zone or trap which is thought to contain oil, and also to compare the stratigraphic section at the well being drilled with that predicted from sections observed at the surface and those taken from nearby wells. We have seen that the rock units can change in lithology in short distances as in facies changes. There may be other changes caused by deformation or compaction of loose sediments. These must be taken into account if the well is to be successfully completed. As a well is drilled, samples of rock are collected. These may be rock fragments or solid cores taken by means of special core drilling. Much information can be obtained from a core, but the process of collecting the core is expensive. It usually necessitates taking all the pipe, or drill stem, out of the well, putting on the coring tube, lowering this tube, cutting and collecting the core, withdrawing all the pipe again to take the sample out, and then lowering all the pipe into the well again to continue drilling (called "making the trip"). Because of the expense of this process other methods are often used. These include use of the fragments of ground rock that are carried to the surface in the mud used as a lubricant in drilling. This mud is forced down the drilling pipe and out through holes around the drill bit. Pressure causes it to return to the surface through the space left between the pipe and the wall of the hole. This mud serves several purposes; it not only cools and lubricates the pipe and bit as it turns in the hole but it removes the ground-up rock and tends to stabilize walls of the drill hole in unconsolidated sediments.

Fig. 2-8. Correlation by continuity of outcrops. Study the outcrop patterns along the east side of the main stream. Notice how it would be possible to trace the units over a relatively large area by the continuity of outcrop. You can recognize identical sequences across valleys making correlation by position in a sequence possible. View of backbone ranges in the Mackenzie Mountains. (Photo by courtesy of the Royal Canadian Air Force.)

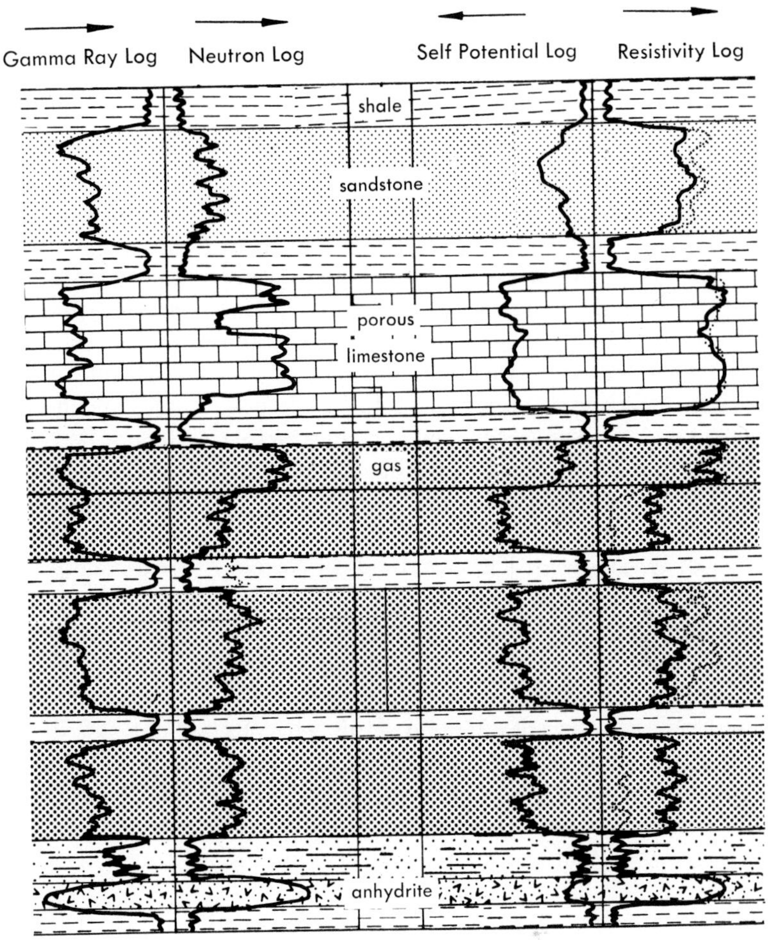

Fig. 2-9. Well logging. Gamma-ray, neutron, self-potential, and resistivity logs are shown for a hypothetical section to illustrate how various common sedimentary rock units might appear on well logs. Both the radioactivity log and the electric log reflect the lithology of the units. (Modified after *Oil and Gas Journal* drawing.)

What observations are made of the lithology after the samples are collected? Many of the same techniques used to analyze well cuttings are applied to other samples collected at the surface. Some of these are:

1. Analysis of the mineral assemblage to obtain the percentage of different minerals present, or the presence of rare or unusual minerals.
2. Chemical analysis of the rock. In this case the percentage of each element present may be determined.
3. Analysis of the size and shape of the fragments which make up the rock. Sand particles tend to become more rounded as they are transported by water for long distances. Wind-blown sand tends to be frosted (small fractures caused by impact of the grains). Such observation helps in the interpretation of the conditions under which the sediment was deposited.
4. Examination of rock by etching with strong acids (HCl and HFl) to reveal small structures or acid-resistant components.
5. X-ray analysis of clays to determine exactly which clay minerals they contain.
6. Differential-thermal analysis. This technique gives both quantitative and qualitative information on the mineral composition of the rock. This new method is proving very practical because it is cheap in relation to many of the other methods of analysis which give comparable data. The differential-thermal

analysis is a measurement of the physical and chemical reactions induced in a substance or mineral assemblage by change in temperature.

7. Thin-section study. Studies are made with the petrographic microscope, which is especially designed to make it possible to observe the changes that take place in polarized light on passing through a section of a rock cut about .03 mm thick. It is used to identify the mineral constituents of the rock.
8. Radioactive minerals. If the rock unit being correlated contains radioactive minerals it may be possible to recognize the unit by this means.

E. *Well logging.* These methods of correlation might be considered as a part of correlation by lithologic similarity, but they have become so important and their use is so widespread in correlation of subsurface units that they deserve special attention. It is not our purpose to go into all the techniques that have been developed in this rapidly expanding field, but several of the more important ideas should be reviewed. Well logs are records showing the variation in different conditions found in wells. Some of the logs that may be obtained during the drilling of a well are electrical logs, radioactive logs, micro logs, caliper logs, temperature logs, and drill-time logs.

Electrical logs. These logs record the resistance of the rock units to the passage of electric currents through them, and the self-potential (the spontaneous potential difference in the well opposite a rock unit). In the resistance-type logs a current is generated and applied to the drilling muds in the hole. In the second case no artificially generated current is used.

The self-potential is caused by a salinity contrast between the mud in the hole and the rock unit. It is generated by an electrochemical process. The amount of the self-potential depends on the nature of the beds and the solutions they contain. A dry rock ordinarily does not conduct electricity; neither does oil or gas. But water is a conductor, and the more chemicals there are in solution the more conductive it is. The potential is thought to be due to electromotive forces caused by electrofiltration and electro-osmosis. Electrofiltration sets up forces which are due to the pressure and resistivity of the liquid (water in the mud of the well in this case). If the hydrostatic pressure in the mud exceeds the hydrostatic pressure in the rock unit the mud will tend to flow into the pore spaces in the unit. If the reverse is true, liquids from the rock unit will cause a bulge out into the mud. The flow from the well into the formation gives a negative potential, and flow from the formation into the drill hole a positive potential.

The second cause of the self-potential, electro-osmosis, is due to the generation of a current where two electrolytes come in contact with one another. In the well the electrolytes are the water in the mud and the solutions held in pore spaces in the rock units. If the salinity of the solution in the rock unit is greater than that of the mud, the current goes into the unit and is recorded as a negative value. If the reverse is true a positive value is obtained. If the two are equal no value is recorded. Some of the characteristics of the self-potential curves illustrated in Fig. 2-9 are:

1. It is flat, a straight line opposite a shale unit.
2. It is high, a long, outward curve opposite units that are highly permeable and contain interconnected pores.
3. It increases generally with improved permeability.
4. It decreases with oil content in the pores.
5. It decreases with higher temperatures.

Resistivity is a measure of the resistance a unit offers to the movement of a current through it. The factors which affect the resistance most are the relative amounts of oil, gas, water, and concentration of salts in the water of the rock units. Principal characteristics of several frequently encountered rock units are:

1. Shale has a low resistivity unless it has high organic content.

2. Limestone and sandstone are intermediate in their resistivity.
3. Oil sands have higher resistivity than water-bearing sands.
4. Fresh-water sands offer more resistance than salt-water sands.

Radiation logs. There are two principal types of radiation logs. One measures the natural radioactivity of the rock unit, gamma-ray logs, and the second measures the effect of bombarding the unit with neutrons from an artificial source. Different kinds of rocks have different amounts of natural radioactivity and therefore emit different amounts of gamma rays. Fig. 2-10 shows the relative values for some of the more common rock types associated with oil fields.

When a rock unit is bombarded by neutrons, gamma rays are artificially produced. Hydrogen has the effect of absorbing the gamma rays, and thus low readings will be obtained opposite units containing abundant hydrogen atoms. The materials that contain an abundance of hydrogen include water, oil, and shales. The radiation logs offer certain advantages over many other logging methods:

1. They can be run through the well casing.
2. They can be run through the mud.
3. They give a distinct indication of certain shales.

II. Methods of correlating biostratigraphic units

The basic unit for the purposes of biostratigraphy is the zone. This includes all or part of a rock unit which is characterized by the presence of a particular assemblage of fossils, faunizones or florizones. The methods of correlation of biostratigraphic units are easily understood in principle. No student of paleontology or comparative anatomy who examines all the data is left with any doubt that there are processes of evolution that have tended to bring about changes in the populations of the animals that have inhabited the earth throughout geologic time. As a result of these changes, there are different populations of animals preserved in the sedimentary rocks of different ages. We know that animals and plants are not evenly distributed over the face of the earth today. There are some forms such as the corals that prefer to live in warm, agitated, and clear waters, while others prefer the frigid temperatures of the Arctic. For this reason we would not expect the same assemblage of animals to be found in all rock units of any single age. Thus the fossil assemblages of any past geologic age are related not only to the time in

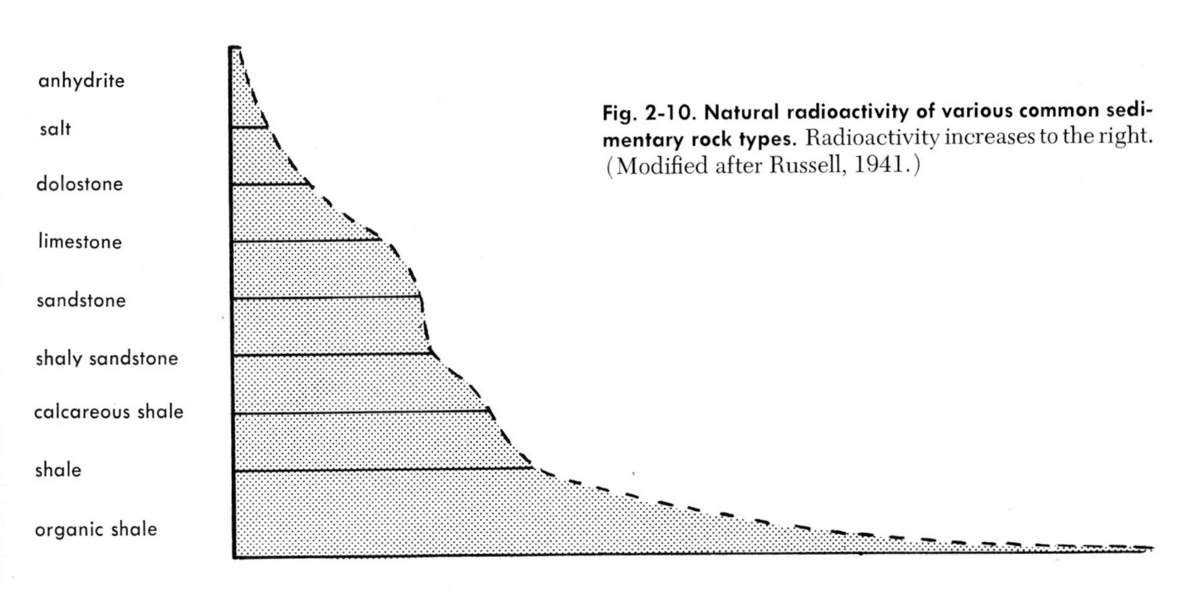

Fig. 2-10. Natural radioactivity of various common sedimentary rock types. Radioactivity increases to the right. (Modified after Russell, 1941.)

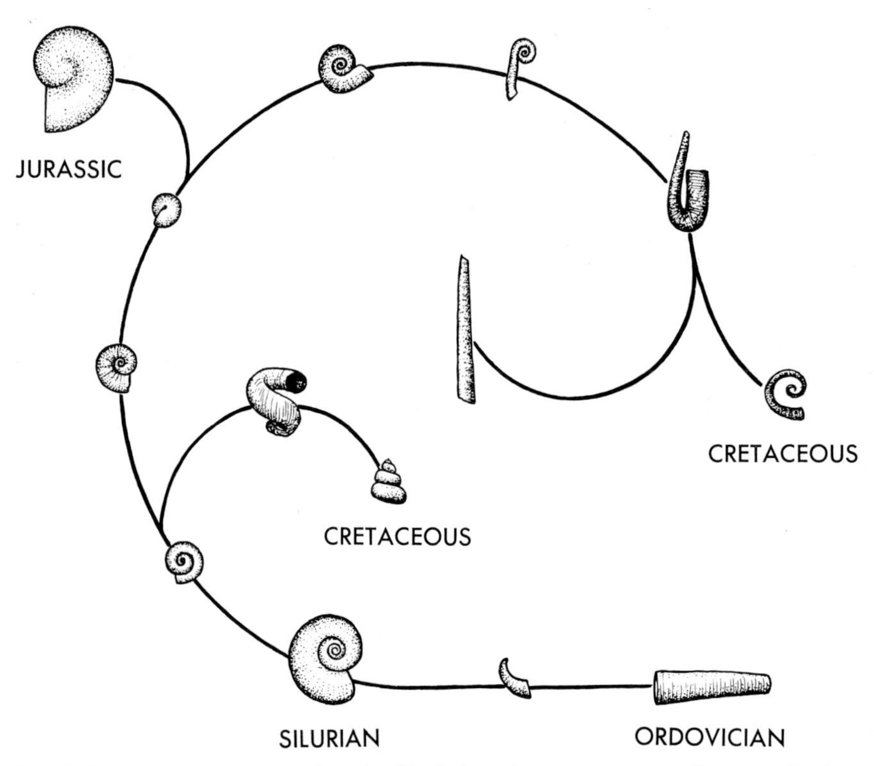

Fig. 2-11. Evolution of cephalopods. Cephalopods are marine molluscs with chambered, cone-shaped shells. Straight at first, the shells became in time more and more tightly coiled. Several stages of coiling can be recognized, each of which continued for millions of years after the next was developed. Gas within the chambered shell made the animal buoyant under water. The various types of coiling brought the lifting force above the animal's body—a compact and efficient design. (Drawn from exhibit at the Chicago Natural History Museum.)

Fig. 2-12. Correlation of zones. A zone may be defined as a bed or group of beds characterized by one or several special fossils, which serve as indices. In some zones almost identical assemblages of fauna may be found. In others a few species are representative, but a great variety of others may or may not be present. Study the two sections to see how the zones may be used for the purpose of correlation. Notice that the lithologies in the two top zones are not identical.

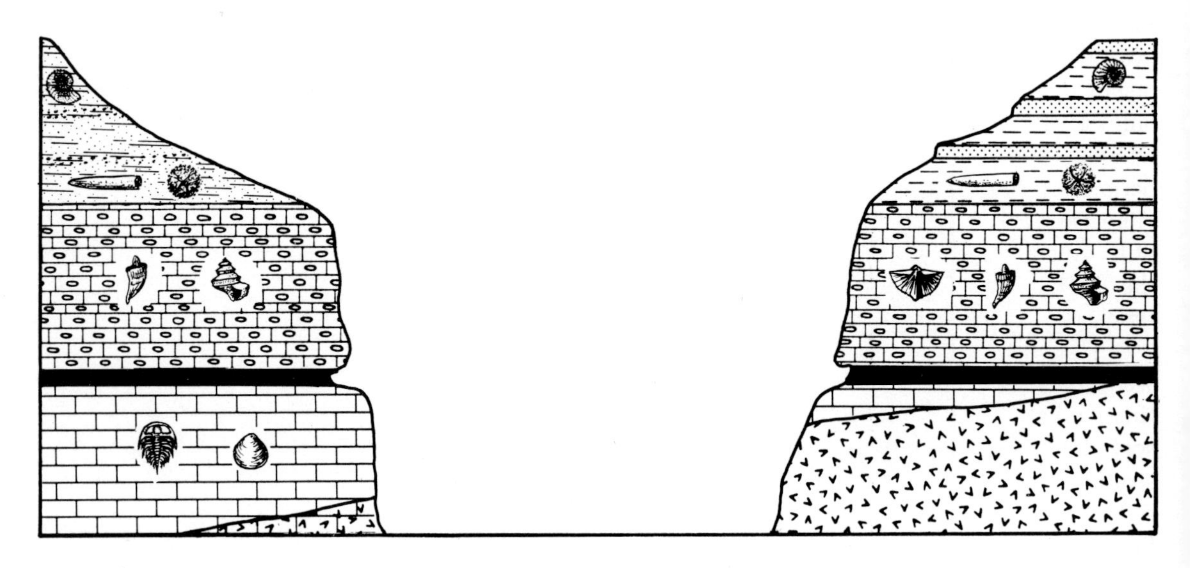

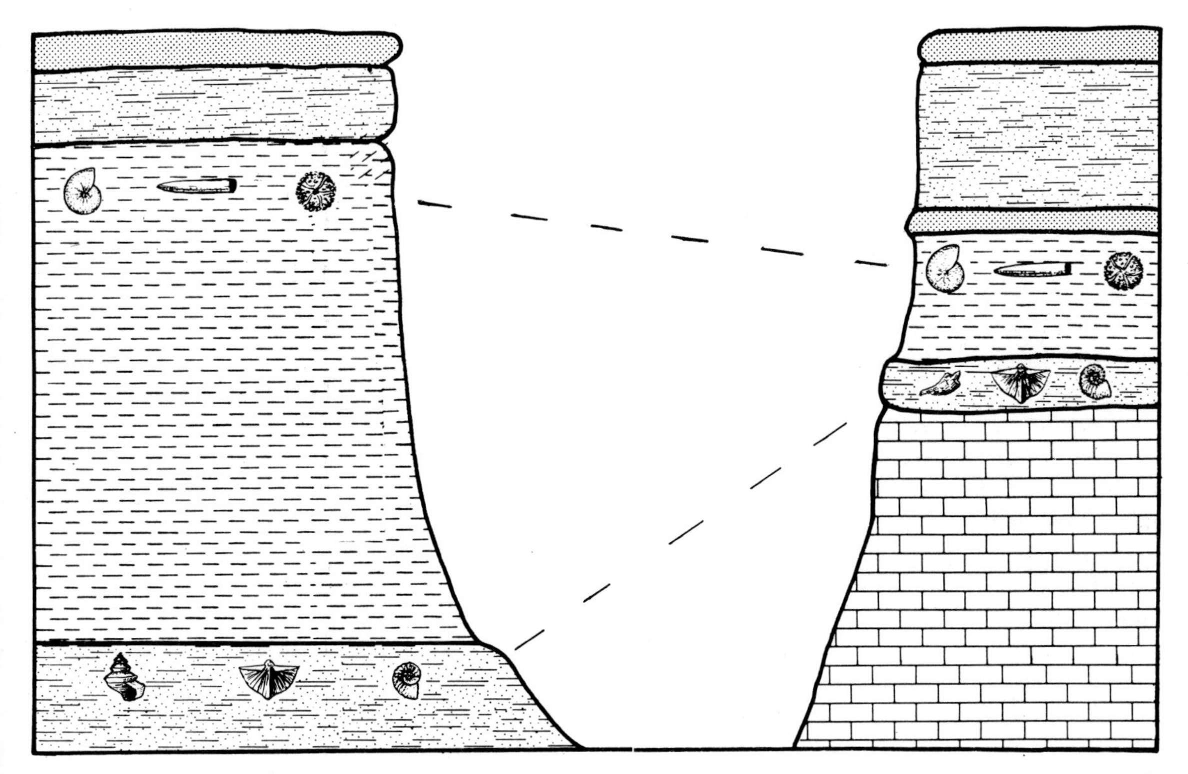

Fig. 2-13. Correlation by zones. Zones are not characterized by certain lithologies nor are they separated by identical thicknesses of rock units in various places.

which they lived but also to the environment they inhabited.

The histories of the different groups of animals are highly varied. A few groups represented in the oldest fossiliferous rock units survive to this day. Some apparently survived for millions of years with little change in the over-all size of their populations. Then they began to expand rapidly in size and diversity only to become extinct a short time later. Others expanded in numbers through long periods of time before starting a gradual decline which eventually led to their extinction. Still others appeared and disappeared from the fossil record in relatively short periods of time.

Those groups of animals and plants that were relatively abundant and possessed distinctive hard parts which could be readily preserved have been used as guides to the biostratigraphic zones. The span of time in which a particular group lived from the time of its first appearance to its extinction is known as the "range" of the group. Obviously the most useful guide fossils are those that are widely distributed and easily recognized, are abundant, and have a short range.

In summary, biostratigraphic units, or zones, are correlated on the basis of the presence of certain guide fossils or more generally on the basis of the similarity of the assemblages of fossils. This should not be interpreted to mean that the assemblages in two equivalent zones must be identical. Correlation may also be established by the position of a zone in a sequence of biostratigraphic zones. This is essentially the same technique as that used to identify a rock unit by its position in a sequence of known rock units.

III. Methods of correlating time-stratigraphic units

A time-stratigraphic or time-rock unit is a sequence of strata deposited during a given span of time. We have seen that relatively few rock units qualify as time-stratigraphic units. It is also true that only a few biostratigraphic units can be rigidly considered as time-stratigraphic markers. But they ordinarily come much closer to meeting the requirements than rock units do. Therefore, in practice biostratigraphic zones are often considered as time markers. Let's examine how far short of the goal they fall. What factors prevent a zone from being a time marker? (1) New forms are not simultaneously evolved in all parts of the world. (2) Time is required for a newly evolved form to migrate throughout the world. (3) Environmental conditions may prevent or at least limit the inclusion of certain animals in the sedimentary record.

An animal or plant which tends to migrate rapidly, lives in many environments, and has a short range (guide fossils) can approximately represent a time marker. If such a guide fossil is quite widely distributed in rocks of a certain age, it may be called an index fossil, and used as a key to that age. Do such animals and plants exist? Yes, in this respect several groups are particularly important. These include the free-swimming (nektonic) and floating (planktonic) marine organisms. Another outstanding group is the animals living in the waters of the continental shelves. Marine invertebrates are particularly abundant among index fossils, and of these protozoans, minute, single-celled animals stand out.

Assemblages of fossils are used for purposes of biostratigraphic correlation. An assemblage gives an even closer age determination than a single index fossil, since the index fossil represents the entire length of time during which that species existed. Some have had relatively short ranges on the order of a few million years, but this is the exception to the rule. Therefore if precise dating is required an assemblage must be used.

In the course of evolution many forms undergo progressive changes in their shapes or structures. These changes have been studied in great detail for certain groups of animals and plants, so that it is possible to identify the age of a fossil if particular species are present in the strata.

Radioactive dating methods serve as checks on other means of time-stratigraphic correlation. Radioactive dating as a means of correlation has been used extensively in the older igneous and metamorphic rocks which contain few fossils. Carbon-14 is coming into widespread use for dating units less than 50,000 years old. This leaves a gap between 50,000 and 500,000,000 years in which radioactive dates have been of very little use as a method of correlation as compared with other methods.

Of great importance in the thinking of early stratigraphers was the idea that the crust of the earth undergoes periods of intense deformation causing rocks to be folded or arched. They believed that these periods occurred almost simultaneously throughout the earth. If this had been the case then the record of this deformation, recorded as an angular unconformity, would provide a time marker. On the basis of other means of dating, these unconformities are now believed by most stratigraphers to be of different ages, invalidating the previous idea of contemporaneous deformation.

Eustatic changes in sea level are worldwide changes in the levels of the surface of the seas in relation to the continents. These changes may occur as glaciation causes the volume of water in the oceans to be reduced. They may also be brought about by changes in the shape of the ocean basins, or warping of the sea floor. Whatever the cause, there is good evidence to suggest that fluctuations in sea level throughout the world have occurred many times in the geologic past. We are now experiencing such a change as the ice caps of the Pleistocene melt, adding more and more water to the oceans. When a eustatic rise occurs, the seas begin to advance across the continents. When a eustatic lowering takes place the seas begin to retreat. The turning points in these advances and retreats serve as approximate time markers. However, complexities are introduced by the fact that local deformation of the continents may cause part of a continent to rise. If the continent rose without an accompanying rise of the sea level then, obviously, the effect would be that of a relative lowering of sea level at that locality.

Problems arising in correlation

It may be possible to correlate units without difficulty for thousands of miles, or it may be an extremely complex problem to correlate those in a relatively small area. In general, correlation is made on the basis of fossil content or lithology. The farther apart two rock sequences are, the more difficult it is likely to be. The following list shows some of the more important causes of trouble when correlation is attempted:

1. Problems when fossil content is used:
   a. Different sedimentary environments will support different assemblages of animals (i.e., fossils are not identical in different types of rocks even if they are exactly the same age).
   b. Some animals are isolated in one part of the world, and this must have been true in the geologic past also.
   c. Even those animals that can migrate across the oceans require some time to do so. For example, new forms may evolve in the Caribbean and migrate throughout the world eventually, but the spread may require many thousands or even millions of years.
   d. The range or life span of a particular fossil species may be different from that generally accepted. Thus a fossil may be found in an older rock than it is thought to occur in. When this happens the rock unit may be assigned to the wrong age, or a controversy may arise that will require much work to resolve.
   e. Some rock units do not contain fossils. Some environments do not support many living organisms.
   f. Fossils may be poorly preserved or extremely limited in numbers in certain units.
2. Problems regarding use of lithology:
   a. Time lines are not necessarily parallel to rock-unit boundaries.
   b. Lithology of a unit may vary laterally from one facies to another.
   c. After it is deposited a rock unit may be altered by processes of metamorphism making it difficult to identify the original lithology and compare it with unmetamorphosed equivalents.
   d. Over long distances rock units almost invariably change in lithology.
3. General problems:
   a. When an area is lifted above sea level, erosion begins to remove the sediments. During the time that an area is above water no marine record is formed. Not only is there no deposition for the time of emergence, but a large part of the previous record may be destroyed by weathering and erosion. Unfortunately the record of deposits representing millions of years of sedimentation has been lost in this manner.
   b. During deformation of the earth's crust units of rock may be folded, broken, and faulted. This deformation breaks up and separates parts of the record which were formerly together. This is one of the main causes of trouble in the correlation of units in the Basin and Range province of the western United States. Blocks of the crust have been broken and displaced by faulting, so that between two uplifted blocks there is a downthrown block which is not exposed.
   c. The geologic literature itself may present many problems. Each stratigrapher depends to some extent on previous work. Unless the greatest care is exercised some errors will get into the work. They may arise from a faulty correlation by a previous worker. It may be that the error has already been discovered and corrected in a later paper in one of the periodicals. If the stratigrapher does not know of this correction, he may incorporate the error from the earlier work in his own research on the assumption that the earlier work was

correct. How do such errors occur? Taking everything into consideration, it is easy enough to see the reason. A fossil may be misidentified, or its age may not have been known exactly. Much cross checking is done to prevent errors of this type. A geologist must try to compile and read everything that has been written on the area or problem with which he is concerned. Often there is a great quantity of data available from different areas and sources. Others in his field may also check on his work, but despite all of this effort mistakes are occasionally made.

REFERENCES

AM. GEOL. INST., 1957, *Glossary of Geology and Related Sciences.*

DUNBAR, C. O., and RODGERS, JOHN, 1957, *Principles of Stratigraphy:* John Wiley and Sons, New York, 356 p.

KRUMBEIN, W. C., 1956, Regional and local components in facies maps: Am. Assoc. Petroleum Geologists Bull., v. 40, p. 2163-2194.

KRUMBEIN, W. C., and SLOSS, L. L., 1953, *Stratigraphy and Sedimentation:* W. H. Freeman and Company, San Francisco, 497 p.

WHEELER, H. E., 1958, Primary factors in biostratigraphy: Am. Assoc. Petroleum Geologists Bull., v. 42, p. 640-655.

II THE PRESENT IS A KEY TO THE PAST

3 Reconstructing the Past

Historical geology is largely concerned with our efforts to reconstruct the history of the earth and with the results obtained through these efforts. That the history of the early ages of our planet is held in a rock record has already been stressed. Now we may consider how we can go about deciphering this record. By now you are aware that the rock record is complex, and that we can succeed in interpreting it only by careful observation and determination of the age and distribution of the various rock units. Once we have as complete a record as possible of the nature and distribution of the rocks laid down or formed during one particular period of the past, we can begin to fit these pieces of information together, creating a picture of what the particular area or region under study was like during that period. At this point in our work, we utilize the concept of uniformitarianism.

UNIFORMITARIANISM

The concept of uniformitarianism is that the same processes and principles that govern natural changes on the earth today have acted in the past to produce similar changes. In other words, "the present is a key to the past." Since there is no way for us to actually observe that uniformity has prevailed, this concept must be considered an assumption. It is one of the most important, fundamental assumptions of geology. The strength of an hypothesis, or for that matter a whole science, is based on the strength of its basic assumptions. Therefore it is worth while for us to examine this assumption. There are two reasons for its general acceptance among geologists.

First, in the time that man has been actively observing and recording the nature of natural processes, there appears to be no evidence of any change in the way in which they operate. The so-called laws or principles governing physical and chemical reactions and interactions have remained constant. Thus we assume that they may be applied to events of the past. We see no reason to think that the law of universal gravitation was in any way different during the Cambrian Period from what it is at present. It seems logical to assume that limestone, exposed at the ground surface during the Silurian Period or any other time, was dissolved by rain water carrying carbon dioxide in solution just as it is today. This does not mean that we assume that there was necessarily the same amount of carbon dioxide that we find in the rain water today, or that limestones were as widely distributed as we now find them.

Second, geologists feel that further proof of the validity of uniformitarianism is found in the ease with which the geologic record of the past can be interpreted by its use. This in itself may not be a very persuasive argument, but it is hard to dispute the fact that when several lines of investigation are used, each one based on this assumption, they inevitably all lead to the same or compatible conclusions about a past event. An example will serve to illustrate the point. Exposures of limestone are common in many parts of this country. Assume that you study one such outcrop and find (as you almost certainly will) the fossil remains of some invertebrate animals. If these particular animals presently live only in marine waters, then you have one line of evidence pointing to a marine origin of this limestone unit. As you know, there are many types of limestone. But, if this one is composed of limestone in a form now deposited only in the sea, you have a second line of evidence pointing to a marine origin of the unit. Wells drilled deep into such units may obtain cores which contain connate water (water trapped in the sediment at the time of its deposition). If the connate water has the composition of sea water, then a third line is established. All of these different lines of evidence point to a marine origin for the limestone unit. Each of them is based on the assumption that the present is a key to the past. The need for this vital key of knowledge is the primary reason for requiring a semester of physical geology before allowing students to study historical geology. It should be readily apparent that you need a firm knowledge of the earth as it is and also a clear understanding of the nature and effects of the processes now acting upon it before attempting to apply this knowledge to rocks formed in the past. If you stop to think of some of the things you learned in physical geology you will soon see how they may be applied. Consider the following examples:

1. You know that the kind of soil developed on certain rock types depends on the climate under which the soil weathered. If you discover a buried soil how would you decide what general type of climatic conditions prevailed when that soil formed?
2. What conclusion would you draw from the discovery of ventifacts in a sandstone layer millions of years old?
3. Could you explain a serpentine-shaped ridge of assorted debris buried under marine sediment?

In the first problem (1) you need to know that in humid climates the soils are likely to contain only small amounts of soluble minerals. The iron will probably be oxidized to limonite. In arid climates soluble minerals may be prominent in the soil. Calcium carbonate may accumulate near the surface under such climatic conditions. In the second case (2) the ventifacts are a good indication that the area was arid or semiarid and that there was abrasive material such as sand in the wind. Even

Fig. 3-1. Ancient cross-bedding. This cross-bedded sandstone is about 130 million years old. It was deposited during the Jurassic Period in southern Utah. From exposures such as this we can decifer the record of the past. Here is evidence of the climatic conditions, even the wind direction, that prevailed when these sands were deposited. (Photo by Edgar W. Spencer.)

the direction of the wind could conceivably be determined if the sandstone in which the ventifacts are buried also contains cross-bedding. The third case (3) might be explained as an esker, formed during glaciation on the land mass and later buried as the region was lowered beneath the sea.

Using this type of information it is often possible to make remarkable restorations of conditions long past. From the examples cited above it is evident that past climatic conditions may be postulated. But much more is possible. The position of the coast lines, mountains, the depth of water and even its temperature at a given time in the past may be judged on the basis of uniformitarianism. These are the subjects of the following chapter. What can be learned of past geologic ages must be obtained from the rocks formed during those ages and preserved since that time. This imposes several restrictions on our interpretations and makes the problem a much greater challenge. How can we possibly discover whether or not there was a mountain range in a certain area 100 million years ago, if the mountain range itself disappeared from the face of the earth 90 million years ago? The answer is that the material removed from the mountain was deposited on its flanks and in the areas around it. If it was located near a sea, it is probable that the sediment accumulated there. The presence of the mountains will have to be inferred from the character of the deposits in the sea. Thus the nature of sedimentary deposits is extremely important, and in order to understand them we must know the conditions under which they were formed. The solution to this situation is found in the theory of uniformitarianism. By studying the environments in which present-day sediments are deposited we will know how to interpret those of the past. It is worth while not only to study the type of sediment that is formed in a certain place, but to consider the animals that live there. These animals die, and their remains become incorporated in the sediment and are as much a part of the rock as the mineral fragments around them. Just as different animals live in different climates or regions on the land, so different marine organisms live in certain particular marine environments. The fauna and flora of a swamp are strikingly different from those of the continental shelf or those of the deep-sea floor. Some marine organisms live only in warm waters, others only in cold water. Some require currents to bring them food, others move about and collect their food. Here then is a valuable means of interpreting the past environments by knowing the environments in which similar animals and plants live today. This is one of the important fields of research in geology at the present time. It is the field of Ecology and Paleoecology.

Fig. 3-2. Old lake level. The contour-like lines on the side of the hill are terraces marking former levels of the Great Bear Lake in the Northwest Territories. From these we can tell that the lake was once much larger than its present margins. Lake and sea shore lines are also found preserved in the rock record and enable us to establish the position of ancient seas. (Photo by courtesy of Royal Canadian Air Force.)

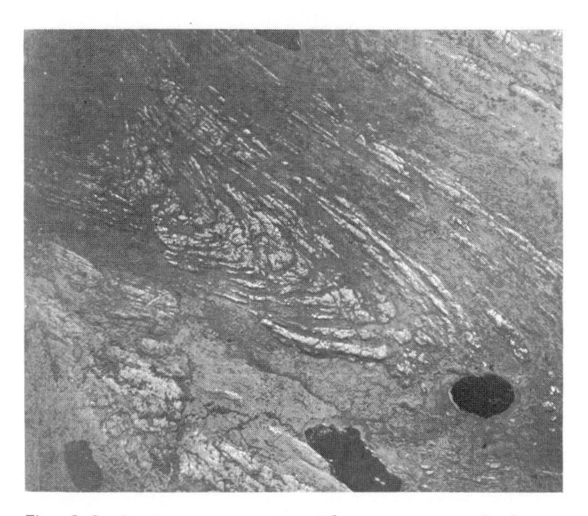

Fig. 3-3. Ancient mountains. This is a vertical photograph of a plunging syncline in Precambrian strata near the Herb Lake area, Manitoba. There is obviously little physiographic evidence of the mountains which once stood here over a billion years ago. About twenty million years are sufficient to reduce even the highest mountains to a plain, but the structures formed during the folding and deformation of the crust which brought the mountains into being are still in existence. Here even after a billion years we can not only determine that there were once mountains but we can determine the trend of these ancient highlands. (Photo by courtesy of Royal Canadian Air Force.)

Limitations of uniformitarianism

The limitations that must be placed on the concept depend largely upon its interpretation. If it is used only in the strictest sense of its meaning as in the above discussion there is no need to limit its application. It is restricted to mean that the nature of processes and the physical and chemical laws have remained the same through time. This does not imply that, because we have ice caps at the poles today, there have always been ice caps at the poles, nor does it suggest that sea level has always tended to rise to where it is today, or that climatic variations have always been as great as they are now. An example of how the concept may be somewhat stretched is the use of rates of sedimentation to judge the length of time involved in the formation of a sedimentary rock. We discussed this method earlier. In principle the present rate of accumulation for a particular sediment type is measured. Then the thickness of an ancient deposit of similar nature is measured, and, by assuming that the same rates of sedimentation applied in the past, the length of time required to form the ancient deposit is calculated. The adherent to a strict interpretation of the concept of uniformitarianism will not accept this line of reasoning. He will point out that uniformitarianism may be used to evaluate the mechanism or mode of deposition, but not its rate. The rate would depend on many other factors. What are some of them? Conditions have certainly not been the same throughout the earth's history. During the greatest part of its history, there were no land plants and very few land animals. When the plant cover is lost from an area today as a result of poor farm practices or deforestation we see erosion accelerated. If this condition existed for the continents as a whole in the past the amount of sediment flowing into the oceans may have been much greater than it is today. This might certainly have affected the rate of sedimentation. Thus as we go back into the earlier parts of the earth's history we should expect that conditions were quite different from those with which we are familiar.

Uniformitarianism vs. catastrophism

One of the first principal objections to the idea of uniformitarianism was the amount of time required for the completion of all the work accomplished by natural processes. In the eighteenth century most people believed that the earth was no more than 6000 years old. This would hardly leave time enough for a feature the size of the Grand Canyon to be formed by a stream cutting in the manner and at the rate of the Colorado River. Even if we accept the possibility that the river might have cut more rapidly in the past than it is now cutting, 6000 years is not conceivably enough time. One apparent solution to the problem is to accept the principle of uniformitarianism but with a modification. That modification is that the earth has from time to time experienced great catastrophies. It has even been

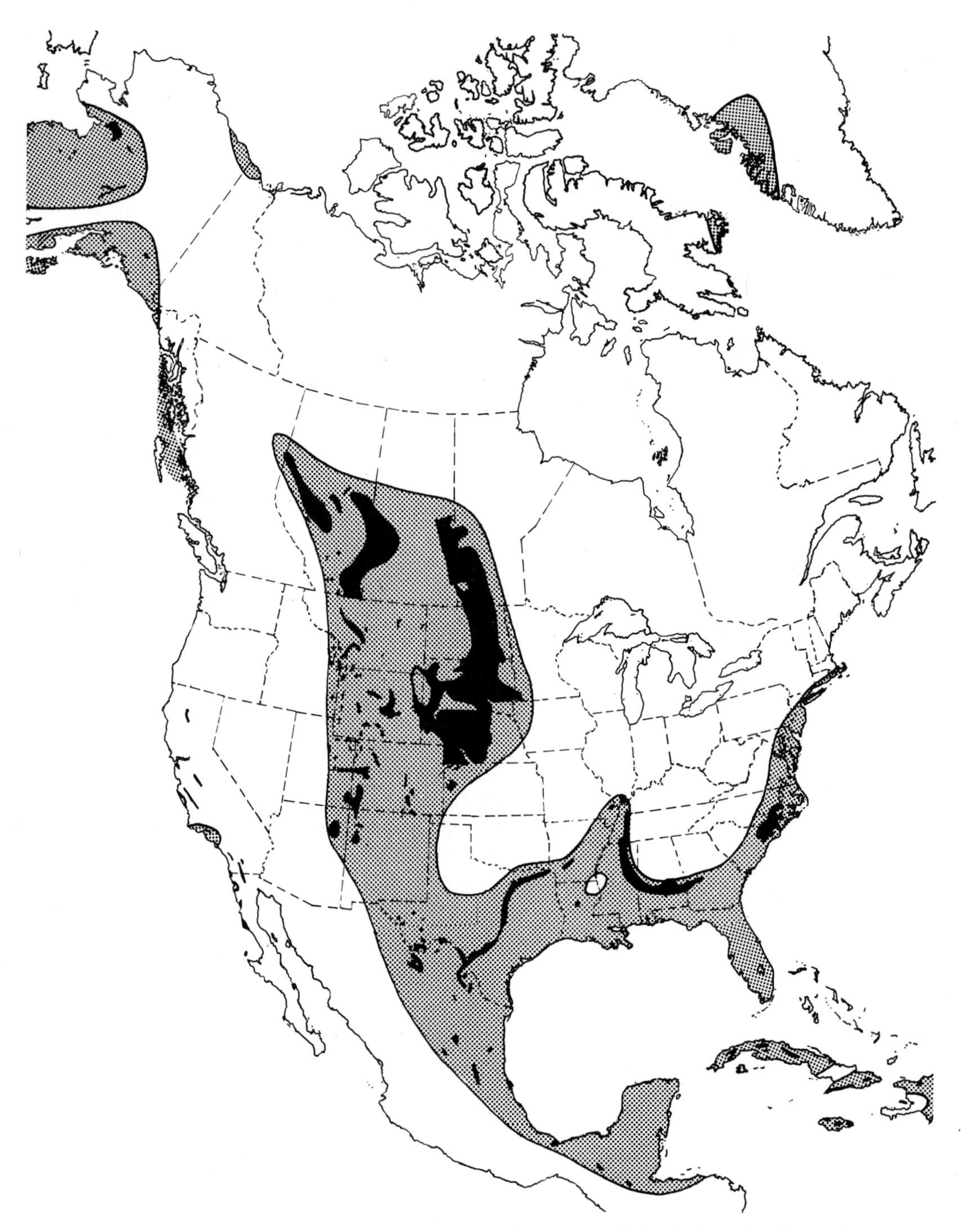

Fig. 3-4. North America 70 million years ago. This outline map of North America shows the outcrops of Upper Cretaceous (Campanian) strata in black. Because these strata contain marine fossils and are composed of sediments such as those now formed in the sea the position of the Upper Cretaceous Seas on the continents may be approximated. This was the last time seas spread extensively across the continental interior. The exact borders of the sea are exact only where ancient beach deposits are found. There are few such exposures, but the type of sediment and the fossil assemblages it contains are an indication of the water depth and distance from shore. (Reprinted with permission from Charles Schuchert, *Atlas of Paleogeographic Maps of North America*, John Wiley & Sons, Inc., 1955.)

proposed that the Grand Canyon is a huge rift in the earth's crust, torn apart in as short a time as a day or a week, and that the rift has simply been modified by subsequent erosion. As you might expect there is absolutely no field evidence for any such catastrophic event. In our discussion of the development of the time scale, it was brought out that periods of mountain formation marked breaks between the eras. Many have envisioned these mountains as rising rapidly, in a matter of a few hundreds of years. With the advent of accurate dating methods and with a greatly improved idea of the age of the earth, it is unnecessary to call on catastrophic events to explain the changes we observe. Uplifts of as little as a fraction of an inch a year may eventually create mountains. That slow rates of this order of magnitude have been the usual order of mountain formation is demonstrated by the unconformities that characteristically occur around the margins of major uplifts. Instead of sudden uplift, mountains rise slowly. They may become stable for a period of time while they are eroded, and the products of that erosion are laid down as sediments around the ranges. Then, when uplift is renewed, the sediments are uplifted; they are beveled off by erosion; and then new sediments from the mountains are laid down over them. Thus a series of angular unconformities are formed at the margins. From observations of the erosion and deposition of sediments at the present, we can say that the amount of time involved in these events is great. Radioactive dates obtained in the Rocky Mountain folded belt show that the mountains continued to be active over millions of years. This is typical of all the major mountain belts.

Uniformitarianism and catastrophism

If we must choose between these two concepts then uniformitarianism is the obvious choice. The very word "catastrophism" has a bad connotation for most earth scientists. They are so adamant in refuting the more extreme views of the catastrophists that they prefer not to use the word at all. However, events which may be called minor catastrophies are rather common on the earth today. The earthquakes which struck Agadir, Africa, and Chile in 1960 and the typhoon that hit Japan in 1959 are good examples of such catastrophic events. You can probably name other similar events that have occurred recently. Often the effects are pronounced. Each of the following occurs many times during every year:

1. Rivers flood and wash away huge amounts of top soil in a matter of a few weeks.
2. Hurricanes hit the eastern coast of North America. Storm beaches are formed, and ordinary beaches are washed away in the processes.
3. In deserts most of the annual rainfall comes in downpours within a period of just a few days. At these times most of the alteration of the desert landscape for that year takes place.
4. Strain is built up on opposite sides of faults for periods of many years; then the release of this energy and subsequent displacement takes place in a matter of a few hours.
5. Volcanoes may stand dormant for many years and suddenly begin to eject great quantities of lava, dust, or other pyroclastic material.
6. Tidal waves break up rocks along the sea cliffs around the oceans of the world and inundate the low land areas in short periods of time.
7. Masses of loose sediment or decayed rock stand on steep slopes for years until they become unstable. Then the slightest disturbance sets huge landslides in motion. The counterpart of this process in the oceans is the turbidity current. Some occur with the seasons, after large quantities of sediment have been deposited on the steep submarine slopes off the mouths of rivers.

These serve to illustrate the importance of minor "catastrophic" events in accomplishing erosion and deposition. The cumulative effects of the constant downslope creep of soil, the gradual decay of rocks under the atmosphere, and the gradual removal of material by streams hour after hour, day in and day out, over millions of years are probably much greater than the effects of these minor catastrophes. Nevertheless, the minor catastrophes should not be discounted. The two together constitute the nature of the operation of natural processes today.

FINDING ANCIENT LANDS

We often hear that the frontiers of the world have been pushed back until there is no longer a dark, unknown, and unexplored continent. Mount Everest has been climbed, the Antarctic has been crossed; yet there remain, unknown to most people, many unexplored lands, many lost continents and seas. These are not continents or seas in the usual sense of the word, for they are no longer distinct physiographic features. To discover them we must explore the past. The continents we find there are vast, the mountains high and rugged, the lands and the seas inhabited by strange animals. Even the plants found on many of these long-hidden lands bear no resemblance to those we see growing today. Parts of these lands are vast swamps, other parts are shallow seas rimmed by reefs. There are those who explore these ancient lands and seas for buried treasure such as oil and minerals; others seek the excitement and thrill of discovery. The results of these explorations are the subject of a later part of this book. Before turning to the story, we should first examine a few of the techniques used.

Now you should be able to see that the first important requirement in this exploration is to learn to determine the age of certain bodies of rock. They alone hold the key to the riddle of these ancient times. If we want to reconstruct a region or a continent as it

Fig. 3-5. Multiple unconformities. The margins of most major mountain belts contain unconformities. These indicate that the uplift was relatively slow, and intermittent. The top section shows conglomerate eroded from the top of the uplift and deposited on the flanks of the mountain. In the lower section the earlier unconformity has been warped upward and younger erosion products from the mountain are laid down across the unconformity. This structure is typical of the margins of many ranges in the Rocky Mountains.

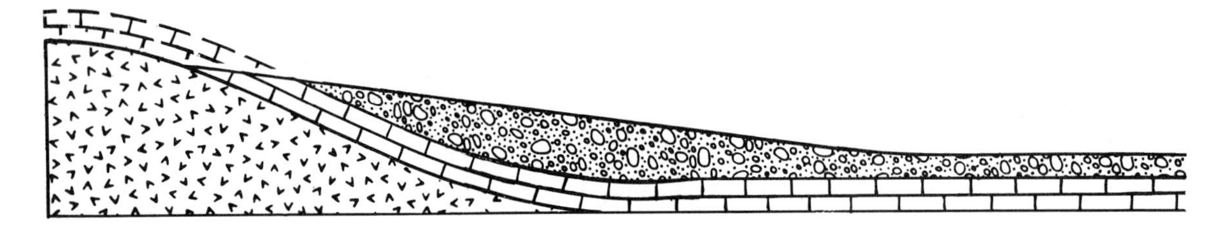

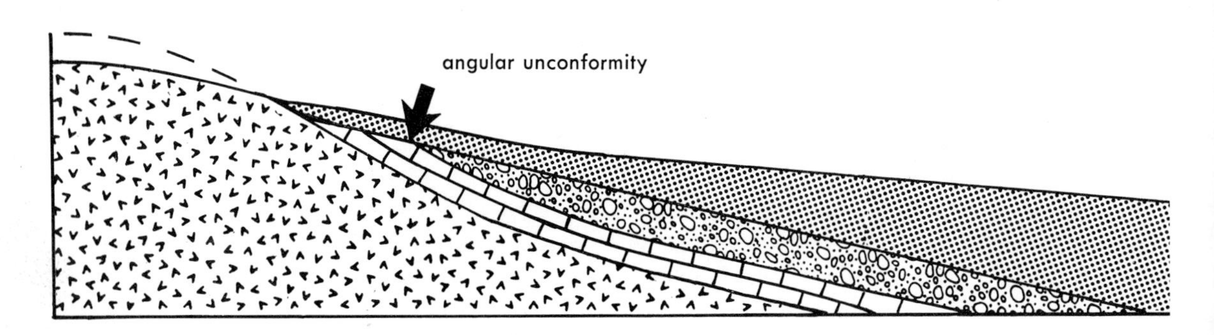

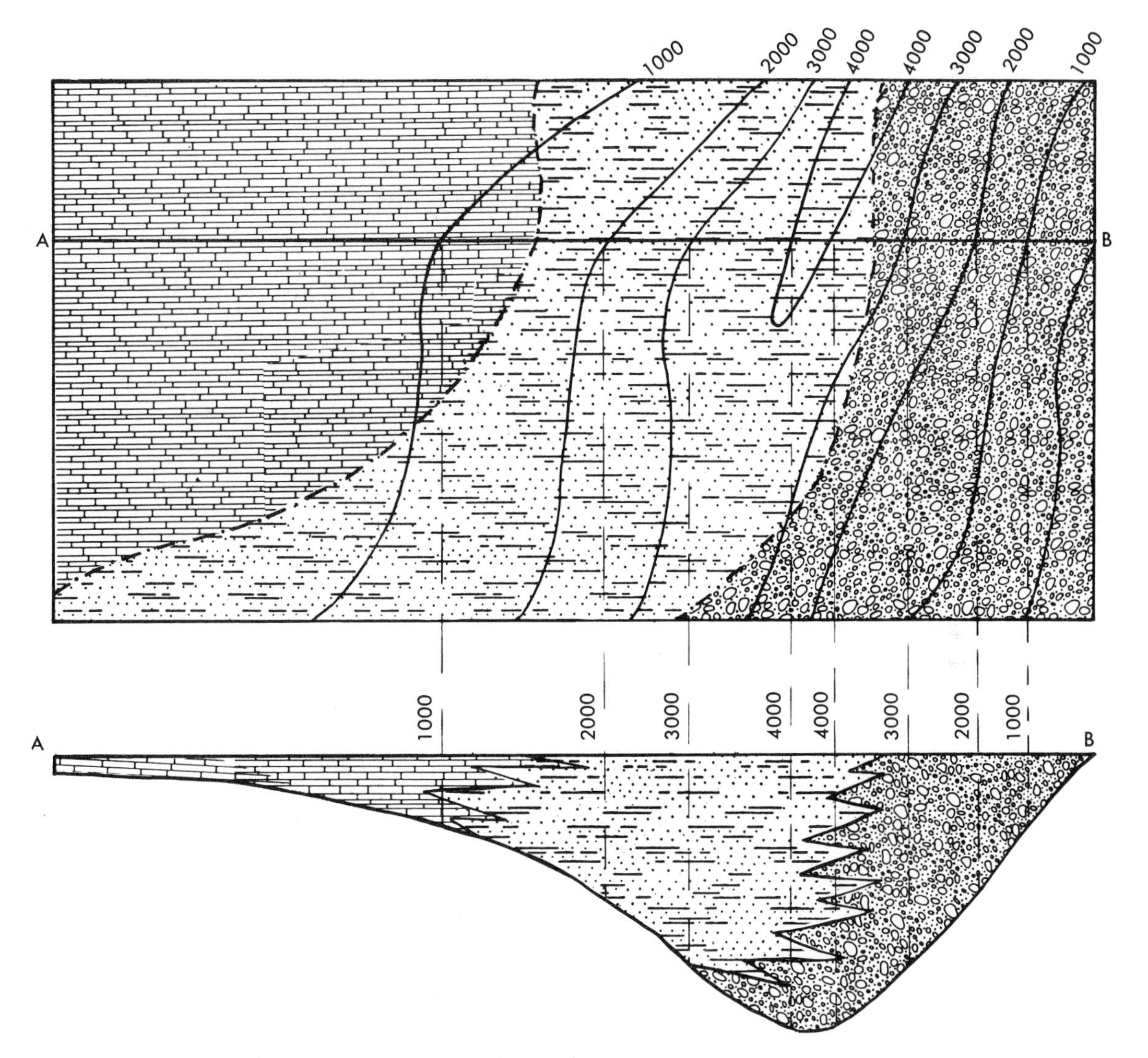

Fig. 3-6. Isopach map. The distribution of rock types is shown as an overlay on an isopach map. The top section is a map view on which the isopachs are drawn and labeled. They are somewhat similar to contours except that they represent lines of equal thickness of a particular rock or time-stratigraphic unit. Below is a cross section showing the variations in thickness along the line A-B on the map. The top of the unit is drawn here as horizontal and thicknesses are plotted directly below. When the isopachs and nature of the rock types are considered together we get a good indication of the conditions which prevailed when this section was deposited. The coarse conglomerates on the east side must have been eroded from a highland area. Further out sands and shales were laid down in a zone that was subsiding. In the west limestones were deposited in shallow relatively clear waters on the stable shelf. Here the geosynclinal accumulation trended north northeast.

was, we must first of all know what rocks were formed at that time. The reconstruction is complete only after the geography, climate, ecology, and stability of the crust at that time are known. We can go a long way toward obtaining this goal by studying surface outcrops, but the picture is often incomplete until there is a good sampling of subsurface data to supplement surface observations. The first step is to find the rocks that were formed during the time in which we are interested. This can be done by the methods already described such as radioactive dating, or by the use of guide fossils. Once the age of a few units has

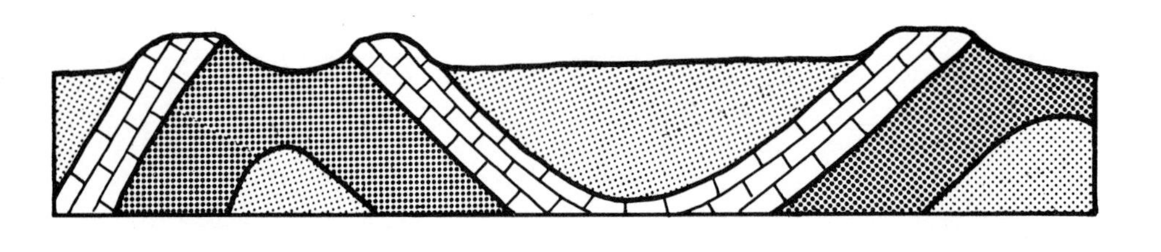

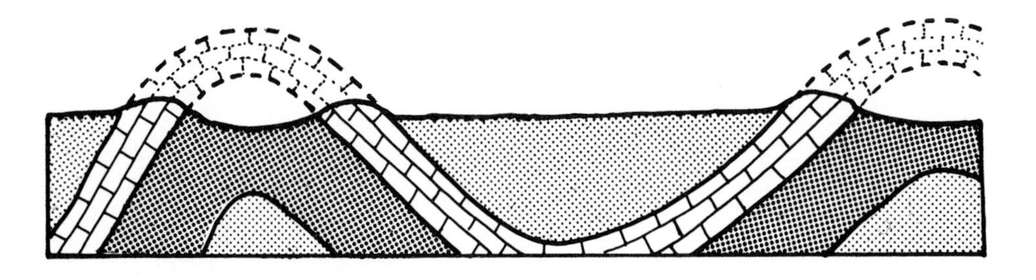

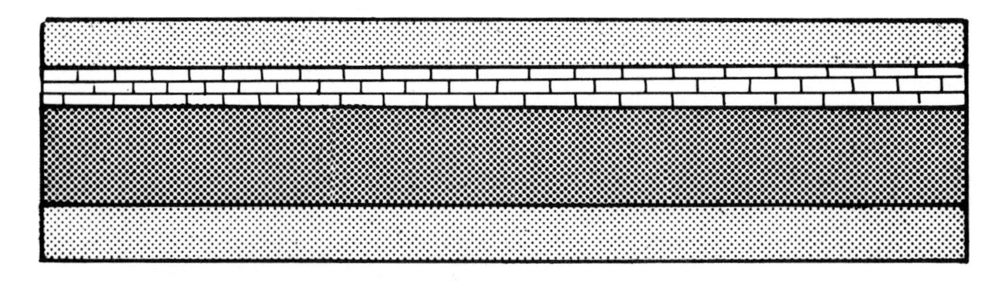

Fig. 3-7. Unfolding deformed strata. In this simple case the sedimentary rock sequence is shown in three cross sections. At the top the folded sequence has been eroded to form a valley and ridge topography somewhat like that of the Appalachian Mountains valley and ridge province. To reconstruct the conditions when the top sand was laid down the outlines of the folds are dotted in and then returned to a horizontal position approximating their attitude when the sediments were deposited on the sea floor.

been determined, others are dated by the various techniques of correlation. This eventually leads to relatively complete knowledge of the distribution of rocks of this particular age. We would probably start by making a map to show the distribution of these rocks at the present time. Then to this outline we might add more specific symbols to indicate the different types of rocks and their location in the overall picture. Thus the sandstones of this age would be differentiated from the igneous rocks, the shales, limestones, conglomerates, etc. From our understanding of the conditions under which these various types of rocks are formed today, we begin to see certain possible correlations between present conditions and those prevailing in the past.

Careful analysis of the rock units and of their fossil content is necessary to obtain all the information possible about the climates and the ecology of this period. From this we construct a paleogeographic map, one showing the geography of this period of time. It should include the continental margins and the features found along them such as beaches, offshore bars, continental shelves, continental slopes, swamps, deltas, and reefs. Also it may reflect the general nature of the land masses near the shore lines such as mountains, swamps, and plains or lowlands. Definition of the physiography farther from the continental margins is generally poor. (Why?) Paleontologic studies can reveal the correlation between the fossils and the various environments in which they lived. From them we may learn something of the temperatures, depths of water, and strength of currents in the seas. It is sometimes possible to infer climatic conditions from the nature of the sedimentary deposits.

The last important aspect that we may want to investigate concerns the stability of the crust during the period in question. It is not an easy matter to determine what happened in the areas that moved up, since they received no deposits and were usually the areas from which material was derived to be laid down elsewhere. But where regions went down and accumulated sediment it is possible to determine the extent of the deformation. This may be done by measuring the thickness of the time-stratigraphic units—rock units laid

Fig. 3-8. Reconstruction of strata. The folded, faulted, and tilted section at the top may be returned to its position at various times in its past history by determining the sequence of events and then systematically removing the effects of each. The first step is to reconstruct conditions before faulting, then reconstruct the eroded units and tilt section back to a nearly horizontal position such as that at the time of deposition of the top sedimentary sequence on the angular unconformity. Reconstruction might be continued by removing the top strata, and then proceeding as in Fig. 3-7 to reconstruct the conditions before folding.

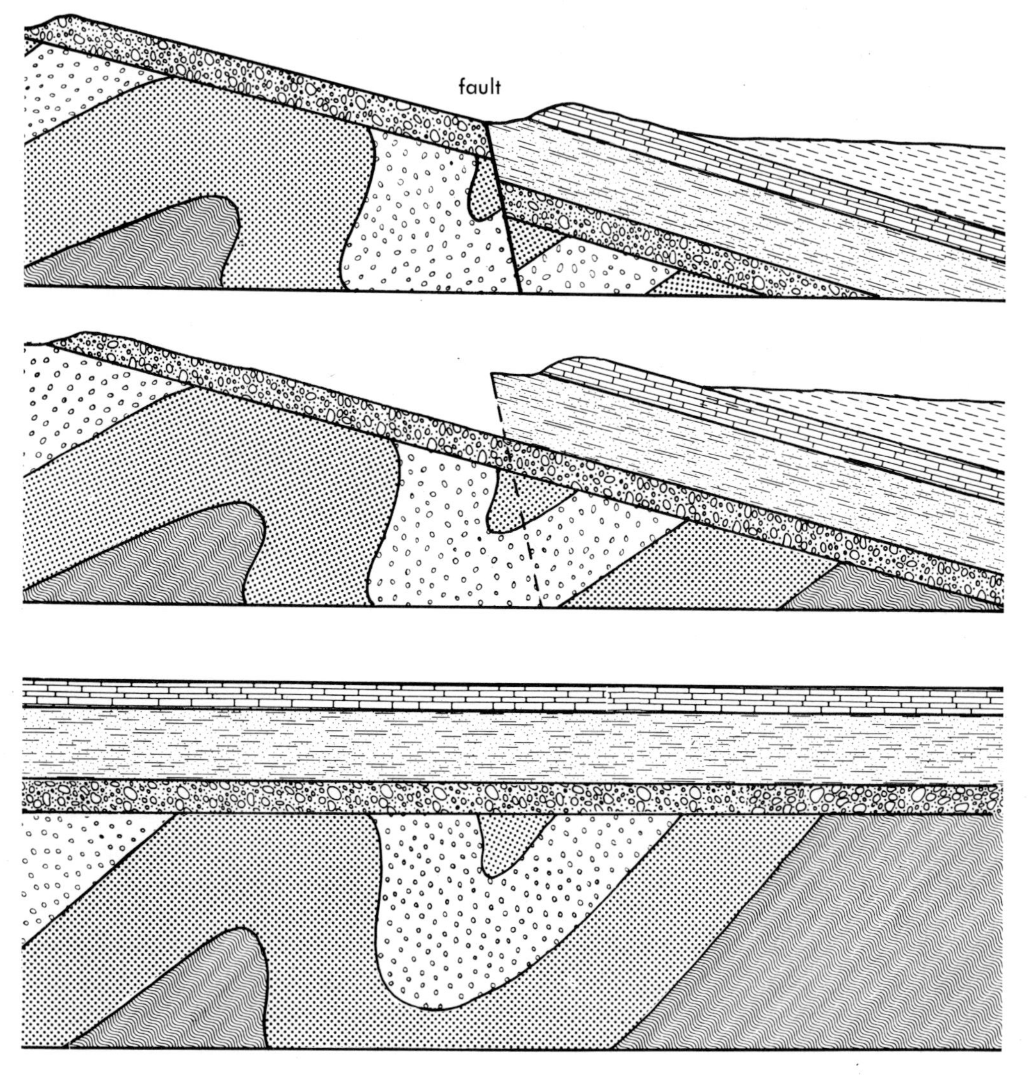

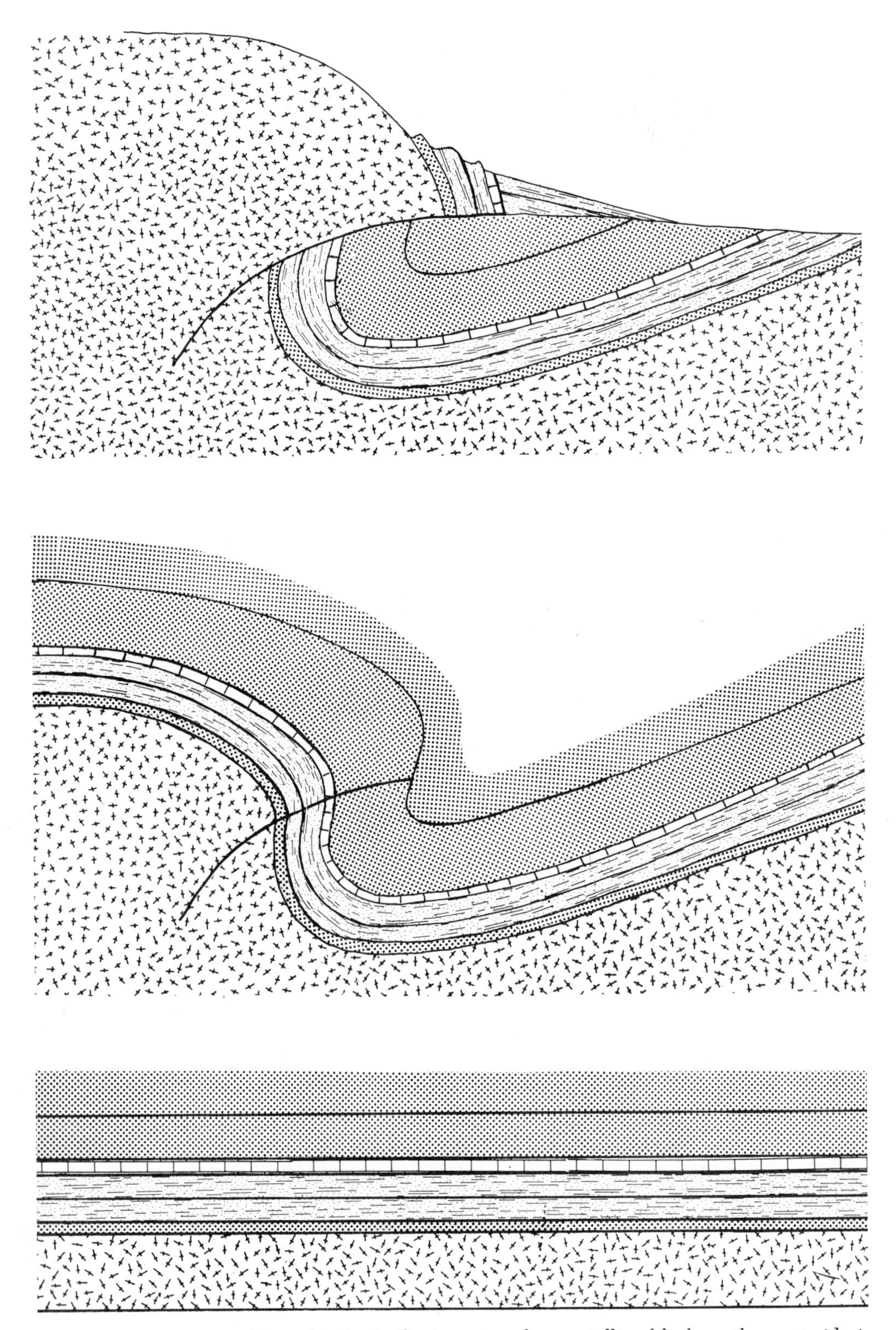

Fig. 3-9. Reconstruction of thrust block. In the top view the crystalline block on the west side is shown thrust up on a sedimentary sequence. At the bottom conditions such as they were before uplift and thrusting started are reconstructed.

down during the time period in which you are interested. These thicknesses are recorded on the map already constructed to show the distribution. It is often useful to prepare a map to help visualize these thicknesses. Such a map may be prepared by drawing lines connecting points of equal thickness. The result looks something like a contour map. In fact the lines are labeled systematically in the same manner as contour lines with a definite interval; the difference is that the interval is an increase of thickness instead of elevation. Where the lines are close together the units formed in this time are thickening rapidly. Where the lines are widely spaced the thicknesses are varying only slightly. Such a map is called an isopach map. The –0– isopach is the line separating units of this period from those that are older. The positions of deep accumulation are obvious from such representation, and this combined with the map showing distribution of different rock types may be extremely useful in interpretation. Assuming that there has been no later erosion, the areas covered by thin sediment were relatively stable. Those areas in which great thicknesses accumulated were near an abundant source of sediment such as a mountain range.

Unfolding deformed rocks

If the time we want to investigate lies far back in geologic history, it is highly probable that at least part of any extremely large area, such as one approaching continental dimensions, will have been deformed since the end of the period. This means that before we can construct an accurate paleogeographic map or isopach map, the effects of the deformation must be removed. This requires determination of exactly what happened during the deformation. If for example a large fault displaced the strata formed during the time in which we are interested, the original position of the strata is found by hypothetically moving the displaced strata back into their original position. Likewise, if the strata were thrown into folds, these must be restored by removing the folds. If the deformation has been complex and extensive this reconstruction is likely to be difficult or perhaps even impossible. The job of making restorations is not quite so difficult a task if you remember that many sedimentary bodies, such as those laid down on the continental shelves, are nearly flat-lying at the time they are formed.

REFERENCES

SCHUCHERT, CHARLES, 1955, *Atlas of Paleogeographic Maps of North America:* John Wiley and Sons, Inc., New York, 177 p.

4 Environments of Deposition

The main lesson to be learned from the theory of uniformitarianism is that the past can be successfully reconstructed in large part from the nature of the sedimentary deposits, the presence and distribution of igneous and metamorphic masses, and the structures formed in the past. "Change" more than anything else has characterized the face of the earth throughout its history. The surface conditions we find in an area today are no indication of what they were like in the past. We can often determine what they were like because we are familiar with a great variety of different conditions and environments on the earth today. It would not be an easy matter to explain ancient glacial deposits if there were no glaciers today, nor would we understand features characteristic of deserts if there were no arid regions, but fortunately both of these extremes do exist.

Most of the record of the past is left in sedimentary rocks. About three-quarters of the face of the land masses on earth is covered by sedimentary rocks. For this reason it is essential that particular attention be given to the formation and nature of unconsolidated sediments being laid down at the present time. You have studied the mechanisms of deposition. Now you should relate these to the environments in which deposits form. What exactly does the phrase "sedimentary environment" mean? It is used here to include all the physical, chemical, and biological conditions under which a sediment accumulates. Two obvious and widely variant environments exist, the continents and the oceans. Within each there are many smaller environmental niches. Factors responsible for these variations include:

1. The medium in which the rock is formed—water, air, ice.
2. The geography of the environment—the depth of the water, the external extent of the environment, and its general configuration.
3. Temperature.
4. Pressure and other climatic factors.
5. The nature of the movements in the medium in which deposition occurs. Was deposition from the wind, wave action, longshore currents, stream deposition at the base of a waterfall, or gradual silting from a slowly moving river? Consider the difference between the environment of deposition in the quiet of a lake and that of the turbulent mass of a density current. Each of the above will leave certain characteristics on the texture, fabric, or primary structures of the sediments formed.
6. The numbers and types of organisms present. Some animals secrete calcium carbonate, others use calcium carbonate to build their shells. Some animals are scavengers and will destroy the remains of other animals. In many environments the remains of one or more groups of animals or plants will be the dominant constituent of the sediment. In other environments no animal or plant remains are found.

Finally, of course, we must not overlook the nature and composition of the materials supplied to the environment. This is the material which will be deposited. It is the mass which to some extent reflects the conditions of the environment. Some materials are much more sensitive to variations in conditions than others.

Classification of the environments

It would require an exhaustive study of the deposits being formed in every part of the world in order to completely cover all types of deposits and to demonstrate all known relationships between them and the environment in which they are found. Few places have identical environments, but it is possible to classify the environments into workable groups which have essentially the same characteristics. Such a classification is manageable and serves to illustrate the range of variation as well as the principal types of environments we may expect in the rock records of past times.

The following classification is by Krumbein and Sloss, 1953:

MARINE ENVIRONMENTS
- Neritic (shallow water)
- Bathyal (water of intermediate depth)
- Abyssal (deep water)

TRANSITIONAL ENVIRONMENT
- Deltaic
- Lagoonal
- Littoral (beach)

CONTINENTAL ENVIRONMENTS
- Terrestrial (desert, glacial)
- Aqueous stream (fluvial)
- lake (lacustrine)
- swamp (paludal)
- cave (spelean)

Relative importance of the environments

The type of environment that should be considered most important depends entirely upon your point of view. The marine environment is by far the most important in terms of the quantity and extent of the deposits formed. Deposits formed in marine waters are the ones most frequently encountered in the rock records of past times. The continental deposits are formed above sea level where erosion is actively taking place. We have seen that, if there were no processes of construction, the earth's surface would be eroded to a nearly flat plain almost at the level of the sea in a period of about 23 million years. Although erosion goes on continually the land masses are uplifted in places, and continents tend to persist through periods much longer than 23 million years. However, their shapes do change. One result of this continual removal of material from the continents and shifting of it to lower levels is that continental deposits tend to be short-lived (geologically speaking). For most periods of geologic history one indication of the positions of land masses is the absence of deposits in the area. Some continental deposits are preserved and become part of the more or less permanent record, but these are rare compared with the number of marine deposits preserved. In general the continental deposits were buried by the advance of a sea that covered the area so fast that waves did not have a chance to break up and rework the deposits. In these cases the continental deposits are overlain by marine deposits, or transitional deposits.

Fig. 4-1. Arctic coastal plain. Most of the sedimentary rocks now exposed on the continents were originally deposited in shallow seas such as the one lying off this coast. The sediments deposited will bear tangible evidence of the cold water and low land areas which are important factors in the environment of deposition here. (Photo by courtesy of the Royal Canadian Air Force.)

Although the greatest volume of sediments is marine, the transitional or continental deposits may provide crucial clues to such questions as the climate, position of shore lines, nature of the land masses, and fluctuations in sea levels. Continental deposits are of great value in the interpretation of the Cenozoic Era. Many such deposits are exposed on the continents. These include the debris eroded from the Rocky Mountains and spread across the continent on both sides of this range. Other important deposits are those laid down during the Pleistocene, the ice ages. In general the abundance of continental deposits is inversely proportional to the time since their deposition. As we go back into the Mesozoic and Paleozoic fewer sedimentary rocks originally deposited on continents are found. In the long run the marine deposits have a far better chance of survival.

In the following discussions greater attention is given to the deposits of marine and transitional environments than to continental deposits. There are several reasons for this. First, the majority of people are less familiar with these environments. Secondly, cave deposits, desert deposits, stream beds, and glacial deposits are adequately explained in physical geology, and they are not commonly encountered in rocks more than a few million years old. The glacial deposits will be covered later in a discussion of the history of the ice ages.

Deep-sea sedimentary environments

How deep is the deep sea? The boundary between the region treated here as the deep sea and the shallow water is 100 fathoms (600 feet). This corresponds approximately to the edge of the continental shelves throughout most of the world. Water depths between 100 and 1000 fathoms are called bathyal, and from below 1000 fathoms to the bottom of the deepest sea trenches is the abyssal zone. Compared with other sedimentary environments, the deep seas and their environments are little known to us, although they cover more than half the face of the earth. Until the Second World War the deep seas received little attention from oceanographers. Exploration there was too expensive, too time-consuming, and the necessary tools were not available. Since the Second World War there has been considerable interest in the ocean basins, and governments have recognized the importance of spending the necessary money to obtain a better understanding of them. Until this time it was generally assumed that most of the deep-sea basins were very similar and that the conditions within them showed little variation. Now we are aware that the variations are much greater than expected, even though a great number of the details are still unknown.

From the point of view of sedimentary environments there is little reason to treat the bathyal and abyssal zones separately. Other than the fact that the bathyal zone grades into the neritic zone, the two zones are similar. Both receive sediment from:

a. Finely suspended material in sea water.
b. Remains of the abundant floating and swimming life, mostly protozoans, in the surface water.
c. Meteorites.
d. Debris which slumps and slides downslope in density currents from the edge of the continental shelf.
e. Marine plants, especially the diatoms.

Both zones are almost free of surface-wave disturbance and current action (except for density or turbidity currents). Internal tidal currents may affect them; however, very little is known about these. Neither zone receives light, nor do they contain nearly as abundant a benthonic (bottom dwelling) population as the shelf waters. Hydrostatic pressure is high, more than 2000 pounds per square inch, in both areas, and temperatures are low, close to freezing in the abyssal plains.

Deep-sea sediments

Red clay is the most extensive deep-sea deposit. Its actual color is from brown to reddish. It contains films of manganese or manganese nodules. Red clay is found in the greatest depths. Its origin is subject to considerable debate. Scientists believe that it is derived

Fig. 4-2. Radiolarians. Radiolarians such as these make up oozes which cover large areas of the sea floor. Their remains are siliceous. These are greatly magnified. (Photo by E. W. Spencer.)

Fig. 4-3. Diatoms. Diatom remains, like radiolarians, are siliceous. The diatoms are microscopic sized plants. They provide a source of food for a large part of the animal population of the ocean. A variety of diatoms is shown in this greatly magnified microphoto. (Photo by E. W. Spencer.)

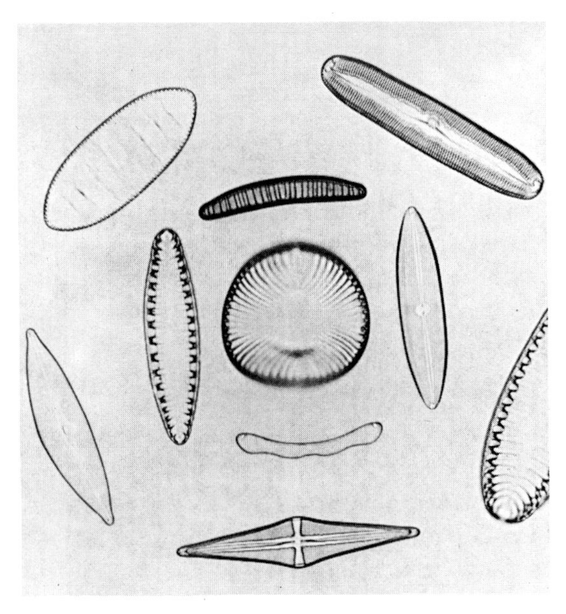

from the finest clay fractions taken into the oceans from the land areas. It has also been attributed to submarine weathering of basic volcanic material and to the accumulation of meteoric dust.

***Globigerina* ooze** is the second most extensive deposit of the deep seas. It is a calcareous mud formed from the shells, called tests, of the Globigerinas, protozoans of microscopic size which have a globular-shaped shell. The tests are made of calcium carbonate. There is almost no *Globigerina* ooze found below depths of 2500 fathoms, because calcite is soluble under high pressure and at low temperature. Clays are usually mixed with the *Globigerina* tests in these sediments and may take up more than 50 per cent of the deposit.

Diatom ooze is a deposit consisting of siliceous remains of the microscopic-sized plants, diatoms. Most of these are located between latitude 40° South and the Antarctic Circle. The beautiful but minute plants contain droplets of oil and may be the source of most petroleum.

Coral sand and mud is locally abundant in the deep-sea areas around coral reefs, having been carried out and dropped by surface currents.

Less widely distributed sediments include muds which are named for their color (red, blue, green) and volcanic sand and mud. Red is confined to the coastal areas close to the mouths of the Amazon and Yangtze Kiang Rivers. Blue and gray muds of continental origin occur in shallow to deep areas near land masses. Green muds probably get their color from the mineral glauconite or chlorite. Volcanic muds and sands are frequently mixed with other deep-sea sediments in the volcanic belts throughout the world.

Deposits from density currents exist in an abundance which is as yet undetermined. Some oceanographers suspect that these may account for a large part of the total volume of sediment of the ocean basins. Many years of research will be required to establish how extensive they really are. There is little doubt that they are important. Activated through slumping along the edge of the continental shelf, sediments of the neritic zone move down into the deep water. The fact that these sediments can move down low slopes for hundreds of miles has been definitely established. They account for the presence of neritic fossil fauna, ripple marks, and coarse sands in the abyssal environment.

What factors affect the distribution of deep-sea sediments?

1. Those deposits carried by density currents are lobate in form. The lobes originate from areas on the shelf which have slumped. Most of these are slopes which have become over-steepened as a result of long-continued or rapid sedimentation. For this reason, density-current deposits are most likely to occur off steep continental shelves, where sediment is carried out in the ocean by large rivers, and where there are no deep-sea trenches off the coast in which the deposits might be trapped.

2. Red clays are extremely widespread. They appear to be abundant where other types of sediment are lacking. It may be that the materials which make them up are deposited uniformly everywhere but that they are inconspicuous when mixed with large amounts of other sediment.

3. The chief source of other pelagic, deep-sea sediments is marine animals and plants. Diatoms are most abundant near the surface in high latitudes where the ocean waters are upwelling and fertile. Of the single-celled animals the radiolarians and Foraminifera are most abundant toward the equator; they are also more abundant near shore than away from it since their food supply is most abundant in shallow waters. Although they are of little importance in shallow-water sediments, they are the main constituents of the sediments of deeper waters. Why? Because most of the clastic (fragments such as sand) sediments are heavier and have dropped to the bottom long before they can be carried into the areas of deep water. The protozoan remains make up a small fraction of sediments dominated by sand, silt, and limestone.

4. An important factor determining the dominance of siliceous sediment over calcareous sediment is the depth of the water. Calcium carbonate is much more highly soluble in deep, cold waters of the oceanic deeps. Thus siliceous remains of diatoms and radiolarians dominate these waters.

Fig. 4-4. Deep-sea ripple marks. This picture was taken with a camera which was lowered to a depth of 700 fathoms in the North Atlantic Ocean. The presence of ripple marks there is a positive indication of current action. Likewise sandstones which contain ripple marks formed millions of years ago are indications of the currents which moved in ancient seas at the time of their formation. (Photo by courtesy of the Lamont Geological Observatory, Columbia University.)

Deep-sea sediments of the Indian Ocean

Sediments of the Indian Ocean have been described by Wolfgang Schott in the following words:

> The Indian Ocean contains almost all known types of recent deep-sea sediments. In the equatorial and temperate latitudes Globigerina ooze, red clay, and radiolarian ooze are found, as well as . . . blue mud, coral mud, and others . . . in subpolar and polar regions, diatom ooze and glacial-marine sediments occur.
>
> All these deposits consist dominantly of two types of substances, mineral and organic. The mineral constituents come from the adjacent mainland

or from islands. They reach the sediment in different ways:

1. Suspended fluvial material;
2. Material eroded from the coastline;
3. Glacial debris from icebergs; or
4. Dust from volcanoes and deserts.

. . . The organic constituents depend on the animals and plants living in the sea water or on the sea bottom. Near the coast and in areas of shallow water the organic world of the sea bottom is the decisive factor. . . . If the organic components are distinctly subordinate to the mineral ones, or are completely lacking, in the open ocean the sediments consist of red clay, but near shore the sediments consist of . . . blue mud, green mud or in polar regions, of glacial marine sediments.

Deep-sea sediments of the Pacific Ocean

In many ways the Pacific is distinctively different from other oceans of the world. Its great size and the small number of rivers flowing into it offer two reasons for this conclusion. In addition the marginal zone and the southwestern part are highly active seismically and volcanically, and deep-sea trenches located around the margins act as sediment traps to prevent continental debris from being carried far out. The deep water is more alkaline than that of most oceans and contains a high concentration of silicate and phosphates. Finally the equatorial current system is well developed, and plankton are extremely abundant in these waters.

Fig. 4-5. Distribution of sediments in the Indian Ocean. By studying the distribution of modern sediments and the conditions under which they are deposited we can unravel the history of ancient deposits. (After Wolfgang Schott, *Recent Marine Sediments*, 1955.)

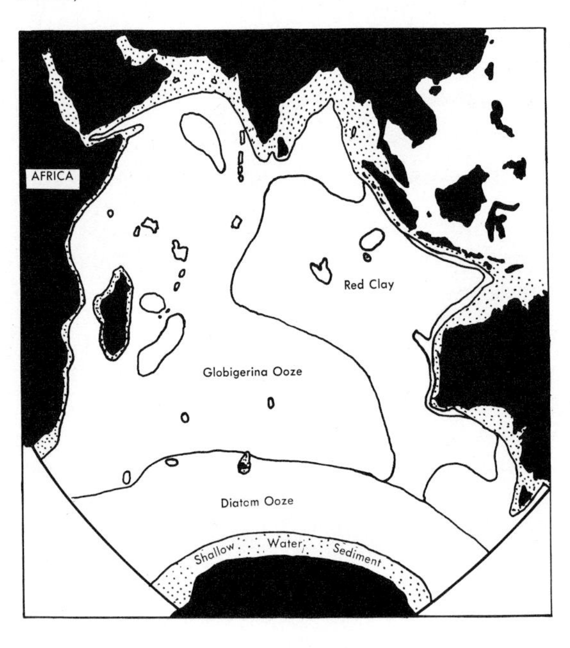

Diatom ooze forms bands across the northern part of the Pacific and across the Antarctic Ocean. A belt of calcareous oozes is found at the equatorial belt and particularly in the southern Pacific. Radiolarian ooze borders this calcareous belt on the north, and red clay dominates most of the bottom sediment in the northern Pacific and in large scattered areas of the southern Pacific. This clay covers almost twice as much area in the Pacific as in the Atlantic, probably because of the greater areas of deep water in the Pacific. Turbidity-current deposits are known to be present in great abundance off the west coast of North America. In the areas of active deformation, high mountains near the coast, rapid erosion, and consequently rapid supply of terrigenous sediment to the narrow continental shelf which margins the west coast combine to favor oversteepening of deposits and slumping.

Neritic environments

The outer margin of the neritic zone corresponds roughly to the edge of the continental shelves, and the inner margin is the position of the lowest tides. In this zone the water depth varies from almost zero to about 100 fathoms. The neritic environment covers about 10 per cent of the face of the world, but it is by far the most important zone or area in so far as the formation of sedimentary rocks now exposed on the continents is concerned. The environment and its sediments are more diversified than are those of any other environment. The sediments are derived in part from the continents and animals that are dependent on the shore and sea bottoms and in part from

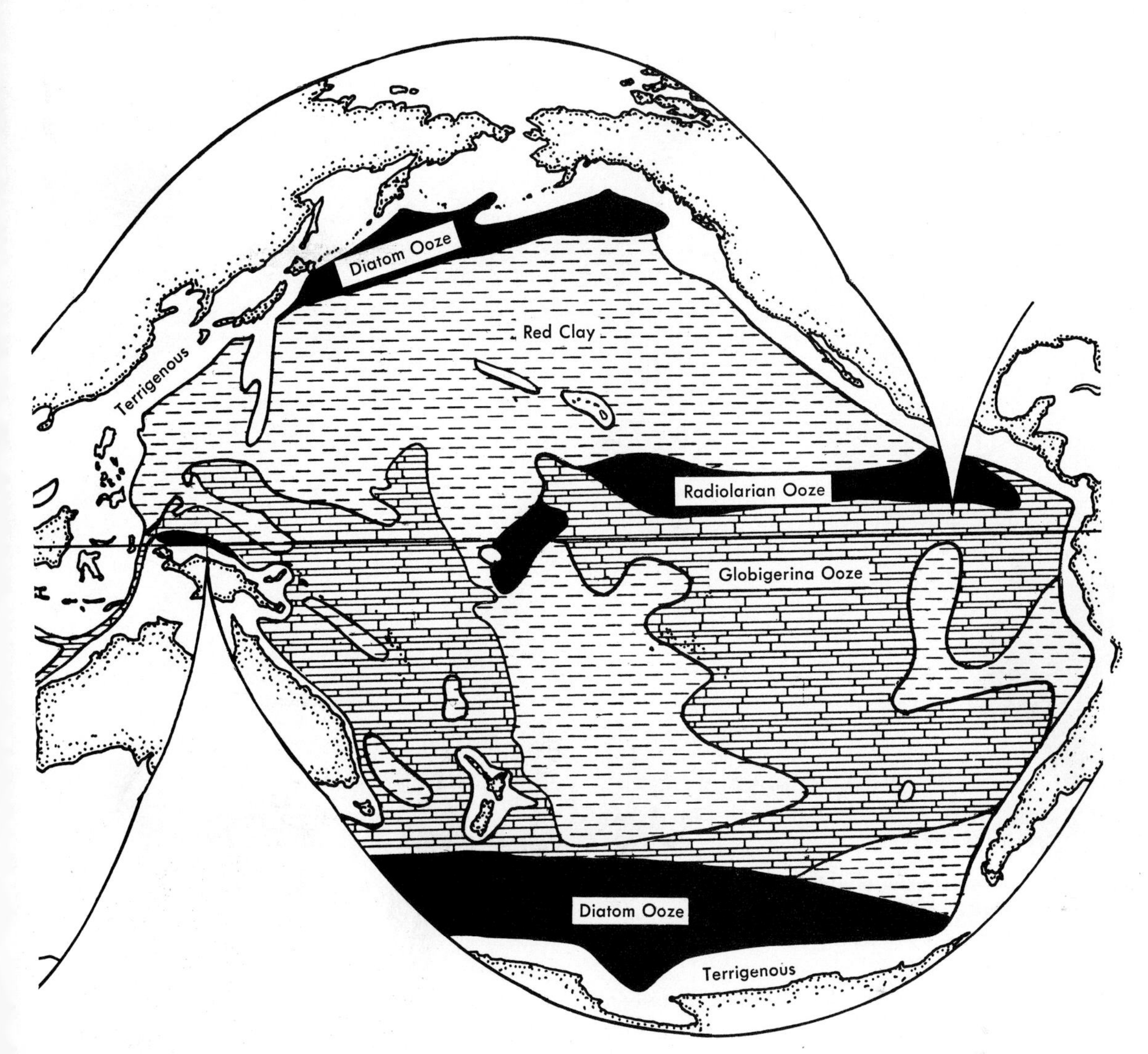

Fig. 4-6. Distribution of principal marine sediments in the Pacific. Note the extensive areas of red clay and globigerina oozes in the central part of the ocean. The siliceous diatom oozes concentrated in the high latitudes; the radiolarian oozes along the equator; and the distribution of terrigenous sediments near shore surrounding the ocean. (Adapted by permission from *The Oceans: Their Physics, Chemistry and General Biology,* by H. U. Sverdrup, Martin W. Johnson, and Richard H. Fleming. (C) 1942. Prentice-Hall, Inc. Reprinted by permission of the University of Chicago Press, copyright by the University of Chicago.)

the pelagic communities. Pelagic communities are groups of marine organisms which live free from direct dependence on the bottom or shore; the two types are the free-swimming forms, nektonic, and the floating forms, planktonic. Because the neritic environments are important and highly diversified several noteworthy examples are considered. These include an estuary, an atoll, and the Bahamian platforms in addition to the general treatment of continental-shelf deposits.

General features of the continental shelves

The continental shelves are far from uniform in nature. Off the eastern and southeastern coast of the United States a lowering of sea level to the edge of the shelf would reveal a wide, gently sloping land surface. Florida would appear roughly twice its present width. Off the southern coast of California the shelf area is very irregular and includes deep basins

Fig. 4-7. An aerial view of old mountains nearly buried in their own debris in an arid climate. Deposits such as these are not as likely to survive long ages of erosions as are shallow marine sediments. This area is in Arabia. (Photo by courtesy of the U.S. Air Force.)

and high mountain blocks situated between the coast line and the steep escarpment which borders the deep Pacific basin. The outer margin of the shelf off the Mississippi delta is also very irregular. These are probably the results of subsidence and slumping of the edge of the shelf and may be related to a major fault zone bordering the deep parts of the Gulf of Mexico.

The shape and extent of the shelf is determined by the nature of the continental margins. Along coasts characterized by young folded and faulted mountains the shelf is narrow. Wide shelves appear most often off coasts characterized as broad low lands, off glaciated lands, and off many of the world's largest rivers. The biggest shelf area is in the Arctic where the width reaches 800 miles in places. Shelves are commonly between 10 and 20 miles wide.

The shelf environment, unlike the deep sea, is penetrated by light. This tends to make it warmer and more suitable for a large number of marine organisms. The main energy factors in the environment are waves and current action and, to a smaller extent, chemical activity. Almost all the shelf is disturbed periodically by wave motion that extends down from the surface. Even the outer margins are affected by storm and tidal waves, and currents move continuously over the shelves. These are the longshore currents set up by the oblique impact of incoming waves on the shore. They tend to move along parallel to the shore and are responsible for the transportation and sorting of sediments. Temperature is an important environmental factor. It depends primarily on the temperatures of the water brought onto the shelves by the oceanic currents and on the latitude of the shelf.

Sediments on the shelves are dominated by terrestrial debris near the shore, but at greater distances offshore biological factors become increasingly important. Maps showing the distribution of sediment types on the shelves off the northeastern and northwestern coasts of the United States are shown (Figs. 4-8 and 4-9). From these examples generalizations may be drawn regarding sediment distribution.

1. Sediment textures do not vary systematically either along or perpendicular to shore lines. Many areas show a progressive decrease in size of sands or silts out from the beaches for several thousand feet. But this often grades back into coarser sediments again. Several explanations have been offered to account for the coarsening of sediment toward the continental-shelf margins. One is that storm waves have carried both coarse and fine material out to that position, and that later the fine sediment has been sorted out and removed by lesser current and wave action. Along the

Fig. 4-8. Distribution of marine sediments off the coast of the northeastern United States. (Modified after Francis P. Shepard, *Recent Marine Sediments*, 1955.)

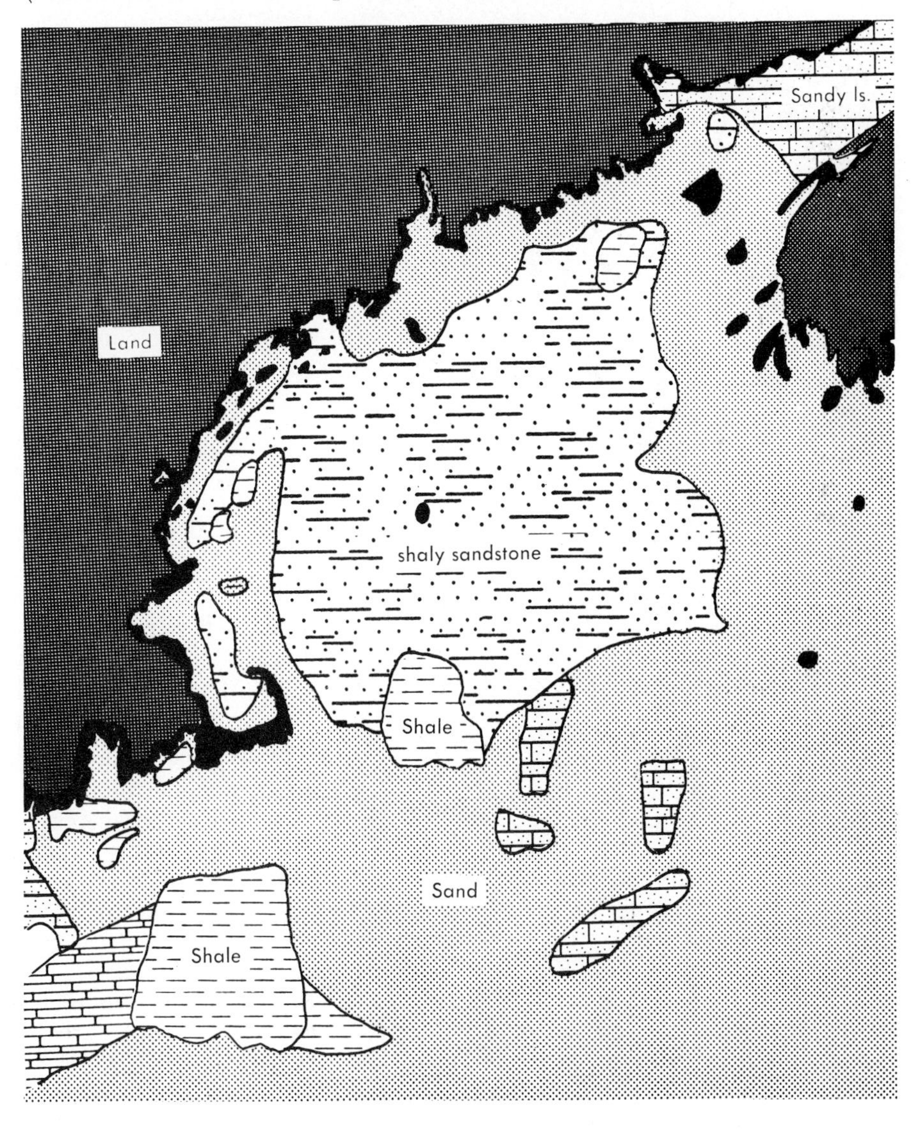

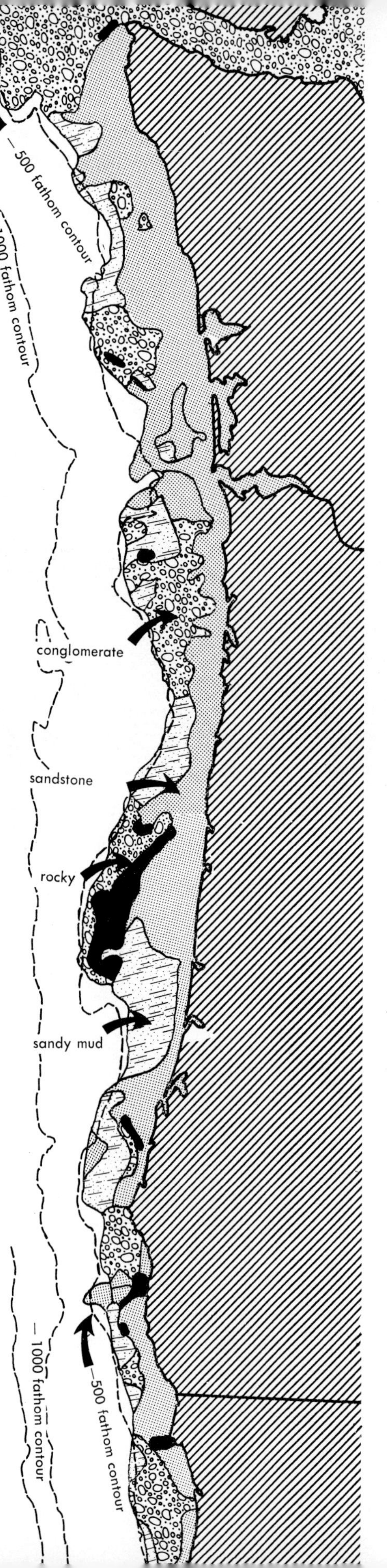

edge of the shelf off the eastern coasts it may be that wave action has sorted the sediments and that the Gulf Stream has removed the finer sizes and carried them into deeper waters. A second hypothesis is that the coarser sediments were laid down near the edge of the shelf during the ice ages, the Pleistocene, when the continental shelves were at least partially exposed. Such a lowering of sea level throughout the world would necessarily accompany the ice ages as water from the oceans was stored on land as snow and ice. That sea level was lower in the Pleistocene is generally accepted, but there is considerable doubt that the coarse sediments we find at the edge of the shelf are those deposited near shore many thousands of years ago.

2. Not all shelves have coarse sediments at their outer margins. Some show a progressive decrease in the size of sediment from the shore line out to the margin of the shelf, just as we might predict.

3. Bare-rock bottoms are found on some shelves. They are more likely to be found on the narrow shelves than on the broader ones. Most of them are covered by a thin veneer of sediment that is in the process of being transported across them to deeper water. For many years it has been assumed that these were wave-cut and wave-built terraces. Photographs taken under water now show us that the outer margins are not all wave-built terraces composed of deposits. Instead rocky outcrops appear right at the edge of the shelf. The sediment that is deposited near the edge of these solid shelves periodically slumps off or slides down slope in turbidity currents.

4. The character of sediments on the shelves is closely related to the types of lands that are located near them. Muddy sediments are generally found on shelves beyond the mouths of large rivers such as the Amazon, the Mississippi, Elbe, Yangtze Kiang, and the Indus. On shelves off parts of the continents that were recently scoured by continental

Fig. 4-9. Distribution of marine sediments off the northwestern coast of the United States. (Modified after Francis P. Shepard, *Recent Marine Sediments,* 1955.)

Fig. 4-10. Deposition of continental sediments. Continental sediments are being deposited in these glaciated valleys. (Photo by courtesy of the Royal Canadian Air Force.)

glaciers the sediment is a mixture of rock fragments, sands, and mud such as that produced by glacial erosion. This is typical of the Barents Sea north of Norway and Sweden, Baffin Bay between Greenland and Canada, the Ross Sea in the Antarctic, and the Gulf of Maine. Where high mountains border the coasts an abundance of coarse sediments such as gravels and coarse sands flood out onto the shelves. If the rate of burial is rapid, feldspar fragments as well as insoluble minerals may be found in the sediments. If lowlands or plains border the sea the sediments are usually fine, and the remains of animals and plants may make up a large portion of the sediment.

Littoral environment

The littoral zone is that part of the shore between the average position of the highest flood tides and the lowest ebb tides. Among the most important factors that play a role in determining the nature of the deposits in the littoral environment are:

a. The configuration of the shore line.
b. Stability of the shore (whether it is stable, emerging, or submerging).
c. The quantity and type of sediment being brought to the shore.

There are three distinctly different types of littoral environments: those characterized by sea cliffs and wave-cut terraces; those located along low, open shores similar to areas along the central Texas coast; and those, called the tidal flats, extensive, nearly level plains, submerged twice daily by tides. Deposits of the littoral zone are not too important in terms of frequency of their occurrence in the rock record. Few instances are known, but, of these, a number have been important oil-producing zones. The recognition of such environments can provide important information since they clearly define shore lines.

Cliffed shore lines. Rugged shore lines have cliffs ranging in slope from 10° or 15° to vertical and even overhanging. Usually there is a platform of more gentle slope at the base of the cliff, but some plunge into water of great depth leaving no littoral zone at all. On others, particularly in bays, the platform is covered by a beach, but usually the cliff is terminated at a wave-cut terrace just below the level of the water. More than any other environment this is dominated by wave action and mechanical energy. The sediment type supplied from the immediate vicinity depends to a large extent on the type of material making up the cliffs. If hard, crystalline, igneous, or metamorphic rocks or compact sedimentary rocks are exposed in the cliff, angular blocks and boulders will be found along the narrow littoral zone. These are broken up by wave action, and the small fragments are shifted seaward and deposited at the edge of the platform. If they are sand size they may be carried on along the shore by currents. If the cliff is composed of poorly consolidated sediment, the masses which slump into the sea will tend to be broken up and carried off much more rapidly by current action.

Low shore lines. Like the cliffed shore, these are dominated by wave action; however, most of the wave energy is spent before reaching the upper parts of the beach. Sand is by far the most common sediment along these shore lines, although cobbles, pebbles, silt, or

Fig. 4-11. Bermuda beaches. Coral reefs and coral sand are seen in this view of the beaches of the south shore of the Bermuda Islands. Sand here is composed of calcium carbonate rather than quartz. It is a product of the wave erosion of the reef building organisms. (Photo by courtesy of Bermuda News Bureau.)

even clay may be found. The type and distance of the source from the beach and the strength of the longshore currents govern which of these sediments will be found in any particular location. In seas that contain a high concentration of calcium carbonate, the sand may be composed of shell or reef fragments or even calcareous oölites. These appear on the shores of the Bahamas platform and on some atolls. In some areas olivine or volcanic ash may make up the sand. In the Azores, after the eruption of a new volcano in 1959 the beaches were composed of black sand, volcanic cinders, and ash. Silts and colloids may appear in this environment, where rivers carrying them in suspension enter the sea.

Not all beaches are exactly alike, but most may be divided into three parts.

1. The offshore zone extends seaward from the position of sea level at low tide. This part of the shore is always under water.
2. The foreshore is located between the inner margin of the offshore zone and the level of the highest tide. Part of this zone is in and out of water at least once a day, and the lowest part of it is washed by every incoming wave. A part of the foreshore, sometimes called the upper beach, is under water only during storms. The sand found here is coarser than that making up the lower beach. This part of the beach tends to rise up to a crest.
3. The backshore, or berm, is built up by successive high-water levels and by high storm waves. In a few instances, the berm is as much as 50 feet above the average level of the sea.

Beaches and bars. Although this subject has been treated in your course in physical geology, it is well to review briefly some of the deposits found along low, open coasts. If there is a bay, then beaches are very likely to occupy a position at the head of the bay. As waves enter the bay they hit the beach margins of the bay and are refracted. This sets up longshore currents on either side of the bay that are directed toward the head of the bay. Sand and silt are shifted along toward the bay head and eventually accumulate to form a beach. Sometimes cuspate beaches or bars will form along the sides of the bays. As a general rule bays are catchment areas for sediment more than they are sources of it; therefore they have a tendency to be filled in. Erosion is concentrated on the headlands near the mouth of the bay.

If there is plenty of sediment and a longshore current capable of moving it, bay-mouth bars will form across the entrance to the bay. Such a bar may grow until it completely cuts the bay off from the sea.

Offshore, submerged bars or long narrow barrier beaches may form approximately parallel to the shore line. A few of these are founded on ridges or rock formations such as reefs, but most of them appear to have no solid foundation. Various explanations of their origin have been offered. They are probably deposits of sand thrown up from the sea floor by the agitation of breaking waves. This sand would come from the zone immediately in front of the bars, and there is frequently a shallow depression in this position. The bars grow until they emerge above sea level. Then they may continue to grow when unusually large waves or storm waves carry more sand up on them.

Other features of relatively minor importance are the curved bars known as spits and the bars called tombolos that connect islands with the land.

Tidal flats are favored by low-lying land near sea level but protected from wave erosion and strong currents. They are generally located near an abundant source of sediment such as the mouth of a large river. The sediments on tidal flats often consist of soft water-soaked slime. There is a large amount of fine silt and clay and a little sand, all mixed with varying amounts of shell fragments, minute sea-urchin spines, fine plant detritus, and fragments of diatoms, Foraminifera, and ostracods. In some areas excrements of worms and other invertebrates make up a significant part of the sediment. Many invertebrates inhabit the tidal-flat environment. These include gastropods,

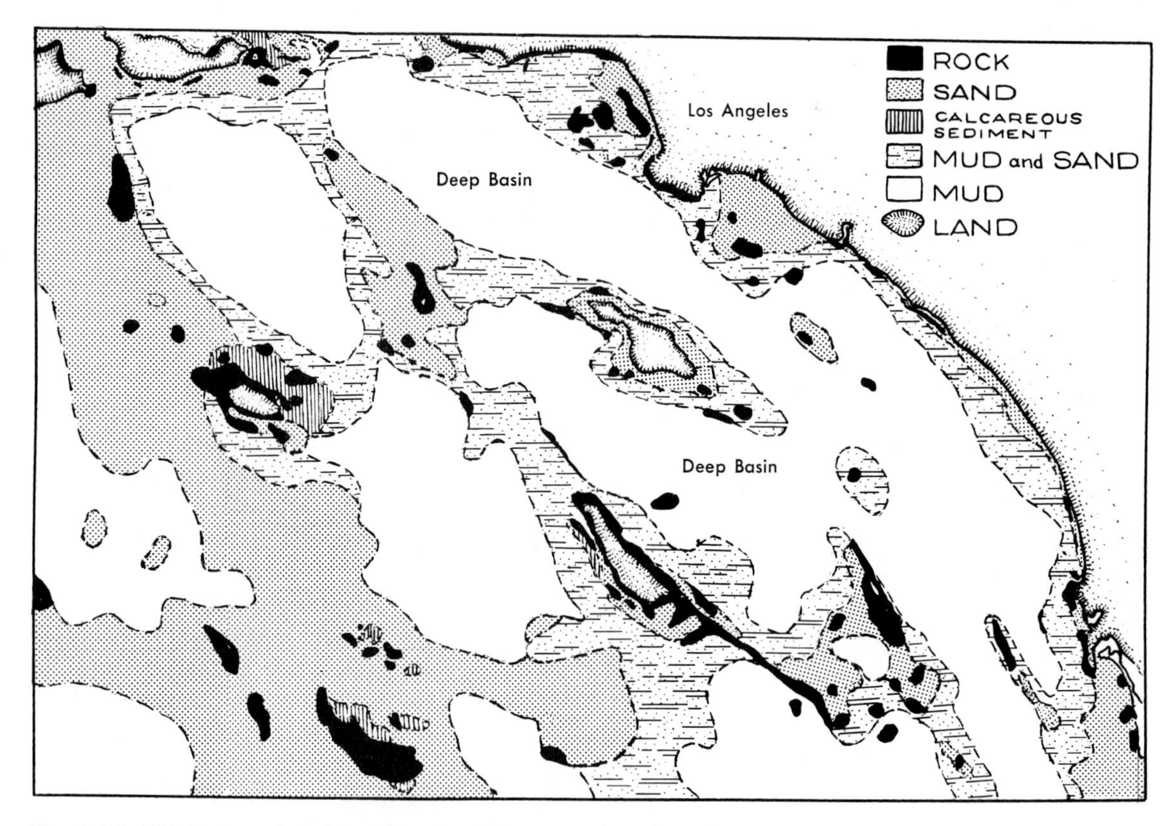

Fig. 4-12. Distribution of marine sediments off the coast of southern California. Compare the distribution of sediments here with those along the Texas coast and the northeastern coast of the United States. Here the shelf is very narrow and the region is characterized by deep basins separated by blocks which stand high and in a few cases appear as islands. (Modified after Revelle and Shepard, *Recent Marine Sediments,* 1955.)

worms, pelecypods, and many smaller animals.

The deposits on tidal flats are finely stratified. The sands and silts are stratified and cross-bedded, reflecting the reworking of the sediment by shifting currents. The amount of sediment and rate of sedimentation on certain present-day tidal flats are truly surprising. Hantzschel reports as much as 7.3 m of sediments deposited within 3 years in the harbor entrance to Wilhelmshaven, Germany. The rate is sufficient to make continuous dredging necessary to keep the channel open for shipping.

Sources of the muds vary from place to place. Some tidal flats are thought to originate almost entirely from the deposition of suspended matter from streams, but others appear to be reworked swamp or glacial deposits. Animal excrement accounts for a large amount of sediment in certain areas of some tidal flats, and it contributes to making a very rich soil. In Holland when the tidal flats are built up close to sea level or slightly above by storm waves, dikes are built around part of the flat, and it is then used for agricultural purposes.

Marine environments off the coast of Southern California

Unlike most of the deep seas, the submarine landscape off the coast of Southern California is made up of a number of deep basins separated by higher blocks. The basins are as deep as the abyssal zones in some parts of the area, and the blocks rise above sea level in a few places. Where these blocks have been elevated above sea level, they are bare of sediment, and the shallow waters around them are typical of the neritic environments. This particular area is of special interest, because it is an example of a region in which the topography has acted as a controlling factor in the distribution of the sediments.

Near the shore line there is a narrow continental shelf. On this we find the sand and silty sediments carried into the sea by rivers. They are sorted by the wave action and the longshore currents before they are transported very far down the shore. In this nearshore zone there is an almost perfect distribution of sediments according to size. The coarser materials are dropped nearest the shore, and these grade into finer materials which are carried progressively farther from the shore. This progressive change does not, however, continue all the way out to the edge of the shelf. There the sediment begins to get coarser, and even sand and gravels may be found. It is possible that storm waves are responsible for these sediments. Storm waves are often large enough to cause movement in the water down to the depth of the edge of the shelf. This movement causes shifting of the sediments and consequently sorting near the edge. In this way the finer sediments may be removed periodically.

Submarine canyons cut across the shelf in a number of places. These are deep enough to be relatively free of any surface-wave disturbances that might tend to sort the sediments. The sediments found in the canyons are generally fine silts and sands, but there may be patches of coarser sediment where the sides of the canyons apparently slumped into the gorge.

In the deep basins that are found out beyond the continental shelf the sediments are much less well sorted than are those on the shelf. In the centers of the basins, which have relatively flat floors, mud is the most characteristic material. These muds are composed of the fine matter carried out in suspension. Around the edges of the basins sands and silts appear mixed with the muds from the shallower water. The greatest variety of sediments is found on the banks and ridges of the uplifted blocks. Here we find that rocks are exposed. These are the source of part of the sediment found near

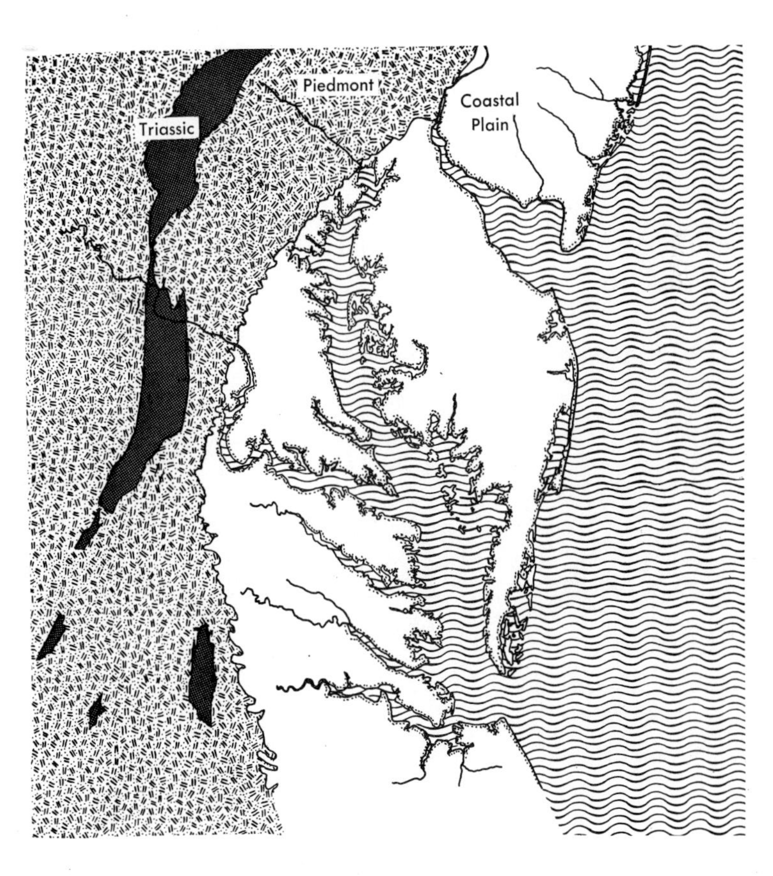

Fig. 4-13. Chesapeake Bay region. The region is divided into several provinces: the continental shelf, the coastal plain, piedmont, and the lowlands underlain by Triassic sedimentary rocks.

them, and this sediment ranges in size from pebbles and cobbles to the finer sands and silts.

An estuary as a neritic sedimentary environment

An estuary is an inland extension of the sea following the path of a submerged or drowned river valley. The largest estuary in the United States is Chesapeake Bay. Among the large rivers flowing into the Chesapeake Bay are the Susquehanna River at its northern end and farther south the Potomac, Rappahannock, and James Rivers. The bay has been investigated by the Office of Naval Research and the United States Hydrographic office as well as the Chesapeake Bay Institute. A distinct pattern of sedimentation is found in this estuary. Along the fresh-water stream channels coming into the bay cobbles, pebbles, and sand occupy the channel bottoms, and mud occurs in the shallow water on shoal areas. After the stream enters the bay, however, the pattern begins to be reversed with coarse material on the shoals and fine clays in the channels. Such a reversal is not easily explained. Sand may be picked up and transported along the channel floor by less current than is required to move clay. The reason for this is that sand occurs as small discrete particles which may roll and bounce along the floor of the channel, but clay is held together by strong cohesive bonds and thus tends to remain stuck together in large clumps once it has been deposited. One explanation for the observed reversal is that eddy currents in the bay are strong enough to transport finely suspended clay colloids toward the channels, but are not strong enough to move the sand on the shoals. Once the clay is deposited in the channel it further retards the movement of sand into the channel by sticking to the sand and holding it in place.

A second aspect of the pattern of deposition is the presence of elongate, lenslike bodies of clay in the channels. These lenses begin near the contact of fresh water and salt water. They thin down the stream channel for many miles. The lens originated as a result of the flocculation of the clay at the salt-water contact. Flocculation is the process by which clay colloids aggregate forming small lumps of clay. These lumps are often too heavy to be carried in the slow-moving waters of streams on low gradients and thus they settle to the bottom.

One interesting aspect of these clays is that they have a tendency to become adjusted to the various types of marine environments. Thus the alteration of the clay minerals may be a key to other environmental factors. For example the alteration is at least partially dependent on the salinity of the water. This can be used in the analysis of ancient deposits as

Fig. 4-14. Bikini Atoll. Schematic section showing the various parts of the reef. (After J. W. Wells, *Jour. Geol.*, v. 58.)

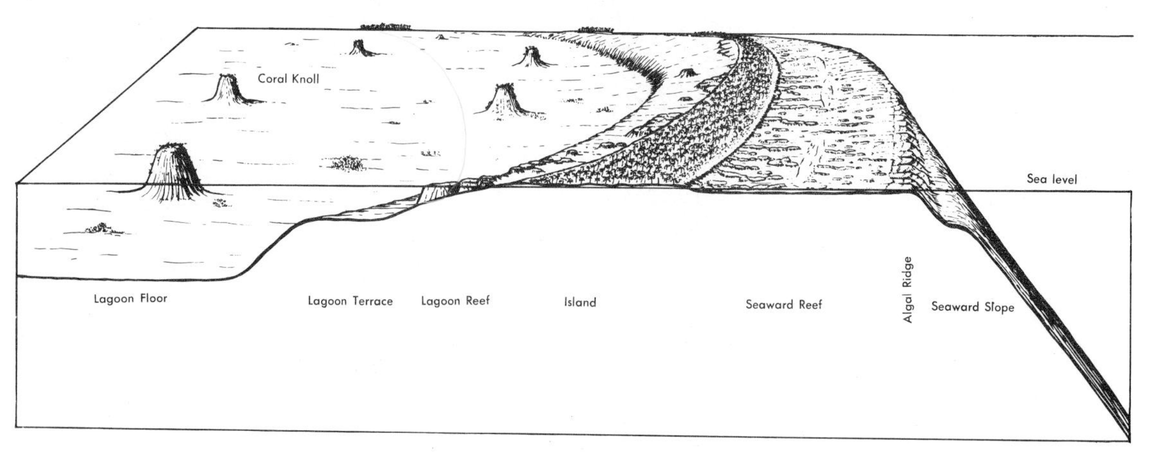

Fig. 4-15. View across the Great Barrier Reef. This reef fringes the northeastern shore of Australia. (Photo by courtesy of Qantas Empire Airways Ltd.)

well as of modern deposits. You have probably learned to identify at least one type of clay. Actually there are many different types, but their physical properties are so similar that it is nearly impossible to distinguish them without special equipment. One of the most successful means of studying them is by what is known as differential thermal analysis. The clay is subjected to steadily increasing temperatures, and the reactions of the clay minerals are noted.

Environment of an atoll

An atoll is a ringlike coral reef or reefs encircling or nearly encircling a lagoon. Thousands of these small reefs dot the southwestern Pacific Ocean and the Indian Ocean. The deposits around them are primarily carbonates, of organic origin. The Bikini Atoll is chosen as a typical example because it is one of the most thoroughly investigated atolls in the world.

Bikini is an oval-shaped group of islands about 26 miles long and 15 miles wide. Marginal reefs are almost continuous around the atoll. In places they are a mile wide. The central lagoon, which has an average depth of 26 fathoms (156 feet), covers approximately 250 square miles. Twenty-six islands surround the lagoon and stand at a maximum height of 25 feet above sea level. A number of passes a mile wide cut through the reef.

Reefs are quite vital on the seaward side of the islands. There they are in direct contact with the open sea which brings in a constant supply of water rich in food and nutrient salts.

Fig. 4-16. Air view of an atoll, Cocos Island. Waves are seen breaking on the shallow portions of the reef. (Photo by courtesy of Qantas Empire Airways Ltd.)

The nature of the marginal zone and of the assemblages of organisms that live there is determined by the slope on which it is located, the prevailing waves, currents, and other ecological conditions. K. O. Emery of Scripps Oceanographic Institution classified the reef types as follows:

1. Strongly grooved—those on which the seaward side is cut by well-developed grooves perpendicular to the reef. The grooves are approximately straight. The ridges between the grooves are flattened and covered by massive coralline algae, which appear to be well adjusted to the strong steady surf on the windward side of the atoll. Where the marginal reefs are low, only a few inches above the large reef flat which extends back into the lagoon, there is a rich growth of corals on the flat. Where the marginal reefs are high, 2 to 3 feet above the main reef flat, water circulation is restricted, and few living corals are found on the flat behind.

2. Grooves weak or absent—no massive coralline algae are present. These reefs are usually on the leeward side of the atolls. Some of the reefs of this type are smoothly scalloped. The seaward slope is very steep, plunging into water about 200 feet deep. The marginal zone here contains coral and algae, but they rise only a few inches above the reef flat. On these smooth reefs, growth of the reefs exceeds the rate of erosion. Reefs of a slightly different nature occur where erosion is more active and on the side of the atoll which receives the most severe storms. These storm waves break up the reef into large blocks which slump into deeper water, but they continue to be covered by a growth of new coral.

Fig. 4-17. Grooves on seaward side of Bikini Atoll. (After sketches by P. B. King, *U.S. Geol. Survey.*)

In summary we may say that reef rocks fall into two groups, algal or coral-algal reef limestone and detrital-reef limestone. The coral-algal limestone is formed of organisms mostly in their original position of growth. The detrital limestone includes blocks of reef mixed with finer fragments. The two types are mixed and grade into one another.

Islands. The islands are formed where broken fragments of the reef become piled up on the reef platforms by waves, currents, and wind. Rocks on the islands include some consolidated gravels, conglomerates, and sandstones, but most of the islands are unconsolidated reef detritus made up of sand, gravel, and rubble. Some of the islands are bordered by beach shingles made of cobbles and boulders of reef debris. The sands are composed of Foraminifera tests, coral and mollusks fragments, fragments of algae, and some finer material.

Lagoons. A shallow terrace borders much of the lagoon. The terrace is covered by 50 or 60 feet of water. It has a few enclosed depressions which suggest solution depressions. If they are, it would be an indication that the terrace stood above sea level at one time and was later lowered in relation to sea level. The main basin of the lagoons is flat except for coral knolls which are growths of isolated mounds of coral. The main sediments in the lagoons are tests of Foraminifera, a coral (Halimeda), and shells of mollusks.

Outer slopes. Near the top of the outer slope numerous large blocks of reef broken off from the outer margin are mixed with sand- and silt-sized detritus of Foraminifera and other organisms. Farther out, at depths of approximately 1000 fathoms, *Globigerina* sand covers the bottom. At still lower levels sediment of volcanic origin is found below the *Globigerina* ooze. Two of the core sections obtained by drilling on the Bikini Atoll reveal the following sequences:

Inches	
0-2	Buff *Globigerina* ooze
2-4	Light-gray *Globigerina* ooze
4-6	Green-gray *Globigerina* ooze
6-9	Buff *Globigerina* ooze
9-13	Light-gray *Globigerina* ooze
13-15	Buff *Globigerina* ooze
15-16	Light-brown *Globigerina* ooze containing weathered basalt
16-24	Light-gray stiff *Globigerina* ooze
0-4	Light-buff *Globigerina* ooze 1/2-inch pebble of tuft-breccia
4-5	Light-brown granular ash
5-6	Dark-brown ash with 1/16-inch grains of black volcanic glass
6-7	Light-brown fine-grained ash
7-7 1/2	Green ash with 1/16-inch grains of rock
7 1/2-9	Dark-brown ash with black volcanic glass
9-11	Oxide lapilli tuff with 1/16-inch crust of manganese

Bahamian platforms

The Bahama Banks, which are located south and east of Florida, cover more than 100,000 square miles of the Caribbean Sea. They are most notable as an extraordinary example of a modern shallow-water area in which almost pure limestone is being formed. This condition is not new for the area. Calcium carbonate sediments have been forming there for approximately 130 million years, since the Early Cretaceous. Since that time virtually no sediment other than limestone has been deposited. These beds have an accumulated thickness of more than 14,000 feet, indicating a probable slow subsidence of the platforms as the limestone was deposited near the surface by precipitation of calcium carbonate ($CaCO_3$) and the accumulation of organic remains. The probable explanation of this subsidence is that it represents a slow isostatic adjustment of the crust to the weight of the sediments. There is no evidence suggesting other deformation. The absence of sands, silts, and muds which might have come from any nearby high land supports this deduction.

The banks are low-lying platforms covered for the most part by approximately 5 fathoms of water and separated by broad, flat-bottomed, deep channels. Coral reefs form the rims of the banks which are islands separated by broad lagoons. Beyond the reef rims the water deepens rapidly toward the ocean basins. Only a small part of the exposed limestone is made up of reef debris. Most of it has been precipitated. Professor Newell of the Museum of Natural History suggests that the platforms developed from Early Cretaceous oceanic coral atolls which gradually became incorporated into the continent by the spread and coalescence of calcareous deposits. "During the Pleistocene epoch the reef communities were nearly exterminated and blanketing oölite deposits were laid down over the Tertiary reefs. Recently, renewed reef growth has been resumed around the bank margins."

The platforms may be thought of as typical of the shallow seas in which many of the limestones of the geologic past accumulated. For this reason the environmental conditions that have led to the deposition of $CaCO_3$ here are especially important.

1. The region is for the most part completely free of terrigenous, land-derived, sediment.

2. A second factor to consider is the climate. The region in which the Bahamas are located is usually covered by warm dry air.

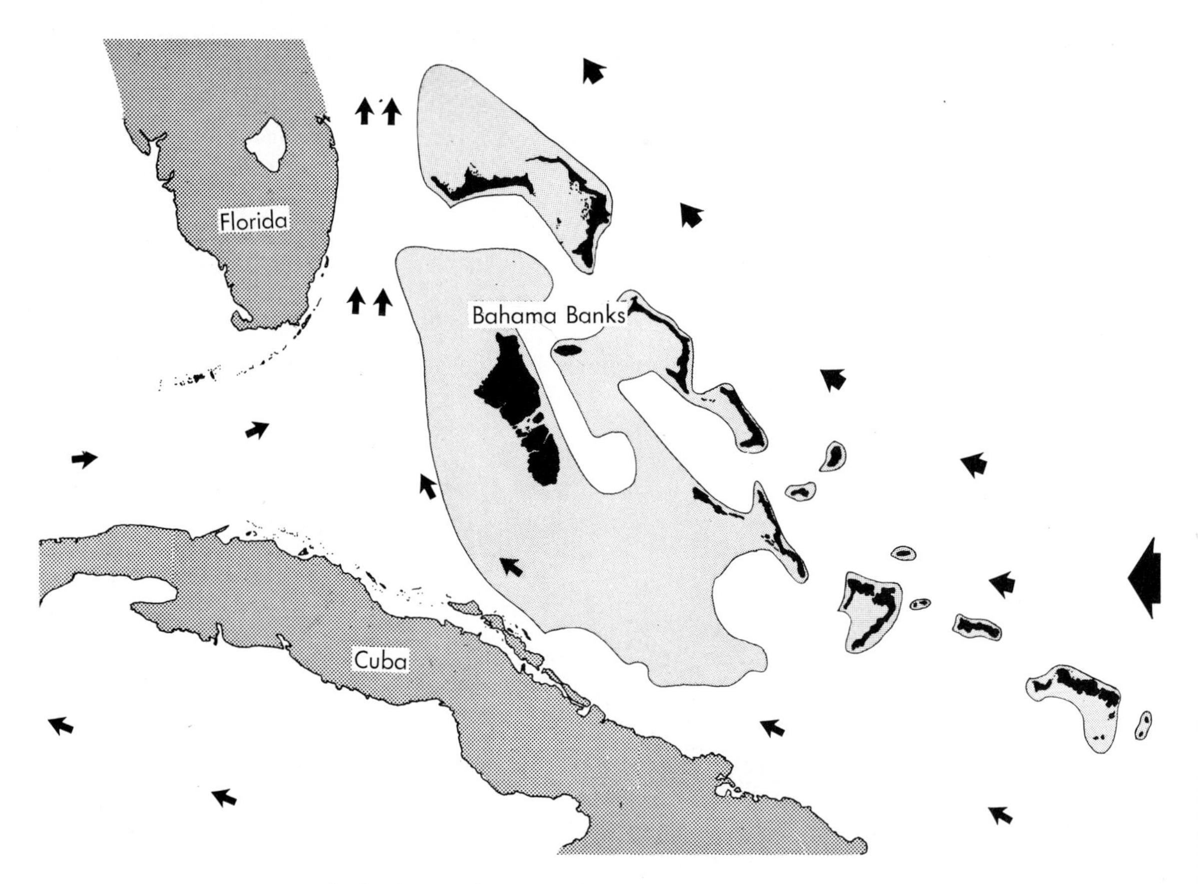

Fig. 4-18. Bahama Banks. The banks are shown in black; the shallow water surrounding them is shaded. The shallow water surrounding Florida and Cuba is not shaded. The arrows indicate the direction of prevailing ocean surface currents. They bring warm waters rich in calcium carbonate up from the equator.

This favors precipitation, since the rate of evaporation of water is accelerated. The average temperature in the winter is 70°, and rainfall averages approximately 50 inches per year. The banks lie in the path of the easterly trade winds, which also accelerate evaporation.

3. A third factor is the abundance of calcium carbonate. The surface waters of the Caribbean Sea are close to 40 per cent above saturation in calcium carbonate. As these waters are carried across the shallow banks there is naturally more surface evaporation. This causes the calcium-carbonate content to concentrate further, and the agitation and heating which take place cause a loss of carbon dioxide. These conditions accelerate the precipitation and accumulation of $CaCO_3$ over the shallow banks.

Sediments. The platforms may be subdivided into several sedimentary regions: the barrier rim, a shelf lagoon, an outer platform, a marginal escarpment, and the deep channels between the platforms. Sediments on the barrier rim are dominated by silt and sand composed of oölite grains and skeletal fragments of the reef faunas. The sand is produced by wave action breaking up the shell and reef remains. Just behind the reef there are many lime-secreting organisms, which also account for a large part of the rim sediment.

Over the platform as a whole much of the limestone is chemically precipitated ooze, oölite sand, and faecal pellets. Oölite sand is originating near the edge of the banks. Oölites tend to form in agitated waters where the supersaturated waters first break and lose carbon dioxide. The oölites are made of concentric layers of calcium carbonate built around a central nucleus of aggregate grains of lime or faecal pellets.

The shelf lagoon is the site of accumulation of calcium-carbonate ooze. This is a mud which consists of microscopic-sized crystals formed by direct precipitation.

The marginal escarpment and outer platform are kept clear of sediment by currents and by wave motion.

Marine environments along the central Texas Coast

There are four principal types of environments along the coasts of central Texas: deltas, protected bays, barrier islands located off shore, and the open continental shelf of the Gulf. Among the main factors influencing the processes of sedimentation and the types of sediments being formed are variation in the salinity of the sea water, effects of wave and current action, depths of water, and variations in supply of source material for the sediments.

Deltas. The deltaic environments are similar to those of the Mississippi River delta, although there are no streams approaching the size of the Mississippi, and most of the deltas are relatively small. In general, deposits are high in clay and organic content on the top, marshy parts of the delta. Coarser sands and silts are found in the channels of streams now flowing across the delta surface and also where old stream channels have been abandoned. At the margin of the delta, silt containing wood fibers and calcareous aggregates are common.

Bays. The shallow bays are protected from wave and current action by the offshore barrier beaches. The water in these bays is calm, in general influenced by the daily tides and, at several points, by fresh-water streams. Like deltas, the bays are not uniform throughout. There are a number of subenvironments. These arise from slight differences between the conditions in the middle of the bays, where open water prevails, and around the margins, where the waters are influenced by sediments washed in around the edge. Other variations are found in the straits between bays and near the mouths of streams entering the bays.

1. Margins of the bays are covered by sandy shores composed of quartz sand mixed with shell fragments, but this mixture grades into muds composed of clay and silt within a very short distance of the shore.
2. Shallow bays are usually covered by no more than 3 feet of water. As in the marginal zone, there is a higher percentage of sand than any other material, although the amount of silt, clay, and particularly shell fragments is much higher than at the margins. The shells are those of snails, Foraminifera, and ostracods. They are mixed with plant fibers of various marine plants.
3. Near the mouths of rivers the mixture of fresh and salt water, the presence of a current, and the supply of sediment from the stream all alter the environment. The ostracods are particularly plentiful, and oyster reefs may be present. Near the oyster reefs the sediment consists primarily of the shell fragments of oysters mixed with a few sponge remains. These are seldom widespread on the bay floor. They grade laterally into silt and clay sediments on either side.
4. In the narrows between the Gulf and the bays or in the straits between two connected bays, the sediments are composed mainly of sand. The movement of water through the narrow gaps caused by tides and the outflow of waters brought into the bays by streams wash these straits clean of the finest sediments.

Barrier islands. The coastal bays and lagoons are separated from the open waters of the Gulf by a long narrow belt of barrier islands and offshore bars. These bars are similar to others bordering most of the Gulf Coast and the eastern coast south of Cape Hatteras. In order to go from one of the bays out to a barrier island it is necessary to cross a low swampy area. This is a shallow belt, partially submerged and affected by the tides. The bottom of this swamp is covered by an intricate

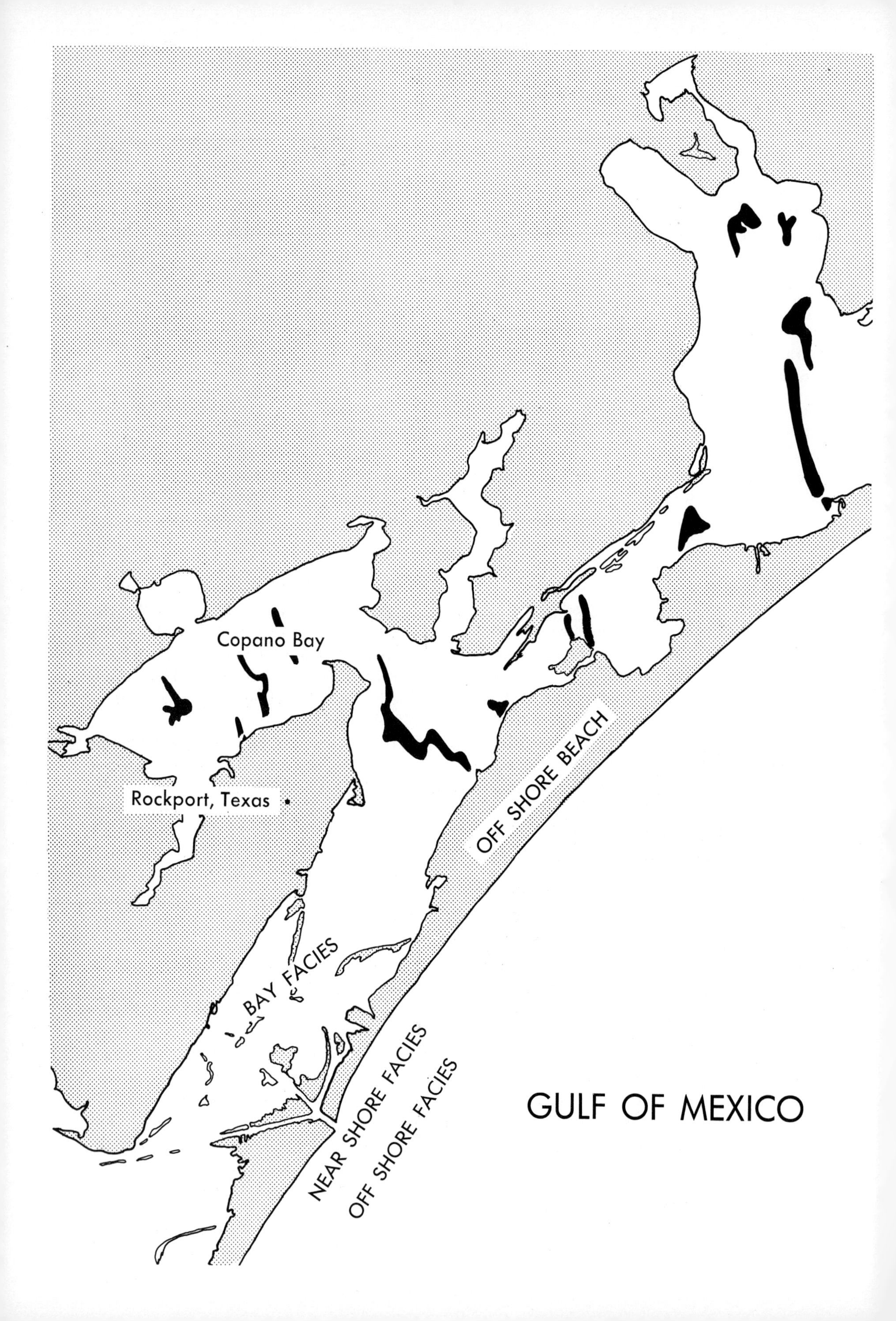
Copano Bay
Rockport, Texas
OFF SHORE BEACH
BAY FACIES
NEAR SHORE FACIES
OFF SHORE FACIES
GULF OF MEXICO

Fig. 4-20. Marine invertebrates. Schematic section showing some typical marine invertebrates found in each part of this marine environment. (After Robert H. Parker, *Am. Assoc. Petroleum Geologists Bull. 43.*)

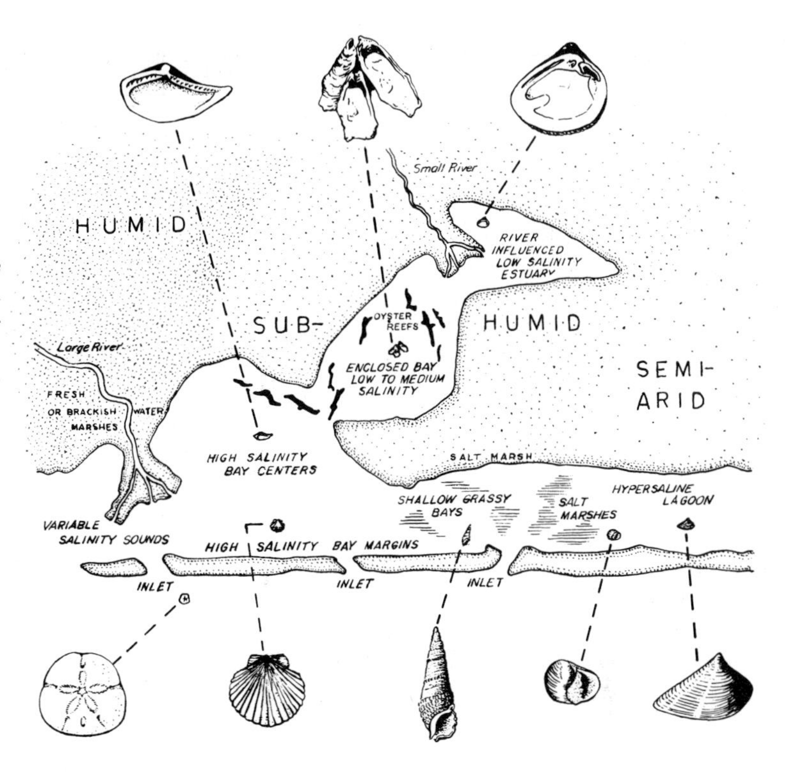

pattern of small channels carrying water from the islands into the bays and ponds where circulation of water is restricted. In places the emerged parts of the swamp have narrow sand beaches around them, but elsewhere the swamp floor is covered by sand mixed with soft silt and clay (30 per cent of sediment). A large part of the coarser sediments in the swamp is made up of aggregates of clay and silt which harden together during low tides when the bottom sediments are exposed to sun and wind. At these times evaporation of the moisture in the sediment takes place, and, as the water in the pore spaces near the surface evaporates, more water is pulled upward by capillary action. This water contains calcium carbonate and salts. As the water continues to evaporate, these salts are precipitated, and the top part of the sediment is cemented together. There is also a large amount of organic matter in the swamp sediment composed primarily of wood fibers, decaying plant matter, Foraminifera shells, and the remains of echinoderms.

The barrier islands are largely covered by sand dunes. The sediment found in these is almost 100 per cent sand. The dunes are cross-bedded, and the sand is well sorted as a result of having been transported by the wind. The sand here is very much like that found on the beaches on the Gulf side of the island. The source of supply for these sands is the beach. They are washed up by waves and then blown farther up on the island by winds. Most movement of the sand takes place during low tide when there is time for the sand grains high up on the beach to become dry. As long as they are being washed over by every incoming wave, the water in the pore spaces between the grains of sand holds them together on the beach. Additional large quantities of sand are deposited above the high-tide level during storms. The beaches are composed of well-sorted sands which differ from the dune sediment mainly because they contain more shell fragments, particularly Foraminifera tests. These are too large to be moved by the wind and they

Fig. 4-19. Map of part of the central Texas Gulf Coast. This map shows the location of several of the sub-environments in relation to one another in this marine environment. The solid black areas are oyster reefs.

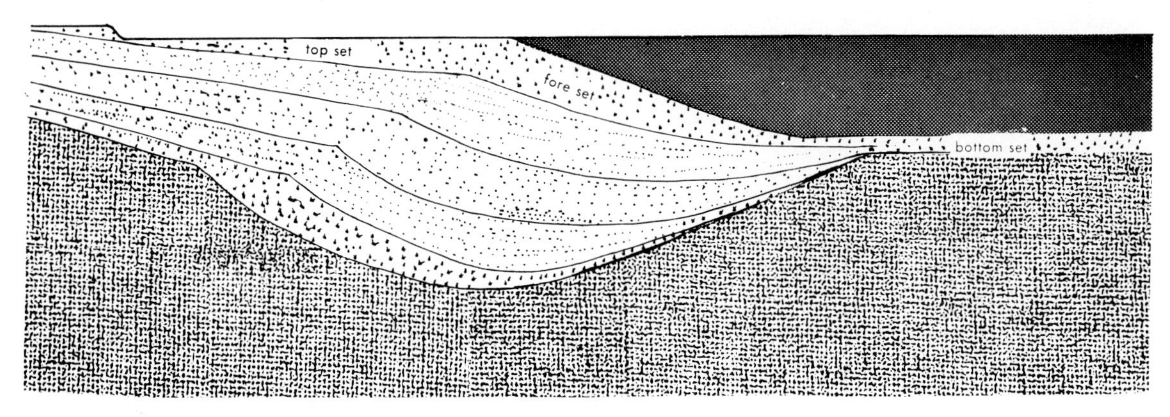

Fig. 4-21. Idealized section across a delta. The top set, fore set, and bottom set beds are shown. The delta shown here has been subsiding through time, deforming the older deltaic deposits.

are therefore almost absent from the dunes.

Continental shelf. The Gulf bottom slopes off irregularly from the beaches for several hundred feet into water that is about 20 feet deep. Irregularities in this zone are offshore bars and depressions apparently formed during storms. The essential differences between the sands on the beach and those found in this near-shore belt are the size and roundness of the sand. The near-shore sand is smaller and less well rounded. The faunas are essentially the same as those on the beach. By far the most distinctive features of these sediments is the presence of the mineral glauconite in them.

Deltas

Deltaic environments are composites of a number of different types of sedimentary conditions. No other environment contains the intimate association of so many different physical, biological, and chemical conditions. In this connection you should take note of deltas located along the coasts where streams transporting sediments as bed load, in suspension, and in solution flow into marine waters. The environment is truly transitional; it is partially above sea level and partially below.

A delta forms when the amount of sediment being deposited from the stream exceeds the amount of erosion and removal accomplished by wave action and oceanic currents. If the stream supplies more than can be distributed, the delta grows seaward. If a balance is reached, the delta becomes stabilized in size, and if wave and current action exceeds deposition the delta will eventually disappear. Deltas are by no means confined to the oceans and transitional environments. They form in lakes, and in streams where tributaries supply more debris than the trunk stream can transport.

Fig. 4-21 is a generalized diagram showing the internal structure of the classic example of a delta. Usually the stream enters and flows across the delta on a low slope. The fresh water and sediment are carried out to the edge of the delta where the river enters the ocean (or lake). At this point the stream is no longer flowing down a gradient; it loses its potential energy and its transporting power. Most of the coarse sand, silt, and other sediment is deposited. Clay colloids, which are in suspension in the fresh water, are deposited when they enter and become mixed with the salt water, thus forming an extensive deposit of clay. The heavier substances are deposited on the slope of the ocean or lake front of the delta, and finer matter is carried farther out in suspension or solution before it settles to the bottom. As a result of the delta's shape and the nature of its formation, three sets of bedding planes are being formed almost simultaneously. The thickest units are the sediments laid on the front slope of the delta; these units are inclined and called the foreset beds. Beyond them the finer sediments settle on a

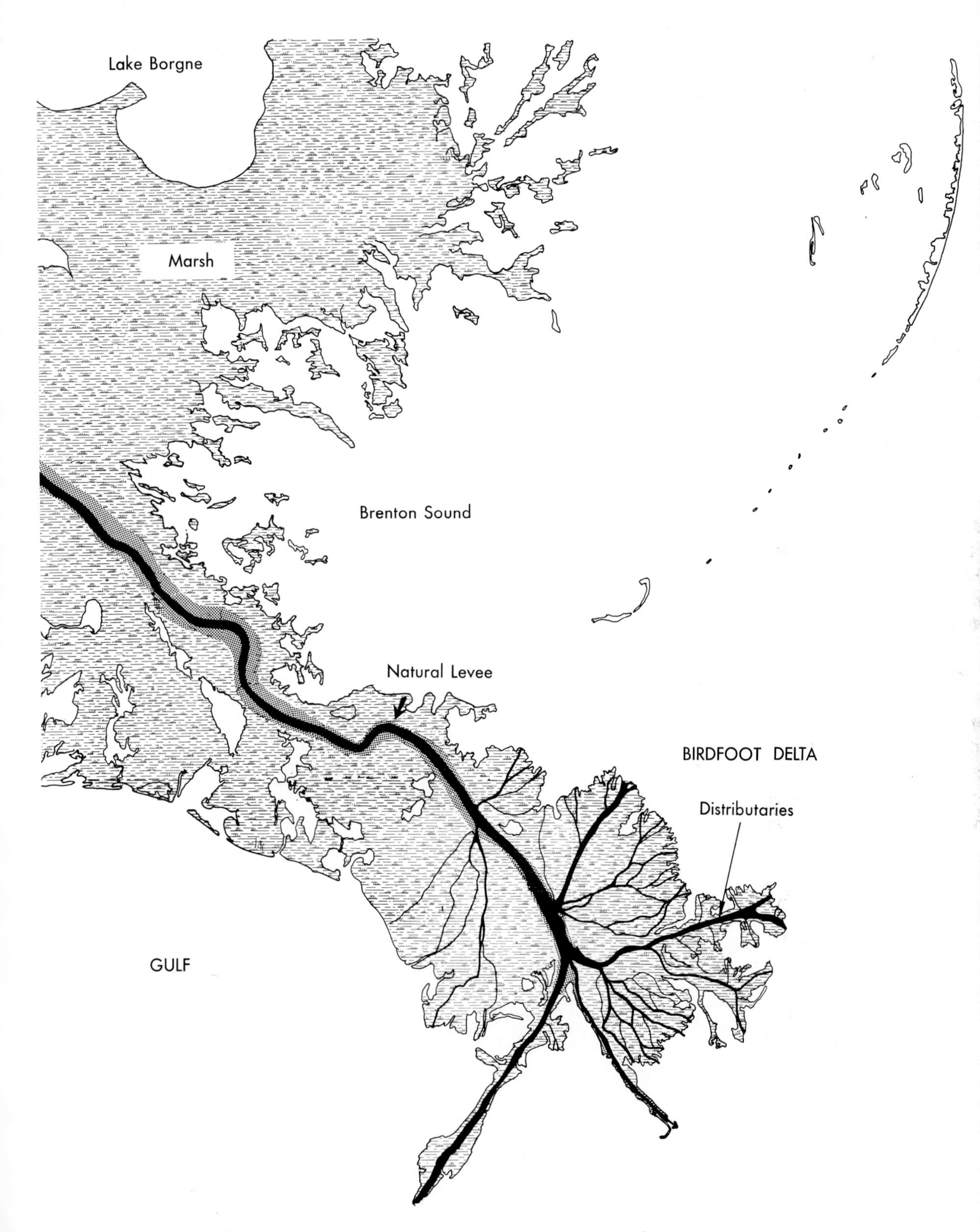

Fig. 4-22. Map view of the delta of the Mississippi River, the Birdfoot Delta. The various environments depicted are described in the text.

nearly flat bottom, creating the bottom-set beds. The third set of beds, the topset, is formed by the sediments which are flat-lying on top of the delta. These are sediments in transport by the streams flowing across the delta marshes, or low areas to either side of the streams. These topset beds truncate the foreset beds as the delta is built seaward.

Mississippi delta

One of the most intensively studied deltas in the world is that of the Mississippi River. During the last 10,000 years the Mississippi River has carried more than 8000 cubic miles of sediments into the Gulf of Mexico. Most of this has been deposited in the delta and near the coast. The weight of this mass has caused the continental shelf to be depressed an estimated 300 to 500 feet under the delta.

The Mississippi River flows over an extremely low slope along its lower reaches. As it approaches the delta the river begins to break up into a number of smaller streams called distributaries. The pattern formed by these resembles that of a braided stream. These distributaries, carrying a heavy load of silt and dissolved material, flow outward into the Gulf across the delta. Seen from far above they resemble the veins of a leaf or the bones of a bird's foot. This pattern gave the delta its present name, "the Birdfoot Delta." Between the distributaries there are extensive areas slightly above sea level, covered by marshes. The streams are actually above the level of these marshes over a large part of the area. Natural levees formed during seasonal floods build barriers confining the stream channels. As the distributaries reach the end of their channels, the stream loads are dropped on the delta front in the form of large lobes. The

Fig. 4-23. Photo of tidal flats near Mont St. Michel. (Photo by French Cultural Services.)

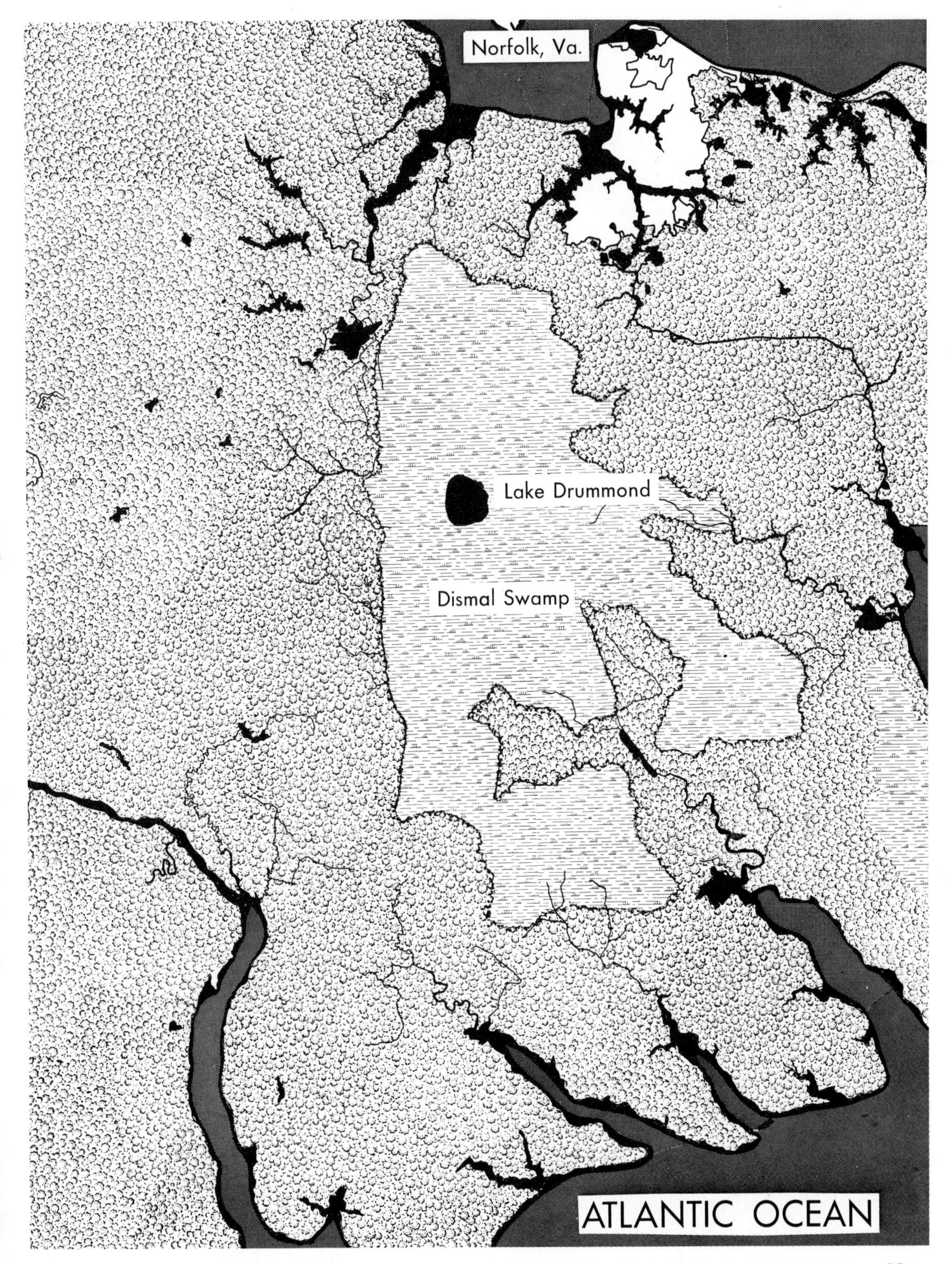

Fig. 4-24 Map view of the Dismal Swamp region of southern Virginia and northeastern North Carolina. Note that the streams drain into the swamp.

Fig. 4-25. View of swamp in the Mississippi Valley. (Photo by E. W. Spencer.)

Fig. 4-26. View of swamp in the Mississippi Valley. (Photo by E. W. Spencer.)

streams have built out great distances on these lobes leaving bays and troughlike depressions between them. Farther out the slope of the delta diminishes and grades onto the nearly flat bottom of the continental shelf. Some of the diverse environments which are combined on deltas are classified and described below:

Summary of environments on the Mississippi delta

I. EMERGED PART OF THE DELTA (that part of the deltaic plain that stands at or above sea level).

1. Distributary channels. The sediments in these channels have been sorted over long periods of time. The finer fractions have been removed leaving heavier sand, pebbles, and some marine silts. This environment is marked by the absence of many living organisms, and for this reason the sediments contain very little organic debris.
2. Natural levees. The sediments here are silty clays laid down during flood stages on the river. The deposits are bedded, but unfossiliferous. They may be broken by mud cracks during dry seasons or when the river is low.
3. Marshes are the most extensive areas on the deltaic plain. The sediments on them are characterized by their organic, rich, clayey silts. They are soft, spongy masses of brown or black clays and grass roots. These poorly bedded materials grade laterally into the natural levees and into the open-water deposits of the bays. The faunas found in these marsh deposits include ostracods, crabs, crayfish, and some snails. This is the only emerged environment that has many animals living in it, but the inhabitants are few in number compared with most of the submerged environments.
4. Sand bars. These are found at the mouths of the distributaries where they enter the Gulf. Other bars may be found along the edge of the marshes where longshore currents have carried in sand from other parts of the shore line.

II. SUBMERGED PART OF THE DELTA. These are the submerged environments around the delta which receive sediments from the delta. The influence of these deposits extends more than 30 miles out into the Gulf from the emerged margin of the delta.

1. Platforms. Nearly flat areas surround the marshes and distributaries. This flat platform is covered by very shallow water. Large bays and broad elongate troughs between the distributaries lie on such platforms. The sediments deposited in these areas are silts, sands, and clays. They may be distinguished from the adjacent marsh deposits by the relative absence of organic matter. They are also better sorted than the marsh sediments. These platforms are not formed in the same manner as the top part of the delta. The platforms were probably extensive wedges of marine clay laid down before the present-day birdfoot delta started to develop. The fauna on the platforms is composed of Foraminifera, pelecypods (scallops), some clams, and a few snails. The assemblage is typical of brackish-marine bays.
2. Delta-front slope. Beyond the mouth of the distributaries the delta front slopes very gently onto the continental shelf. The deposits on this gently sloping surface are made up largely of laminated clay which contains wood fibers and mica flakes carried out in suspension. The most abundant organisms are Foraminifera and various mollusks.
3. Continental shelf. Beyond the slope of the delta front the bottom-set beds are laid down. These are poorly stratified clay and silt which contain large quantities of the remains of Foraminifera and echinoids and other large marine organisms. One unusual component of these sediments is the mineral glauconite, an iron-potassium silicate.
4. Open lagoons. Breton Sound is a salt-water lake nearly enclosed by land. The sediments and faunas found within it are similar to those of the open bays on the platform.

Swamp environment

The names swamp, bog, or morass are applied to geographically low, spongy land that is generally saturated with moisture. They are not confined to areas near sea level or even to flat land, although they are much more likely to form and less likely to be drained when they are situated in one of these positions. Swamps cover large areas of the continents. Some estimates put the amount of land covered by swamps of one sort or another at more than 1 million square miles. Not only are they important environments today, but there is a rich and extensive record of this type of environment in the geologic past. At various times swamps have covered much larger areas than they do today. Late in the Paleozoic Era the swamps became so extensive throughout the world that the periods are named for the carbonaceous rocks formed in them. The term Carboniferous is applied throughout the world to the Mississippian and Pennsylvanian periods.

Two general types of swamps are recognized. These are the marine swamps located along coasts where both brackish and fresh waters are present, and fresh-water swamps. Most fresh-water swamps are located in basins or on flat to gently sloping land surfaces that may be far removed from the sea. The most favorable position for the location of a swamp is near sea level, thus explaining why this particular type is so commonly preserved in the rock record. They are covered by slight, relative elevations of sea level and preserved under marine deposits. For this reason swamp deposits usually appear mixed with marine sediments in stratigraphic sequences.

Certain environmental factors are particularly important in swamps. One is the supply of water. Abundant rainfall, or some other type of water supply, is necessary for the continuance of a swamp, which is generally characterized by slow circulation of water or by near stagnation in parts. Biological factors dominate. The swamp environment is especially favorable for the growth of plant life. Therefore it is not surprising that the remains of plants make up the largest part of the sediment. The energy sources for this lush environment are largely chemical reactions and thermal energy supplied from the sun.

Marine swamps. Marine swamps are not uncommon along the coasts of the eastern and southern United States. Many of them have been formed behind the offshore bars that parallel the sea shore. These were initially lagoons that have since been filled by sediment from the continent and by the remains of plant matter. Other marine swamps originate when the sea floor is slightly elevated, exposing a broad, nearly flat plain during at least part of the day. Plant life is most abundant where there is little or no agitation of the water. For this reason swamp conditions are favored where there is a relatively small range between high and low tide. Quite a few swamps, however, are at least partially and some completely covered by sea water during high tide each day. Within a marine swamp different plants are favored by certain special conditions; however, a very large percentage of these swamps are at least partially covered by moss, and most contain grasses and reeds in abundance. In tropical climates the marine swamps contain mangrove or cypress forests. As these plants die they fall into the water and begin to decay. If they can be buried rapidly enough by other plant remains or by marine sediments there is a good chance that they will be preserved and may eventually be transformed into coal. If burial is not rapid, oxidation and bacterial action will soon break them down. For this reason only thin accumulations of swamp deposits are found if the level of the swamp remains stable. Probably no more than a few yards of plant matter can accumulate, since the water depth is seldom great. The thick sequences of swamp sediments that are so common in the stratigraphic sequences of the Carboniferous must indicate at least slight changes in the position of sea level relative to the swamp. A slowly subsiding area would obviously be the most favorable site for the preservation of great thicknesses of such sediment.

The Dismal Swamp of Virginia and North Carolina is one of the largest marine swamps in the United States, and in many ways it is a typical example of this type of swamp environment. A thick, matlike body of plant matter and terrigenous sediment covers most of the swamp. These deposits fill a broad and very shallow basin-like structure. It is a saucer-like depression on one of the terraces characteristic of the coastal plain of the southeastern United States. This is a recently emerged sea bottom which now stands a few feet above the level of the sea. The depression is bordered by higher ground on the western side, but on the north, east, and south rims the ground does not rise above that of the other parts of the swamp.

The mat of organic matter holds the level of the water table above that generally found in the surrounding region. This is accomplished by a simple process. The mat of swamp sediment, acting like a huge sponge, is able to soak up and hold the water at a higher level than normal for the region. In the center of the swamp, there is a large body of water called Lake Drummond. The surface level of this lake is more than 20 feet above the border of the swamp. There is doubt that the swamp will be able to continue building up a thicker accumulation of sediment. In all probability the mat is now drawing water to as great a height as it can maintain. Therefore, this is a good example of a swamp in which the accumulation has reached the maximum depth possible without subsidence of the area. If subsidence should occur, then the area would accumulate new sediment, and the mat would slowly be built back up to its present height above sea level.

Below the level of the mat of organic debris, sediments are marine deposits of silt and sand that are interbedded with continental deposits. From this we conclude that the area has been one alternately covered and exposed above the sea. Terrigenous silts and clay are being brought into the swamp from the west today; they are being interbedded with the decaying remains of reeds, grasses, and other plants. A few small stream channels wind through parts of the swamp, and these are the only sites in the swamp that are covered by sand and silt.

Fresh-water swamps. These are usually located around the edges of lakes. Generally the water table is at the surface near the edge of a lake, and this, plus rainfall and occasional rise in the level of the lake, favors the growth of large quantities of vegetation. A ringlike pattern of vegetation is likely to surround the fresh-water lake. Each type of vegetation is best adapted to water of a certain depth. Moss, grasses, and reeds are abundant in many of these swamps, and they also may abound in cypress, spruce, cedar, tamarack, alder, and sumach. Plants such as water lilies are found floating on the surface of the lake. These may grow very thick, until they form a mat in which sediment is caught. Quaking bogs are composed of thick accumulations of such mats that are in a state of partial decay. Most lakes are temporary features in the process of being filled in by sediment. Mud and silt are brought into the lake by streams and also are washed in from around the edges. As the lake is progressively filled, the depth of water tends to

Fig. 4-27. Drainage pattern within a lagoon behind one of the offshore beaches along the eastern United States. Note the recurved spit at the sea shore, and the sluggish drainage which characterizes the swamp behind the beach.

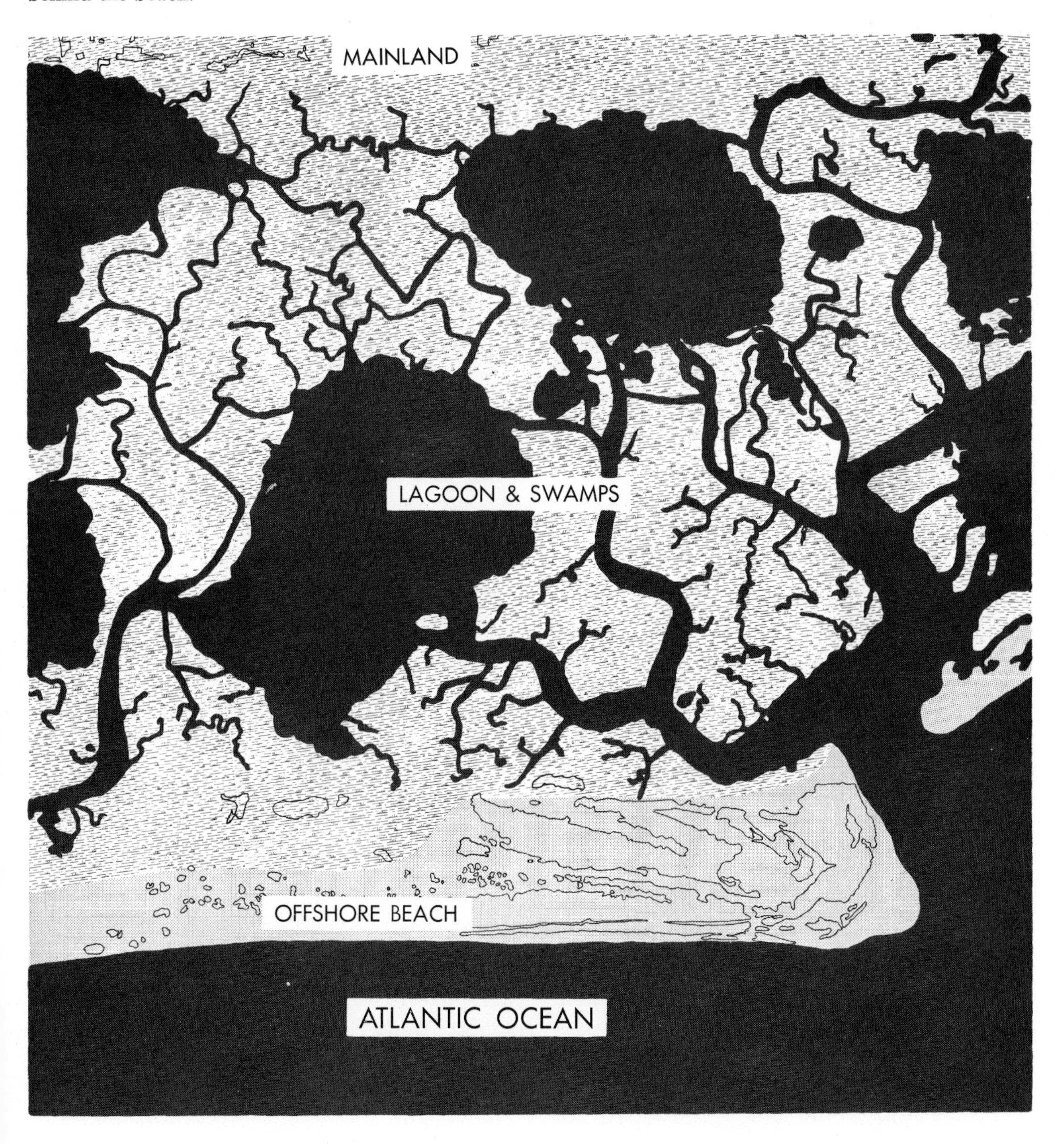

decrease, and the shallow-water plants grow closer and closer to the center until the lake, as such, disappears. When the lake is gone, the streams that fed it may flow across the lake sediments and cut their channels into them. The swamp may persist on either side of the streams until the streams cut their channels beneath the level of the swamp and drain it. With draining comes oxidation, decay, and erosion of the deposits until they are gone. There are relatively small numbers of fresh-water swamp deposits preserved from past geologic ages. By nature they are transient forms. The best chances for their preservation are found when they are near sea level in a region which undergoes rapid subsidence.

REFERENCES

BURST, J. F., 1958, "Glauconite" pellets: Their mineral nature and applications to stratigraphic interpretations: Am. Assoc. Petroleum Geologists Bull., v. 42, p. 310-327.

EMERY, K. O., 1956, Sediments and water of Persian Gulf: Am. Assoc. Petroleum Geologists Bull., v. 40, p. 2354-2383.

TRASK, P. D., Editor, 1939, *Recent Marine Sediments, A Symposium:* Am. Assoc. Petroleum Geologists.

EMERY, K. O., *et al.*, 1954, Bikini and nearby atolls, Marshall Islands, U. S. Geol. Survey Prof. Paper 260-A, 265 p.

GINSBURG, R. N., and LOWENSTAM, H. A., 1958, Influence of marine bottom communities on depositional environment of sediments: Jour. Geology, v. 66, p. 310-318.

HEDGPETH, J. W., Editor, 1957, *Treatise on Marine Ecology and Paleoecology: Volume 1, Marine Ecology:* Geol. Soc. America Memoir 67, v. 1, 1296 p.

KRUMBEIN, W. C., and SLOSS, L. L., 1953, *Stratigraphy and Sedimentation:* W. H. Freeman and Company, San Francisco, 497 p.

KUENEN, PH. H., 1950, *Marine Geology:* John Wiley and Sons, New York, 568 p.

MC KEE, E. D., 1958, Geology of Kapingamarangi Atoll, Caroline Islands: Geol. Soc. America Bull., v. 69, p. 241-278.

NEWELL, N. D., 1955, Bahamian platforms: Geol. Soc. America Sp. Paper 62, p. 303-316.

SLOSS, L. L., 1958, Paleontologic and lithologic associations: Jour. Paleontology, v. 32, pp. 715-729.

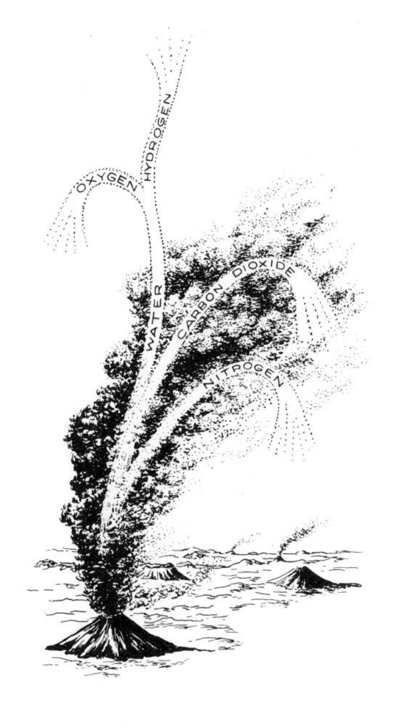

III THE DAWN OF EARTH HISTORY

5 Origin of the Earth

Few problems in science capture the imagination as quickly as does the question of the origin of the earth. Many answers to the question have been proposed. No one of them can be said to be perfectly correct, but with the development of new techniques and instruments an ever-increasing amount of information is being obtained about our universe. With each new bit of information we come closer to a full understanding of the origin of the earth. New facts sometimes refute hypotheses; sometimes they confirm predictions made on certain hypotheses, thereby lending support to them, but they always narrow down the possible solutions to the problem and therefore lead us closer to the answer.

OUR UNIVERSE — THE MILKY WAY

Although the earth is the central object of man's attention it is by no means an outstanding object as compared with others in the universe. It is highly probable that life exists

Fig. 5-1. A Spiral nebula in *Ursa Major*, the Big Dipper. Our galaxy, the Milky Way, might resemble this if seen from a distance of several hundred million light years. 200-inch telescope. (By courtesy of Mount Wilson and Palomar Observatories.)

abundantly on other planets in the universe, and it is entirely possible that our earth doesn't even have the distinction of being the only planet inhabited by mammal-like organisms. Some care is required in the use of the term "universe" because it may have several connotations. In its broadest sense the term is applied to all the stars, their satellites, and groups of stars. Stars are not evenly spread across space. This is apparent when we look into the heavens on a clear night. One distinct band across the sky appears to contain many more stars than other parts of the sky. We call this band the Milky Way. Most of the stars you see in the Milky Way belong to the group of which our own sun, which is a star, is a part. Such a group is called a galaxy. The galaxy of which we are a part is called the Milky Way. This galaxy is disc-shaped or somewhat like a lens. It contains an estimated 100,000,000,000 stars spread over a space that is 100,000+ light years in diameter. A light year is defined as the distance light will travel in one year. Light travels at the rate of 186,000 miles per second. That makes one light year a distance of 5,865,696,000,000 miles. Consequently even 100,000 million stars are not crowded within the galaxy. Of course many of these stars may have planets around them, and these in turn may have satellites such as our moon moving about them. For this reason you see why it is highly probable that there may be other planets somewhat like the earth within our galaxy. Chances are much greater if we take into consideration the fact that our galaxy, the Milky Way, is only one of countless similar galaxies in the universe. These other galaxies appear as stars to the unaided eye, but with telescopes it is possible to see the difference and photograph their shapes. The closest of the other galaxies is Andromeda which appears to be somewhat similar to our Milky Way. Its distance is between 1 1/2 and 2 billion light years. It is the most distant object visible to the unaided eye.

OUR EXPANDING UNIVERSE

One of the techniques for study of stars and galaxies is the analysis of spectrograms. The spectrograph is used to break up the light coming to us from these bodies into its component wave lengths. Analysis of spectrograms has made it possible for us to obtain information on the composition and structure of stars. One of the most interesting observations that has been made from the spectra of the galaxies is that the lines of the spectra are displaced toward the red end of the spectrum. The amount of this red shift is approximately proportional to the distance of the galaxies from us. This effect is similar to the common experience of hearing a horn on a car or train

Fig. 5-2. A Spiral nebula in *Andromeda,* seen edge on. Photograph with 60-inch telescope. (By courtesy of Mount Wilson and Palomar Observatories.)

moving past you. When the horn passes you the pitch is lowered. It seems to become more bass. This effect is produced because the source is moving away from you tending to lengthen the waves. In a similar manner waves of light are lengthened and shifted toward the longer wave lengths (red light has a longer wave length than green, yellow, or blue). The interpretation of this observation is that the galaxies are moving away from one another. The paths of movement have been calculated, and it is found that these paths converge in one general area of space. There is no galaxy in that position. All the galaxies appear to have moved out along paths radiating from that point. The galaxies farthest from the point are traveling fastest. These observations have led to the formulation of a theory that our universe is expanding, that all the galaxies originated from the same general area, and that they all started to move out away from that point about the same time.

AGE OF THE UNIVERSE

On the basis of the theory of the expanding universe it has become possible to estimate the age of the universe. It is computed to be about 5 billion years old. That is the amount of time it would take for the galaxies to return to their point of origin if they returned along the same paths and at the same velocity with which they are now moving away.

A second independent method is available to us as a means of estimating the age of the universe. That is the idea of determining the age of the elements. One assumption is made: that the elements were all formed at about the same time, and that some of the original constituents have been modified by radioactive decay. Earlier we investigated this method of determining the age of rocks containing varying amounts of uranium-238 and the end product of its decay, the stable lead-206. In this case the uranium is called the parent element, and lead-206 the end decay product. Other parent elements are: uranium-235, thorium-232, rubidium-87, and potassium-40. They decay to form stable end products which are respectively: lead-207, lead-208, strontium-87, and argon-40. The age of the elements can be determined from the time when all the naturally radioactive series consisted entirely of the parent elements. In order to make this determination we need to know how abundant each of these elements was when radioactive decay started. The problem is greatly simplified by the observation that the abundances of all the elements with atomic numbers greater than 40 are about the same. Thus originally there was about the same amount of uranium-238 as there now is of some of the stable elements. With this understanding plus knowledge of the half life of the various radioactive series it is possible to estimate the amount of time since the radioactive decay began. The analysis yields a figure of about 5 billion years. Thus there is essential agreement between this line of reasoning and the theory of the expanding universe. Further evidence is found in the analysis of meteorites. The relative amounts of lead derived from radioactive decay and lead that has been stable since its origin are analyzed. These studies yield an age of about 4 1/2 to 5 billion years for most meteorites.

ORIGIN OF THE SOLAR SYSTEM

If our present hypotheses are sound all of the matter of the universe was concentrated in a relatively small space about 5 billion years ago. It is likely in this case that the temperatures within that initial cloud of matter were extremely high, and that great internal pressures were built up. Elements, as such, did not exist. Instead, matter consisted of a soupy cloud of neutrons. From this state the matter of the universe began to expand. With this expansion and reduction in temperatures elements began to form, and finally condensation of these clouds of matter began within the cells of turbulent movement which would be expected within such a hot mass of gases. With expansion these cells of matter became separated into large clouds or masses that eventually became the galaxies. Within each of

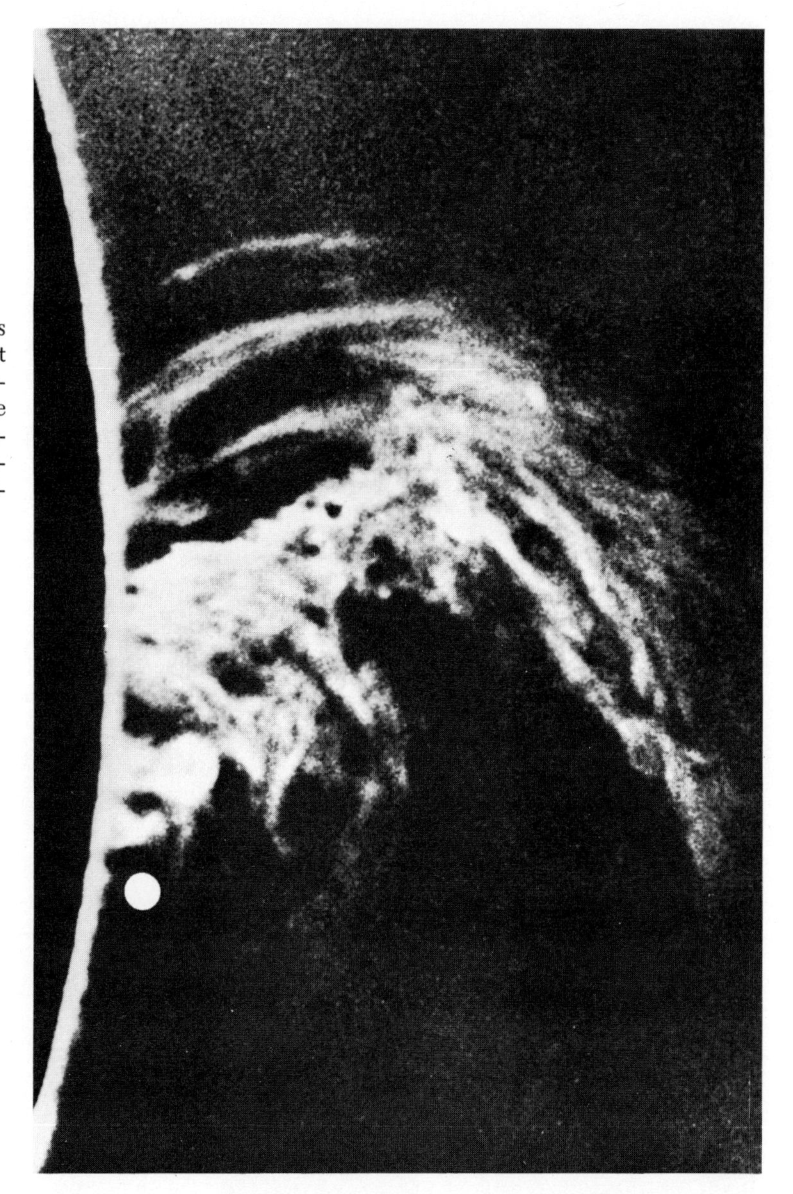

Fig. 5-3. Prominence on sun. This large, active prominence is about 140,000 miles high. It was photographed in light of calcium. These explosions occur above the photosphere in the lower part of the corona. (By courtesy of Mount Wilson and Palomar Observatories.)

these presumably other cells of turbulence existed which eventually condensed into the stars. Our sun is one such star.

EVOLUTION OF THE SOLAR SYSTEM

A number of important theories have been advanced to explain the evolution of the solar system, including the formation of the planets. Before considering these, it is important that we review some of the basic facts about the solar system. These impose limitations on any acceptable theory, and any satisfactory hypothesis of the evolution of the solar system must explain them.

1. The mass of the solar system is concentrated in the sun. It contains about 99.8 per cent of the total mass. The 9 planets contain the remaining .2 per cent.
2. The planets move in orbits about the sun. These orbits lie approximately within a single plane.

3. The planets rotate about their axes, and all of them rotate in the same direction about these axes.
4. The direction of rotation about the axis is the same as the direction of revolution of the planets about the sun.
5. The planets are spaced in a regular pattern. They form two groups. One, the inner group, includes Mercury, Venus, Earth, and Mars. The other, the outer group, includes Jupiter, Saturn, Uranus, and Neptune, much larger planets, and Pluto, a smaller planet.
6. Angular momentum (mass multiplied by the angular velocity) of the solar system is concentrated in the planets. About 98 per cent of the angular momentum is held in the planets.
7. The sun is a perfectly typical star. It differs from other stars only in that it is close enough to the earth to permit us to examine it in greater detail. The sun is about 432,000 miles in radius which makes it a medium-sized star. Its interior is at a temperature of 15 million degrees absolute, and its surface is

Fig. 5-4. The sun's corona. This thin gaseous layer of the sun is not normally visible except when the moon covers the photosphere during total eclipses. In this photograph the corona is shown at a time of little sunspot activity. During greater sunspot activity the corona is extended farther out and it is more nearly circular. Parts of the corona extend over a million miles above the photosphere, and even in its most dense parts the corona is only about a million-millionth of the density of the earth's atmosphere at sea level. (Photo by courtesy of Yerkes Observatory.)

	Mass Earth = 1	Radius (Km.)	Density	Gases in Atmosphere	Distance from Sun
Sun	332000	695000	1.4	many	
Mercury	0.05	2500	5.1	none	36 million mi.
Venus	0.81	6200	5.0	carbon dioxide	67 million mi.
Earth	1.	6371	5.5	many	93 million. mi.
Mars	.11	3400	3.9	carbon dioxide water vapor	141 million mi.
Jupiter	318.	71000	1.3	methane ammonia	483 million mi.
Saturn	95.	57000	.7	methane ammonia	886 million mi.
Uranus	14.6	25800	1.3	methane	1783 million mi.
Neptune	17.3	22300	2.2	methane	2793 million mi.
Pluto	.03	2900	2.?	unknown	3666 million mi.

Fig. 5-5. The Solar System. The mass of other bodies in the Solar System is given in relation to the mass of the earth.

about 6000 degrees absolute. The solar atmosphere which consists of hot gases extends out from it a distance of 9000 miles. Great tongues of luminous gas, primarily hydrogen, extend outward from the solar atmosphere to heights of several hundred thousand miles. These are called prominences. About the solar atmosphere and the prominences is the corona. This is a rarefied, filmy atmosphere of gases which extends at least a million miles from the sun.

Fig. 5-6. Bode's Law. The top line gives the names of the planets in order of increasing distance from the sun. Bode's law is an empirical series formulated in the top two rows of figures. The third line is the total of the top two lines. The bottom line gives the actual distances of the planets from the sun in terms of the earth's distance from the sun which is taken to equal 10. Note the close correlation between the two. Asteroids occupy the gap between Mars and Jupiter, and Neptune does not fit into the series. The agreement suggests that the planets are arranged systematically. The system of their arrangement must be related in some way to their mode of origin. The important thing to be learned from this law is that the planets are not scattered haphazardly.

	Mercury	Venus	Earth	Mars	Vacant	Jupiter	Saturn	Uranus	Pluto
	4	4	4	4	4	4	4	4	4
	0	3	6	12	24	48	96	192	384
Totals	4	7	10	16	28	52	100	196	388
	3.9	7.2	10	15.2	. .	52	95	192	395

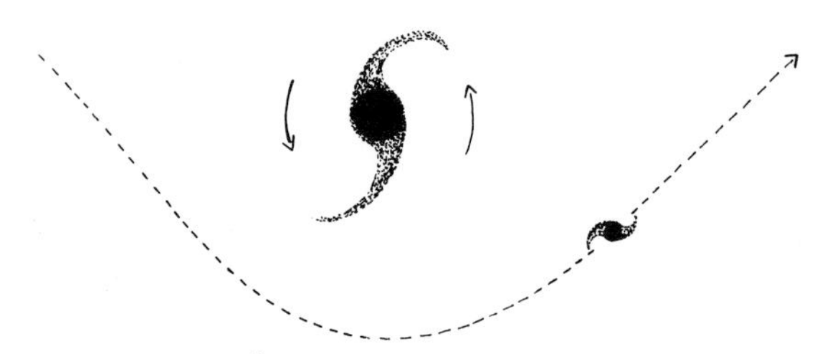

Fig. 5-7. Dynamic Encounter hypothesis of the origin of the planets. According to this theory the planets were formed from material pulled out of the sun by the tidal forces set up by the close approach of another star. As the stars' paths crossed material was ejected and set in rotation around the sun.

8. The chart of Fig. 5-5 gives dimensions and other information about the planets of the solar system.

The principal theories that have been advanced to explain the origin of the planets may be classed in two groups. All of these theories have in common the idea that the planets evolved from the sun. They differ as to the manner in which this occurred. In one group, material is pulled out of the sun by an external force such as gravitational pull resulting from the dynamic encounter or near collision of our sun with another star. The second group holds that the planets became isolated masses of matter as the material of the solar system condensed into the sun.

Dynamic Encounter theory

The theory that the planets were formed as a result of the near collision of the sun and another star was first proposed by the French philosopher Buffon in 1749. It was later elaborated by Chamberlin and Moulton. These theories propose essentially that as another star approached our sun tremendous tides were set up on the surface of the sun, and these tides or filaments of hot gases were pulled out from the sun. As the star passed, these arms of gas were given a rotational motion. After the star was gone the gaseous matter in these arms condensed into solid material and gradually drew together to form planets. Because the two arms would probably be very similar in size and shape it would be logical to expect that similar-sized planets would form at similar distances from the sun. The size of the potential planets would be a function of the amount of matter distributed at different distances from the sun. Thus this theory explains the occurrence of pairs of planets of approximately the same size at about the same distances from the sun. Pairs of this nature are: Mercury and Mars, Venus and Earth, Jupiter and Saturn, and Uranus and Neptune. The rotation of the arms of gas would also account for the concentration of angular momentum in the planets rather than in the sun itself.

At the present time this theory has fewer followers than it has had in the past. Some of the important objections to it are:

1. It appears likely that the gases drawn out from the sun would disperse throughout space rather than condense into planets.
2. The chances that another star would come close to the sun are extremely small. There is no evidence to suggest or prove that this actually did happen.

The Nebular Hypothesis

Kant and Laplace. The first Nebular Hypothesis was advanced by Kant and Laplace about 1796. It was the most generally accepted hypothesis for more than a century before Dynamic Encounter theories supplanted it. According to the Nebular Hypothesis, the solar system evolved from a single, large, flat, rotating nebula that extended out beyond the position of the most distant planet. As this nebula contracted the mass became increasingly concentrated toward the center. Anyone who has twirled a weight on the end of a string around a finger knows what happens when this occurs. As the weight nears the finger the speed of rotation increases. Rotation was visualized as slowly increasing. As the velocity increased the centrifugal force around the equator of the mass eventually became equal to the gravitational attraction between the material at the outer rim of the disc and the central mass. As a result a ring of matter was left while the contraction of the remaining matter continued. In this manner successive rings of matter were left behind the contracting mass. Subsequently the material within each ring was drawn together, and planets and their satellites were formed. The formation of the satellites from the planets was essentially similar to the formation of the planets from the sun. Thus this theory accounts for similar directions of rotation of all the planets and most of their satellites. It also leaves the planets within about the same plane of rotation, and the theory does not require any special conditions for the development of planets in this solar system that might not be expected in other solar systems as well.

The theory was refuted when it was learned that the angular momentum of the solar system is concentrated in the planets and not in the sun. This is not compatible with the idea that the mass of matter rotated more rapidly as it condensed. Since the original theory was advanced much theoretical work has been done on the nature of the turbulence in rotating and contracting clouds of gas and dust. These advances have led to the formulation of new theories which bear similarities to the original hypothesis of Kant and Laplace.

Fig. 5-8. Spiral nebula in *Virgo*, seen edge on. The diameter of this nebula is millions of light years. The general shape and distribution of materials is highly suggestive of a stage in the origin of the Milky Way or even our Solar System according to the Nebular Hypothesis. (Photo by courtesy of Mount Wilson and Palomar Observatories.)

Fig. 5-9. Saturn. The second largest planet in the Solar System, Saturn is distinguished by the rings of matter which surround it, and its relatively flattened shape. There are three of the flat rings, one inside the other, and all in the same plane. The exact nature of the rings is still unknown, but they may well be particles which have been kept from coalescing into a satellite by tidal forces exerted on the planet by one or more of its moons. (Photo by courtesy of Mount Wilson and Palomar Observatories.)

Von Weizsäcker. In 1944 a German physicist, C. F. von Weizsäcker, proposed this modification of the Nebular Hypothesis. The sun consisted of a hot central concentrated mass that was radiating light and heat much as it is presently doing. At that time the sun was surrounded by a thin, flat, rapidly rotating cloud of matter that encircled its equator. This disc of material consisted primarily of hydrogen, helium, and a small amount of heavier elements. It had about the same temperature that planets at varying distances from the sun now have. Radiation from the sun drove off most of the hydrogen and helium which are extremely light in weight. The heavier elements left behind collided with the escaping hydrogen and helium, and angular momentum was transferred to them. This accounts for the concentration of momentum in the planets. von Weizsäcker postulates that eddy-like vortices would form within the disc-shaped cloud of matter, and that there would be local ac-

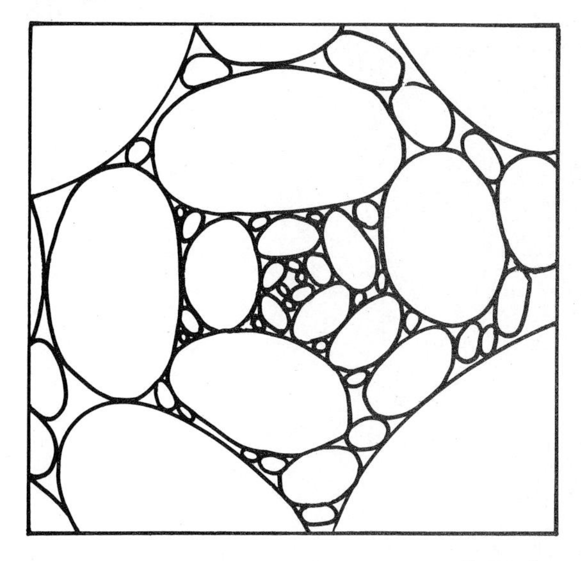

Fig. 5-10. Convection cells. Convection cells in the larger dust cloud from which our solar system evolved, according to Kuiper. (From *Astrophysics*, by J. A. Hynck. McGraw-Hill Book Co.)

cumulations of matter within these cells or vortices. These accumulations of small cool bits of matter became the planets. This theory explains a number of observed facts:

1. His calculated positions for the cells are in agreement with the spacing of the planets.
2. The inner and outer groups of planets differ in density and size. Temperatures would decrease out from the sun in the postulated disc of material. For this reason more material could condense in the outer parts than in the inner parts. The lighter-weight material would be driven out. Thus we find the inner planets are small and dense, whereas the outer planets are large and have low density.

Protoplanet Hypothesis of Kuiper. One of the most popular hypotheses within the past few years is one devised by Gerard P. Kuiper at Yerkes Observatory. It differs in some respects from the ideas of von Weizsäcker. Kuiper visualizes a slightly flattened and slowly rotating disc-shaped solar nebula bulging out from the equator of the sun. In composition this cloud is similar to the sun and contains mostly hydrogen and helium with small amounts of heavier elements, but the disc and the sun itself are thought of as being cool. The disc containing about a tenth the mass of the sun finally becomes internally unstable and breaks up into smaller concentrations called protoplanets. The amount and type of material in each protoplanet are the natural result of the original distribution of material within the solar nebula when it became internally unstable. Within each protoplanet the heavier elements tend to settle toward the center, and the lighter particles and gases remain in outer shells. When the sun contracted it started to radiate, and this radiation drove off the atmospheres from the closer and smaller planets. This means there must have been a great reduction in the original amount of matter in the planets. Kuiper has extended his hypothesis to explain many of the eccentricities of movement of the planets and their satellites. This has brought his theory into particular favor among astronomers.

REFERENCES

JEFFREYS, H., 1952, *The Earth:* Cambridge University Press, Cambridge, 392 p.

KOZYREV, N. A., 1959, Volcanic activity on the moon: Inter. Geol. Review, v. 1, p. 40-45.

KUIPER, G. P., Editor, 1954, *The Earth as a Planet:* University of Chicago Press, Chicago, 751 p.

LATIMER, W. M., 1950, Astrochemical problems in the formation of the earth: Science, v. 112, p. 101-104.

MASON, BRIAN, 1958, *Principles of Geochemistry*: John Wiley and Sons, London, 310 p. (p. 57-62)

POLDERVAART, ARIE, Editor, 1955, *Crust of the Earth:* Geol. Soc. America Sp. Paper 62, 762 p.

UREY, H. C., 1951, The origin and development of the earth and other terrestrial planets: Geochim et Cosmochim. Acta, v. 1, p. 209.

6 Origin and Development of the Hydrosphere and Atmosphere

ORIGIN OF THE ATMOSPHERE

The earth's atmosphere is in contact with the ocean, with the sediments and rocky crust of the earth, and with the animal and plant life near the earth's surface, and it is bounded above by space. The atmosphere is not completely independent of the other parts of the earth. Chemical reactions take place between them, and there is an exchange of materials between them. Thus the composition of the atmosphere has not necessarily remained constant through time. A record of these changes may be left in the sediments that were forming at different times in the earth's history. The problem is to find out how these changes are recorded and then to piece the information together. In order to accomplish this we must recognize that certain characteristics of rocks are related to the presence of particular elements in the atmosphere. For example, in a sedimentary unit the presence of fossils of animals that require oxygen to sustain life must mean that the atmosphere contained oxygen at the time that animal lived. If we find oxidized minerals of Precambrian age, there must have been oxygen in the atmosphere when those minerals were oxidized. Geochemists are best suited to handle this problem since they have an understanding of possible reactions between certain elements that might have been in the atmosphere and compounds found in the sediments of various ages. The data obtained from geologic field studies then must serve as the limiting conditions for any geochemical hypothesis. Any acceptable hypothesis must explain at least a large part of what the field geologist observes.

As in dealing with such questions as the origin of the earth, the origin of life, and the origin of continents, in dealing with the origin of the atmosphere we are forced to rely largely on indirect evidence usually subject to two or more interpretations. Even though the same data and observations may be analyzed, varied interpretations usually arise as a result of the use of different basic assumptions.

The various hypotheses which have been advanced to explain the origin of the earth's atmosphere and hydrosphere fall into two groups depending on the assumed nature of the origin of the earth. One group of theories is based on the assumption that the earth was once a molten globelike mass of gases and liquids which was derived from the sun, and which cooled first to a liquid and then slowly developed a solid crust. The atmosphere and hydrosphere according to this theory are residual materials from the primitive atmosphere which enveloped the earth. This means that the earth has had an atmosphere almost from the beginning with additions and losses of gases through time.

The second theory is derived from the idea that the earth was formed by the accumulation of small bodies called planetesimals which were in a liquid or solid state when they accumulated. William Rubey has analyzed much of the most recent work on this theory. According to this theory the atmosphere has accumulated from the "degassing" of the earth's interior and through chemical reactions that took place when the solid planetesimals accumulated. The heat required to melt the earth's interior would come from decay of radioactive minerals.

Residual Atmosphere Hypothesis

If the earth formed from a part of the sun which was separated in a gaseous state as in the Dynamic Encounter theories, it would be logical to assume that the earth's early atmosphere was similar to that indicated by the spectra of the sun and other stars. Most of the elements found in the sun are known on the earth; however, the relative abundance of some of the elements is notably different: hydrogen, helium, xenon, and krypton all are less abundant on earth than they are in the sun.

The amounts of hydrogen and helium in the sun greatly exceed all other elements in abundance. Therefore, a large quantity of these would be predicted for the primitive atmosphere of the earth according to this theory. Methane (CH_4) and ammonia (NH_3) are the most abundant gases in the atmospheres of several of the major planets of the solar system, the earth excluded. Since both of these gases are stable in the presence of an abundance of hydrogen and helium it is predicted that they were present in the primitive atmosphere of the earth. Nitrogen and water vapor are also thought to have made up a part of the early atmosphere.

At first there would have been considerable loss of those gases that are so light that they are not held to the earth by the force of the earth's gravitational attraction. Hydrogen and helium would be included among these. The rate of loss would decrease with time, and as the earth cooled, compounds would form, and these would tend to retain hydrogen in the earth. Helium, because it is an inert gas, does not tend to form compounds which might retain it in a similar manner. With the continuation of cooling the gases were gradually transformed into liquids, and these in turn into solids which formed near the surface where the rate of cooling was most rapid. This idea provides a ready explanation for the existence of a molten core in the center of the earth. It is

Fig. 6-1. Craters of the moon. The force of gravitational attraction on the moon is not sufficient to hold atmospheric gases such as those blanketing the earth. Thus the moon has no atmosphere and weathering does not take place. Because of this condition the craters on the moon may be ancient. Similar features may once have dotted the face of the earth. The origin of the craters has long been attributed to the impact of meteorites when the moon was in a semi-molten state. However, smoke has been seen rising from one of the craters, suggesting that they are not impact features. It is probable that they are collapse features. calderas, associated with volcanic activity. If they are of volcanic origin, it is obvious that the amount of activity has been great in the past. This in turn would serve as a good indication of similar activity in the early history of the earth. This lends support to the idea that the earth's atmosphere and hydrosphere have originated through "degassing" of the interior of the planet. (Photo by courtesy of Mount Wilson and Palomar Observatories.)

Fig. 6-2. Crater of Mauna Loa in the Hawaiian Islands. This air view of the volcano crater shows a distinct similarity to the craters of the moon. They may indeed be features of similar origin. Volcanoes may be the ultimate source of the waters of the oceans and atmosphere. (United States Air Force Photo.)

simply a residual liquid from the initial stages of the formation of the earth. Cooling of the gases to liquids would not completely remove all gases. Some remained as a primitive atmosphere, and these underwent changes through losses and additions. These changes are treated separately since they are independent of the initial stages in the formation of the atmosphere.

Accumulated Atmosphere Hypothesis

Late in the 1950's and early in 1960 data became available which strongly support the theory that the earth's atmosphere accumulated gradually as a result of "degassing" of the earth's interior and is not in fact a residual mass of gases. These new findings suggest that the earth may have never been totally molten. Much of the evidence has been derived from studies of the moon including its shape and the distribution of its surface features. One of the strongest arguments for a molten origin of the earth has been that the earth and moon probably originated at the same time. The surface of the moon is covered by a large number of craters. Most frequently these have been interpreted as features formed by the impact of large meteorites on the moon during the early stages of its formation when it was supposedly molten. The craters resemble frozen splash features. Now we have good reason to

Fig. 6-3. Mt. Aso, Kyusyu, Japan. This is part of the largest crater in the world. It is fifteen miles in length from north to south, ten miles in width, and seventy-five miles in circumference. If our atmosphere originated through "degassing" of the earth's interior the gases should be very similar in composition to the early atmosphere of the earth. (Photo by courtesy of Japan Tourist Association.)

question this interpretation of the origin of the craters, and therefore the whole idea that the moon or the earth was molten. Both Russian and American astronomers have seen smoke rising from one of the craters on the moon. This is almost definite proof that the moon is volcanically active. Other studies have shown that the surface is covered by a layer of dust. How could this form on a body such as the moon, which has no atmosphere, no winds, and no weathering if it originated from a molten mass? It is easy to see that this dust could be the outpourings of dust and ash from volcanoes. We have recorded great quantities of dust from some eruptions on the earth. These observations have prompted more careful analysis of the morphology of the craters of the moon. It is found that the ratio of the depth to the width of the craters is more comparable to that found in the collapse features such as calderas associated with volcanism on earth than it is to the dimensions of impact craters produced experimentally. The size of the craters is of little help here. The craters are generally much larger than any caldera or impact crater known on earth. Some of the rays that extend out from the craters may actually be faults or fractures in the moon's surface. Many of these craters are aligned, suggesting that they may be related to the rays (faults) that extend out from them. If there were random impact of meteorites on the moon and if the rays were shatter fractures radiating from the center of the craters like fractures formed where a bullet hits a window, then there should be no alignment of craters and rays. The alignment suggests that the craters are volcanic by origin and that molten rock and gases came up along the fractures. This is supported by the observation that many of the craters lie at the intersection of two or more aligned fracture zones. Finally, with the publication of the first photographs of the back side of the moon, we learned that craters are much more common on the earth's side of the moon than they are on the opposite side. What does this mean? The moon is affected by the gravitational attraction of the earth in the same way that the earth is affected by the moon. On earth the tides are pulled out by this force, but the solid crust of the earth is also slightly deformed in the direction of the moon. The same is true of the moon. Since it always keeps the same side toward the earth, that side is deformed and pulled out in a bulge toward the earth. This pull combined with fractures that might have formed as a result of the bulge might well influence the distribution of volcanic activity on the moon.

If the atmosphere were derived from the accretion of planetesimals it would appear unreasonable to assume that it ever had exceedingly large concentrations of hydrogen and helium, since these would have been lost more readily from small planets than from large ones which have a much greater gravitational attraction. It is particularly noteworthy that

Composition of Volcanic Gases from Kilauea Volcano, Hawaii	
Constituent	*Per cent of total volume*
H_2O	67.7
CO_2	12.7
N_2	7.65
SO_2	7.03
SO_3	1.86
S_2	1.04
H_2	.75
CO	.67
Cl_2	.41
A	.20

Fig. 6-4. The composition of volcanic gases escaping from Kilauea Volcano, Hawaii.

even heavier inert gases might be lost from small planetesimals. This could be the explanation for the relative deficiency of krypton and xenon on the earth. These two inert gases are thousands of times less abundant in the earth than some of their close nongaseous neighbors in the periodic table.

What then would the initial composition of the earth's atmosphere have been? Since the planetesimals would be meteorites, analysis of gases in meteorites should give some ideas. Meteorites yield carbon dioxide and nitrogen. A second source of information might be the composition of gases coming from volcanoes on earth today. The main constituents are water vapor, carbon dioxide, and oxides of sulfur.

Fig. 6-5. Composition of the Earth's atmosphere.

Composition of the Earth's Atmosphere		
Constituent		*Per cent of total volume*
N_2	nitrogen	78.00
O_2	oxygen	20.30
A	argon	1.30
CO_2	carbon dioxide	.05
Ne	neon	.001
He, CH_4, Kr, N_2O, H_2, O_3, and Xe less than .001 each.		

Oxygen in the atmosphere

The nitrogen in the atmosphere is easily explained by either theory on the origin of the earth. It is present in meteorites and in volcanic gases, and it would be derived from the decomposition of ammonia if the earth had a primitive atmosphere like that of the sun.

The history of the atmosphere's oxygen is more debatable. Holland (1958) has shown that the earth's atmosphere about 2 billion years ago consisted primarily of carbon dioxide, nitrogen, and relatively little free oxygen. His calculations hold equally well under either of the theories. They are based on studies of the presence of particular oxygen-bearing compounds (minerals) in rocks of Precambrian age. Most of his studies have been made on $Fe_3O_4 - Fe_2O_3$, $UO_2 - U_3O_8$, and $PbS - PbSO_4$. From studies of compounds which were actually formed in rocks of different ages it is possible to estimate the partial pressure of oxygen in the atmosphere at various times.

The first oxygen in the atmosphere was probably freed from water vapor by solar radiation in the upper layers of the atmosphere, a process called photochemical disassociation. This process is taking place today at a rate which, if continued throughout geologic time, would provide several times the amount of oxygen presently found in the earth's atmosphere. Of course much of the oxygen that has been produced in the past has been incorporated in oxygen compounds in the minerals of the earth's crust.

A second source of oxygen is from the process of photosynthesis by green plants. This process may be responsible for maintaining the present oxygen content of the atmosphere, but it could not account for oxygen in the Precambrian atmosphere because the higher order of plants which produce oxygen by photosynthesis did not appear on the earth in abundance until the Devonian Period. Lower plants which might have been present in the Precambrian time absorb oxygen and expire carbon dioxide. Thus this process does not explain the observed oxygen content of the Precambrian atmosphere.

Losses from the atmosphere

Through rock-weathering processes the atmosphere and rocky crust of the earth react. These reactions tend to remove certain constituents from the atmosphere as they combine to form compounds. Examples of some of these losses are:

1. When the partial pressure of carbon dioxide reaches a certain level, reactions begin which may be symbolized as follows:

   $$CaSiO_3 + CO_2 \rightarrow CaCO_3 + SiO_2.$$

   Stated without chemical formula this means that the carbon dioxide of the atmosphere reacts with the minerals formed from the crystallization of rock melts to produce carbonate rocks such as limestone and dolomite, and to produce free silica. It has been pointed out that the absence of large quantities of limestone in the Precambrian rocks is an indication that the atmosphere did not originally consist of carbon dioxide and nitrogen. Although the above equation symbolizes the reaction it is apt to be very misleading. Rubey (1955) defines the actual steps symbolized in the above equation:
   a. Carbon dioxide, sunlight, and water favor the growth of plants on the land and in the sea.
   b. Plants support the growth of all other organisms.
   c. Decaying organic matter yields carbon dioxide which, dissolved in ground water, forms carbonic acid.
   d. Calcic feldspars, pyroxenes, and amphiboles (common rock-forming minerals) in crystalline rocks and carbonates in sedimentary rocks are decomposed by weak solutions of carbonic acid, with the formation of clay minerals and the release of calcium and other bases into aqueous solution.
   e. Ground waters carrying the calcium and other dissolved materials discharge into streams and so into the ocean where solar evaporation causes gradual concentration of $CO_3^{=}$ ions in sea water.
   f. When the solubility product of calcium ions and carbonate ions exceeds a certain value, limestone is deposited. Consequently carbon dioxide alone will hardly result in the formation of limestone.
2. Carbon dioxide is also taken out of the atmosphere as plants and some animals use it, and they in turn may be transformed into coal, petroleum, or disseminated carbon in rocks.
3. Oxygen combines with other elements through the process of oxidation.
4. The light gases are lost from the earth's gravitational field (notably hydrogen and helium).
5. Nitrogen is removed by bacteria in the soil to form oxides of nitrogen.

Summary

The evolution of the atmosphere may be summarized as follows (Poldervaart, 1955):

1. The primitive atmosphere probably consisted of water vapor, hydrogen, nitrogen, ammonia, and methane (according to Urey) if the earth was originally molten. It consisted of nitrogen, carbon dioxide, and water vapor if it has derived from degassing.
2. The primitive atmosphere evolved to its present nature through photochemical reactions, accession of gases to the atmosphere by degassing of the earth's mantle, and finally photosynthesis by green plants.
3. The main photochemical process involved was oxidation of methane by

water vapor and decomposition of ammonia. Thus carbon dioxide, nitrogen, and hydrogen were formed, and the hydrogen escaped into space because it is light in weight.

4. When the partial pressure of the carbon dioxide reached a certain level, reactions started, and silicate and carbonate minerals were formed.
5. At first the atmosphere had a strongly reducing character (oxygen was given up rather than combined). Photochemical decomposition of water vapor contributed oxygen to the atmosphere at first, and later more was supplied by the process of photosynthesis by green plants. The atmosphere thus changed from a reducing to an oxidizing atmosphere.

ORIGIN OF THE OCEANS

The origin of water in general and the ocean specifically must be closely related to the origin of the earth's atmosphere. Water probably was present on earth as soon as the temperatures of the surface cooled down to the

Fig. 6-6. Composition of the Earth's hydrosphere.

(Water makes up about 98 per cent of total.)

Constituent		Per cent of total volume of dissolved constituents
Cl	chlorine	55.0
Na	sodium	30.0
SO_4	sulphate	7.7
Mg	magnesium	3.7
Ca	calcium	1.2
K	potassium	1.1
Br	bromine	.2
HCO_3, F, H_3BO_3, Sr		all less than .1 each

Fig. 6-7. Origin of the atmosphere. Water vapor, carbon dioxide, and nitrogen are shown coming from a volcano. The water vapor is broken down by photochemical processes high in the atmosphere – oxygen is liberated and hydrogen, being light, is lost.

critical temperature for water. That is, the temperature at which a fluid cannot exist as a liquid. For water this temperature is 365° Centigrade. We cannot say exactly when this happened, but we find many sedimentary rocks in the early Precambrian. The oldest are 3.3 billion years old. These sediments are like those deposited by running water now, so we may assume that by that time there were considerable quantities of water present on earth.

Several alternative hypotheses about the rate of the formation of ocean waters exist. These are:

1. If the earth possessed a primitive atmosphere initially, then the first oceans that formed in the early Precambrian after the earth cooled might have been almost as extensive as those we know today.
2. The atmosphere and the hydrosphere evolved from the degassing of the earth's interior, and the oceans accumulated gradually as gases came out of volcanoes in the form of steam. The proponents of this hypothesis are divided on the rate at which water has been produced through degassing. Some believe that the water must have been added from the interior most rapidly during the early Precambrian. At that time the surface was covered by a thin crust; thus we might expect more igneous activity than at later times, and this would account for more rapid additions of steam from volcanoes. A second possibility is that the amount of water being added to the surface has proceeded at a nearly steady rate throughout geologic time. The third alternative is that the rate has tended to become more rapid in the later part of geologic time.

Unfortunately we have not as yet been able to establish definitely which of these alternatives is correct, although there is increasing agreement that the oceans came from the earth's interior through volcanism. Large quantities of water are continually being brought to the surface of the earth through volcanoes. Steam is by far the most prominent gas given off by volcanoes; it composes about 98 per cent of those emitted. Many volcanoes are located near the margins of the oceans or within the ocean basins. Thus it is possible that a large part of the steam that comes from them seeps into the volcano from the ocean. Consequently there is the possibility that water is being recycled instead of added continually, but, even if no more than .8 per cent of the water brought out of volcanoes today is truly juvenile, magmatic, this would still provide enough water through geologic time to account for the quantity now found in the oceans.

REFERENCES

LEES, G. M., 1954, The geological history of the oceans: Deep-sea Research, v. 1, p. 67-71.

RUBEY, W. W., 1955, Development of the hydrosphere and atmosphere with specific reference to probable composition of the early atmosphere: Geol. Soc. America Sp. Paper 62, p. 631-650.

7 Unraveling the History of the Precambrian

ORIGIN OF THE CONTINENTS

Something within man drives him to seek that which he discerns as the "ultimate," whether this be to climb the highest mountain peak, descend to the greatest depth in the ocean, or seek the first appearance of his own species. Such a goal, for those who explore the geological past, is the discovery of the first continents that appeared on earth in the earliest stages of its history. Two of the most important obstacles encountered in this search are:

1. The extreme antiquity of any such feature and consequent probability that it has been altered beyond recognition.
2. The probability that the remains of such continents are now covered by younger sediments.

Earlier we discussed the age of the earth and found that it is estimated to be approximately 4 1/2 billion years old, although the oldest rocks that have been dated by radioactive decay are 3 1/3 billion years old. That leaves a period of slightly more than a billion years for which we have no positive evidence of a rock record. This is particularly discouraging since it is almost certainly within this period of time that continents first began to appear on the earth.

Two theories of the origin of the earth have been discussed. In one the earth originated as a hot gaseous cloud, cooled to a molten liquid, and finally crusted over. According to the other theory the earth originated as an accumulation of cool dust or planetesimals that became hot and partially or entirely molten through the heat liberated by radioactive decay. Each of the theories accounts for the presence of the observed stratification of the earth's interior through a sort of gravitative separation, with the more dense materials sinking into the interior and the lighter substances remaining on top. However, the two most widely accepted concepts of the origin of the continents are independent of the mode of origin of the earth. Thus we cannot hope to solve the problem of the origin of the continents by solving the mode of origin of the earth.

The oldest theory of the origin of the continents maintains that they originated as the outer parts of the molten earth cooled and solidified. They were what might be considered an end product of the process of gravitative separation. Throughout the cooling history of the earth various minerals crystallized at different temperatures. When heavy minerals crystallized, they sank toward the earth's interior. When light-weight minerals crystallized they rose to the surface, if they were less dense than the magma. This action created a crust composed of minerals that were light in weight or that had crystallized after the temperatures dropped. This explains why the continents are composed of sialic rocks. The most common minerals in the principal rock types of the continents are the light feldspars and quartz which crystallized at relatively low temperatures. The continents are supposed to be large platelike or raftlike accumulations of these minerals, floating on a more dense, basaltic subcrust.

At the other extreme is the idea that the original solid crust was entirely basaltic. In places this crust was fractured during and following consolidation. These breaks through the outer crust provided zones through which gases, lavas, and solutions could come out of the mantle of the earth. As soon as the atmosphere and oceans began to develop, the materials extruded on the earth's surface began to be affected by weathering and erosion. The effects of chemical weathering such as carbonation, oxidation, and hydration combined with the addition of silica from solutions brought out from the mantle led to the differentiation of the basaltic lavas and pyroclastic debris and to the formation of granitic rocks. These early lands may be visualized as somewhat like the present-day island arcs. According to this theory the continents grew by the successive addition of new sedimentary rocks at the margins of the land. One chain of island arcs after another developed along the margins and eventually became incorporated into the continents by diastrophism. Those who support this general point of view call our attention to:

1. The location of island-arc systems around the margins of the continents today, and to the diastrophism which currently characterizes them;
2. The fact that most of the oldest rocks that have been dated by radioactive methods lie in the central parts of the continental shields;
3. The location of most young folded-mountain belts along the margins of shields or continents;
4. The tendency for successively younger belts of folding to be located at progressively greater distances from the center of the shields.

The origin of the first continents along with the development of the atmosphere, the first oceans, and even the first forms of life took place during the first billion years of the earth's history. No positive evidence in the form of a record left from these times exists. We must infer the early history and development of the earth from what we know of the past 3 billion years and from information we can learn through geochemical and geophysical studies. The story of the earth's history as deciphered by interpretation of the sedimentary-rock record begins only after the earth's surface had become cool and after processes of weathering, erosion, and sedimentation had begun to take place. These processes require the presence of an atmosphere and large quantities of water. The oldest rocks in Southern Rhodesia dated at 3 1/3 billion years are conglomerates. We know that they formed through erosion and sedimentation in water, and so the story begins.

There are two ways to approach the study of history. We might start with the present about which we know a great deal and then, by examining successively older rocks, we would begin to unravel the historical data stored there. However, as in the case of the history of civilization, we find on probing into the earth's history that our resolution of past events becomes less certain as more remote events are considered. Instead let us use the second method and consider first the most remote parts of the past and from there try to reconstruct the sequence of events leading to the present. This technique has the advantage of establishing a basic background against which the events of any period can be viewed. It has disadvantages too. The early history of the earth is more difficult to unravel because the events of later periods have affected the rocks formed earlier. They have been deformed and altered in later orogenies and they have been covered by younger sediments. The nature of the record of the history of the earth is such that we know many more details about the last million years than we do of the first 3000 million.

Fig. 7-1. Indian Shield. Like the other shields, a number of trends of folded mountain belts are clearly indicated by the structures of the metamorphic rocks of the shield. Some of the structures cut directly across others indicating several periods of major orogeny in which folded mountain belts must have formed. The Deccan Basalts which are similar to those of the Columbia River Plateau of the northwestern United States cover a large part of the Indian Shield.

PRECAMBRIAN TIME

Characteristics of Precambrian rocks

The name Precambrian is applied to that part of the earth's history that predates the appearance of the first abundantly preserved animals in sedimentary rocks. These sediments were formed in the early part of what is called the Cambrian Period. They have been dated by radioactive dating methods as being approximately 520 million years old. This then is the upper boundary of Precambrian time. The lower boundary is uncertain. It may be considered to be the age of the formation of the oldest rocks in the crust of the earth. In 1950 this age was considered to be 2 billion years, in 1960 it was 3.3 billion years; it may be pushed still farther back into the past with each succeeding decade. Assume that the beginning of the Precambrian was 3 1/2 billion years ago. That means that Precambrian time

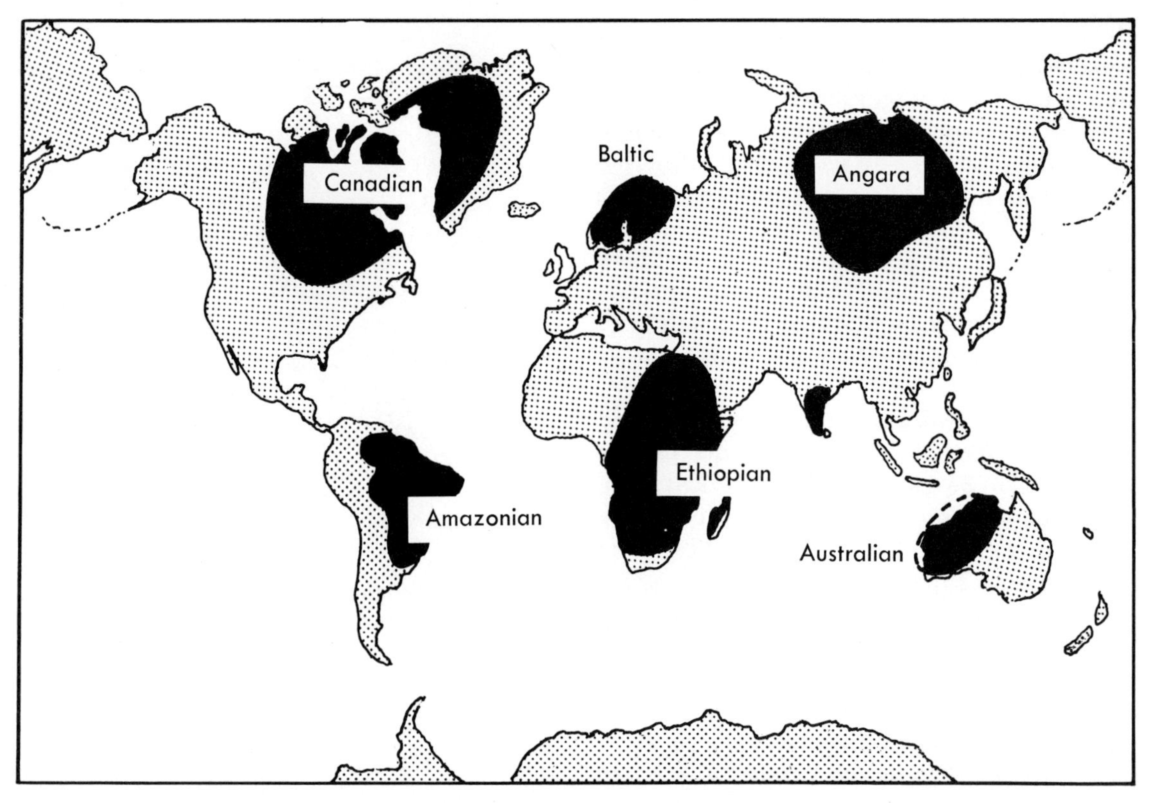

Fig. 7-2. Precambrian Shields exposed on all continents. These areas are seismically stable, covered by thin veneers of recent sediments and small patches of post Precambrian rock units. Most of the rocks exposed in these shields are unfossiliferous metamorphoric units which have been intruded by various types of igneous rocks. Structures obviously related to ancient mountain systems may be traced in the shields.

represents five-sixths of the geological history of the earth. If the earth's origin 4 1/2 billion years ago is taken as the start of the Precambrian then the Precambrian represents nine-tenths of the earth's history. If we knew as much about the Precambrian as we do about the Paleozoic and Mesozoic eras, and treated them equally, then most of the remaining part of this book would be devoted to the history of the Precambrian. But we do not.

First of all, our knowledge is restricted by the distribution of Precambrian exposures. By far the largest number of the Precambrian rock units are exposed in the continental shields (Fig. 7-2). Others are exposed in blocks of the crust that have been uplifted and deeply eroded, or in the cores of several major folded-mountain belts. The distribution of Precambrian exposures in the United States is illustrated in Fig. 11-1. The largest single exposure of Precambrian rocks in the world is found in Canada in the Canadian Shield. The shield continues southward into the northern United States including large parts of Wisconsin, and all of Minnesota.

Within the United States the Precambrian system is exposed along the central part of the Appalachian mountain system and in the dome uplifts in the Adirondack, Ozark, Arbuckle, Wichita, and Llano Mountains. In the western United States the most extensive outcrops are in the Rocky Mountains of northern Montana and Idaho, in the cores of the ranges in the Middle Rocky Mountains, and in the Front Range of the Colorado Rockies. The system is sporadically exposed in uplifts of the Basin and Range province of Arizona and Southern California.

A second important limitation to our knowledge of the Precambrian is the complexity of the rocks. They have been deformed, metamorphosed, and intruded. Frequently the alteration is so great and so variable that it is impossible by conventional methods to recognize and correlate an originally homogeneous rock unit over long distances.

Our knowledge of the Precambrian at the present time allows us to make certain generalizations about it. These serve as an introduction to a more detailed analysis of several particular areas which are well exposed.

1. Precambrian rocks are unfossiliferous. Carbon of organic origin is abundant, and there are many objects which are interpreted as fossils, but most of these are either of questionable origin or are not suitable for correlation.
2. All three types of rocks are found in the Precambrian. Metamorphic rocks are the most abundant type, but there are large quantities of sedimentary and igneous rocks as well.
3. Most of the Precambrian rock units have been at least partially metamorphosed and deformed by post-Precambrian crustal movements.
4. Correlation of Precambrian sedimentary and metamorphic rock units over short distances is possible, but over long distances correlations based on ordinary techniques are not reliable. Thus it is difficult to relate the history of two widely separated regions.
5. The most reliable basis for correlations of time-stratigraphic units of the Precambrian is radioactive dating. Because this technique is relatively new there are not yet enough dates to establish the equivalence in time of events recorded in the rock units of widely separated areas.
6. The extensive areas of gneisses found in the Precambrian shields may have originated in one of two ways. Originally almost all of them were assumed to be igneous intrusions, but many are now known to be highly metamorphosed and "granitized" sedimentary rocks.

Precambrian history of the Canadian Shield

The Canadian Shield covers more than 1 ½ million square miles of the central part of Canada and the northern edge of the central United States. Parts of this area are covered by

Fig. 7-3. Subdivisions of the Precambrian.

PRECAMBRIAN	*Upper*	*Keweenawan Series*		*Killarney Granite*
	Middle or Algonkian	Upper Huronian	*	Animikie Series
		Middle Huronian	*	Cobalt Series
		Lower Huronian	*	Bruce Series
		Major	Angular Unconformity	
	Lower or Archean	Timiskaming Series	*	*Algoman Granite*
		Keewatin Lava Series	*	Knife Lake Series
		Coutchiching Series	*	*Laurentian (?) Granite*

* These series are not exact time equivalents.

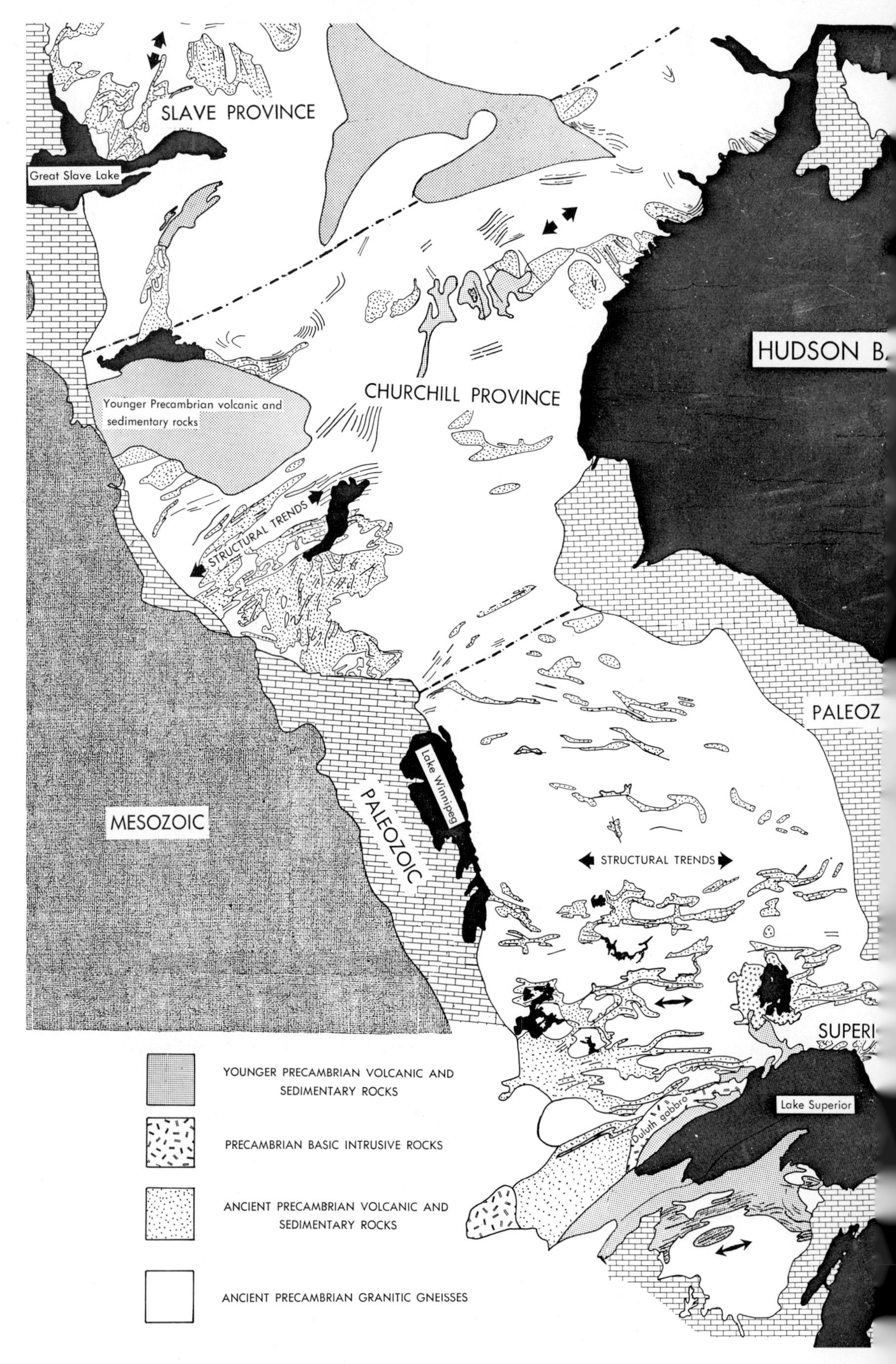

Fig. 7-4. Map of the Canadian Shield.

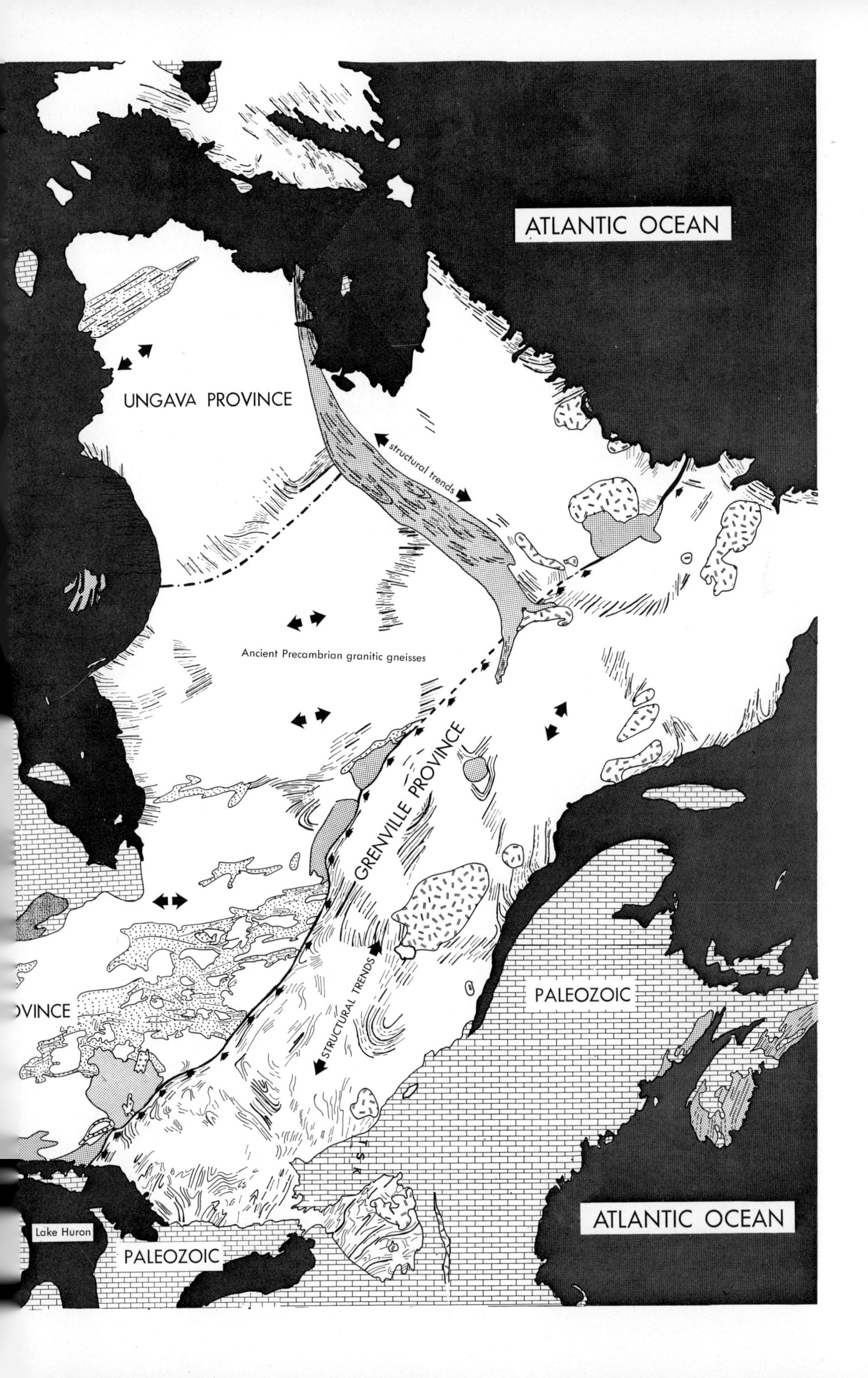

ATLANTIC OCEAN
UNGAVA PROVINCE
structural trends
Ancient Precambrian granitic gneisses
GRENVILLE PROVINCE
STRUCTURAL TRENDS
PALEOZOIC
VINCE
ATLANTIC OCEAN
Lake Huron
PALEOZOIC

the waters of Hudson Bay and Baffin Bay, swamps, glacial deposits of the last ice ages, and Paleozoic sedimentary rocks, but this shield still has by far the most extensive outcrop of Precambrian rocks in North America. As a whole the shield is slightly saucer-shaped. The central part is nearly flat, but slightly higher elevations are found toward the margins in every direction.

We would not expect such an extensive area to have a uniform history throughout billions of years. This expectation is fully realized, for the history of the shield is quite diversified. Even though it is an extensive and inaccessible area, there has been sufficiently detailed mapping of parts of the shield to establish that numerous folded-mountain belts occur within it. Each of these belts is characterized by distinctive structural trends and by internal features that closely resemble the features of the younger folded-mountain belts such as those that now stand out prominently on the face of the earth. At least six major orogenic belts can be separated by their distinctive trends as illustrated (Fig. 7-4). Within these, 15 different orogenies occurred during Precambrian time. Obviously some of these belts have been affected by two or more orogenies at different times. It must be emphasized that not all of these orogenic belts existed in the shield at the same time, nor did single orogenies affect the entire area of the shield at any one time. Just as our present mountains are confined to certain parts of the continent, so they were in the Precambrian. Until there are enough radioactive dates to make it possible to correlate the events in the six different orogenic belts, it is necessary to consider the history of each of them separately. These belts or provinces are:

a. Grenville Province, which extends as a band across the eastern portion of the shield. It includes the Adirondack Mountains, large parts of Ontario, Quebec, and Labrador.
b. Superior Province, which makes up the south-central part of the shield north of Lake Superior. It is the best known of the provinces.
c. Churchill Province, occupying parts of Alberta, Saskatchewan, Manitoba, and the Northwest Territories.
d. Slave Province, located in the region around Great Slave Lake.
e. Yellowknife Province, located between Great Slave Lake and Great Bear Lake.
f. Ungava Province, located in the central northern part of the shield. It is known only through reconnaissance studies.

The boundaries between these provinces are not exact. Further study will probably reveal that some of them should be divided. The Superior Province is already subdivided into three subprovinces.

PRECAMBRIAN HISTORY OF THE SUPERIOR PROVINCE

This province of the shield is named for Lake Superior which is located near its southern edge. The Grenville Province bounds it on the east; it extends northward across the southern part of Hudson Bay and northwestward to Lake Winnipeg. It contains more proved mineral wealth than any other part of the shield. Because of this wealth, and the accessibility and relatively mild climate of this province, it has been studied in greater detail than the other parts of the shield. Even so, it is not easy to trace its Precambrian history. As in other areas of Precambrian outcrop, the main obstacle is correlating the rock record of different localities. History is most meaningful when such correlations can be made. Therefore, we want to determine if an event recorded in one place occurred before, after, or at the same time as some other event in another region. In short the problem is one of relating the stratigraphic record to time. Without fossils this is difficult, and as yet there are not enough radioactive dates to achieve our goals.

Where radioactive dating has been done the results have unfortunately failed to confirm many presumed relationships. One notable example is the age of a granite known as the Laurentian granite. This igneous rock was first described in the Grenville Province where it is intruded into the oldest rocks known in that province. A granite that resembles the Laurentian granite of the Grenville Province intrudes the oldest metasedimentary rocks in the Superior Province. Consequently, it is called Laurentian granite. The name is now firmly entrenched in geologic literature. In the 1950's samples of these granites were dated by radioactive methods. The dates show that the granites in the Grenville Province are about 1100 million years old, but those in the Superior Province are 2500 million years old. The two are separated in time by more than twice the length of time included in the Paleozoic, Mesozoic, and Cenozoic eras combined. This certainly should clarify why the different provinces must be considered separately, but it does not tell us what to do with the term "Laurentian." Should it be restricted to one province or discarded altogether? To a lesser extent the same sort of problem exists within each of the provinces. Thus Precambrian history, as it can now be told, is most reliable when it is considered in detail in a relatively localized area. Within such small regions outcrops of units can be traced, and correlation by continuity of outcrop is most reliable. Within these areas history can be deciphered by determination of the sequence of formation, through unconformities, and by use of cross-cutting relationships.

Subdivisions of the Precambrian. A brief outline will help simplify the discussion to follow. Precambrian time is here divided into three major divisions: Early, Middle, and Late Precambrian. Correlation and history of the Early Precambrian are much less certain than those of the later parts. Small outcrops of these most ancient rocks are found scattered across the province. Sedimentary and metasedimentary rocks of this time are generally known by the names "Coutchiching," "Knife Lake," or "Timiskaming"; lava flows and volcanic rocks are generally called "Keewatin"; and igneous granites are called "Laurentian" or "Algoman." A pronounced angular unconformity separates these units from the Middle Precambrian but there is even doubt that this famous break in the geologic record is the same age everywhere. If it is approximately the same age throughout the shield then there must have been a period of extensive uplift over a huge area at that time. Otherwise we are seeing evidence that different parts of the shield were elevated and eroded at various times before relatively less altered units were laid down. Subdivisions in the Middle Precambrian are known as "Huronian" or "Animikie"; each of these may be subdivided into two or more groups of units on the basis of angular unconformities. These were deformed and intruded by granites that are 1400 million years old. Overlying these with angular unconformity is the Upper Precambrian. It is exposed around Lake Superior where it is known as the "Keweenawan" series. This thick series of lava flows, intrusive rocks, and sedimenary rocks is broken by faults, but it has never been subjected to strong folding. The igneous rocks are perhaps 1100 million years old. This leaves a gap in the history of the region between the Precambrian and the Cambrian systems that amounts to half a billion years. This is equal to the amount of time since the first-known fossil trilobites were preserved. It is a hard task for our imaginations to grasp the lengths of time represented in the subdivisions of the Precambrian.

Lower Precambrian

The time represented by the Early Precambrian is extremely long, and the history as well as the rocks preserved from that time is quite complex. Over the vast area of the Superior Province most of the exposed rock surface is composed of granites and granitic gneisses. Some of these may be metamorphosed or granitized sediments, but large parts are true igneous rocks. Exposed in elongate patches scattered across this surface we find strongly-folded and highly-altered sedimentary rocks and lava flows that trend roughly east-west. It is difficult to correlate these units from one place to another. The most distinctive of the units are the Keewatin lava flows.

Keewatin lava flows. These are actually greenstones, a dense greenish rock that is formed by the metamorphism of basalt. Many of these flows possess an unusual type of structure. Pillow-shaped masses of lava make up large parts of the sequence. These are thought to form where lava is extruded under water. Associated with these we find other volcanic rocks, such as ash and tuff, and rocks containing poorly sorted sediments including some ironstones and cherts.

Most sedimentary rocks found below the Keewatin volcanic rocks are called "Coutchiching." Those above the sequences are called "Knife Lake" or "Timiskaming." There is no certainty that all the units below Keewatin-type sequences are the same age. It could be that there were several periods of outpourings of similar lavas at widely separated times. If this is the case then the Coutchiching of one area may be the same age as the Knife Lake or Timiskaming of another locality.

"Coutchiching", "Knife Lake", and "Timiskaming." One of the outstanding characteristics of these sedimentary and metasedimentary rocks is that they contain large quantities of feldspar, mixed with the sands and gravels. This signifies either a rapid rate of subsidence and sedimentation or dry deposition, because feldspar will decay if it remains long in the presence of water. We get the impression that rates of deposition may have been very rapid and that there was little time for sorting and washing of sediments. A great variety of metasedimentary rocks are found—quartzites, conglomerates, slates, schists, and gneisses. At Lake Timiskaming the metasedimentary rocks contain pebbles and cobbles of Keewatin-type volcanic rocks. These units overlie the Keewatin volcanic rocks nearby. Thus at this locality the type section known as the Timiskaming series is younger than the Keewatin, but this does not definitely establish that all metasedimentary units that lie stratigraphically above the Keewatin-type volcanic rocks are the same age. Why?

There must have been igneous activity at many times during the Early Precambrian. Two names are most frequently applied to these granitic intrusions. Where two periods of intrusion are seen in a single area the older one is called "Laurentian," and the cross-cutting granite is called "Algoman". We have already seen that intrusive rocks called "Laurentian" are variable in age. At least a few are undoubtedly younger than some Algoman granites, but in general the name Algoman is applied to the younger Early Precambrian granites.

Middle Precambrian

Most of the units of this age are deformed and slightly altered, but not so extensively as those below them. The name Huronian is fre-

Fig. 7-5. Iron Ranges. This is a cross section across the Cuyuna Range of Minnesota. Other important iron producing districts include the Mesabi Range, Vermilion Range, Gogebic Range, Marquette Range, and Menominee Range in the United States and the Steep Rock Lake, Animikie, and Michipicoten districts in Canada. The iron is concentrated in the Middle Precambrian section (Huronian) of the region. The iron-rich strata were folded in the Late Precambrian. The black zones indicate that part of the strata in which iron has been concentrated (up to 60% Fe). Lower grade unconcentrated taconite underlies the hematite rock zones. (After Zapffe.)

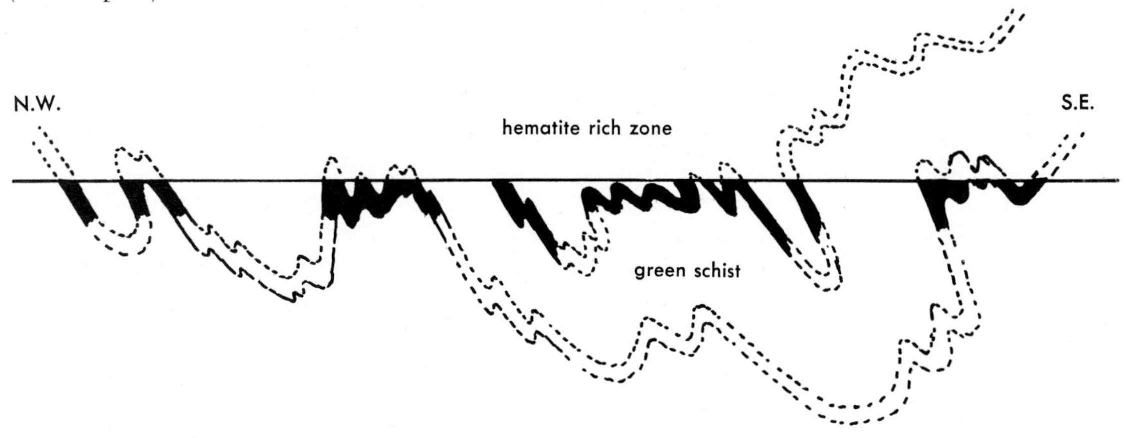

Fig. 7-6. Belcher Mountains. Exposed in the Hudson Bay region these plunging folded sedimentary and volcanic strata outline the former position of the Belcher Mountains, a range which stood here in the late Precambrian. The folds trend northward. In the millions of years since these mountains were uplifted and folded erosion has beveled them into a nearly flat plane. The lines running across the units are fractures and faults caused by the deformation of the units. (Photo by courtesy of the Royal Canadian Air Force.)

quently applied to all or parts of the Middle Precambrian This name is taken from the type locality near Lake Huron where these rocks were first described. Similar units are found farther west around Lake Superior where they are divided into three groups separated by unconformities. Thus in some areas it is possible to subdivide the Middle Precambrian into as many as three parts. For example, around Lake Huron the Middle Precambrian is divided into the Upper Huronian, Middle Huronian, and Lower Huronian. But in Ontario the divisions are called Animikie series, Cobalt series, and Bruce series. However, the subdivisions of the Middle Precambrian in these two localities are not time equivalents. In 1959 the United States Geological Survey adopted the use of Animikie series for the entire section of Middle Precambrian units in northern Michigan.

One of the most important events of the Middle Precambrian was the deformation of the Middle Precambrian rocks as well as the underlying units. They were sharply folded and uplifted to form a major mountain range trending east-west across the Great Lakes region. This mountain range is known as the Penokean Range. The folds of this range were intruded by granitic rocks near the close of the Middle Precambrian. Some of these intrusions contain radioactive minerals, which have been dated as 1400 million years old. Deformation was less intense to the north and west for in those re-

Fig. 7-7. Northwest Territories. This view of the barrens between Artillery Lake and Thelon River in the Northwest Territories is typical of the physiography of a large part of the Canadian Shield. The millions of years of erosion have reduced the ancient structures to a nearly featureless plain. Drumlins show the direction of movement of the continental glaciers which recently occupied the shield. On the left an esker is seen as a light-colored line marking the position of a former stream under the ice sheet. (By courtesy of the Royal Canadian Air Force.)

Fig. 7-8. Mesas eroded in flat-lying Coppermine series, near the Arctic Coast, Northwest Territories. (By courtesy of the Royal Canadian Air Force.)

gions we find the same units, only slightly tilted instead of folded.

Most of the rock units are not particularly unusual. Sandstones, slates, conglomerates, dolomites, and lava flows are all present in quantity. The upper parts formed just before the orogeny contain units that are generally indicative of more crustal activity, such as lava flows and graywackes. Among the most interesting and economically important parts of the entire sequence are the iron formations.

Iron formations. These Precambrian deposits have been extremely important in the development of the American industrial society. Iron ore mined from a number of localities in Minnesota and northern Michigan is the principal raw material for the steel industry in Pennsylvania. The most famous of these mining districts are the Mesabi, Cuyuna, Vermilion, Gogebic, Marquette, and Menominee ranges. The occurrence of iron is essentially the same in all. One widely accepted theory is that

Fig. 7-9. Early Precambrian units intruded by later granites. These units are exposed in this vertical photograph of the region near Duncan Lake, Northwest Territories. The early Precambrian sediments are dark in color. They have been intruded by granite in bodies up to one-half mile in size. Note how the light-colored dikes have filled fracture and fault patterns in the lower part of the photograph. This establishes the age of the fracture pattern. Late Precambrian diabase dikes shown in dark grey cut across both the early Precambrian metasedimentary rocks and the granites. The irregular black areas are lakes. (By courtesy of the Royal Canadian Air Force.)

during the Middle Precambrian, streams carried the products of decomposition of older igneous and metamorphic rocks into the seas of that time. Silica-rich shales and iron-bearing cherts were deposited. The iron was derived from iron-bearing minerals (augite, hornblende) in the older rocks. When the region was later deformed the rocks were partly metamorphosed, and a rock known as taconite developed. Still later these taconite units became exposed at the surface and were subjected to weathering and erosion. Over a long period of time leaching of the units by ground water has concentrated the iron near the surface. This rich iron ore is about 60 per cent iron. The mineral is a pure hematite (ferric iron oxide). The hematite occurs with jasper, a hematite-rich chert. These ores have been important for many years, but with the present high rates of consumption they will be depleted in the foreseeable future. Attention is now being given to the commercial development of the taconite which contains up to 30 per cent iron.

Fig. 7-10. Mesas near Nipigon Village, Ontario, formed by Keweenawan diabase. The diabase was intruded as a series of sills and forms a resistant cap over Keweenawan sedimentary rocks exposed at the base of the mesa in the foreground. Note that these units are slightly warped but not folded. They have not been involved in an orogeny even though they were intruded more than a billion years ago. Further south, rocks of the same age as these are more strongly deformed. (Photo by courtesy of the Royal Canadian Air Force.)

Upper Precambrian

The name Keweenawan series is generally applied to rock units formed during the latest part of the Precambrian. The lower parts of these are thick sections of basaltic lava flows and intrusions of basalt and its coarse-grained equivalent, gabbro. These were followed by a thick sequence of conglomerates, sandstones, and shales that were apparently laid down on the land surface, not under water. The reason for this assumption is that the sands contain ripple marks indicating strong currents such as those common in streams. The shales and silts contain mud cracks which would form where the muds were periodically dried. A tidal zone or lake bottom might contain such features. Large parts of the sediments are colored red by iron-oxide stains suggesting that the sediments were oxidized. These sediments and the igneous activity were probably related to the Penokean orogeny that folded the Middle Precambrian units.

The Keweenawan series is confined to the area around Lake Superior. It is within a structural basin and probably never extended far beyond the present boundaries of this downwarped area.

The amount of magma involved in the igneous activity of this time amounted to thousands of cubic miles. Surface flows aggregated more than 5 miles in thickness in many areas, and in addition there were huge intrusions. Of the latter, the large lopolith that is exposed along the western end of Lake Superior, the Duluth lopolith, is almost 50,000 feet thick and more than 140 miles long. This body is dated as 1100 million years old. This may well be the age of a large part of the igneous activity. A second important intrusion is found at Sudbury, Ontario. The composition of the intrusion there is slightly different; it is a

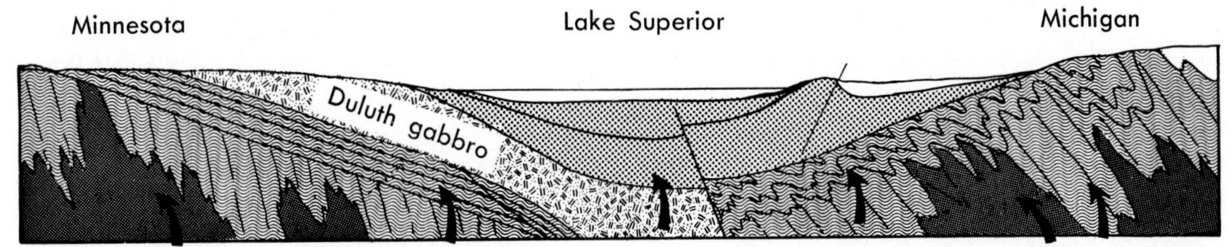

Fig. 7-11. Generalized section across Lake Superior. The lake occupies a position that coincides approximately with the broad synclinal structure of the rocks which underlie it. The Huronian series which is tilted on the Minnesota side of the lake is more strongly deformed in Michigan, indicating proximity to the belt of folding which affected the southern margin of the Canadian Shield in the Late Precambrian.

norite, and associated with it we find rich deposits of nickel ore. This is the principal source of this metal in North America. Another important mineral resource produced from the Keweenawan sequences is native copper. The main source of this copper is the Keweenaw Peninsula of northern Michigan where native copper is found in the porous parts of the ancient lava flows. The copper fills the vesicles left by escaping gases. It is also found as a filling around pebbles of some of the conglomerates that lie above the lavas. The copper was not primary; probably it was brought in and deposited by hot solutions after the lavas and conglomerates had formed.

GRENVILLE PROVINCE

The Grenville Province of the Canadian Shield is separated from the Superior Province by a very sharp line, a fault scarp. Rocks on the Grenville Province side are strongly deformed. The units are intensely folded, faulted, metamorphosed, and intruded. The structural trends of this orogenic belt roughly parallel the abrupt line between the two provinces. Units of the Superior Province side strike into the fault diagonally. The highly deformed rocks of the Grenville Province have been thrust westward over relatively undeformed units of Middle Precambrian age (Huronian) of the Superior Province. The fault may be traced northeastward for a distance of almost 700 miles. At no point along the line are the rock units of the two provinces in contact; so there is no place at which the units of the two regions can be directly correlated by tracing out the continuity of some particular horizon. The histories of the two regions cannot be totally unrelated, but until more accurate dates are available they might as well be.

One of the most important things we can learn from the Grenville is the importance of using concise meanings for scientific terms.

The term "Grenville" was not given a very specific definition when it was first brought into use. As a result, work by various people has led to a number of different meanings, and this has given rise to a serious problem in nomenclature. Because of the resulting confusion some have suggested that the term be entirely dropped from usage. As F. Fitz Osborne puts it, "Grenville is neither a series nor a lithological unit. It is a state of mind." Sir William Logan, one of the pioneers in geological investigations of the Canadian Shield, first used it when he applied the name to a band of marble found near the village of Grenville. Later he applied the name to a whole series of units consisting of quartzites, gneisses, and other rocks as well as marble. Since then the term "Grenville series" has been applied to sequences of rocks of similar lithologies over a region of nearly a quarter of a million square miles in eastern Canada. This has been done in spite of the fact that these units are often widely separated by extensive areas of massive granitic rocks. The reason for doing this was an assumed correlation between similar lithologies. As more and more detailed work was done, however, it was discovered that some of the units graded or interfingered into others, and that they did not appear everywhere in the same sequence. To summarize, we find the term "Grenville" applied to an orogenic belt, to a group of related lithologic units, to a regional province, and sometimes it is even used to denote a certain period of time.

The rocks of the Grenville Province are strikingly different from those of the Superior Province.

1. Marble is abundant in the Grenville Province. None is found in the Superior Province. Marble, which is a metamorphosed limestone, is a certain indication of an abundance of carbon dioxide in the atmosphere at the time of its deposition. These units are known to be more than a billion years old. One of the most interesting features of these marbles is that they contain thin layers of graphite, a form of pure carbon. The most probable source of this carbon is organic matter. This is one of the earliest indications of the presence of life in the Precambrian of North America; however, similar carbon has been found in rocks nearly 3 billion years old in Precambrian rocks outside of North America.
2. Another unusual type of rock found in the Grenville Province is one which contains anhydrite and gypsum. Such rocks are now formed in shallow enclosed bodies of water that are subjected to high rates of evaporation.

Fig. 7-12. Folding in argillite (dark) and greywacke (light) belonging to the Yellowknife group, Gordon Lake Area, Northwest Territories. (Photo by courtesy of the Royal Canadian Air Force.)

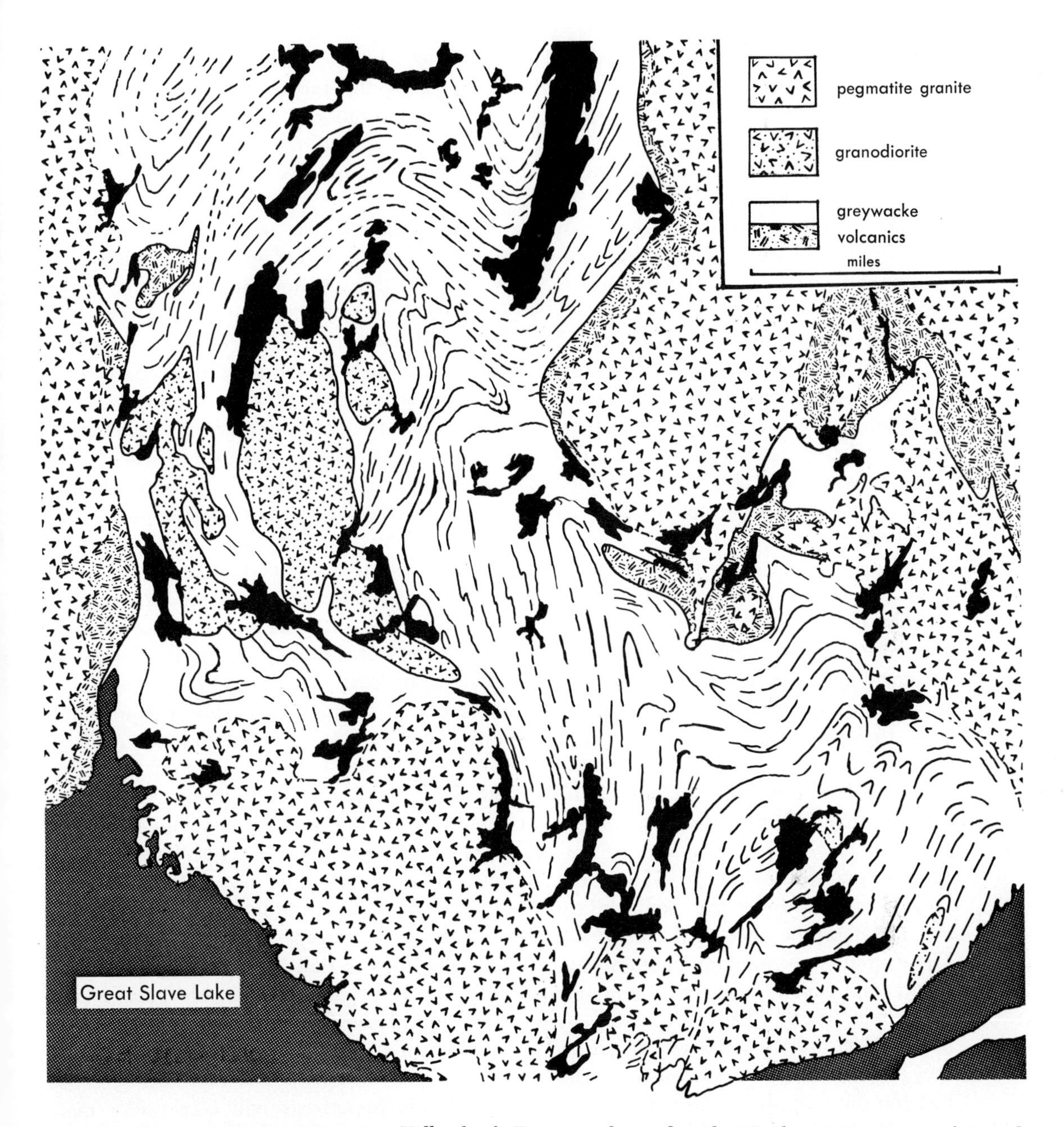

Fig. 7-13. Detail of Yellowknife District. Yellowknife District is located in the Northwest Territories of Canada on the north shore of the Great Slave Lake. The oldest rocks in the region are Early Precambrian (Archean) volcanic flows and sediments of the Yellowknife group. In some places there is an unconformity between the sedimentary and volcanic rocks. The rocks of the Yellowknife group have undergone at least two periods of folding. Each of these periods was accompanied by intrusion of granitic rocks. Middle Precambrian (Proterozoic) strata overlie the Yellowknife group. The entire sequence is intruded by still younger Precambrian pegmatitic granite. The disconnected bodies of rocks as shown in this illustration depict the complexity of the Precambrian history of the shields. (Y. O. Fortier, 1946, *Geol. Surv. Canada.*)

This might mean that there was an arid or semiarid climate during the time of their deposition.

3. Other sedimentary rocks found in the province include sandstones that have been metamorphosed to pure quartzites,

conglomerates, and feldspar-bearing arkose and graywacke. Where feldspars are found in rocks deposited in water, it must be assumed that deposition was rapid and that transportation was a short distance because, as you will remember, feldspar weathers to clay in the presence of water. Graywacke containing feldspar and volcanic ash was typical of the deposits of the Superior Province. There are few quartzites such as those found in the Grenville Province. Quartzites are nearly pure quartz indicating that sediments were deposited slowly or carried for a long distance in water. In the process they become sorted and separated from other materials.

4. Granitic gneisses outcrop over large areas. Some of these may be metamorphosed igneous rocks, but many of them are thought to be granitized sedimentary units. Shales have about the right composition to yield a metamorphic rock of granitic composition. It may be that these zones were highly metamorphosed and altered during the orogeny that deformed the rocks of this belt.
5. Igneous granites known as the Laurentian granite intrude the sedimentary and metamorphic units of the province. These granites fortunately contain pegmatites in which radioactive minerals have been found. They are dated as 800 to 1100 million years of age. Since they cut the folded rock units of the belt the dates apply to the deformation as well as to the granite, but it does not give the age of the metasedimentary rocks other than to indicate that they are older than 800 to 1100 million years. This pegmatite is about the same age as some intrusive rocks in the Huronian of the Superior Province.
6. One of the most unusual rock types found in the region is anorthosite. The origin of this rock composed almost entirely of labradorite feldspar, a plagioclase, is debatable. Large areas of it are found in the Adirondack Mountains and farther north in Quebec and in Labrador. Around the margins of this unit some of the world's largest garnets, more than a foot across, are found.

Synthesis. If we are to fully understand such a diverse group of rocks we must in some way relate them to one another. Most of the metasedimentary units are thought to have been laid down in a broad elongate geosynclinal trough such as the ones that characterize later periods of geologic time. At any one time a great variety of sediments were formed across the area; each was related to its particular environment. Those areas which were close to high lands received conglomerates, sands, and arkoses. Those far away from land but still in a warm climate accumulated limestones. Thus it is probable that the rock units of the province interfinger with one another in some areas, while others of different age lie in vertical sequences. At least some 20,000 feet of sediment accumulated in this geosyncline before deformation began. During the deformation deeper parts of the geosynclinal accumulation were intruded by Laurentian granite and large quantities of the sedimentary rocks became granitized into granitic gneisses. The culmination of the deformation was the folding and thrusting of part of the belt to the west. Thus we arrive at a concept of a Grenville orogenic belt. The idea is that there is a close genetic, temporal, and spatial relationship between the sediments of the Grenville Province and their environments of sedimentation and the intrusions and deformations which followed. The test of this hypothesis will come with more accurate determination of ages of the units and their relationships by radioactive dating.

BEARTOOTH MOUNTAINS

The story of the investigations of the Beartooth Mountains of Montana and Wyoming is of importance because it illustrates two major ideas. First, the studies made there are typical of the continual re-evaluation of established and accepted ideas. Such re-evaluation is an important aspect of the scientific method. Secondly, the methods and techniques of analysis used in the study of the Beartooth Precambrian are of a type that can be applied to many other Precambrian areas. These methods are strikingly different from those generally used in the analysis of the history of rocks younger than the Precambrian. Many different lines of investigation have been brought to bear on the problem of deciphering the earth's history.

This mountain range contains one of the most extensive exposures of Precambrian rocks in the Rocky Mountains. While this discussion may serve to illustrate the techniques used to decipher Precambrian history and the nature of that history in the Beartooth Range, it should not be assumed that other parts of the Rocky Mountain region had exactly the same Precambrian history. In fact the differences in the stories unraveled in many parts of the Rockies are almost as marked as those of the stories of the diverse provinces of the Canadian Shield.

Precambrian rocks of the Beartooth Mountains consist mainly of gneisses that have a granitic composition. Throughout the Paleozoic and Mesozoic eras this region, south-central Montana and northern Wyoming, was buried under great thicknesses of sediment. But toward the end of the Mesozoic the whole Rocky Mountain system began to be uplifted. In that part of the Rocky Mountains known as the Middle Rocky Mountains the uplift took the form of displacements of huge blocks of the crust. A number of large, elongate blocks were uplifted along faults, and the adjacent blocks of the crust were depressed to form basins. Like other blocks of this region the Beartooth block was eroded as soon as it was uplifted above the level of the sea that had prevailed until the end of the Mesozoic. Erosion was accelerated during the great ice ages, the Pleistocene, when large glaciers carved huge valleys in the mountains. Eventually the sediments that had been deposited during the Paleozoic and Mesozoic were eroded away, leaving a bare exposure of the older rocks in the core of the range.

Early ideas

The origin of the crystalline rocks in this range has been a subject of debate for many years. Because these Precambrian rocks contain the same mineral assemblages found in igneous granites, and because the texture is very much like that of granites, the rocks were called granites, and the core of the range was mapped as a batholith. These rocks are very much like the granites and granitic gneisses of parts of the Canadian Shield. Although they are massive they are not perfectly homogeneous. Most of the granitic rocks are faintly banded. In places they contain lenses of darker rocks known as amphibolite (because it contains a large quantity of the amphibole minerals such as hornblende). These lenses are often contorted and drawn out. These were originally interpreted as blocks of the country rock into which the batholith was intruded. It was assumed that they were broken off the top or sides of the magma chamber during the intrusion. After falling into the hot magma they were partially melted or assimilated by the magma. In addition to the granitic rocks and the darker lenses of amphibolite a number of different sets of dikes were known to cut through the Precambrian. Some of these are dark basaltic dikes, and others are light-colored porphyry dikes composed of quartz and feldspars.

Recent studies

Early in the 1950's interest in the Precambrian of the Beartooth Range was renewed. At this time a new, more intensive and detailed study was started. Instead of examination of the gross aspect of the Precambrian and consideration only of the overall composition of the rocks, the methods employed consist of dividing the region into a number of small areas. Within each of these areas very detailed mapping is done. Each outcrop is examined, and the distribution of even the most minor variations in rock types is mapped. Where the granitic rocks appear massive the orientation of the flakes of mica is recorded. All rock types are sampled and studied with a petro-

Fig. 7-14. Gneiss of Precambrian. This photograph shows some of the detail of an exposure of gneiss of Precambrian age which is exposed to the core of the Madison Mountain Range in Montana. These rocks are sedimentary rocks which have been metamorphosed, recrystallized and deformed. They were deformed in the Precambrian. There must have been mountains in the Rocky Mountain states long before the modern range came into existence. Note the flowage. (Photo by E. W. Spencer.)

graphic microscope, and some are even analyzed chemically to establish their exact chemical composition and the quantities of each element present. The efforts of this detailed work are paying off. Maps of the central core of the range reveal a pattern that closely resembles the map of a plunging system of folds in sedimentary rocks. Detailed mapping of true igneous bodies has been done elsewhere, and in these places the structures shown are eddy-like flow patterns in the intrusions such as you might expect in a viscous magma as it is intruded. Thus the presence of these foldlike structures suggests that the granitic rocks of the Beartooth are not of an igneous origin. They appear to be highly altered sedimentary rocks. Furthermore the fact that the folds do exist indicates that this region was deformed in the Precambrian. This might very well have been part of a high folded-mountain belt that rose during the Precambrian, but vanished under the attack of long-continued erosion before the beginning of the Paleozoic Era. That such a mountain range had disappeared before the Paleozoic is shown by the angular unconformity between the lowest Paleozoic rock unit and the Precambrian granites. The contact between them is almost perfectly even. It is undoubtedly an erosion surface created sometime before the end of Precambrian time.

The existence of these folded structures is a positive indication that the rocks were originally sedimentary, but it is not necessarily a conclusive argument; therefore, studies continue. Another of the methods used is to study the nature of the minerals in the granitic rocks. The mineral zircon makes up a very small portion of the rock. It generally occurs as very small crystalline masses or crystals which can be separated from the other minerals by crushing the rocks, placing the crushed minerals in a dense liquid to separate out the light-weight feldspar and quartz. Then the zircon is further separated by use of a strong magnetic field. The reason for making this separation is to study the shape of the zircon crystals. Like quartz, zircon is insoluble in water; thus it does not dissolve when it is transported in a stream, and it usually is deposited in small amounts in many quartz sands. Zircon originates in igneous rocks such as granites. It is one of the first minerals to crystallize as cooling of the magna begins, and since it is usually present in small quantities in the magma it tends to crystallize into a small number of perfectly developed, euhedral, crystals. If the magma is subjected to erosion at some time after it has cooled the zircon is freed through weathering processes. It is carried along in the running water just as quartz is. As it is transported the small euhedral crystals are broken and rounded. Eventually the rounded zircon becomes lodged in a sedimentary deposit. So the shape of the zircon in a rock is a key to the history of the rock. If the zircons are rounded, it is sedimentary; if they are euhedral then it is most likely that the rock in which they are found is igneous. The zircons in the granitic rocks of the Beartooth are rounded like those of sedimentary deposits. We may conclude that these granitic rocks are not really igneous even though they may appear to be. They should be called granitic gneisses.

We may ask what happened to the original sedimentary units to transform them into granitic rocks. The answer is that they were highly metamorphosed under certain conditions which led to their "granitization." The detailed chemical changes need not be dis-

Fig. 7-15. Rock flowage in Precambrian rocks. The flowage accompanied metamorphism and must have taken place at high temperatures when these rocks were altered from their original sedimentary character. The alteration took place when this rock was deeply buried under high pressure and temperatures. The exposure is in the Madison Mountains of central Montana. (Photo by E. W. Spencer.)

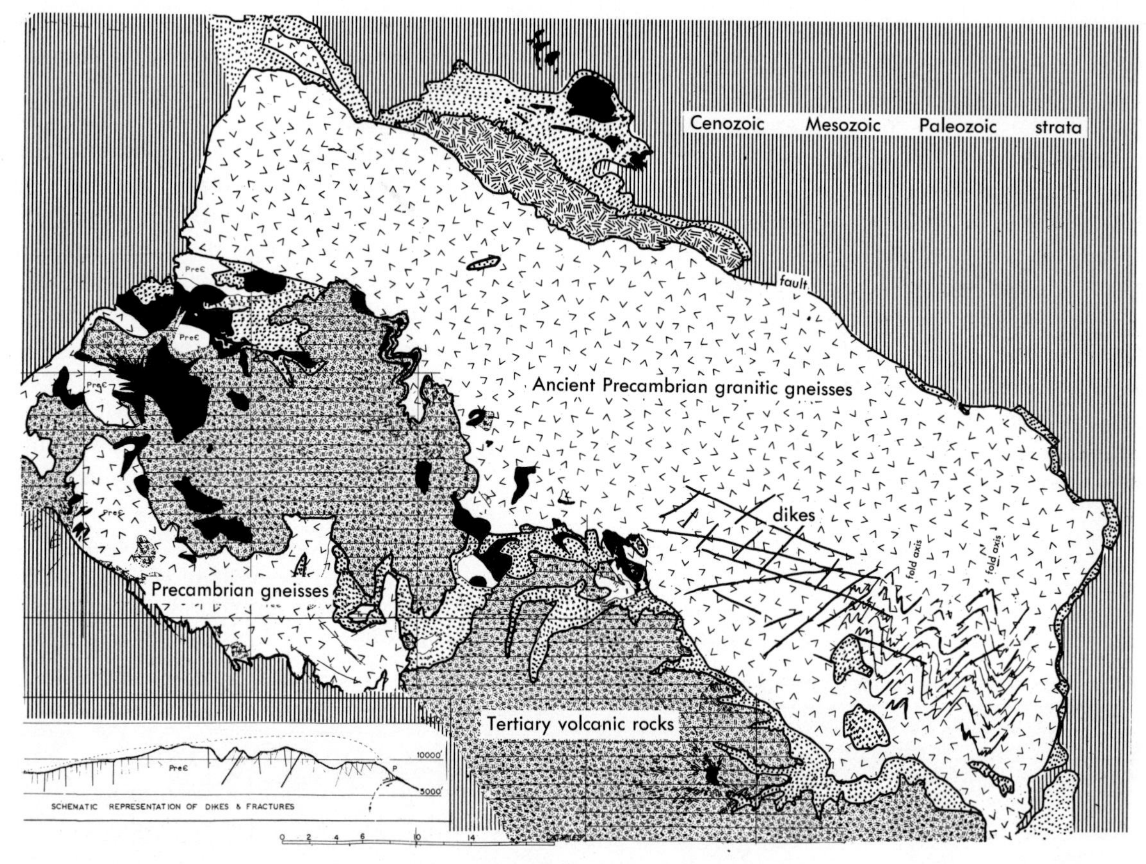

Fig. 7-16. Beartooth Mountains. The Beartooth Range of central Montana is in many respects similar to other ranges of the Middle Rocky Mountains. Precambrian granitic rocks are exposed in the center of the range and at high elevations where they have been stripped of younger rocks by erosion. Paleozoic and Mesozoic units outcrop around the margins of the range. The southern margin of this range is covered by the volcanic rocks which make up the Absaroka Range of Wyoming. The Precambrian core of the range has been elevated as a huge block which has risen through younger strata. In the eastern part of the range the folds and dikes are represented schematically. These folds trend northeast and are cut by several swarms of dikes. See text for description of their origin. (Map by E. W. Spencer.)

cussed here. In general we may say that a thick sequence of sedimentary rocks such as shales, limestones, and silts has the same bulk chemical composition as a granite. That is, the same elements are present in about the same quantities in the two types of rocks. We have already established that these rocks were folded. It is likely that they were deeply buried within a mountain range and that they were subjected to high confining pressures, the weight of the rock masses above them. Furthermore, we can say that they were heated to high temperatures. This is learned from the presence of certain minerals which appear only in rocks that have been heated to within certain temperature ranges. From these we learn that the temperatures within this mass of granitic rock reached nearly 600° Centigrade. Although the temperatures were very high, they were not sufficient for the mass to flow as a magma. Under these conditions of high temperature and pressure the minerals of the original sediments became unstable and underwent changes, recombinations of the elements, which brought about the development of a rock composed essentially of feldspar, quartz, and biotite. During this process of granitization pegmatites formed. Some of these

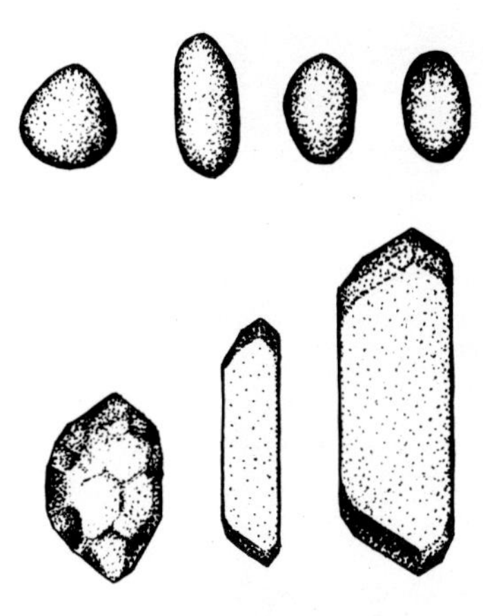

Fig. 7-17. Zircons from metamorphic rocks. The top row of zircons were removed from a granitic gneiss, and the bottom row came from a porphyry dike. That the gneiss was originally sedimentary, not igneous, is indicated by the rounded shape of the zircons. They were transported in a stream and rounded like sand grains before they were deposited and incorporated in the sediment. Later the deposits were metamorphosed and transformed into a granitic rock, but the zircons remained relatively unchanged. Zircons like those in the bottom row crystallize early in the cooling history of a magma. They tend to form euhedral, perfectly shaped, crystals. (Redrawn from R. Harris.)

contain uraninite, a radioactive mineral. This has been dated as being 2700 million years old. Because the pegmatite is related to the granitization, we know the age of this process. Because the granitization is related to the deformation we have a good idea of the age of this orogenic episode in the history of the earth. The age of these activities makes them the oldest known events in the history of the United States.

An outline of the Precambrian history of this area as determined from these studies may be set forth:

1. A thick sequence of sediments was laid down in the early part of the Precambrian. It may be that these sediments were deposited in a shallow sea, although there is no positive proof of this. Cross-bedding is found in some quartzite units in the Beartooth. This indicates deposition of sand in a current, but it does not establish whether the current was a wind or water current. The composition of the sediments was probably that of sandstones and silts.
2. The deposition of these units was followed by an undetermined period of time for which there is no record.
3. Then came a time during which molten rock masses, ultramafic magmas, rich in iron and magnesium, were intruded into the sediments.
4. Shortly after the intrusion of the ultramafic rocks the sediments and the intrusions were deformed and folded.
5. About 2.7 billion years ago the deeper zones in the crust of this area were subjected to high temperatures and great pressure. The sediments in the central part of this orogenic belt were transformed into granitic rocks. The older dikes and intrusions were metamorphosed, and pegmatites formed.
6. Then came another long period about which we have no knowledge.

Fig. 7-18. Hypothetical section in the Beartooth Mountains.

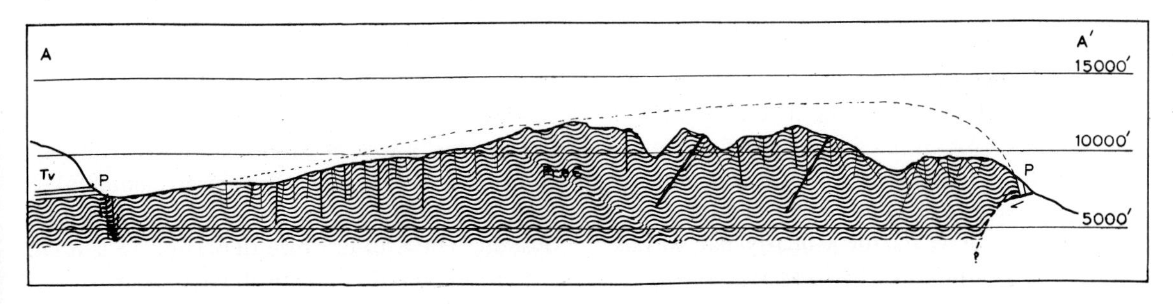

Fig. 7-19. Fossils in Precambrian rocks. This photograph is one of Conophyton Zone 2, Flathead County, Montana. (Photo by U.S. Geological Survey.)

7. In the later part of the Precambrian the region was uplifted a second time, and the rocks were faulted and fractured. This deformation was accompanied by the intrusion of a swarm of basaltic dikes. This may be distinguished from the earlier dikes because these dikes are not metamorphosed, and they cut across the older ones and the granitic rocks. Chilled contacts are found along some of these later dikes.
8. Following the late Precambrian disturbances there was a long period of erosion. This removed the top part of the mountains and elevated parts of the area. It may have required millions of years for a nearly flat surface to be developed across the region.
9. In the early part of the Paleozoic Era a shallow sea transgressed across the region leaving a flat-lying layer of sand.
10. Much later the region was again deformed and uplifted and the present Rocky Mountains began to take shape in the Cretaceous Period.

THE BELTIAN SYSTEM

Many of the spectacular mountains in the Northern Rockies of Montana and Canada are composed of Upper Precambrian sedimentary and volcanic rocks that are part of the Beltian System. These units were deposited in a broad subsiding trough that must have been several

Fig. 7-20. Precambrian gneisses. A large fold is evident in the foliation of these gneisses in the Rocky Mountains, Montana. The fold was formed in the Precambrian. (Photo by E. W. Spencer.)

hundred miles wide and may have extended all the way into the southwestern United States. It has been suggested that the Belt units are about the same age as those situated just below the oldest Paleozoic sediments. Almost 35,000 feet of sediments accumulated on the western side of this geosyncline, while the eastern side received about 12,000 feet. The sediments consist of red, green, and black mudstones, thick sections of limestone, quartzite, and in places large amounts of basaltic lavas. Some of the basalts were extruded as flows on the surface. Others were intruded into the older sediments as sills and dikes.

The lower part of the Beltian System is composed of conglomerates where it is exposed. These conglomerates contain pebbles and cobbles of the older Precambrian rocks that are presently exposed in the core of nearby mountain ranges. This suggests that a source area of this type of rock stood exposed

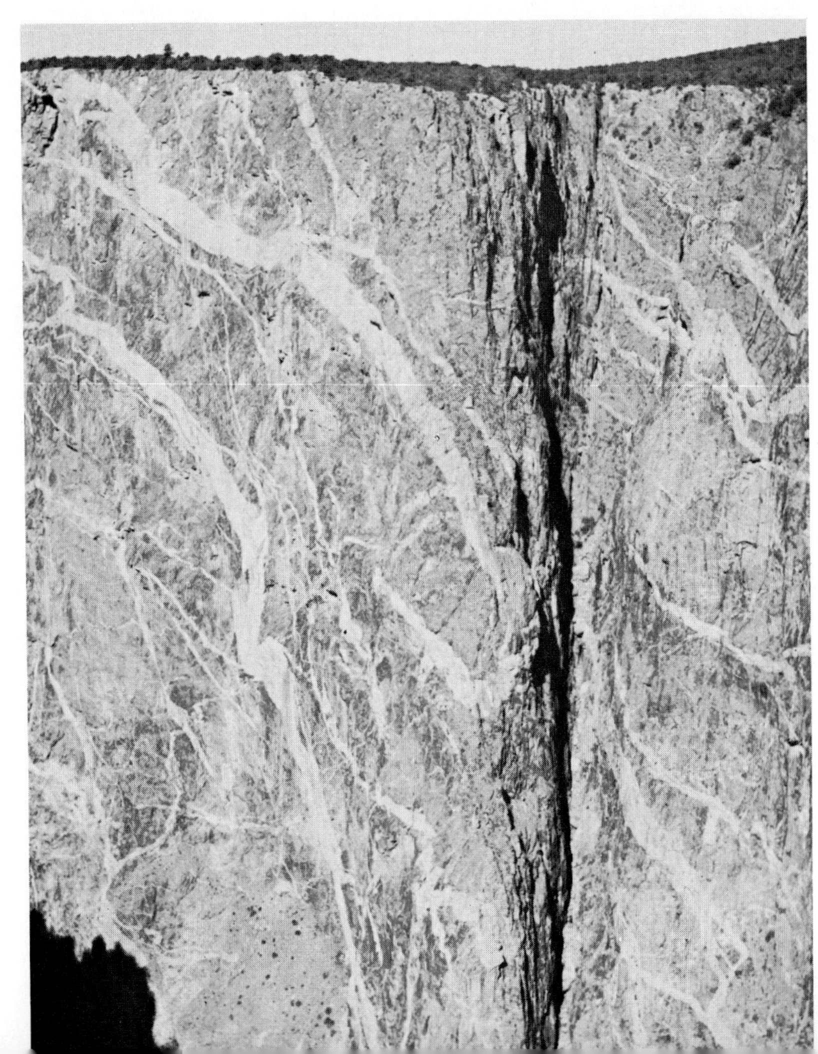

Fig. 7-21. Black Canyon of the Gunnison River, Colorado. (Photo by E. W. Spencer.)

Fig. 7-22. Peaks of the Garden Wall in Glacier National Park, Montana. (Photo by courtesy of Montana Highway Commission.)

to erosion and decay during the time that the Belt was deposited. Since the units are much thicker on the west it is probable that the source lay to the west of the geosyncline during most of the time. Some of the fine-grained clastic sediments are cross-bedded. From these it is possible to determine the direction in which water currents were moving. Studies made on these confirm the position of the western source, but it is apparent that other sources existed from time to time. The muds and shales contain mud cracks and ripple marks as well as cross-bedding. The mud cracks were most likely formed where mud flats were periodically dried out. Ripple marks suggest a shallow water origin for the sediments in which they were found. We now know that such ripple marks can originate in deeper waters, but they are most likely on the shallow continental shelves. The limestones of this age are important because they contain large cabbage-shaped masses of calcareous algae that grew in great quantities almost like reefs.

PRECAMBRIAN OF ARIZONA

The Precambrian history of parts of Arizona and Southern California has long attracted the attention of geologists. Precambrian rocks are exposed at the bottom of the Grand Canyon where the Colorado River has cut through almost a mile of nearly flat-lying Mesozoic and Paleozoic sedimentary rocks. The stream is now entrenched in the Precambrian metamorphic and igneous rocks of the inner gorge of the canyon. Two major divisions of the Precambrian may be discerned in the bottom of the canyon. They are separated by a prominent angular unconformity. The older units are highly metamorphosed and deformed. The younger sequences are less deformed; they are faulted and tilted but are not folded or highly altered like those below the unconformity. These two divisions of the Precambrian are known simply as the Lower and Upper Precambrian. They cannot be directly correlated with the Precambrian divisions of the Beartooth or with those of the Canadian Shield.

Fig. 7-23. Precambrian rocks exposed near the bottom of the Grand Canyon in Arizona. A very prominent angular unconformity separates the block-faulted Precambrian rocks from the nearly horizontal sedimentary layers of Paleozoic age. (Photo by E. W. Spencer.)

Outline of history

An interesting analysis of the history of the older, Lower Precambrian rocks has been made by Gastil (1958). The rocks are not at all like those of the Beartooth Mountains. There is no doubt about the original sedimentary character of the metamorphic rocks in this region, or about the igneous origin of the granites which intrude the metasedimentary rocks. A short summary of the history revealed in the older Precambrian follows. Compare it with the history of the Beartooth Mountains.

1. The earliest event for which there is evidence is the deposition of chemical sediments and fine muds. At the time they were laid down there was considerable volcanic and igneous activity in the region. Basic lava flows intermittently poured out over the sediments. Because these sediments are very fine-grained it is obvious that they must have been laid down at a great distance from any source of coarse debris. So there was no high mountain range anywhere nearby at that time.

2. The first evidence of a change in conditions came with the formation of deposits consisting of mixtures of gravels, sands, muds, and coarse debris. This seems to indicate that the area was becoming less stable and that it was near a land mass which had been elevated above sea level.

Fig. 7-24. Cross section across Precambrian rock units in Gila County, Arizona. This section shows the complex relationships of the Precambrian rock units the origin of which is described in the text. The section illustrates the present configuration of the units. Such sections may be used along with descriptions of the rock types to interpret the history of the region. (Simplified after Gordon Gastil.)

Fig. 7-25. Going-to-the-Sun Mountain in Glacier National Park, Montana. (Photo by courtesy of Montana Highway Commission.)

Fig. 7-26. Hypothetical section in Arizona at the time of a large granitic intrusion in the Precambrian.

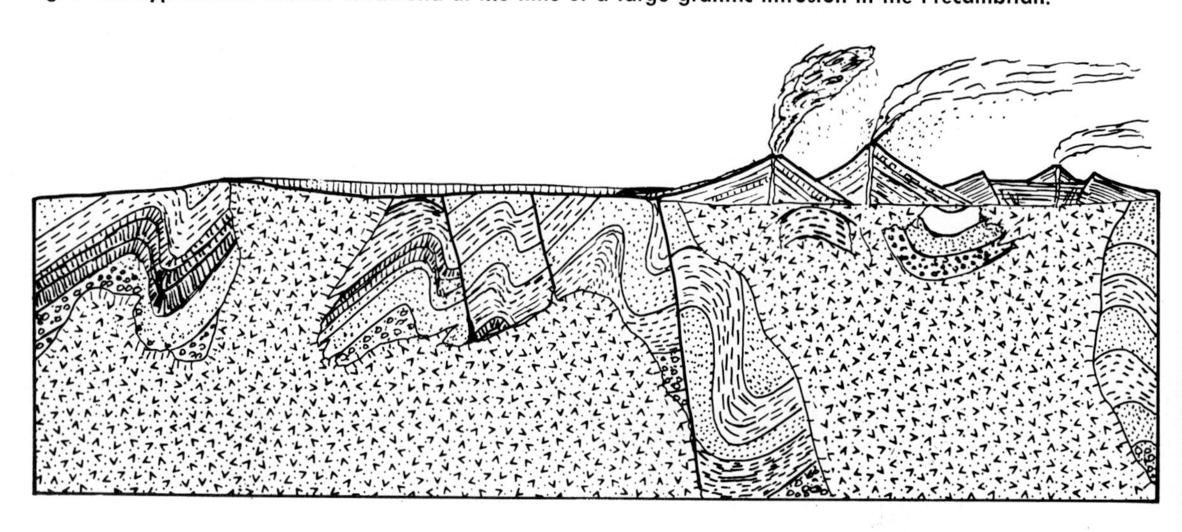

3. Uplift of the surrounding areas continued until finally a large part of the region stood above sea level. At this time erosion was very rapid because of the high relief. As a result conglomerates were formed. These conglomerates contain boulders of the older volcanic rocks, the volcanic rocks on which the conglomerates actually rest. This indicates that the older volcanic rocks were exposed near the site of the conglomerates. Extensive igneous activity accompanied this uplift of the region and the formation of the conglomerates. This time great quantities of rhyolite, siliceous lava, poured out of the earth. So we now find rhyolite flows interbedded with conglomerates. Uplift continued throughout this part of the history so these units of rock are tilted and in some places folded. Where folds developed the uplifted parts of the folds were exposed to erosion and were soon dissected and eventually beveled off.

4. This was followed by a return to the shallow-water conditions that had prevailed earlier in the history of the region. New sediments were once again laid down flat across the older, folded conglomerates and rhyolites, giving rise to an angular unconformity. At first these younger sediments were composed of the erosion products of the rhyolites which had been erupted during the uplift, but gradually these ceased to be a major source of sediment. Sands and muds again made up the bulk of the sediment in the area which at this time resembled a broad continental shelf.

5. Since this region had already been unstable during an earlier period it is not surprising to find that uplift started once again, and volcanic activity was resumed. Just as before with uplift and volcanic activity the sediments laid down during this time were conglomerates and volcanic rocks mixed and interbedded. The amount of igneous activity became increasingly intense and culminated in the intrusion of large quantities of lava. Magmas welled up toward the surface engulfing many of the older rocks. These magmas broke through the surface, and huge quantities of ash were blown out of the volcanoes thus formed. The heat accompanying these extrusions was so great that the ash partially melted in the air giving rise to what is known as a welded tuff. These great quantities of magma were granites in composition. The gases and fluids associated with the magmas permeated the surrounding rocks and metamorphosed them by chemical alteration and by virtue of their temperature.

6. This marked the end of the early Precambrian. It was followed by a long period of time in which these complex and highly altered rocks were weathered and eroded. The high volcanoes and mountains of these earlier times were eventually beveled off.

7. The first rock units of the later Precambrian (most recent) are conglomerates. These form a basal unit laid with angular unconformity on the older highly contorted and intruded sequence. Sometime before the Paleozoic Era there was a renewed uplift of the region. This caused the entire Precambrian section to be faulted, and some of the blocks were tilted. This gave rise to a minor erosional unconformity between the Late Precambrian and the Paleozoic systems.

REFERENCES

COOKE, H. C., 1947, The Canadian Shield: In *Geology and Economic Minerals of Canada*: Geol. Survey Canada Econ. Geology Ser. 1, p. 11-32

ECKELMANN, F. D., and POLDERVAART, ARIE, 1957, Geologic evolution of the Beartooth Mountains, Montana and Wyoming, Part 1, Archean history of the Quad Creek area: Geol. Soc. America Bull., v. 68, p. 1225-1262

FENTON, C. L., and FENTON, M. A., 1937, Belt Series of the North, stratigraphy, sedimentation, paleontology: Geol. Soc. America Bull., v. 48, p. 1873-1970

GASTIL, GORDON, 1958, Older Precambrian rocks of the Diamond Butte quadrangle, Gila County, Arizona: Geol. Soc. America Bull., v. 69, p. 1495-1514

HARRIS, R. L., JR., 1959, Geologic evolution of the Beartooth Mountains, Montana and Wyoming, Pt. 3 Gardner Lake area, Wyoming: Geol. Soc. America Bull., v. 70, p. 1185-1216

MASON, BRIAN, 1958, *Principles of Geochemistry:* John Wiley and Sons, London, 310 p.

PETTIJOHN, F. J., 1943, Archean sedimentation: Geol. Soc. America Bull., v. 54, p. 925-972

RANKAMA, KALERVO, 1948, New evidence of the origin of Precambrian carbon: Geol. Soc. America Bull., v. 59, p. 389-416

SPENCER, E. W., 1959, Fracture patterns in the Beartooth Mountains, Montana and Wyoming: Geol. Soc. America Bull., v. 70, p. 467-508

THOMSON, J. E., 1956, *The Grenville Problem:* Royal Soc. Canada Spec. Publication No. 1, 118 p.

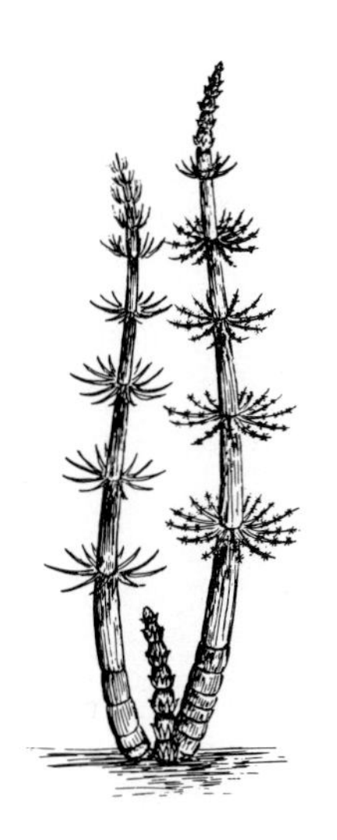

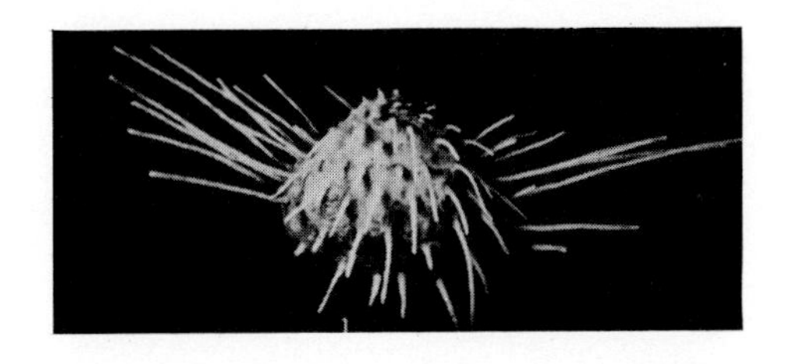

IV THE LIVING AND THE DEAD

8 The Origin of Life

A THEORY OF THE ORIGIN OF LIFE

No scientist will pretend to be able to describe exactly the way in which life began on this planet. The problems involved in bringing together just the right substances in exactly the necessary amounts and in the arrangement necessary for the formation of even the simplest living organism almost exceed the imagination. The probability of the formation of the earliest living forms in what is often described as the "hostile environment" of the early Precambrian may seem negligible. Yet the combined efforts of chemists, biologists, and geologists have thrown much light on this fundamental problem of life. We shall see that the earth's early environments were less hostile to the development of life than even our present-day environment, and that what may seem improbable in terms of the history of man may become highly probable when considered against the background of geologic time.

The following brief discussion presents

some of the modern scientific thought regarding the origin of life. The main question is: "Is it possible to explain the origin of life in terms of inorganic processes affecting the materials that occur naturally on the surface of the earth?" In seeking an answer to this question we must first find answers to the following questions:

1. What materials make up organisms?
2. What is the means by which these organic molecules may be produced by inorganic processes?
3. What forces are acting to bring these molecules together in the arrangements found in organisms?
4. What sources of energy would be available to sustain the first forms of life developing on the earth?

Composition of organisms

The first of these questions is one of the easiest to answer. Essentially the substances of which organisms are composed are water, some salts such as those found in sea water, and organic carbon compounds. These are called organic compounds because they occur very rarely in nature except in organisms. Most of these organic compounds are composed of four types of elements: carbon, oxygen, nitrogen, and hydrogen. These four elements combine in various ways to make up four classes of organic compounds in living matter. These are carbohydrates, fats, proteins, and nucleic acids (Fig. 8-1). The fats and carbohydrates are simpler than the proteins and nucleic acids.

Fig. 8-1. The constituents of living matter.

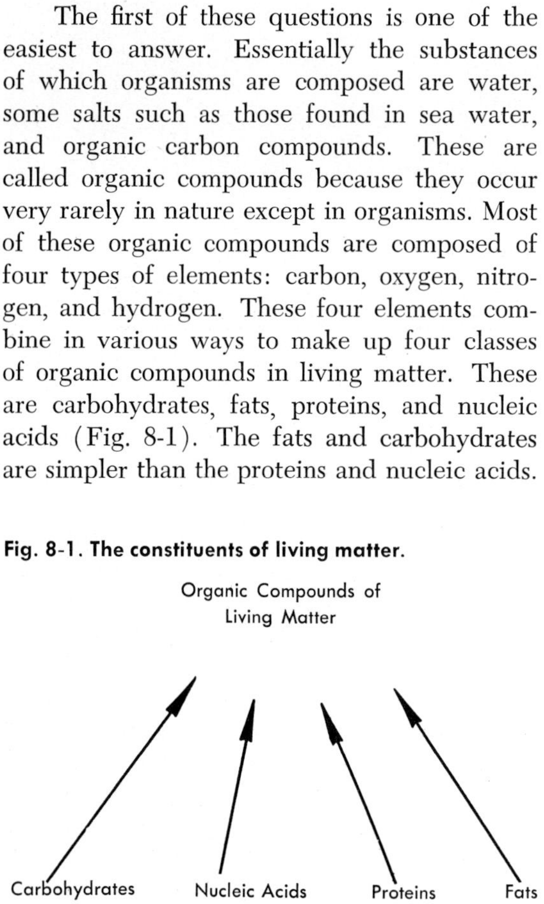

Organic Compounds of
Living Matter

Carbohydrates
Nucleic Acids
Proteins
Fats

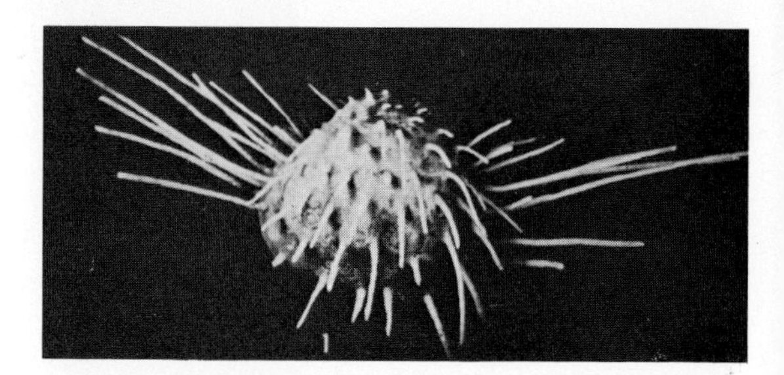

Fig. 8-2. A silicified fossil brachiopod. Even the fine details such as the delicate spines projecting from the shell have been preserved. (Photo by courtesy of the U.S. National Museum.)

The fats and carbohydrates are used by the organism as a source of the energy necessary to carry on the functions of living matter. The nucleic acids are much larger and more complex structures capable of almost endless variety. It is the structure of the nucleic acids that is believed to be the main constituent of the genes. The proteins are still more complex. They include the largest and most complex molecules known in nature. Their structure is built up of a number of different amino acids which are strung together in long chains. The different amino acids may be attached in different orders and many ways to provide literally millions of combinations. It is interesting that no two species of living organisms possess the same proteins.

Formation of organic molecules

The student will profit from a review of the nature of the history of the early atmosphere of the earth for it is within this early evolving atmosphere that life must have originated. There is evidence of living organisms in the Upper Precambrian strata, and the Lower Cambrian is characterized by an abundant and varied fauna. The life of the Cambrian is so abundant, varied, and advanced that its forerunners must have existed far back into the Precambrian time. Were the necessary constituents for living matter present at that time? Of these constituents water began to form very early, and the necessary salts would have begun to accumulate as soon as erosion of the land masses by water had started. The salts derived from erosion of rocks of the crust are carried into the oceans where some of them remain in solution. But the question remains as to how organic compounds, carbon compounds, could have formed before any life existed.

For a little over a century chemists have been able to synthesize organic compounds in the laboratory, and they are now known to form by inorganic processes in nature. Thus one of the most important obstacles is overcome. Volcanic emanations of metal carbides react with water vapor at the earth's surface to yield compounds of carbon and hydrogen. In recent years Dr. S. L. Miller successfully produced organic compounds by circulating a mixture of water vapor, methane (CH_4), ammonia (NH_3) and hydrogen over an electric spark. This experiment simulates electrical discharges in the upper atmosphere in the presence of the constituents postulated for the primitive atmosphere of the earth. The results of the experiment are impressive for several amino acids (the constituents of the complex proteins which form organic compounds) were formed by this inorganic process. This experiment makes the spontaneous formation of amino acids and therefore proteins much more likely than had been thought. However, it does not take into account the enzymes, a special class of proteins that govern the synthesis of organic compounds in living organ-

Fig. 8-3. Calcareous algae found in the Beltian rocks of Montana. These are among the oldest known fossils. (Photo by courtesy of U.S. Geological Survey.)

Fig. 8-4. Petrified wood. This view is of trees found in the Petrified Forest of Arizona. The details of cell wall are preserved in such fossils. As in the case of the brachiopod, Fig. 8-2, silica has replaced the original matter. (Photo by courtesy of Arizona Highways.)

isms. The main effect of these enzymes is to regulate the rate at which the synthesis (formation of the organic compounds from its constituents) takes place. How could enzymes have acted to bring about the original synthesis of organic compounds, since they are proteins, one of the most complex organic compounds? The simplest and best explanation of this is the time factor. Enzymes do not make processes take place which would not take place in their absence. They simply accelerate the process. But acceleration is not necessary because the amount of time covered by the Precambrian is on the order of 3 to 4 billion years. Over this tremendous span of time even the slowest processes of synthesis would yield great quantities of organic molecules.

If such an organic molecule should be formed today by inorganic synthesis it would be short-lived indeed. It would almost immediately become the prey of some living organism or it would be burned up by the process of oxidation in the presence of the oxygen of the earth's atmosphere. Such would not have been the case in the early Precambrian, for there was no life, and oxygen was lacking in the earth's primitive atmosphere. It had yet to evolve from photosynthesis and photochemical reactions in the earth's upper atmosphere. For this reason there was plenty of time for the organic compounds to become integrated into more stable aggregates.

Integration vs. dissolution

Simple organic compounds are found to be subject to a third destructive reaction, the process of spontaneous dissolution. In other words the processes by which the organic compounds may become synthesized are reversible. Actually they are known to go backward much faster than they go forward. This poses a serious problem to the formation of living matter through inorganic processes. Yet this problem is not insurmountable, for we know that living organisms are subject to this same reversible process, and they are able not only to withstand it but to grow as well. This is done through the expenditure of large quantities of energy. That integration should take place becomes more likely when we realize that the attachment of several molecules together makes the aggregate more resistant to dissolution. Larger molecules tend to disintegrate much more slowly than small ones.

Fig. 8-5. Fossil fragments. Fossiliferous rocks often contain the remains of a great variety of animals, and these are usually preserved only in fragments such as those shown here. One of the jobs of a paleontologist is to reconstruct the complete animal from the fragments, and to learn to recognize animals from only small fragments. (Photo by courtesy of the U.S. National Museum.)

Furthermore, the organic molecules have a tendency to form various structures spontaneously. These structures give the aggregate even more stability, and this tendency is so strong that proteins may orient themselves even while in solution. It would be through this tendency to form structures that the organic molecules, once they had become synthesized, would combine in aggregates which would gradually become transformed into more complex structures.

We may visualize many thousands of millions of these structures forming until through a chance arrangement a form is produced that possesses the characteristics with which we associate life. Such a process almost certainly took place in the seas for it is there that the necessary constituents are concentrated and in constant motion bringing many combinations together. That such a process, plus the tendency of organic molecules to form structures, might be responsible for the formation of a live organism is demonstrated by recent experiments. In these experiments pieces of cartilage and muscle were dissolved in a solution of water. The solution was stirred until a completely random orientation of the organic molecules was assured. Then as the solution was precipitated the molecules realigned themselves with regard to one another to reproduce the original pattern of the tissues. If such an experiment is possible with a tissue which has a structure as intricate as that of a muscle then it does not seem unreasonable to explain the origin of much simpler structures in this manner. In the early Precambrian there was certainly time and the necessary materials for many trials.

Once simple structures began to form, the process of natural selection might have begun to operate. As the aggregates of molecules began to form in large numbers some were more favorably organized and situated for survival. As a result they grew while other forms which were less well suited to the environment failed in the competition. Once the most favored molecular aggregates had reached the threshold of life they were confronted with new problems — the problems that confront all organisms. Organisms are dynamic structures constantly taking in matter and energy and disposing of that which is unsuited for their development.

Present-day living plants are able to obtain this energy through the processes of photosynthesis by which they produce sugar from

Fig. 8-6. Brachiopods preserved as actual shells. Many fossils are preserved as molds or casts. A mold is the impression left by the original parts in the sediment. A cast is a duplication of the original parts. (Photo by courtesy of the U.S. National Museum.)

carbon dioxide, water, and sunlight. Animals obtain the necessary energy through respiration by which they convert the sugar to energy. But at the time of the development of the first living forms there were no plants, little or no oxygen in the air, and deadly ultraviolet rays penetrated to the land surface killing off any living forms that were unprotected by waters of the seas. How then did these early organisms obtain energy?

Energy sources

Through the process of fermentation an organism can break down organic molecules into smaller parts with the resultant yield of some energy. The fermentation of sugar by yeast to yield alcohol is an example. How long the early organisms obtained the necessary energy through fermentation is not known. Eventually, however, the process of photosynthesis was developed. The process of photosynthesis could not have developed until there was carbon dioxide in the atmosphere. This might have been very early in the earth's history since carbon dioxide is present in volcanic gases. It would have eventually developed through the process of fermentation in which carbon dioxide is a waste product. Essentially photosynthesis consists of the combination of carbon dioxide with water and sunlight to produce sugar and oxygen. Thus with photosynthesis the problem of finding enough material to ferment is alleviated for the early organisms. As soon as photosynthesis developed there was an abundant supply of energy.

One of the by-products of photosynthesis is oxygen. Once this was available in quantity, organisms could develop a way of using it to produce energy which is much more efficient than fermentation. This process is called respiration. It is a form of combustion in which sugar plus oxygen yields carbon dioxide, water, and energy. The main advantage that this offered the organisms was that the amount of energy yielded from a like quantity of sugar was about 35 times that obtained through fermentation. This abundance of energy provided the organisms with all they needed to carry on life processes. It was out of this surplus that future evolutionary developments took place.

Fig. 8-7. Tracks. Tracks are also indicators of life, and as such are fossils. These tracks and markings are not fossils, but if covered by mud they might become fossils. This photo was taken on the sea floor in the Atlantic Ocean. (Photo by E. W. Spencer.)

With the release of oxygen through photosynthesis and through photochemical reactions in the upper atmosphere a layer of ozone formed high above the earth's surface. This layer of ozone serves as a filter to remove the sun's ultraviolet rays. Once this layer had formed the first stages had been set for the emergence of life from the seas.

THE FIRST SIGNS OF LIFE ON EARTH

Following the initial stages of the development of the earth's crust, temperatures near the surface were much too high for living organisms. The development of the oceans and atmosphere was followed by a period of many years, perhaps even billions of years, during which the first organic compounds formed.

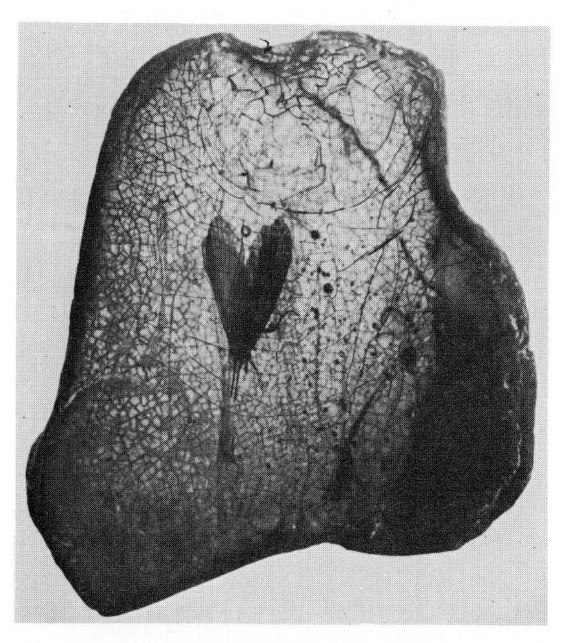

Fig. 8-8. Fossil fly. Preservation of insects as fossils is very rare. This one was caught in pitch from a tree. (Photo by courtesy of the U.S. National Museum.)

This first part of the earth's history would, according to the theory of the origin of life, have been a time of trial and error. In this time synthesis of various organic compounds took place in the seas. Eventually structures formed that resembled the simplest living organisms. It is little wonder then that we find no fossils in the rock units of the early Precambrian time. It may be that no organisms were present on the earth during the first half of its history. When living forms did appear they had no hard parts suitable for preservation, and so our efforts to find them are frustrated attempts to find something that does not exist.

Carbon. The only thing we have been able to find in the units of early Precambrian time that may be associated with living organisms is carbon. Carbon is one of the constituents of all living organisms. In fact organisms are one of the few agents by which carbon becomes fixed in nature. Carbon is abundant in shales, schists, and limestones of Precambrian age. We have learned through studies of recent organic carbon that the ratio of carbon-12 to carbon-13 is higher in organic carbon than it is in carbon formed through inorganic processes. This test has been run on carbon of Precambrian rocks, and it is found that a large part of the ancient carbon is of organic origin.

Fossils. Before the end of the Precambrian sufficient time had elapsed for the development of some organisms of a more complex nature. The fossil record bears this out. There is considerable evidence of life in the Upper Precambrian units. In the limestone units of the Grand Canyon a form that is remarkably like the simple jellyfish has been found. This section also contains the small rodlike spicules that are characteristic of the walls of sponges. The Belt System contains features which are identified as worm borings and trails. The most abundant evidence of life is the great quantity of calcareous algae, a simple plant, found in the Belt, both in the Grenville Province and in the Grand Canyon. In some places these form reeflike masses. Individually they are concentrically laminated structures that somewhat resemble a head of cabbage.

In spite of the relative abundance of fossils in the upper parts of the Precambrian section there remains a vast gap between these fossils and those that appear in the Cambrian strata. Life in the Cambrian is characterized by great abundance and variety. Although there were no vertebrates or higher plants there were many complex invertebrates. Almost every invertebrate phylum is represented among the Cambrian fauna.

FOSSILS

History of fossils

Fossils are the remains or traces of animals or plants that have been preserved. The study of fossils has a long and colorful history. The Greek historian Herodotus was among the first to recognize the true significance of fossils. He realized that the fossil shells he found exposed in outcrops far inland were the remains of marine organisms that had been left where he found them by seas that had occupied that area in the past. History shows that this conclusion has not always been as obvious as it now appears. Many have been persecuted for holding this belief. Even Aristotle failed to see the connection between the "figured stones" and shells. He taught that these objects grew in place in the rock.

The period of greatest controversy over the true nature of fossils came between 1500 and 1700. Many people held that these figured stones were placed in rocks by the devil to mislead people. Such unyielding dogmas as this led to an inevitable conflict between science and religion. Fortunately most of these problems have been resolved, but during the Renaissance they raged furiously. One interesting compromise solution on the origin of fossils was that they had been created at the same time as the earth, and were put there as a picture of great events to come. So it was no wonder that they resembled the life of the present. Others suggested that the creator attempted to form various types of animals and plants and discarded those he didn't like. The fossils thus were the unsuccessful forms that were discarded.

Some of the students of these controversial "figures in stone" went to the other extreme. Johann Beringer, a professor in the University of Wurzburg, often took his students to nearby outcrops to collect fossils. Some of the students decided to play a practical joke on their professor by planting a few home-made fossils in the outcrop. Beringer fell for the hoax, to the delight of his students. They set about preparing all sorts of fossils from clay which were baked and then planted. The first ones resembled the usual assortment of fossils, but in time the students became more daring and made replicas of birds' nests, insects, beehives, and birds in flight. The more of these Beringer found the more delighted he became. Finally he decided to write a book and illustrate the extraordinary fossil find. After the publication had gone to press, in 1726, he discovered a fossil that contained Hebrew characters. One of these when translated read "Johann Beringer." He realized then that he was the victim of a hoax and spent the rest of his life trying to buy all the copies of the book, but his efforts were in vain, for his heirs sold the books as a novelty after he died.

Fig. 8-9. A Pleistocene water hole. The tar pits near Los Angeles, California, have yielded a rich assortment of fossils of many animals including those shown in this reconstruction. Animals gathered to drink from water pools on the asphalt and were sometimes trapped in the underlying asphalt seeps. The wolf on the left and the saber tooth cat on the right, coming to prey on other animals, were sometimes trapped themselves. The large birds were carrion eaters waiting to feed upon the carcasses of mired animals. (Photo by courtesy of Chicago Natural History Museum.)

By 1800 many of the basic ideas concerning the origin of fossils had become well established. The work of Cuvier, Smith, Lyell, and others laid the foundation for the use of fossils through the laws of uniformitarianism, superposition, and faunal succession.

Fossilization

Both the actual remains of organisms and traces of them are considered to be fossils. These are direct and indirect evidences of past life that are preserved in the sedimentary record. They may be classified as below:

DIRECT EVIDENCE:

1. Actual remains.
2. Petrifactions.
3. Prints.

INDIRECT EVIDENCE:

1. Molds or casts of actual remains or altered parts.
2. Coprolites that may actually be partially preserved or the molds or casts of such remains.
3. Artifacts.
4. Trails, tracks, and burrows.

Conditions favorable for preservation. From the very nature of organic matter we know that special conditions favor the preservation of plants and animals. Organic matter decays; it is oxidized and broken down by bacterial action very rapidly if it is left exposed to the atmosphere. Scavengers consume the soft parts of plants and animals both on land and in the seas unless the parts are buried quickly or the environment of the sea floor is such that scavengers cannot live there. Consequently, fossilization is most likely to occur under the following conditions:

a. When there is quick burial of the organism in some sort of protective medium.

Fig. 8-10. Fossil leaf impressions, common in rocks of late Paleozoic age. The organic matter is left on the rock as a thin film of carbon. (Photo by courtesy of Chicago Natural History Museum.)

b. When there are hard parts such as a shell or skeleton which decay slowly or not at all.

Actual remains. Soft remains of organisms are very rarely discovered. Most such fossils have been recovered from oil seeps where animals became trapped in the sticky tar coverings, and from ice and frozen soils of the Arctic. One such discovery was that of the extinct wooly mammoth, an elephant-like beast that roamed the northern Siberian plains during the Pleistocene. When the thawing remains of one of these mammoths were first discovered in 1900 along the side of a stream valley the flesh of the animal was red. It was fresh enough for wild dogs to eat a considerable part of it before an expedition could reach the site. Unlike modern elephants the woolly mammoth was covered by a heavy coat of brownish wool and long black hair. Its head was short and had a high crown. The reconstruction of this animal made possible by these remains is very similar to cave drawings found in France. Herds of these animals must have roamed across northern Europe near the margin of the great ice cap during the Pleistocene. Another example of extraordinary fossilization is the preservation of insects, complete with all the very delicate appendages found on these animals, in amber, derived from the resin of trees.

Unaltered hard parts. Shells and internal skeletons are frequently preserved for long periods of time. Many of the best of these are fossils of marine animals that fell into the soft sediment on the sea floor when they died. Of the land dwellers those that live near swamps, lakes, or sea level are most likely to be preserved. Some of the materials most widely present in hard parts are:

Calcite. Often the living animal possesses a shell that is composed of a special form of calcium carbonate known as aragonite, but this is usually recrystallized to calcite within a few thousands of years. Corals, mollusks, and other marine invertebrates make their shells out of these materials.

Phosphate. A few shells are composed of this very resistant material.

Silica. Some animals, particularly the single-celled animals, the protozoans, and sponges, and a group of plants, diatoms, possess hard parts composed of an amorphous, noncrystalline, hydrous silica. This substance is known as opal. It is insoluble and very likely to be preserved.

Chitin. Your fingernails are composed of chitin. Although it is relatively soft and somewhat less likely to be preserved than most of the other materials described above it is frequently found.

Alteration (mineralization, replacement, and prints). The actual remains of an organism are likely to undergo change through time. These changes are fostered by the slowly circulating ground waters that carry elements in solution.

1. Organic matter is frequently altered through replacement. Such replacement involves a unit-for-unit exchange of mineral for organic matter. In this manner the bones, shells, or plant tissues are transformed into calcite, silica, or pyrite. These processes are known as calcification, silicification, and pyritization.
2. Permineralization is the process by which the pore spaces in a porous and permeable fossil are filled by minerals. It is typical of the preservation of bones.
3. Prints: Organic matter contains carbon. The volatile, gaseous, constituents of the flesh or soft parts are sometimes distilled away leaving a thin film of carbon. Such fossils, which look as if they were printed on a piece of shale or mudstone, are among our best clues to the shape and functions of the soft parts of many plants and animals of the geologic past.

Traces. Molds and casts may preserve the fine details of the structures and shapes of organisms, but most of the other indirect fossil forms are somewhat less useful although they may be extremely important. Anyone who has ever hunted or tracked animals knows how useful tracks can be. They may give us the only information we need to recognize a particular animal. This is particularly true if we know what the animal looks like. But sometimes we find tracks that are unlike any we know from the present or the past. When these are found it is like finding the footprint of an animal you never saw before. You can immediately judge something of the animal's size and you may determine if it is a bird, mammal, or an insect, and maybe you can tell something of how it walked, but you probably cannot tell exactly which order of animals it belonged to.

REFERENCES

BARGHOORN, E. S., 1957, Origin of life: Geol. Soc. America Memoir 67, v. 2, p. 75-86

MASON, BRIAN, 1958, *Principles of Geochemistry:* John Wiley and Sons, London, p. 61-62

MILLER, S. L., 1957, The formation of organic compounds on the primitive earth: New York Acad. Sci. Ann., v. 69, p. 260-275

OPARIN, A. I., 1957, *The Origin of Life on the Earth,* 3rd ed.: Academic Press, New York, 495 p.

WALD, GEORGE, 1954, The origin of life: Scientific American, v. 191, p. 45-53

9 The Tree of Life—Classification

THE TREE OF LIFE

Purpose of classification

The most impressive feature about the living plants and animals is their great diversity. Almost every ecological niche in the world is filled with a great variety of living organisms. Each of these niches contains a far more varied fauna and flora than ordinarily meets the eye, and most of them are much more populous than we even imagine. These living plants and animals represent only a fractional part of the forms which have lived on earth since life first originated. An estimated 2 million different species are living today. We cannot be sure how many millions of others have inhabited the earth in the past. Because we are confronted with such an overwhelming array of different forms it is necessary that we devise a system by which they may be separated into groups that possess some distinguishing characteristics. Otherwise we are certain to be unsuccessful in any attempts to understand the relationships among the living and between the living and the dead. The main purpose of classification is to simplify the study of animal and plant life, and to make it possible to apply certain generalizations to whole groups of animals without pursuing a detailed analysis of each member of the group. Obviously such a classification must be based on significant similarities among members of each group if it is to be meaningful.

Grouping organisms

The first and most obvious subdivision we can make is the separation of the plants and animals into two large groups. There is little difficulty in doing this in the great majority of cases. However, some of the most primitive single-celled organisms are so similar to plants that there is no way to establish in which group they belong. Beyond this the animals and plants are subdivided into groups on the basis of such similarities as:

a. Anatomical characters (particularly the hard parts in fossils).
b. Physiological characteristics.

Fig. 9-1. A minute sea-creature *(Trypanosphoera regina)*. Glass model. (Courtesy of the American Museum of Natural History.)

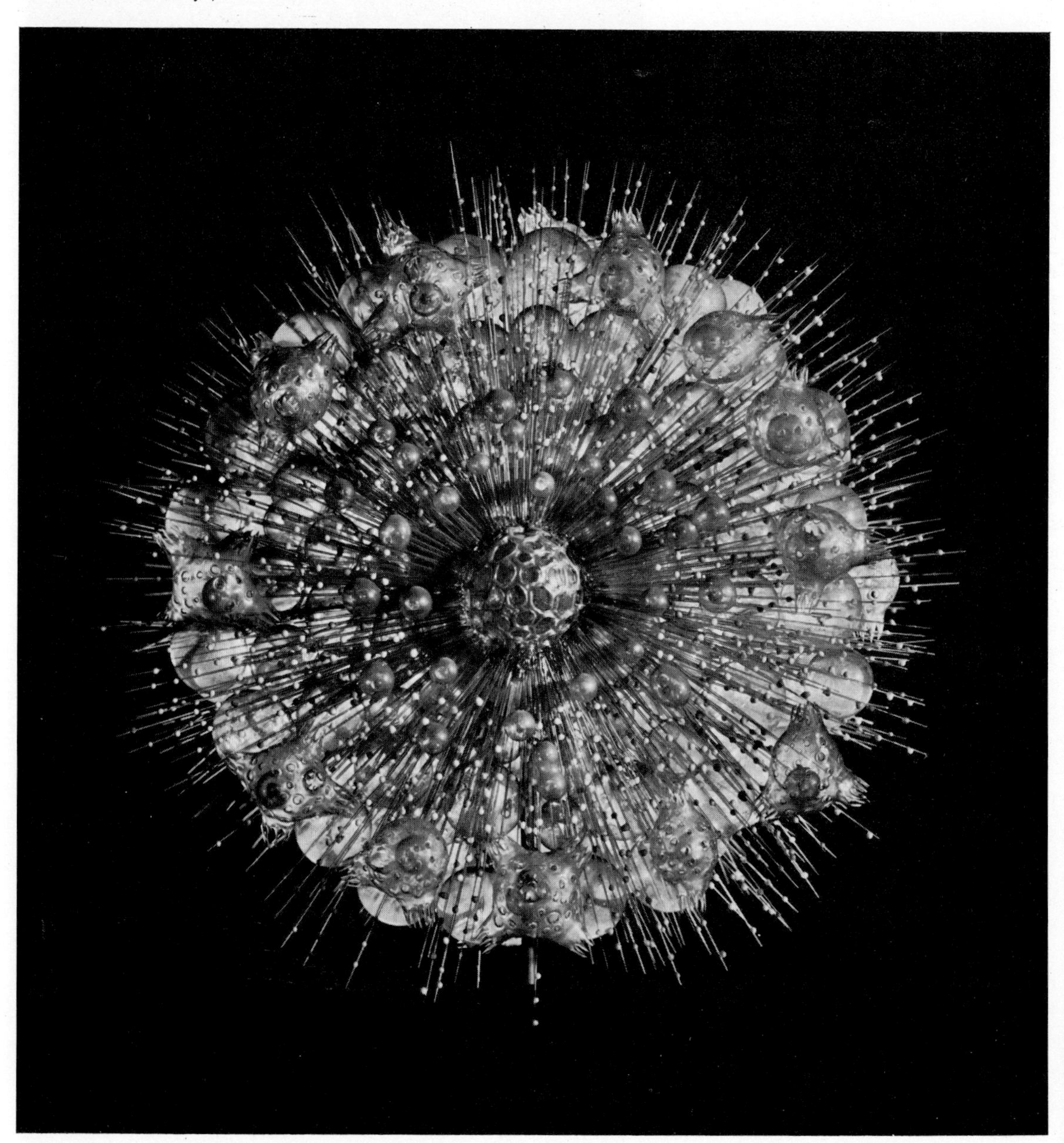

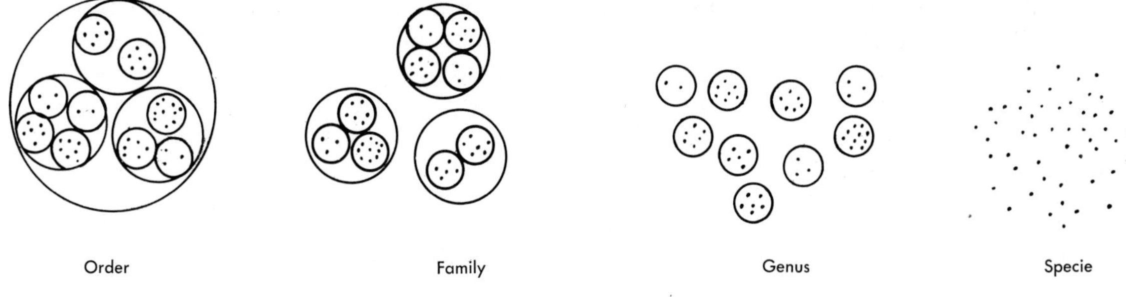

Fig. 9-2. Classification.

Since the first classifications were established by biologists it is not surprising that subdivision is largely based on the similarities to soft parts of the bodies of living animals. However, paleontologists are forced to rely almost entirely on the preserved hard parts of animals such as bones, teeth, and shells. Fortunately the relationship between the hard and soft parts is sufficiently well understood among living animals so that it is possible to make a reasonably good interpretation of the function of most of the hard parts of fossils in terms of a system of classification established by biologists. The main problems arise in dealing with extinct animals and plants. These must be classified solely on the basis of the preserved structures, and they rarely include soft parts.

Influence of the theory of evolution

The system of classification underwent a drastic reinterpretation after the theory of evolution proposed by Charles Darwin became widely accepted. Before, organisms had been classified into groups on the assumption that each group had been especially created. Thus each species should possess distinct characteristics that would be identical from the time of creation until extinction. Darwin introduced the revolutionary idea that the fundamental units of life, the species, were part of an evolutionary sequence. In other words, a single species undergoes change through time and is not a fixed unit. This has given rise to one of the most important problems in the part of paleontology that deals with classification. Biologists generally use the following definition of a species: A species is a group of animals which can interbreed and produce fertile offspring. This definition is adequate for grouping of living organisms, but it poses an important problem to a paleontologist—that of determining which organisms in a fossil assemblage were capable of fertile interbreeding. Obviously we cannot hope to answer this question. Instead we must look for some other answer to the question: what is a species? The answer must be found in features preserved in fossils. In practice the fossil species is identified on the basis of similarity of structural features of the hard parts.

Subdivisions of classification. It should be apparent that a number of species which have very closely related structural forms probably have a common ancestry. Thus all of these species may be put into a single group. A group of closely related species is called a genus. Using the same type of analysis, the animal and plant kingdoms are classified into successively larger groups. The largest categories contain many diverse forms that have few characteristics in common. In the successively smaller groups the animals or plants come closer by being like other members of the group. Consider the classification of man:

Kingdom: Animal
Phylum: Chordata
Class: Mammalia
Order: Primate
Family: Hominidae
Genus: *Homo*
Species: *sapiens*
Individual: John Doe

The effect of classification is to take the many billions of individuals of living and fossil assemblages and to separate them into smaller and smaller groups in such a way as to reduce the essential differences among those remaining in a group after each successive subdivision.

Fossil names

The elementary student is frequently confused by the multitude of names which may be used in reference to a single species and to the groups of which it is a member. Seven names may be applied to each species: one each of the kingdom, phylum, class, order, family, and genus to which it belongs. In addition there are sometimes further subdivisions into subphylum, superclass, subclass, infraclass, suborder, superfamily, subgenus, and even subspecies. A comprehensive knowledge of this terminology as it is applied to each fossil is not expected even of the most advanced students. It is important that you learn the characteristics that distinguish the main phyla and some classes that are particularly important in the fossil record. Special attention to these is given in Chapter 10. In addition you should know where to find a more detailed classification and information when it is needed. The bibliography at the end of this chapter serves this function.

The name of a fossil usually includes both the generic and the specific name, both italicized. The genus name is given first, and it is capitalized; the species name is never capitalized. The name of the person who first described the fossil is sometimes added. For example *Codaster trilobitus* McCoy is the name of a Paleozoic echinoderm first described by McCoy. Throughout most of the discussion in this book the exact name of fossil species will not be used. In general, reference will be made to the larger categories of the classification such as phylum and class.

The following classification may be used as an outline for reference. It is not intended to be complete. Animals and plants that are not important as fossils have been omitted. The next chapter is devoted to the description of those animals, the invertebrates, and plants that are often unfamiliar to the elementary geology student.

THE PLANT KINGDOM

Classification of algae, diatoms, fungi including molds, mushrooms, toadstools, liverworts, hornworts, and mosses is not included.

Phylum Tracheophyta: the vascular plants.
- Subphylum Psilopsida.
- Subphylum Lycopsida: the lycopods including *Lepidodendron* and *Sigillaria*.
- Subphylum Sphenopsida: including *Calamites*.
- Subphylum Pteropsida: ferns and seed plants.
  - Class Filicineae: ferns.
  - Class Gymnospermae: the seed plants. Includes: cycadeoids, cycads, ginkgos, cordaites, and conifers (pines, sequoias, etc.).
  - Class Angiospermae: the flowering plants. Includes: magnolias, eucalyptus, oaks, elms, maples, beeches, peaches, blackberries, and grasses, sedges, lilies, tulips, yuccas, palms, and orchids.

THE ANIMAL KINGDOM

Classification of comb jellies, flatworms, round-worms, arrow worms, segmented worms and Phoronis has been omitted.

Phylum Protozoa: single-celled animals.

Phylum Porifera: sponges.
- Class Pleospongiae (extinct).
- Class Calcispongiae: chalky sponges.
- Class Hyalospongiae: glass sponges.
- Class Demospongiae: horny sponges and bath sponges.

Phylum Coelenterata:

Class Hydrozoa: Portuguese man-of-war.
Class Stromatoporoidea: (extinct).
Class Scyphozoa: jellyfishes.
Class Anthozoa: corals and sea anemones.

Phylum Graptolithina: (extinct).

Phylum Bryozoa: sea mosses.

Phylum Brachiopoda: lamp shells.

Class Inarticulata: unhinged shells.
Class Articulata: hinged shells.

Phylum Mollusca: the mollusks.

Class Gastropoda: snails.
Class Scaphopoda: tooth shells.
Class Pelecypoda: clams, mussels.
Class Cephalopoda: squids, octopuses, nautilus.

Phylum Arthropoda:

Class Trilobita: (extinct).
Class Crustacea: shrimps, water fleas, barnacles, lobsters, crabs.
Class Arachnida: eurypterids, king crabs, ticks.
Class Insecta: cockroaches, grasshoppers, dragonflies, bugs, flies, ants, bees, wasps.

Phylum Echinodermata:

Class Cystoidea: (extinct).
Class Blastoidea: (extinct).
Class Crinoidea: sea lilies.
Class Asteroidea: starfishes.
Class Echinoidea: sea urchins.
Class Holothuroidea: sea cucumbers.

Phylum Chordata:

Subphylum Vertebrata.
Superclass Pisces: aquatic vertebrates.
Class Agnatha: jawless fishes.
Class Placodermi: (extinct).
Class Chondrichthyes: sharks, rays.
Class Osteichthyes: bony fishes such as sturgeon, trout, perch, lungfishes.
Superclass Tetrapoda: land vertebrates.
Class Amphibia: frogs, toads.
Class Reptilia: lizards, snakes, alligators.
Class Aves: birds.
Class Mammalia: including opossums, monkeys, men, anteaters, rats, mice, dogs, cats, seals, whales, elephants, horses, pigs, sheep, and cows.

REFERENCES

DARRAH, W. C., 1939, *Textbook of Paleobotany:* D. Appleton-Century Company, New York. 440 p.

DAVIES, A. M., 1920, *An Introduction to Palaeontology:* Thomas Murby and Company, London, 414 p.

FENTON, C. L., and FENTON, M. A., 1958, *The Fossil Book:* Doubleday and Company, Garden City, 482 p.

MOORE, R. C., LALICKER, C. G., and FISCHER, A. G., 1952, *Invertebrate Fossils:* McGraw-Hill Book Company, New York, 766 p.

NEAVERSON, E., 1928, *Stratigraphical Palaeontology, A Manual for Students and Field Geologists:* Macmillan and Company, London, 524 p.

SHIMER, H. W., and SHROCK, R. R., 1944, *Index Fossils of North America:* The Technology Press, Massachusetts Institute of Technology, 837 p.

SHROCK, R. R., and TWENHOFEL, W. H., 1953, *Principles of Invertebrate Paleontology:* McGraw-Hill Book Company, New York, 766 p.

SWINNERTON, H. H., 1923, *Outlines of Paleontology:* Edward Arnold and Company, London, 420 p.

ZITTEL, K. A., VON, 1927, *Textbook of Paleontology:* Macmillan and Company, London, 839 p.

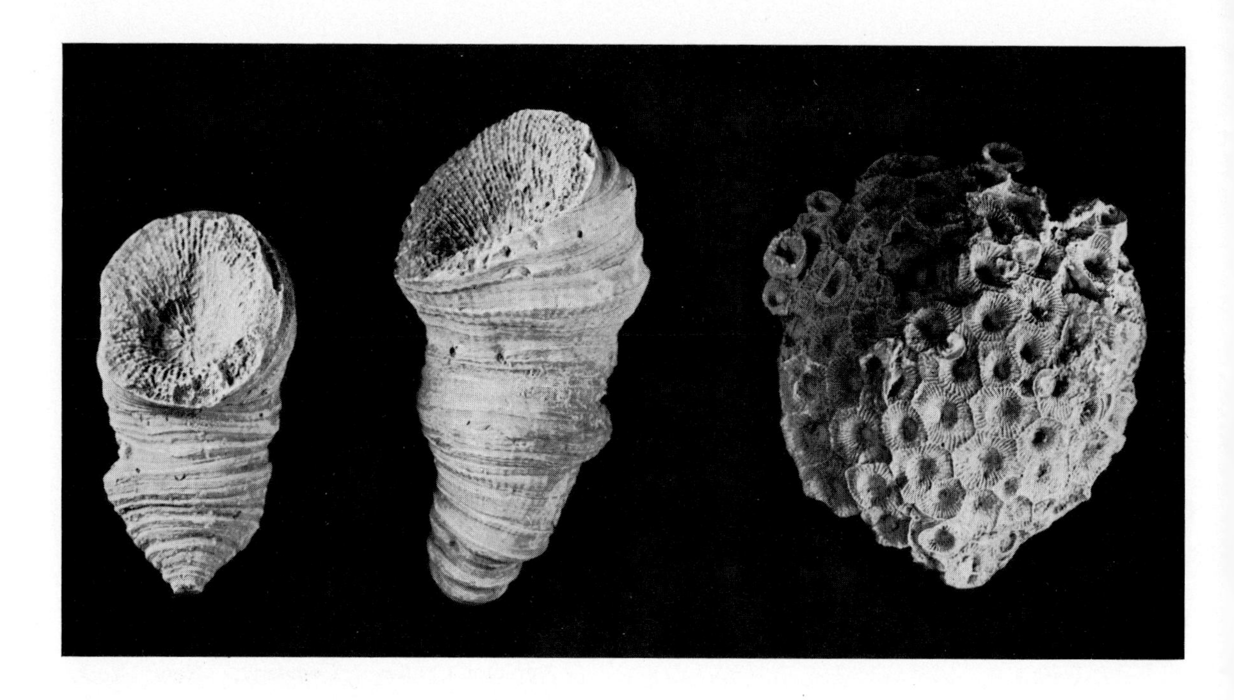

10 Learning to Recognize Fossils

Invertebrates and Plants

MORPHOLOGY OF THE INVERTEBRATES

Invertebrate animals are particularly prominent in the fossil record. It is fossils of these animals that you are most likely to find in the sedimentary rocks exposed near your home or your school. They are much more abundant than the vertebrates of the world today, and all evidence from the fossil record leads us to believe that they have always been more numerous. It is the fossil invertebrates that most frequently provide the clues to identification of rock units and their ages. They make possible most of our correlations; therefore, they are of basic importance in most of the techniques we use to unravel the last half billion years of the history of the earth. For these reasons it is particularly important that we be able to recognize the most common classes and phyla, and to know the principal morphological features that have led to their classification.

Fossils are identified by the shape and structure of the hard parts. Morphological studies are the principal basis for classification of fossils. It is careful study of the successive changes in structure through time that provides most of the data on which invertebrate evolution is based. In this chapter attention will be directed primarily toward the hard parts and, where possible, the relationship between hard and soft parts. It is helpful to understand the function or reason for the existence of the hard parts.

Phylum Protozoa

The protozoans are the most abundant organisms in the world. The only group that comes anywhere close to them in abundance is the insects. Yet most people have never seen even one protozoan. Their shells are a major constituent of many extensive limestone formations, and they cover the floors of large parts of the present-day ocean basins. Several are large enough to be seen with the naked eye, and a very few are as big as a garden pea. But most of the shells of these animals that are of geologic significance are about the size of a pin head. Protozoans are single-celled or noncellular animals. Many of them are so much like plants that there is some question as to which kingdom they belong. For this reason it is a common practice especially among biologists to divide all organisms into three kingdoms, Plant, Animal, and Protista. When this is done the third group consists of bacteria, flagellates, slime molds, ciliates, and the familiar amoeba and its relatives. There seems to be a very good reason for putting the protozoans in this position because they do not show a very close relationship to the multicellular animals nor to each other for that matter. Unlike many of the other groups of animals they have not followed the paths of differentiation through time that is so characteristic of more advanced animals. The earliest known protozoans are not strikingly different from those we find in the seas today.

Of this group the relatives of the amoeba are most important geologically. They belong to the class Sarcodina. The amoeba is famous for the simplicity of its structure. It is a lump of protoplasm without any definite shape and without any evidence of specialized parts. It takes in water and then collapses, expelling the water along with waste products. The amoeba has no hard parts, but its relatives the Foraminifera and the radiolarians do, and they are the most important geologically and the most interesting groups of the Protozoa.

The Foraminifera, often called forams, secrete a shell that is composed of calcium carbonate, calcite. These shells are often beautiful and of an intricate design. The shells of these animals make up a large part of marine sediments. What seems most amazing about the forams is that such an apparently structureless blob of protoplasm can build such a complex and beautifully designed structure. The forams, like the radiolarians and other Sarcodina, possess a network of branched threadlike projections from the protoplasm. These are called pseudopodia or false feet. Most of them live in marine waters, but some also inhabit brackish- and fresh-water environments. Something over 30,000 species of forams have been described. The great variety and the small size of their shells have made them particularly important in geologic investigations. Their shells are so small that they are not destroyed by the grinding of a bit in the bottom of a drill hole. They can be recovered whole from oil wells. Thus they are particularly suitable for geologic studies in areas where the rock units do not outcrop at the surface, and where geologic studies must be based on subsurface data. The greatest use for forams in this re-

Fig. 10-1. Diatoms, microscopic-sized plants.

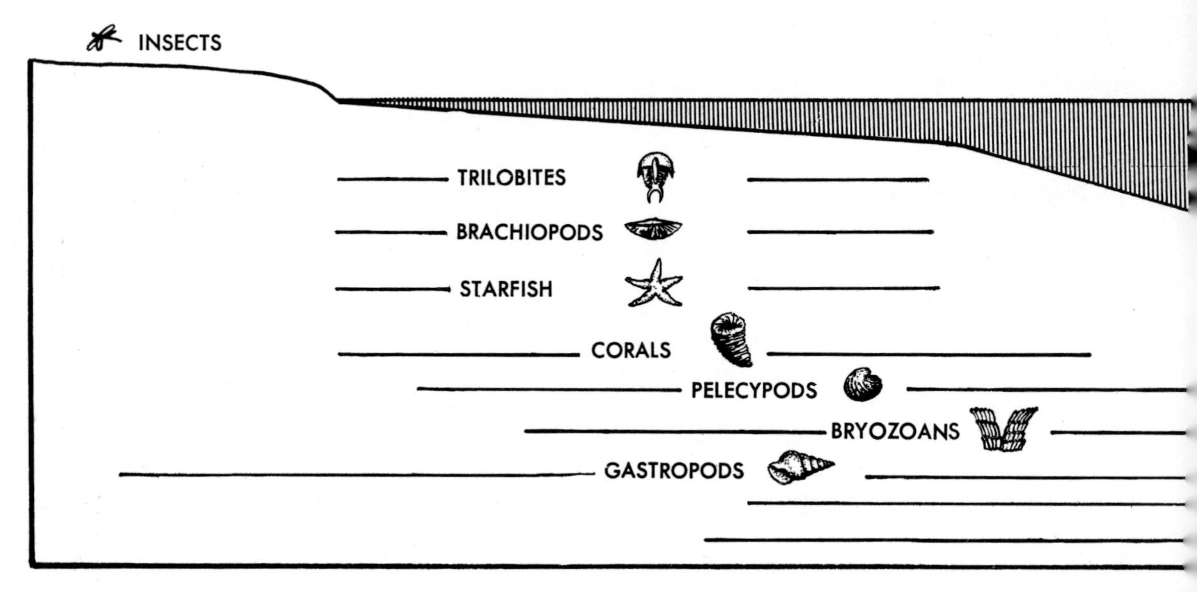

Fig. 10-2. Environments of certain invertebrates. The study of fossils has led to many important discoveries. The theory of evolution is based on paleontological studies. More recently, however, fossils have been con-

spect is for correlation of rock units. But because so much attention has been directed to the study of forams we have learned to use them in other ways as well. They are useful indicators of the environments in which they lived, giving an indication of the temperature of the surface waters and the salinity of the water.

The most common forams are between .1 mm and 5 mm in diameter. The shells are composed of substances that are either secreted by the animal or made of foreign particles from the sediment which are cemented together. Most but not all fossils are composed of calcium carbonate. A few are made of the material that composes your fingernail, chitin. The simplest of all the shells is a single flask-shaped body with a single opening or aperture at one end. It is shaped like a bottle with a neck on it. Most of the shells are composed of a great number of these chambers built one on the other. After the first chamber has been constructed the organism continues to grow, and the protoplasm overflows through the opening to the outside. It then begins to build another chamber connected with the first but not necessarily of the same size or shape. In some of the forams the chambers are arranged in a linear series with each new chamber surrounding the aperture of the last chamber. In others the development of two rows or series of chambers occurs, and in some even three rows of chambers are found. The chambers may become arranged in a planispiral coil, like a disc; they may be fan-shaped, star-shaped, or pear-shaped. One of the most common families of forams, the fusulinids, has shells which resemble a small grain of wheat. Another, the globigerinids, is globular in shape.

Some special structures that have been used for the identification of different species include the structure of the shell walls. Some walls have tiny perforations, while others are solid. Of course, the structure of the wall can be seen only with the aid of a microscope, but it is worthy of mention here because it has been of such importance in classification of the main groups.

Radiolarians: Another group of the Class Sarcodina, the order Radiolaria, make up large quantities of sediment on the sea floor particularly in tropical climates. They are found only in marine waters. They are among the most common of the free-floating and swimming organisms in the upper levels of the sea. The radiolarians are characterized by radiating

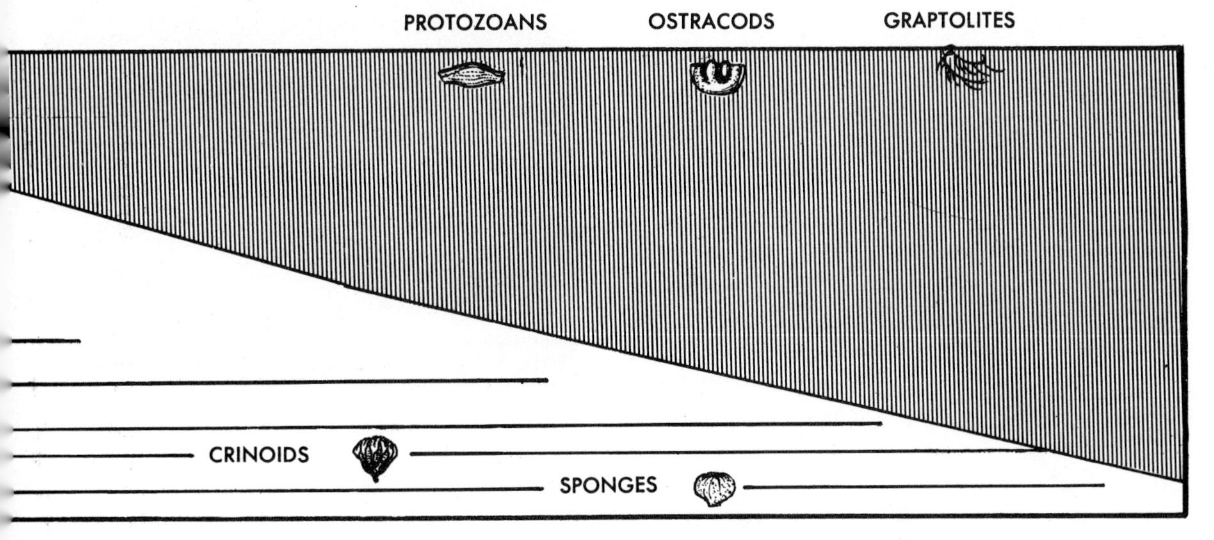

sidered increasingly as indicators of particular environments. This diagram shows the parts of the sea bottom in which different groups are most likely to be found. Several of these groups are extinct.

pseudopodia. The most interesting thing about them is the shape and form of the structures they build out of silica from the sea water. These structures, called tests, are more diverse than any other found in the animal kingdom. Some 6000 species are known. The test is actually an internal skeleton. Silica is secreted by the organism to form a network of rodlike pieces that may or may not be fused together in a pattern. The forms taken by these rods vary from globular to conical, starlike, and other interwoven patterns.

Phylum Porifera

The Porifera or sponges are among the oldest of the organisms, and they have undergone very little change over a period of hundreds of millions of years. Apparently they were well adapted to the life of the marine waters soon after they first appeared and they have continued to remain well adapted. Sponges are not of great value to geologists because they have few hard parts and they have not changed much through time.

Porifera are multicellular animals with a very low level of organization. The body of most sponges is much like that of a vase. It is attached to the sea floor (such organisms are said to be sessile), and it is open at the top. Shapes are not always as simple as that of a vase. They may also take the form of cylinders,

Fig. 10-3. Foraminifera showing the internal structures. The shell shown here in cross section is one of the simplest found.

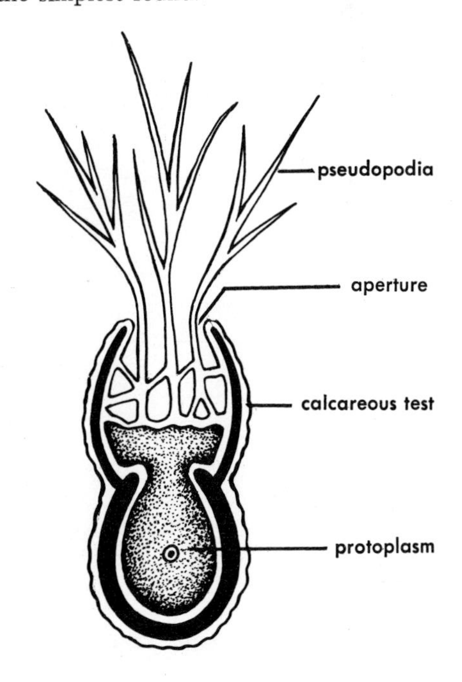

spheres, leaflike masses, and others. The walls are perforated by a large number of canals which open both on the outside and inside of the wall. The main differences among modern sponges involve the complexities of the canal systems which, because they are soft parts, are not preserved in fossils very often. Water is drawn into the canals from the outside and forced through the canals into the center of the sponge. From there it goes through the opening at the top of the body. The sponge takes food from the water as it passes through the canals.

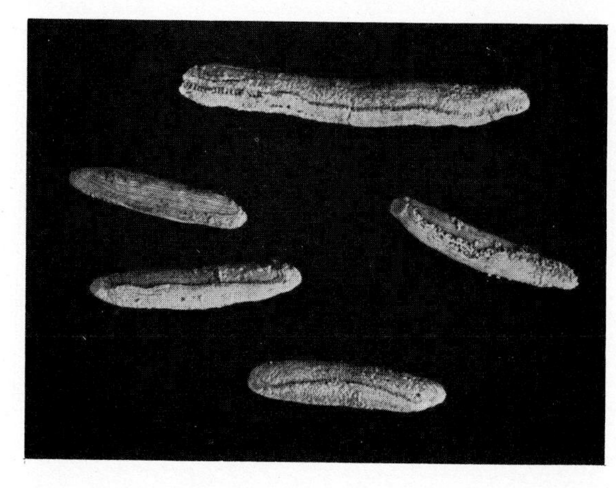

Fig. 10-5. Parafusulina from the Glass Mountains of west Texas. This is one of the important guide fossils for Permian strata. (Photo by courtesy of the U.S. National Museum.)

Fig. 10-4. Models of Cenozoic Foraminifera showing a variety of forms. All are greatly enlarged. (Photo by courtesy of Chicago Natural History Museum.)

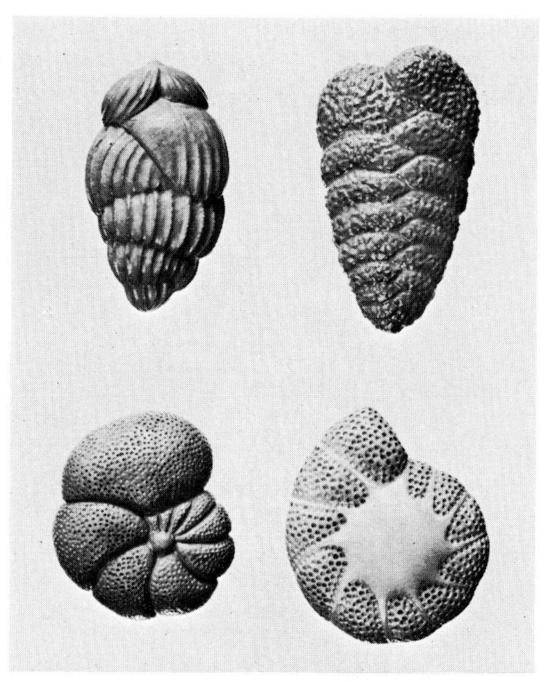

Classification. The soft parts of the sponge are supported by a harder structure called its skeleton. These skeletons are composed of organic fibers or crystalline spicules, or a combination of the two. Some of the spicules are composed of calcium carbonate, and others are made of silicic acid, opal. They vary widely in shape, size, and structure. Some of the more common types are illustrated. The composition and structure of the spicules are used as the basis for the classification of sponges.

Ecology. Most of the sponges are confined to marine waters, but a few live in fresh water and may be found in lakes and streams. Because dirt and mud would clog up the entrances to the canal systems they favor waters that are not agitated and those that contain little suspended debris. Sponges are found growing individually or in colonies and at all depths. They live in waters of tropical, temperate, and frigid climates. About the only indication we get from the sponges about their environment is from the composition of the spicules. The siliceous spicules are restricted largely to sponges that live in waters between 1500 and 3000 feet deep, but some live in both deeper and shallower waters.

Phylum Coelenterata

Corals that secrete a hard calcareous skeleton are the best-known coelenterates, but they are only one representative of this varied and numerous group. Corals have been very important in the fossil record. They date back to the early part of the Paleozoic Era, the Cambrian Period, and have been important constituents of reefs during many periods. All coelenterates have a sac-like digestive cavity with one opening. The cavity is surrounded by tentacles equipped with stinging cells. Coelenterates possess the tissue level of body organization, but they lack true organs. The stinging cells are used to obtain a food supply. Prey may be stung, paralyzed, and pulled into the digestive cavity. The food ranges from microscopic animals to some large crustaceans and even fish.

Fig. 10-6. Sponge and spicules. Cross section through a simple sponge, at the top, and an enlarged view of a variety of spicules, at the bottom. The shape and composition of the sponge spicules are often used for classification of sponges. They are the only hard parts of sponges that are commonly preserved.

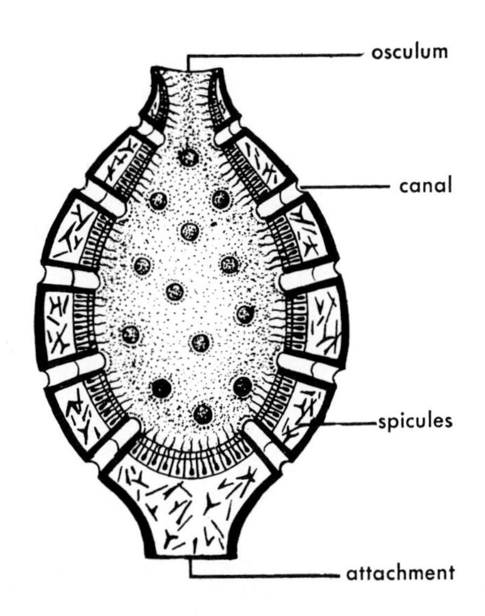

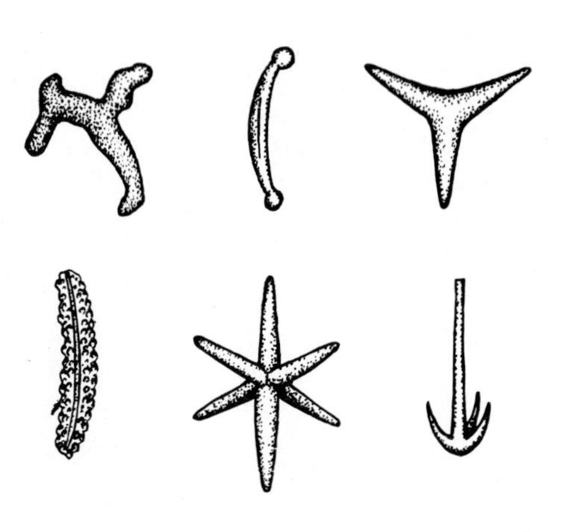

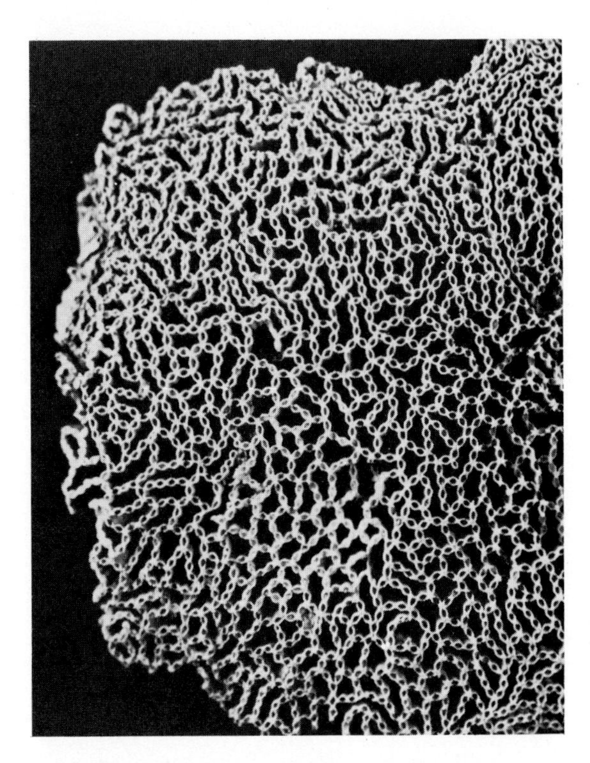

Fig. 10-7. A section through a "chain coral" which belongs to the class Tabulata. This chain coral is known as *Halysites*. It is from the Louisville formation near Louisville, Kentucky. (Photo by courtesy of the U.S. National Museum.)

The body of the coelenterates may take one of two forms known as a polyp or a medusa. The two forms live different sorts of lives, but are essentially similar in makeup. The cylindrical-shaped body of the polyp is attached to the sea floor, but the medusa is a flat or bell-shaped body that is unattached and free swimming. The polyp has one closed end, and the other has an opening or mouth which is surrounded by the soft tentacles. The polyps secrete calcareous external skeletons (which

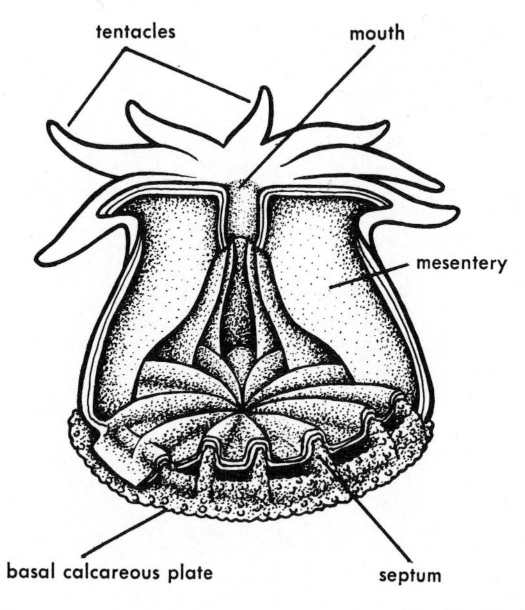

Fig. 10-8. A simple coral polyp of the class Anthozoa.

when built up in colonies form large masses commonly known as coral). In addition there may or may not be an internal skeleton. The medusa has no skeleton of any sort. Polyps and medusae may alternate in the life cycle of a single kind of coelenterate. The medusa grows as a bud on the polyp, then becomes detached and floats away. These forms then reproduce sexually, giving rise to a new generation of polyps.

Hydrozoa. Two classes of the coelenterates are important in the fossil record. They are the classes Hydrozoa, including the Stromatoporoidea, an extinct form that may belong to a separate phylum, and the Anthozoa. The Hydrozoa live both in fresh and marine waters as individuals or in colonies. They secrete skeletons of calcareous material. The colonies resemble a tree with short stubby limbs. The stromatoporoids are much more varied in appearance. They are known only as fossils. Their calcareous skeletons take many shapes including spheroidal, domal, or tree-shaped (dendroidal), and many specimens are laminated crustlike masses. These are composed of numerous closely spaced laminae separated by pillars or curved plates. The pillars may have been built around the individuals of the colony with the laminae separating successive generations. However, we cannot be sure that this is the case because the animals are extinct.

Anthozoa. The largest group of corals are those of the class Anthozoa. Here we include the most abundant reef-forming corals. They

Fig. 10-9. Three Tetracoralla. These are also known as rugose corals. (Photo by courtesy of the U.S. National Museum.)

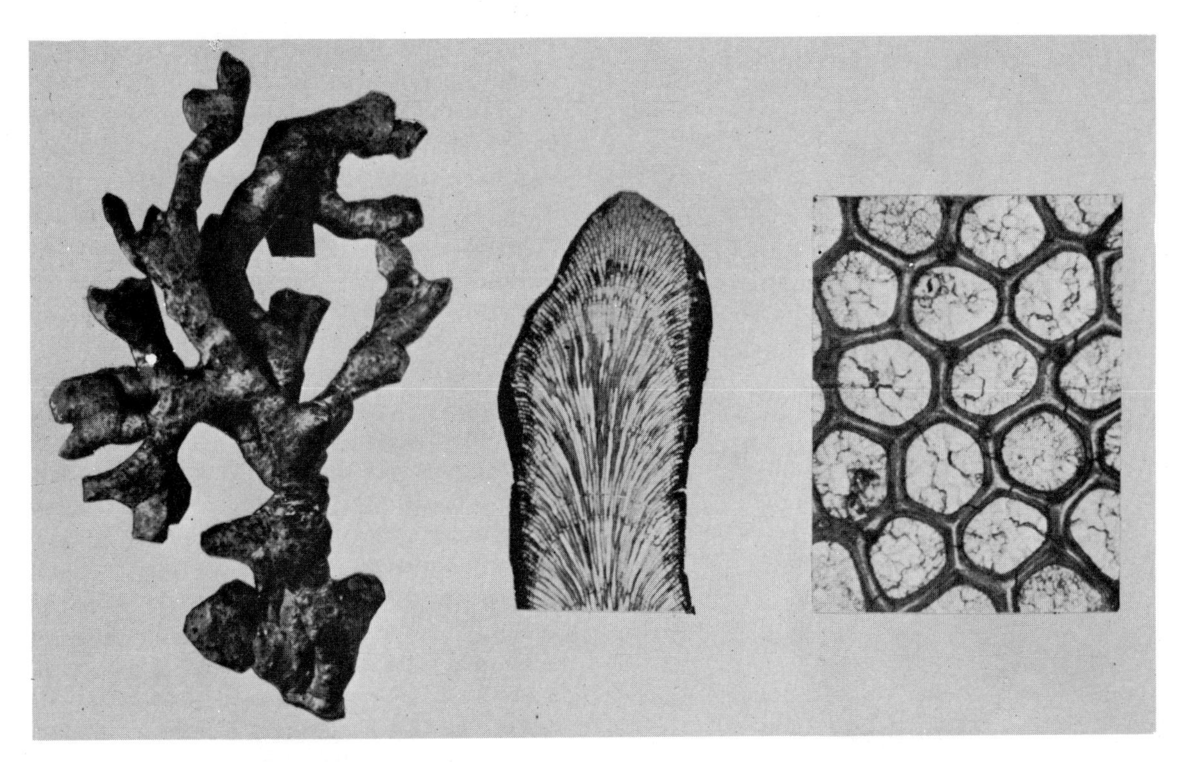

Fig. 10-10. A large stoney bryozoan colony from the Hamilton group of New York. At the left the colony is shown reduced to about one third. In the middle is a section through one branch of the colony enlarged 3x. At the right is a tangential section across a branch of the colony enlarged 50x. (Photos by courtesy of R. S. Boardman, U.S. National Museum.)

are found only in marine waters and may live individually or in colonies attached to the sea floor. The members of this class may be recognized by their symmetry. Their short stout bodies have a four-, six-, or eight-fold symmetry which is expressed in the calcareous external skeleton they secrete. The soft parts are attached at the base to the skeleton. When the tentacles around the mouth are extended the polyp has a flower-like radial symmetry. The tentacles wave creating currents which move food into the mouth and gullet. Food passes into the digestive sac which is divided into compartments by a number of radial partitions which extend across the bottom. These partitions are called mesenteries. Each individual polyp builds a cup or disc-shaped skeleton of some sort. This structure is called the theca. Between the mesenteries the soft parts of the polyp are strongly folded. Vertical plates of calcite grow in these folds out from the wall of the theca to the center where they meet. The plates, called septa, alternate with the mesenteries and are likewise radially arranged. The polyp is surrounded in its colonies by other polyps. In order to keep a favorable position to obtain food the skeleton is built higher as the animal grows. The lower parts of the skeleton are abandoned, and a partial or completely solid horizontal plate, the tabula, is built across the theca. More than 6000 species of the Anthozoa are living today, and many thousands have inhabited the seas of the past. These are subdivided according to the following characteristics:

1. The nature of the colony.
2. The internal structure of the theca.
3. Size, shape, and relationships between thecae.
4. The number and arrangement of the septa.
5. The number and arrangement of tentacles and mesenteries.

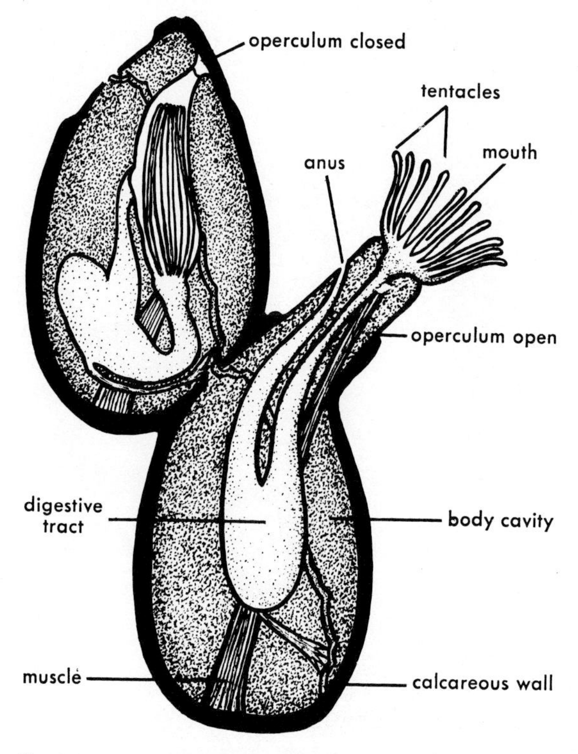

Fig. 10-11. A small section of a bryozoan colony. Two individuals are shown in cross section.

On these bases the Anthozoa are subdivided into three subclasses:

1. Alcyonaria (also Octocorallia): sea fans.
2. Zoantharia (including order Hexacoralla [brain corals]; order Tetracoralla [extinct])
3. Tabulata (extinct).

Alcyonaria. The polyp of the alcyonarians has eight tentacles encircling the mouth and eight mesenteries attached to the base of the enteron. This means there are eight septa; so, it is easy to see why this group has been called the Octocorallia. They live in large colonies that take on a lobate or branching form. The individuals of the colony are connected by means of tubular connections that are embedded in common fleshy material that covers the top of the skeleton. The thecae are attached to a solid or hollow axial structure that is made up of tiny spicules somewhat like those of the sponges. The shapes of the networks of these colonies range from very simple tubes to the more elaborate sea fans.

Zoantharia. This group has six mesenteries and six or some multiple of six septa in those that have skeletons. One group, the sea anemones, are fleshy corals that do not have a skeleton. The other members of this group are distinguished by their prominent septa and the arrangement of the septa. The number of septa is highly variable, but there is invariably a hexameral arrangement of them. Most of the modern corals (including the brain coral) belong to this subclass.

Tetracoralla (Rugosa). This group is now extinct, but the rugose corals were abundant for many millions of years and thus are geologically important. Tetracoralla have six prominent septa, three of which are very close together, dividing the theca into four areas or quadrants. The solitary forms are easily recognized by their curved conical shape. Both the solitary corals and colonial masses have rough exteriors and for that reason are called rugose corals. The colonies were built in dendritic or massive forms.

Tabulata. This extinct group of Paleozoic corals were colonial corals characterized by strongly developed tabulae. Most have poorly developed septa. Walls separating the individuals of the colony are thick. This group is usually cylindrical or prismatic in shape.

Fig. 10-12. A brachiopod shell broken away to show the internal structure.

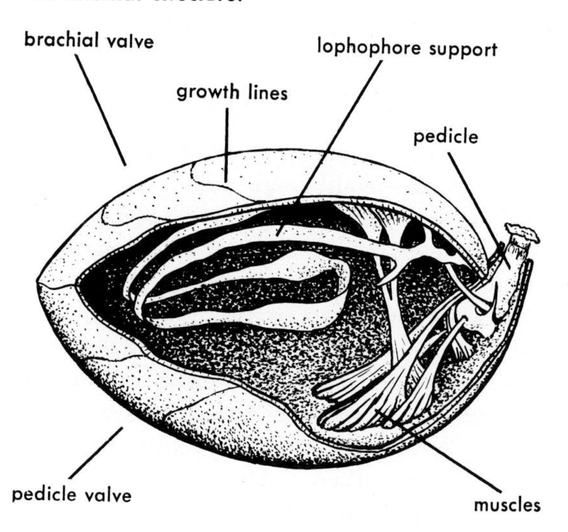

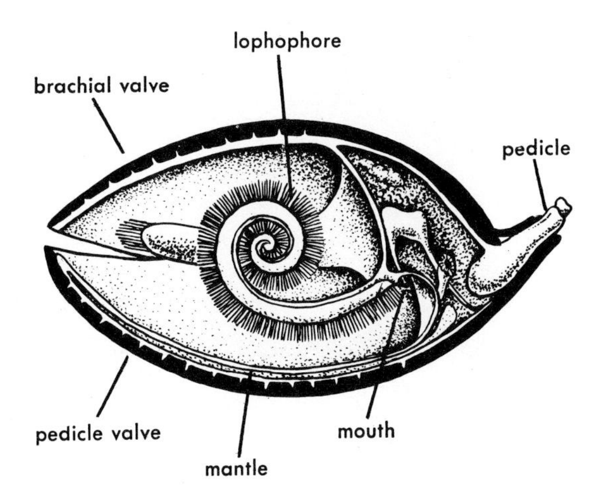

Fig. 10-13. A cross section through a live brachiopod, showing soft parts of the animal.

Phylum Bryozoa

Bryozoans are abundant today in the oceans and in the fossil record of marine sediments. Many of the fossil genera and species have a short stratigraphic range and are widely distributed, making them useful for purposes of correlation. They bear a superficial resemblance to corals in that the individuals of the colonies live in a cup-shaped container that opens at only one end. These cups are fixed to a limy or horny framework to which other members of the colony are attached. They grow to form fans, mats, and branching colonies. Like the coral polyps they possess tentacles around their mouths, but there the resemblance ends. The tentacles of the bryozoans are different in that they cannot be used to sting their prey. The function of the tentacles is to bring food to the mouth. The tentacles are lined by very fine thread-like cilia. These move systematically through the water creating a slight current of water which transports water and food to the bottom of the tentacles and into the mouth. Internally they are much more complex than corals. The digestive system is a complete tube, doubled into a U so that the anus is near the mouth. Such an arrangement is undesirable, but it is necessary since there is only one opening in the cup which houses the soft parts. The animal also possesses a rudimentary nervous system and a well-developed muscular system. The opening to the cup is covered by a hard disc called the operculum. It operates like a trap door. The animal pulls it down over the aperture when it retreats into the protection of the hard cup.

The bryozoan colonies live in cold, warm, and hot water and at depths ranging from near surface to the abyssal plains. They are attached to the sea floor, to shells of other animals, or to objects on the bottom. Like the sponges they prefer clear water, but they seem to thrive in agitated waters. Most, but not all, live in marine water.

Bryozoans are divided into two classes depending on whether they lived in marine or

Fig. 10-14. Three articulate brachiopods, showing variations in external form. The top is an internal view of the shell. (The photo of *Rafinesquina* at the bottom is by courtesy of the U.S. National Museum.)

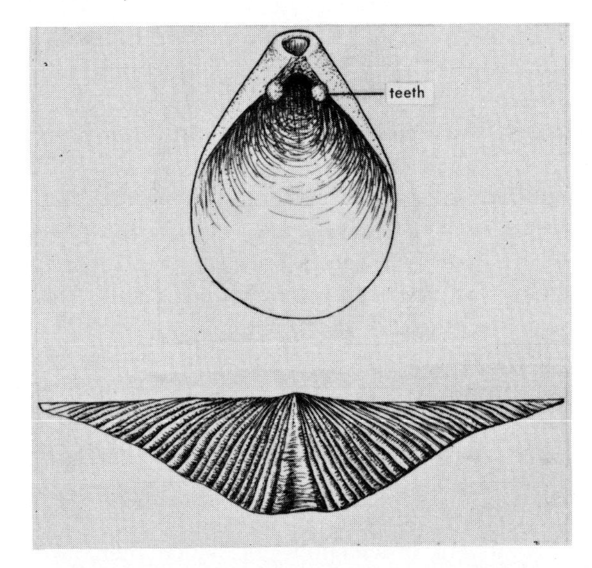

fresh water. The further subdivisions are based largely on the presence or absence and structure of the covering of the aperture, and on the composition of the cup or enclosure for the soft parts.

Phylum Brachiopoda

Brachiopods are undoubtedly one of the most important groups of fossils for stratigraphic correlation. Their shells are commonly found well preserved in the sedimentary rocks of the Paleozoic and Mesozoic eras. They have undergone many changes through time making them useful in correlation. The soft parts of the animal are enclosed in two approximately but not quite equal shells. Brachiopods may sometimes be confused with clams, which do have two equal shells, but the shells of the clam are located on either side of the body while those of the brachiopods are above and below the body. Brachiopods are much more complex internally than either the corals or bryzoans. Brachiopods have a gut or coelom and a well-developed nervous, muscular, digestive, circulatory, excretory, and reproductive system. These soft parts are rarely preserved in fossils, but markings and structures within the shell related to them may be preserved. Most notable of these is a firm internal support for tentacles that are found in some brachiopods. This structure is called the lophophore support. The lophophore possesses cilia which move to set up currents to bring food to the mouth and to aid respiration. Brachiopods are solitary animals which are usually attached to the sea floor by a fleshy stalk that protrudes through the back of the lower shell.

Modern brachiopods, of which there are some 200 species in the South Pacific Ocean, vary in size from a quarter of an inch to about 3 inches. In the past they have been both smaller and larger. Some have been no more than a millimeter in diameter, while other fossils are as much as a foot across. They inhabit shallow water, usually no more than 100 fathoms deep, or in other words they occur mainly on the continental shelves.

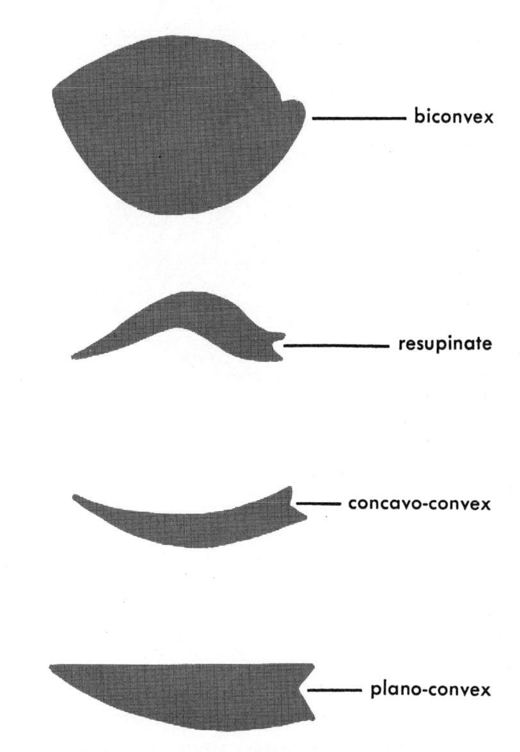

Fig. 10-16. Four brachiopod profiles. The shapes of brachiopods show great variation. These four profiles are shown as they appear when looking at the specimens along the hinge line.

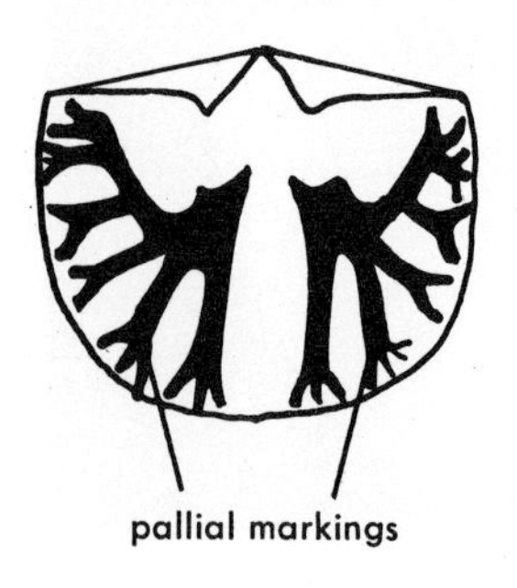

Fig. 10-15. Sketch of the pallial markings on the inside of a brachiopod shell. These markings are found where the circulatory sinuses in the mantle of the animal came in contact with the shell.

The largest subdivision of brachiopods is made on the basis of the nature of the connection between the two shells. Some, usually the smaller "brachs," have shells held together without the benefit of a hingement, the inarticulate class. Others possess some form of teeth-and-socket joints which function like a ball-and-socket joint and are used for articulation along the edge of the shells, the articulate class.

Articulate Brachiopoda. An important feature used in classification of the articulates is the structure of the shell walls. In some groups fine rodlike extensions of the soft mantle of the body project outward into the shell. Where these rods occur there is a small corresponding hole in the shell. The shell appears perforated and is said to be perforated or punctate. Other large groups either do not have these perforations at all, or they are pseudopunctate.

The animal has no heart, but there is circulation of a body fluid through a branching system of passageways that lead into the mantle, a soft tissue which encloses the organs and muscles. From the mantle these passageways lead outward toward the margins of the shell. They leave very interesting branching patterns on the inside of the shells, called pallial marks.

The pedicle valve is the shell through which the pedicle or stalklike support for the brachiopod projects. The other shell is known as the brachial valve. Space must be provided within both shells for the large round stalk. The pedicle valve is usually somewhat longer than the brachial valve, but both are slightly pointed in the region of the pedicle opening. This end of the shell is known as the beak. Inside the pedicle valve there is a broad shelf-like area at the beak end. This shelf is broken by a triangular area that opens into the pedicle opening. On either side of this deltaic-shaped structure the teeth or dental plates are situated. These are not teeth in the ordinary sense of the word. They are not used for mastication of food but serve as a means of hingement for the two shells.

The brachial valve is somewhat smaller than the pedicle valve. There is a triangular-shaped space for the projection of the pedicle through the beak end of this shell also. Situated in a position directly opposite the teeth of the pedicle valve are dental sockets in which the teeth may pivot. Almost directly between the sockets there is a small projection from the inside of the shell to which muscles are attached in the living organism. From this projection there is a ridgelike growth called the median septum which extends from the beak end toward the outer margin of the shell. Extending out into the shell from the region of the dental sockets is the lophophore support. These supports are often broken off in fossils because they are delicate, but when present they provide an excellent means of identification. Some are simple ribbon-like loops, others are coiled either vertically or laterally within the shell.

Scars are found where the muscles were attached to the interior of the shell. The articulate brachs have two sets of muscles which are attached to both the pedicle and brachial shells. One set is used to open the shell. These extend from the central part of the pedicle valve to the brachial valve where they are at-

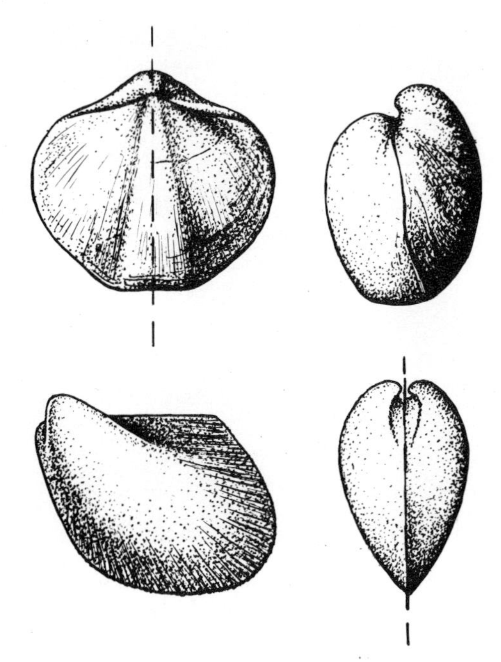

Fig. 10-18. Comparison of a brachiopod shell with a pelecypod shell. These two groups are frequently confused by beginning students. The planes of symmetry are indicated for each. The pelecypod is symmetrically bisected by a plane through the hingement, but the brachiopod is symmetrically bisected by a plane at right angles to the hingement.

Fig. 10-17. Shell structure of brachiopod shells. The variations in the structure of the shell walls is used as a means of classification of brachiopods. (After R. C. Moore, *Invertebrate Fossils.*)

Fig. 10–19. A fossil gastropod, *Ananias*. (Photo by courtesy of U. S. National Museum.)

tached behind the hinge line along which the shell moves when opening or closing. As a result of this arrangement the shell may be opened by contraction of these muscles which causes the shell to pivot along the hinge line. The second set of muscles is attached from the central interior of the pedicle valve to the central interior part of the brachial valve. These are used to close the shell; this purpose is accomplished by contraction also. The animal simply relaxes one set of muscles while contracting the other in order to open or close the shell. The muscles used to open the shell are attached to the small projection near the beak on the brachial valve already mentioned. The other attachments are to the inside of the shell itself.

Shell structures. A number of features on the shells may be useful in the identification of certain brachiopods. The shell may have an almost perfectly smooth surface, or it may be characterized by many small ridges or folds which radiate out from the beak region. Some of these actually are small folds in the shells, but others are simply local thickenings of the shell wall. The folded shells are said to be plicate, while those with alternate thickening and thinning are called costate. In addition to these small plications there may be a large fold on the brachial valve. This fold extends from the beak toward the lower margin of the shell. On the pedicle valve directly opposite this structure there is a troughlike depression along the midline. This affects both the outer and inner surface of the shell and is called a sulcus. Some of the shells are highly decorated with spines that project from the surface of both shells.

Finally there are differences in the external form or shape of the shell. It should be noted that all brachiopods are symmetrical. They may be divided by a plane of symmetry that cuts through the beak and pedical opening down to the outer margin. The mollusks with which brachiopods are sometimes confused do not have this symmetry. A great diversity of shell shapes is known, but all of them are symmetrical. If the shells are turned so that you have a side view (that is, looking along the hinge line), they will have one of four shapes as illustrated (Fig. 10-16):

Fig. 10-20. Gastropod shell showing various morphological features.

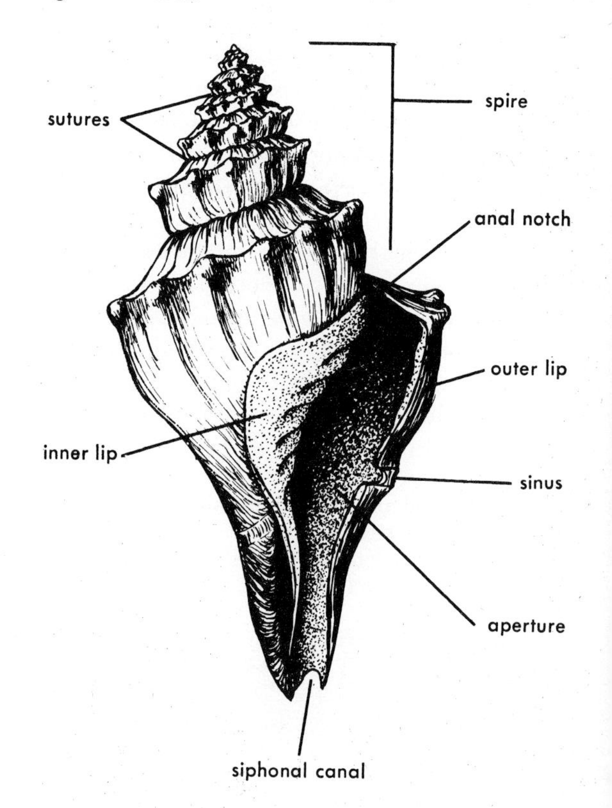

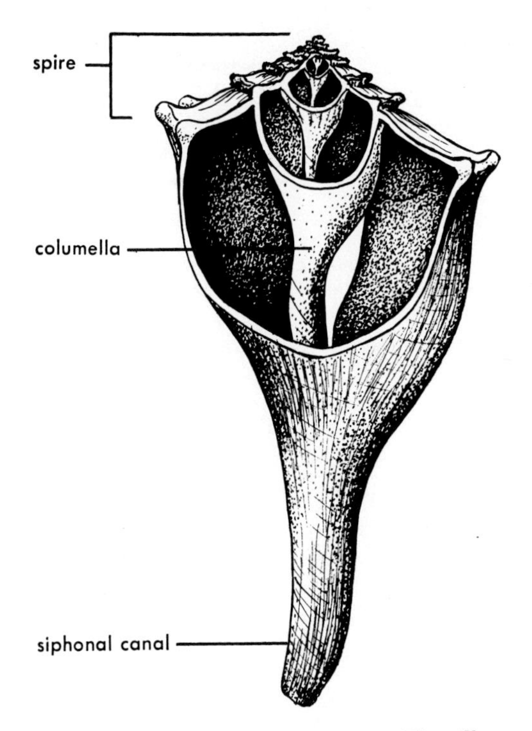

Fig. 10-21. Gastropod shell sectioned. This illustration shows the way in which the inner lip becomes coiled to form the columella. (After Shrock and Twenhofel, *Principles of Invertebrate Paleontology.* McGraw-Hill Book Co.)

a. Biconvex.
b. Resupinate.
c. Concavo-convex.
d. Plano-convex.

Ecology. The brachiopods that are found today live exclusively in marine water, and from the sediments most generally found associated with them we assume they have always been confined to the seas. Almost all of them live in shallow water between the strand line (shore line) and the edge of the continental shelf at about 100 fathoms. A few are found in the deeper waters on the continental slope. Most are attached to the sea bottom by a pedicle, but others are fixed to the bottom by the spines that project from their shells.

Phylum Mollusca

Mollusks are another of the largest groups of animals living today. You can get some idea of their abundance and diversity when you consider that there are some 60,000 living species. They inhabit the land, fresh and marine waters, but most of them are marine. Some of the common members of this group are the nautilus, octopuses, cuttlefishes, squids, scallops, mussels, oysters, and snails.

One of the most characteristic features of the group is the muscular region located behind the mouth. It serves as a means of locomotion in many forms and is called the foot. The body is normally elongate and bilaterally symmetrical. The foot is the lower part of a fleshy covering for the other soft parts of the animal. Unlike the other groups we have considered, mollusks show a concentration of sensory structures in a head. There are sometimes well-developed eyes and other sense organs. The digestive system is well developed, and some have a rasping device to help prepare food for digestion. The circulatory system includes a heart, and the respiratory system consists of complex gills. Oxygen diffuses through these gills into the blood stream. There are also muscular, reproductive, and excretory organs. Many of the mollusks build shells of calcium carbonate. In size they range from a fraction of a millimeter to over 53 feet, the giant squid. From these features it should be apparent that the mollusks are much more complex than the previously discussed animal groups.

Three groups of the mollusks are very important. They are the Gastropoda, snails; Pelecypoda, clams; and Cephalopoda, squids and nautilus.

Fig. 10-22. A modern gastropod shown carrying the shell.

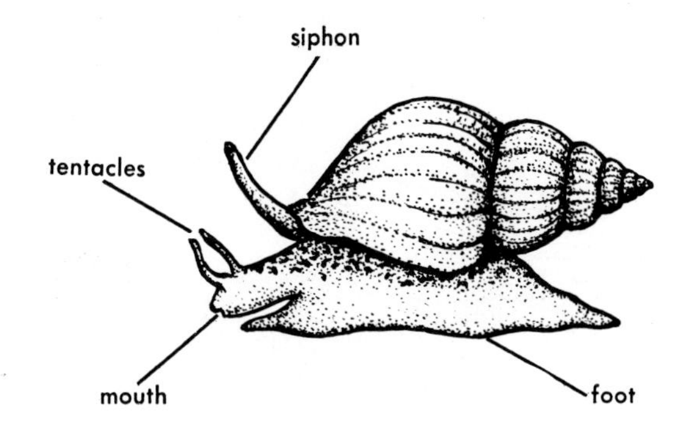

Class Gastropoda

The name gastropod literally means stomach foot. This foot is the means of locomotion, slow as it is, for the snails. They carry a shell around on their backs for protection. This shell contains a single opening. The animal is bilateral in its early larva stage, but as it grows it undergoes a change in which the internal organs become twisted in a loop. This brings the anus from a position behind the mouth and foot to a point over the mouth. Although this is an unsanitary arrangement it is a very practical one for an animal that lives in a shell with a single opening. The internal organs on one side of the snail fail to develop after the twisting takes place. This and a sort of lopsided growth gives a spiral turn to the body covering and in turn to the shell secreted by the body covering. Consequently the shells of most gastropods are curved in spirals.

Gastropods are world wide in their distribution. They are most abundant in shallow well-lighted marine waters, but some live on land in the mountains, and others inhabit waters as deep as the abyssal plains, 18,000 feet. They crawl on the sea floor, and a few can swim. Most gastropods eat plants, which they cut up with a toothlike mechanism called a radula. The radulas would be most helpful in classification if they were preserved more often in the fossil record. The gastropods are able to drill holes into solid rocks, and some of them drill holes in the shells of other mollusks to feed on the soft parts of their prey.

Fig. 10-23. Cephalopod shown in section. The air chambers are sealed off from the outside providing the animal with a balance system which has been used to buoy up his weight.

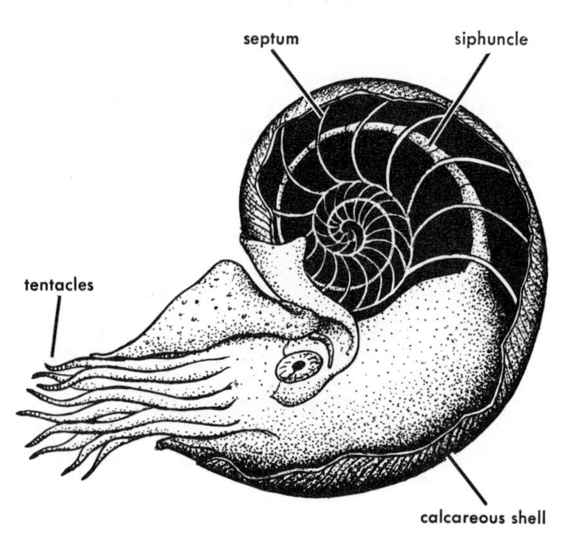

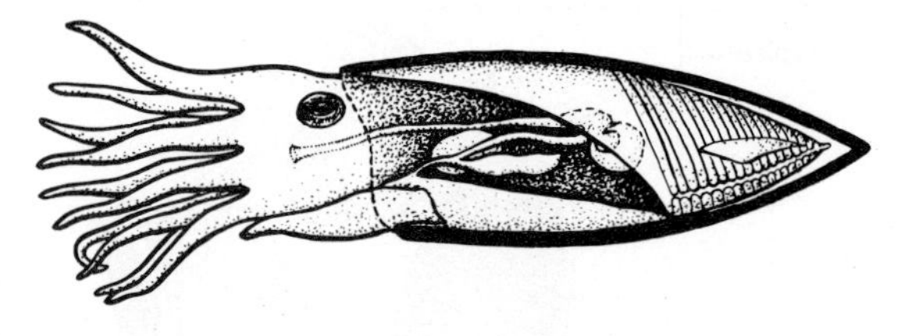

Fig. 10-24. A *Belemnoida* cephalopod. The cigar-shaped remains of these extinct cephalopods are commonly found in the upper Paleozoic strata. The animal resembled the modern squid.

The shell. Gastropod shells are coiled, but these coils take several different forms. The coils are generally found to increase in size with the growth of the soft parts. The coiling may be either right-handed, clockwise coiling, or left-handed, counter clockwise, and it may be within a single plane, or the coils may be extended up or downward. Some of the most outstanding morphological features of the shells are described here:

Aperture: the opening into the shell through which the animal moves in and out. It may be circular, oval, slitlike, or elliptical. The margin of the aperture is divided into an inner lip, called the columella, around which the shell coils in many species, and an outer lip.

Operculum: a horny or calcareous platelike covering of the aperture found in some gastropods.

Whorl: the term applied to one complete volution about the axis of coiling.

Suture: the line marking the trace of the contact between adjacent whorls.

Siphonal notch: The outer lip of some gastropods is interrupted by a troughlike depression or canal which serves as a protective cover for the siphon. The siphon is a fold in the mantle which brings in fresh water to the mantle. A siphon is required for this purpose because of the sanitation problem involved in having the mouth and anus so close together.

Anal notch: A second recess in the outer lip occurs where the waste products are removed from the anus. This notch is usually at the opposite end of the lip from the siphonal notch.

Ornamentation: Several types of ornamentation are common on gastropod shells. There may be rounded ridges which revolve with the whorls. Growth lines give rise to transverse markings which indicate positions of the shell margins at different times. Fine raised threads and fine grooves may run transverse to the whorls or revolve with them. Perhaps the most prominent features are keels, flanges, or spines that run across the whorl.

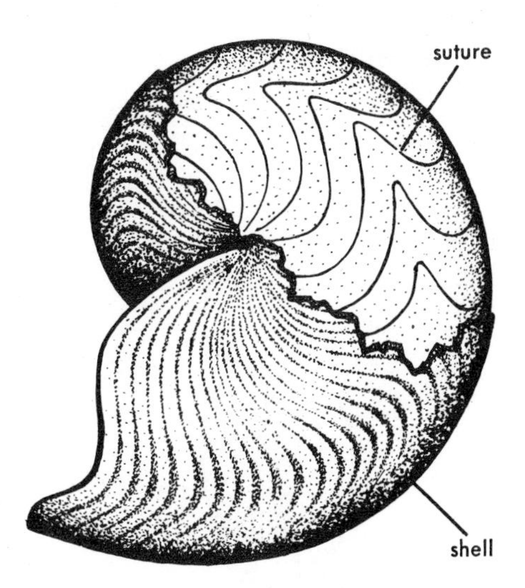

Fig. 10-26. Ammonoid. The outer shell is broken away to show the suture pattern, a comparatively simple curved line marking the intersection of the internal partitions and the shell.

Class Cephalopoda

The name of this class comes from the close association of the head and the foot. The group is the most highly developed class of the mollusks. It includes such familiar animals as the squid, cuttlefishes, and octopuses. In past geologic times the nautiloids and ammonoids of this class were important. The animal is bilaterally symmetrical, that is, it may be divided into two sides that are mirror images of one another. The head is closely surrounded by a number of long muscular tentacles which are usually equipped with hooks or suckers. The eye is one of the most outstanding features of the head. It is very much like the eye of the vertebrates. There is also a well-developed hearing organ, and the mouth is furnished with powerful jaws and a radula which can be used to chew food. The skin of the cephalopods contains cells of pigment that is black, brown, or reddish yellow. When the animal becomes alarmed different sets of these cells are pulled out by tiny muscles attached to their edges. Thus the octopus can change color in a flash. Many cephalopods also have a bag filled with an inklike fluid that can be ejected into the water. This provides a shield behind which the animals can escape from their enemies. This is needed by those cephalopods which have no shells or other protection for their soft bodies.

Fig. 10-25. A Cretaceous ammonoid. The early ammonoids had a very simple suture pattern such as that seen in Fig. 10-26, but toward the end of the Mesozoic Era the sutures became increasingly complex as seen here. The specimen is *Scaphites*. (Photo by courtesy of U.S. National Museum.)

Water is taken into the mantle cavity and forcibly ejected through a funnel-shaped siphon. This creates a jet stream of water that forces the animal through the water. The squids normally swim forward by means of fins located on either side of the body, but they may also swim by means of the expelled water.

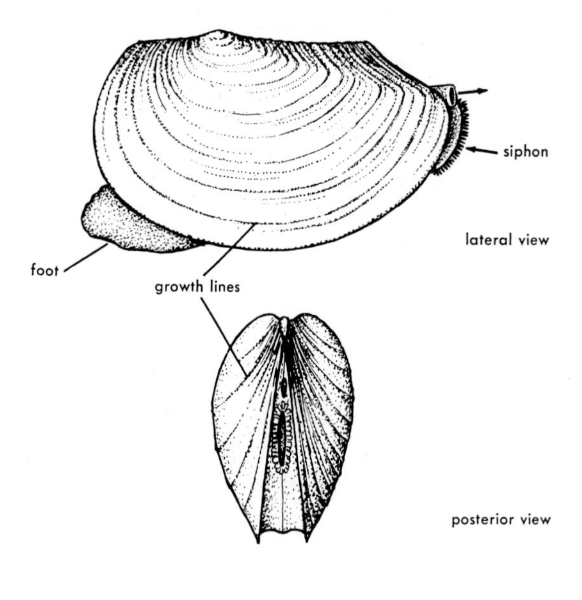

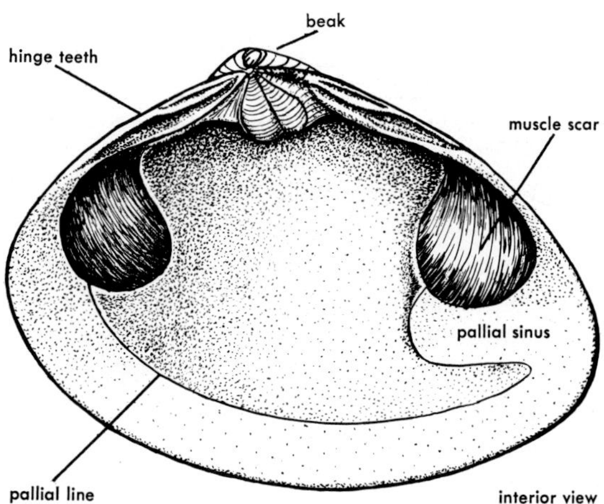

Fig. 10-27. Morphological features of pelecypods.

They dart either forward or backward by pointing the siphon in the direction opposite from that in which they wish to travel.

The biologists' classification of cephalopods is based on the number of gills that the animal has, but this is not at all satisfactory for the purposes of the geologists, since there is no way to find out how many gills the extinct groups had. The problem is complicated by the fact that the vast majority of cephalopods are extinct. We recognize three main groups, Nautiloidea, Ammonoidea, and Dibranchia (squid, octopuses).

Nautiloidea. They have straight or coiled shells which are divided into chambers separated by gently curved partitions or septa. The lines where these septa meet the wall of the shell are called sutures. They are simple smooth lines in most of the nautiloids. The pattern formed by these sutures is one of the best means of identification of the cephalopods. When the shell is coiled it is coiled within a single plane, and that plane bisects the shell into two symmetrical parts.

Ammonoidea. This group is extinct. The shells are coiled, and the septa between chambers are irregular or wrinkled surfaces. Thus the intersection of these septa with the walls of the shell gives rise to a very irregular suture pattern.

Dibranchia. This group includes most of the modern cephalopods. They have 8 or 10 tentacles. If they possess any hard parts at all they are in the form of an internal uncoiled vestigial shell. Belemnites belong to this group.

Morphology of the shells. In the nautilus, one of the few modern cephalopods that possesses a shell, the animal occupies the last or living chamber of the shell. As the animal grows, it builds cell walls for a larger chamber and shuts off the last living chamber by secreting a septum. The middle of this septum is perforated by a hole through which a slender tubelike mass of the fleshy parts of the animal extends back to the very first chamber. These chambers are used as a buoy by the animal. They contain air and help support part of the weight of the shell. The shells of all the cephalopods are very similar in structure, although not all are coiled.

Class Pelecypoda

The pelecypods include many familiar sea animals such as the clams, oysters, mussels, and sea scallops. Most of them are marine, and with a few exceptions they are bilaterally symmetrical. They have two shells or valves which are nearly symmetrical. The plane of symmetry however extends between the valves not through them as is the case of the brachiopods. We ordinarily think of the snails as the slowest animals, but even they move more rapidly than most pelecypods, which seldom move very far in their entire lifetimes; some pelecypods like the oysters become attached to the sea floors. They are simpler in organization than are the other cephalopods. They have no head, and very few sensory receptors. Food is obtained from the water which surrounds them, for none lives on land. The water is filtered by a gill-like organ. They eat all sorts of food. Some are known to have eaten men who allowed themselves to become trapped in the huge shells. Although a few have shells as large as this would indicate, most are much smaller, but the range is great.

The animal has a mouth, esophagus, stomach, intestine, and anus, but lacks the radula that is present in other mollusks. The circulatory system consists of a heart and a system of tubes. The foot is a large extension of the internal soft parts specialized as a muscular organ for locomotion. Some forms have developed siphons to bring in and take out water. These siphons grow to be several times the length of the shell itself and can be extended or withdrawn by the animals.

Morphology of the shell. The shells are composed of calcium carbonate. They vary in shape and ornamentation but are usually articulated along a hinge line at the back of the shell. The shells possess a rounded and raised part that is somewhat pointed and called the beak or umbo. Other morphological features are:

Pallial line: a mark on the inside of the shell along which the mantle was connected to the shell.

Pallial sinus: an embayment in the pallial line.

Muscle scars: The muscle attachment in pelecypods is very different from that in the brachiopods. The muscles are not attached behind the hingement line, in the same way. A strong ligament behind the hingement tends to spring the shell open. The other muscles directed from the central parts of the two valves simply pull the shell together.

Teeth: The shells are hinged by means of teeth and sockets that lie along a straight or curved line called the hinge line. The nature of the teeth is highly varied—so much so, in fact, that this is often used as a means of classification. Four types of dentition are:

a. A series of very small alternating teeth and sockets on each shell.
b. A few large teeth with or without the smaller one on the side.
c. Equally developed teeth, each shell possessing two.
d. No teeth at all.

Externally the shell may have many forms of ornamentation. These include growth lines which parallel the edge of the shell; very fine radial lines, costae; local ridgelike thickenings of the shell; radial fluted lines where the margin of the shell has developed large folds; crenulate structures formed by slight closely spaced folds of the shell margins; and spines.

Phylum Arthropoda

This group is by far the largest of all the phyla including both plants and animals. Its size is due mainly to the insects and spiders, but it also includes the crustaceans and an extinct group, the trilobites. It is by far the most diverse group and with the exception of the vertebrates it is the most complex in structure and behavior. The number of living species has been estimated as high as 10 million. They have been dredged up from the deep-sea floor, they fly, hop, swim, crawl, and just sit.

Among the features that commonly characterize the arthropods are:

a. A hard external coating that serves as an external skeleton.
b. Legs that are divided into distinct, movable segments – jointed legs.
c. Well-developed jaws that open from side to side.
d. Segmented body structure.
e. Location of their muscles in definite groups mechanically related to certain body movements.

Insects in spite of their great number and diversity are not important in the fossil record. A few have been preserved in the resin of

Fig. 10-28. Perfect preservation of an arthropod in resin. (Photo by courtesy of the U.S. National Museum.)

trees, but these are rare indeed; so, they will be omitted from the following discussion.

An extinct group of the arthropods, the trilobites, were very numerous in Cambrian time, and one or another of the arthropods has been prominent throughout the Paleozoic, Mesozoic, and Cenozoic history of the earth. Their sizes range from fractions of a millimeter to more than 10 feet (the giant crabs).

The bodies of most arthropods may be divided into three segments, a head, thorax, and abdomen. These in turn may be composed of many segments. Those of the head are fused together, and segments of the thorax have pairs of jointed appendages. These appendages function as legs, for respiration, grasping, mastication, and as sensory organs. The animals have highly developed nervous, circulatory, and respiratory systems. The soft parts of the body are enclosed in a hard exoskeleton. This hard covering cannot be increased in size as the body grows. So, the animal molts or sheds the exoskeleton periodically and grows another larger one to accommodate its increased size. During the periods of molting the soft parts of the animal are exposed, and it is particularly vulnerable to attack. Not all arthropods grow during the molting period. Some even become smaller if the food supply is not adequate.

The arthropods are very similar to the annelid worms in many respects, and for this reason it seems probable that they evolved from the worms. Both of them have segmented bodies, similar nervous systems, and muscles. If the arthropods did evolve from worms they

Fig. 10-29. Morphological features of trilobites.

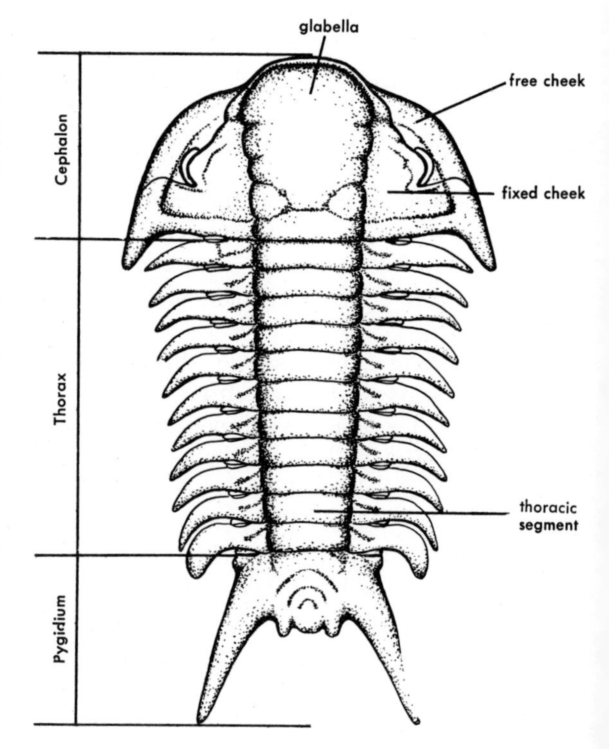

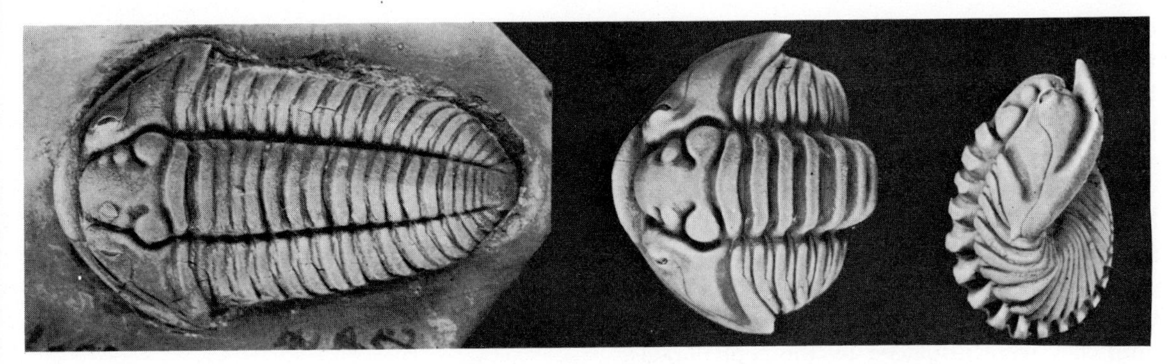

Fig. 10-30. Three fossils of the same trilobite, *Flexicalymene*. (Photo by courtesy of U.S. National Museum.)

did so long before the Cambrian Period, for the trilobites were well developed by the earliest part of that period.

Ostracoda. These minute crustaceans are about the size and shape of a lentil or lima bean. They range in size from 1 mm to as much as 20 mm. Although they are not very impressive in size or appearance they are very valuable in stratigraphic correlation. Their segmented body is covered by a bivalve shell somewhat like that of the pelecypods. It is composed of chitin or calcium carbonate. They live only in water, where they are part of the mass of small animals that swim and float near the surface. They are most abundant in the oceans, but live in fresh waters as well. Their bodies are indistinctly segmented, but they possess eyes and seven pairs of appendages including two antennae. The fresh-water forms have one more pair of legs than the marine varieties. The outer surfaces of the shells are often rather plain. They may be smooth and glossy, or granulose, pitted, or striated.

Trilobites. This group lived only during the Paleozoic Era. They are named for the trilobate form of their bodies which may be

Fig. 10-31. Fossil of an extinct arthropod, *Eurypterid*. (Photo by courtesy of the U.S. National Museum.)

divided into a head or cephalon, thorax, and abdomen or pygidium. The sizes and shapes of the trilobites are highly varied. About 1500 genera are known, and most of them were small, about 2 or 3 inches, but a few were very small, and others were more than 2 feet long. They appear to have inhabited shallow marine waters only, and they probably dwelt on the bottom. They dominated sea life of the Cambrian and most of the Ordovican Period until they were displaced by the cephalopods. The soft parts of the trilobites have not been preserved. We can only infer what they were like from the hard parts that remain. These hard parts are mainly the exoskeleton.

Cephalon: The central part of the cephalon is called the glabella. It is arched above the two cheeks on either side which are divided into two parts by a suture, a cut. These sutures may mark the place where the eyes were placed. The thorax consists of a large number of thoracic segments each of which has a pair of appendages attached. These were almost certainly the legs of the trilobites. They are jointed and could have been moved. The pygidium covered the abdominal part of the body. It is composed of a number of segments that are fused together. In some species it looks very much like the cephalon. In others the pygidium seems to be lacking altogether.

The trilobites have been classified according to a number of characteristics including:

a. The nature and position of facial sutures.
b. The number of thoracic segments.
c. The presence of eyes and their structure.
d. The structure of the cephalon or pygidium.

Phylum Graptolithina

Members of this extinct group have at one time or another been classified as coelenterates, bryozoans, and at present as hemichordates. The hemichordates are organisms which fall between the invertebrates and the true chordates or animals with backbones. Most hemichordates are small, soft-bodied, wormlike animals that possess some characteristics of the chordates and some of the invertebrates.

The graptolites were abundant during the Paleozoic Era. They occur in rocks from the Middle Cambrian to the Early Mississippian when they became extinct. About 6000 species of them have been described. They were colonial organisms that had external skeletons made of chitin. These skeletons consist of rows of cups or tubes that develop from a single

Fig. 10-32. Fossil of a graptolite. This group is extinct. It is thought to be related to the hemichordates such as Rhabdopleura, Fig. 10-33. (Photo by courtesy of the U.S. National Museum.)

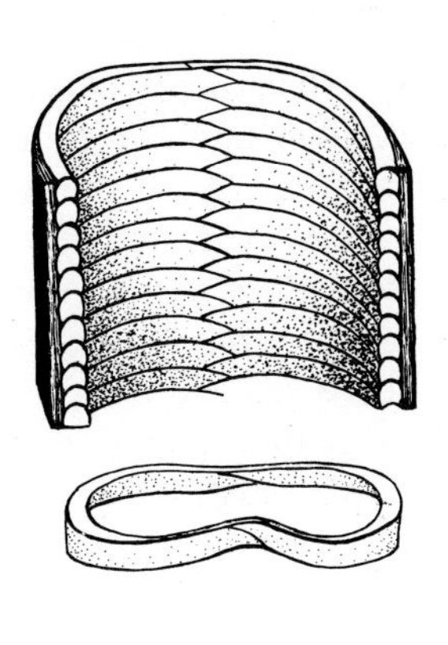

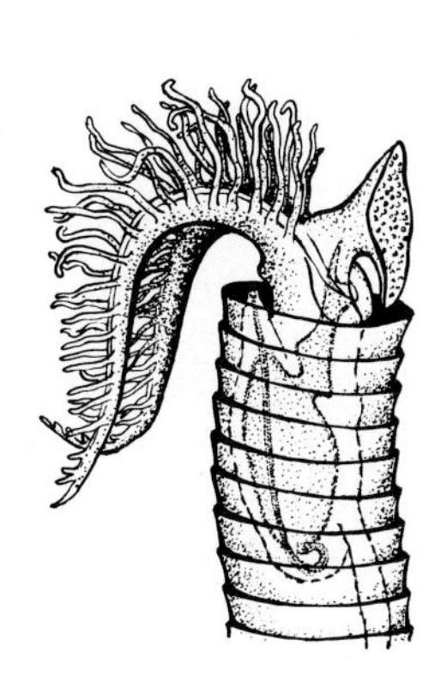

Fig. 10-33. Graptolite theca. At the top is a greatly enlarged section of one of the theca, housing the individuals of a colony. The structure is similar to that found in Rhabdopleura, a modern hemichordate. Such similarities are used to help establish the relationship between extinct animals known only in the fossil record with those living today. (After Lankester, 1873.)

initial cup called the sicula which is distinctive by nature. These colonies apparently hung down below a floatlike mass that kept them near the surface of the ocean and allowed them to drift with the sea currents. A few fossils of these bulbs have been found. They are important guide fossils because they occur throughout the world. The fact that they could float was probably a very important factor in distributing them so widely. The fossil remains are for the most part carbon deposits on the bedding planes of black shales, in which they are most frequently found. A few have been found in near-perfect states of preservation, however, and these have made it possible for us to find out a great deal more about their structure.

The colony hung down from the float, or whatever else they may have been attached to, by a hollow thread called the nema. The first individual of the colony built a tiny chitinous cone called the sicula. From this the budding pattern found among the graptolites started. Three theca or cup-shaped containers developed from each bud. There are obvious difficulties in finding out exactly what the function of each of these theca was, but they have been compared with living hemichordates and explained as follows by Kozlowski (1948). Both male and female individuals are developed among the hemichordates. One theca is thought to have housed the female individuals, a second the somewhat smaller males. The third theca was built by the immature females. Thus two of the thecae may have been secreted by the same individual. The rows of thecae form long strings of individuals called stipes. These branch and may be connected in some forms.

Phylum Echinoderma

The name echinoderm comes from the Greek words *echinos,* spiny, plus *derma,* skin, and refers to the spiny skin of the animals. Many of them have calcareous plates in the skin which may or may not be firmly fused together. These plates are especially important since they are the hard parts that may be preserved. All the echinoderms are marine animals. Some are attached to the sea floor, while

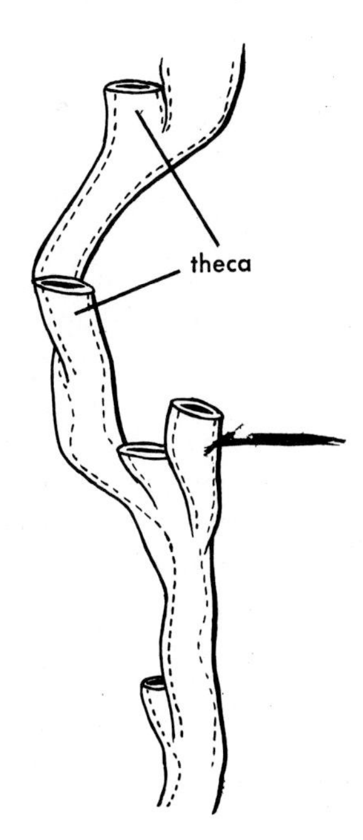

Fig. 10-34. A restored section of a graptolite showing the theca.

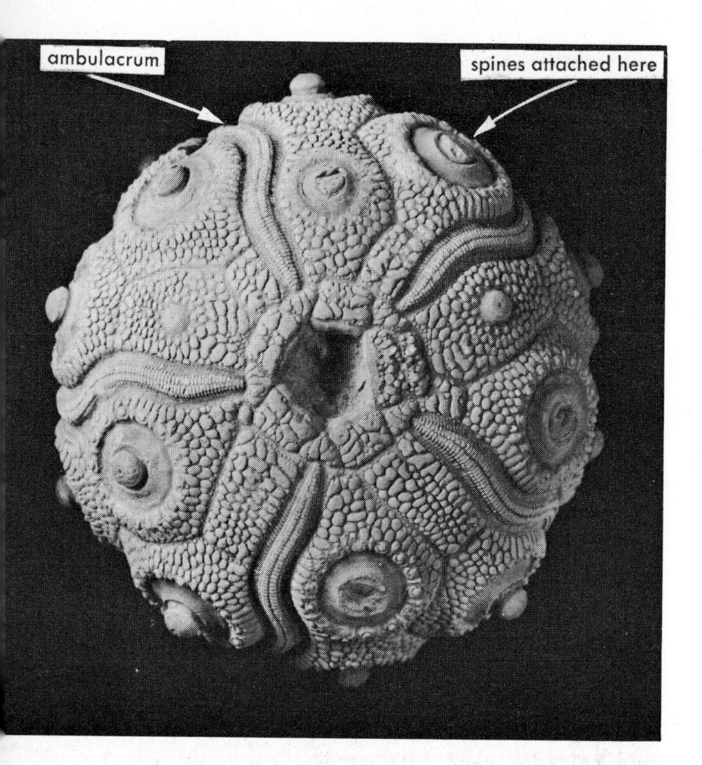

Fig. 10-35. A beautifully preserved specimen of *Stereocidaris*. This is an echinoid, one of the main groups that belong to the phylum Echinoderma. (Photo by courtesy of the U.S. National Museum.)

others move about freely. They are relatively complex animals having a digestive tube, a gut, and specialized excretory, reproductive, nervous, and circulatory systems. They are much more complex than the coelenterates, but there is a superficial resemblance in that both are radially symmetrical. Although the larvae seem to be bilaterally symmetrical the overall shape of the adults is radial. The starfish is perhaps the best example.

One of the most unusual features about the echinoderms is the circulatory system. They have a poorly developed true circulatory system, and in addition a water circulatory system. This second system uses filtered sea water brought in through a specialized sieve plate. In many of the animals this water-circulatory system is connected to tubelike feet. They are operated by hydraulic pressure and are used for locomotion and for grasping. Increased pressure forces the tubes to extend out, and they retract as pressure is reduced.

The body of most echinoderms may be divided into five radial components. These are the arms of the starfishes. Sea urchins have five radial areas, and the holothuroids, sea cucumbers, have five internal compartments. Regardless of what form these radial components take there are five external radial grooves, or bands of porous plates, along which water currents move toward the mouth. These carry food to the mouth. The grooves or bands of plates are called ambulacra or rays. Classification of the echinoderms has been based on:

a. The nature of the water-circulatory system.
b. Presence or absence of fixed or movable arms.
c. The mode of life.

Twelve classes are now recognized, but we shall limit our discussion to five, all of which are important geologically. These are the cystoids, blastoids, crinoids, asteroids, and echinoids.

Echinoidea. This class is often confused with the phylum as a whole because of the similarity of the names. The echinoids are known by many common names such as sea urchins, sand dollars, sand shillings, or shield

Fig. 10-36. A schematic section through an echinoid showing internal structure. The tube feet and sieve plate are attached to the water circulatory system.

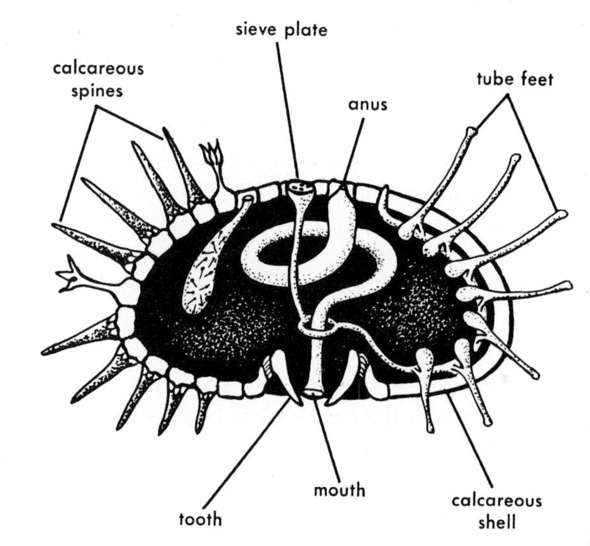

Fig. 10-37. A cystoid, *Pleurocystites*. Compare the calyx of the cystoid with that of the blastoid and crinoid.

urchins. The soft parts of the body of the animal are encased in a rigid and spinose test or shell composed of many symmetrically arranged plates. These shells are usually flattened on one side and globular or oval on the other. Unlike others of the echinoderms they do not have free arms or a stem. One group has a regular radial pentamerous (five-sided) symmetry, but a second group known as the irregular echinoids has an irregular arrangement of the plates. The earliest known echinoids have been found in the Middle Ordovician rocks, and they have continued to inhabit the seas of the world ever since.

Cystoidea. This group first appeared in the Middle Ordovician, and the last of them have been found in rocks of the early part of the Permian Period. Some cystoids have stems, and others are stemless. They have globular or rounded tests that are composed of calcareous plates. These vary in number from 13 to as many as 200, and they may or may not be arranged systematically giving the plate arrangement symmetry. The central part of the animal, the calyx, is covered by a large number of calyx plates that are tetragonal, pentagonal, hexagonal, or irregular. In some these are arranged in patterns; others lack arrangement. Each of the calyx plates is perforated by a tiny tube. The cystoids are classified according to the type of these pores. The cystoids have arms that waved in the water probably

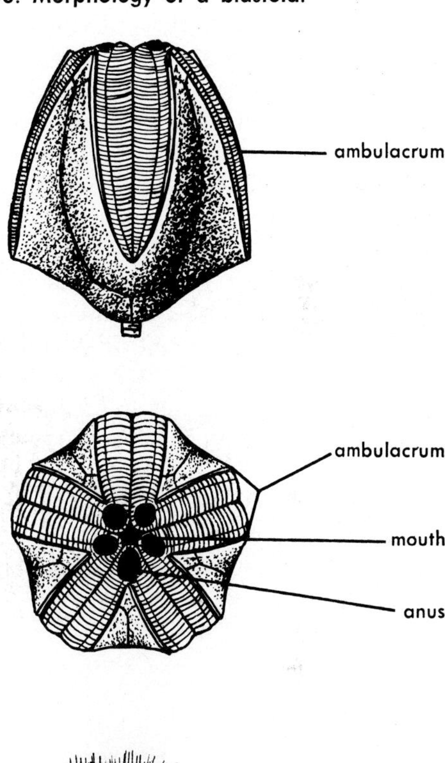

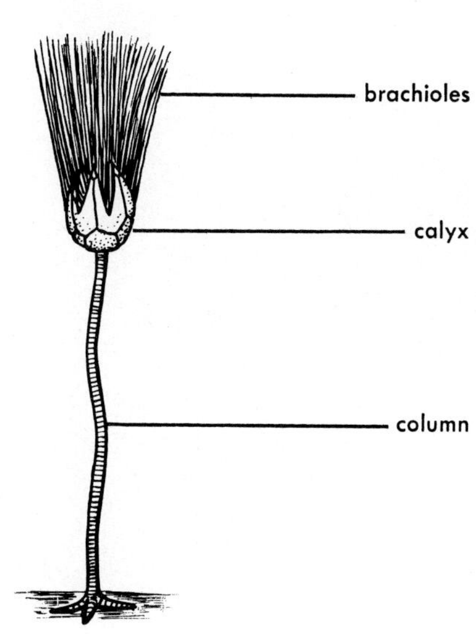

Fig. 10-38. Morphology of a blastoid.

aiding in the gathering of food by setting up currents moving toward the mouth.

Blastoidea. The blastoids possess a budlike calyx in which there is a definite number and arrangement of the plates. A large number of arms called brachioles extends up from the calyx which is connected by a stemlike column to the sea floor.

Crinoidea. This group, the modern sea lilies and feather stars, has been common since the Early Ordovician. They live in large groups sometimes called gardens. Evidence of this comes from dredging of the sea floor which has occasionally produced as many as 10,000 individuals in one dredge. They live in the reef environments and seem to prefer clear water. The skeletons of crinoids are extremely complex. This makes them somewhat difficult to describe, but it increases their value for stratigraphic correlation. Essentially the animal consists of three parts, a calyx which encloses the principal soft parts and organs, the arms which extend above to provide currents moving food-bearing water toward the mouth, and the stem which connects the calyx with the sea floor. In this respect they are similar to cystoids. They also have a globular body, the calyx, enclosed by an armor of symmetrically arranged calcareous plates to which the arms are attached. They lack the pores in the calyx plates which identified the cystoids.

Fig. 10-39. A fossil crinoid, *Aesiocrinus*. (Photo by courtesy of the U.S. National Museum.)

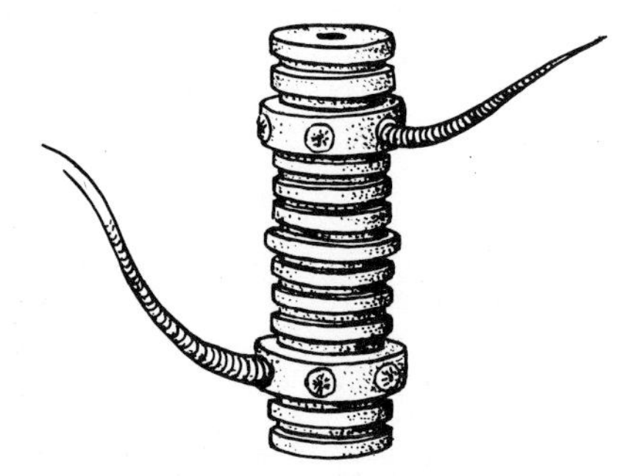

Fig. 10-40. Part of a crinoid column. The stem is the most commonly preserved part of the crinoid, or sea lily.

Asteroidea. The starfishes are very familiar inhabitants of the modern sea. They are star-shaped, having five or more flattened arms that radiate from a central disc. On the top side a small vent is located through which waste products are expelled. Near this opening is a pore called the madreporite through which water enters the water-circulatory system. On the bottom side the ambulacral grooves extend out from the centrally located mouth to the tips of the arms. A light-sensitive organ is located at the tip of each of these arms. Each of the ambulacra is bordered by a great many small tube feet, each of which has a suction disc. By variations in the water pressure within the water-circulatory system the tube feet may be extended or retracted, enabling the starfish to move or grasp with its feet. The top and sides of the arms are covered by small short blunt calcareous projections. Starfish have the amazing property of being able to rebuild an arm if it is torn off, and in some instances where the animal was cut into two nearly equal pieces each has survived, and two individuals have developed. Starfish date back to the Middle Ordovician as do most of the other echinoderms.

Fig. 10-41. A "garden" of sea lilies, crinoids, growing on the sea floor. (Photo by courtesy of the Chicago Natural History Museum.)

PLANTS

With the exception of algae, fossils of plants are rare in the stratigraphic record until the middle part of the Paleozoic Era. Since that time land plants have been relatively abundant, and the study of them has given us a sharper insight into the nature of physical and climatic history of the world at different times. You have undoubtedly noticed that the plants that thrive in various environments are strikingly different. In a swamp you find entirely different assemblages from those on a high mountain slope, in the great plains, or in a desert. So fossil plants are keys to ancient climates and environments. Plants have not been as useful in correlation as invertebrate

Fig. 10-42. One arm of a starfish. This illustration shows the water-circulatory system which is used to control movement of the tube feet.

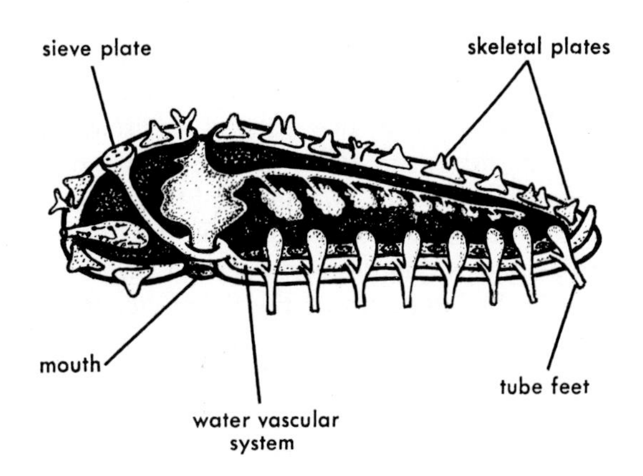

Fig. 10-43. A restoration of one of the first plants which has a vascular system. It is *Psilophyton.* Note that it does not have leaves. (After Dawson.)

fossils because most plants that are likely to be preserved as fossils do not live in marine waters. The continents are not often the sites of long-term deposition, and plants that fall to the ground on land are usually oxidized and decay rapidly. This leaves one type of environment that is particularly suitable for the preservation of plants. That is the swamps, and these are by far the best-documented part of the record. The peak of swamp development in the world came in the later parts of the Paleozoic, and it is from these swamps that our best and most dramatic plant fossils have been recovered. It would be misleading to mention no other way in which plants are preserved. Although they are relatively less abundant some important fossil plants are discovered in deposits of ash and dust, and occasionally in other continental-type deposits.

Correlation with plants' spores. One of the most important uses of plants for purposes of correlation has been found in the use of spores and pollen. These are microscopic in size and require special techniques of preparation and analysis. One reason they have great potential is that they may be blown around in the wind and thus be spread across all types of depositional environments. It is possible for them to become incorporated in sediments that will survive, whereas the trees from which they come may not be preserved.

Most of the fossils of plants are preserved through carbonization. The fossils are like pictures in carbon drawn on a piece of shale, coal, or some other rock. A great many of them look a lot like the pressed flowers made by putting a flower in a book and placing weights on it.

For those who have not had a course in botany a few simplified descriptions of some of the more important plant groups may be helpful. We have already mentioned the algae as the first well-preserved fossil we know, but unfortunately it is not possible to differentiate the various groups of algae. The blue-green algae, green algae, yellow and brown algae, brown algae, and red algae are all classified as separate phyla by the botanist, but we cannot make such distinctions. Most of what we find in the fossil record is calcium carbonate that apparently became trapped in the loosely suspended algae. Likewise most of the other very simple plants are not well represented in the fossil record, with one notable exception, the diatoms.

Diatoms. These single-celled plants are geologically the most important of all plants. Over large areas of the earth, mainly the oceans, they are the main organisms that carry on photosynthesis. They are the main food source for animals ranging in size from the single-celled animals to whales which consume tremendous quantities of these microscopic-sized plants. Probably more animals depend on them for food than on any other plant.

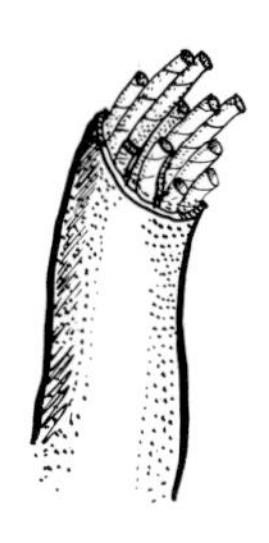
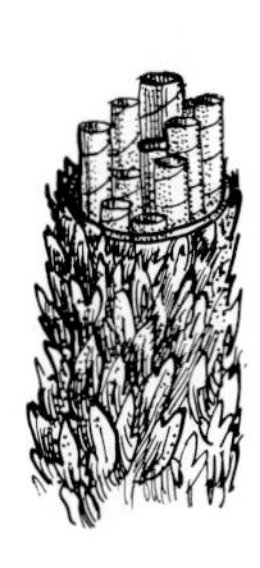
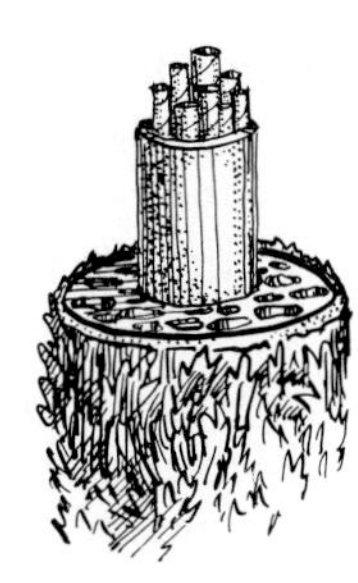

Fig. 10-44. Three plants. Increasing complexity has characterized the evolutionary development of plants. The simple plant at the left possesses tubes used to carry water and nourishment to the plant from the ground. In the middle the tubes are somewhat specialized so that some carry sap and at the right the stem is thick enough to support the plant making it possible to grow high above the ground. (Redrawn from *The World We Live In.*) (Courtesy of James Lewicki.)

Diatoms are very unusual in other respects also. They secrete a skeleton-like structure that is composed of silica. This remains after the plant dies and sinks to the sea floor where it is the dominant sediment over extensive areas, particularly in deep cold waters. The diatoms are highly varied in form. They possess some of the most beautifully intricate patterns. Each diatom possesses a droplet of oil, and for this reason and because of their abundance they are now considered as one of the most probable sources for the petroleum found in sedimentary rocks. They live individually and in small colonies in fresh and salt water.

Vascular plants

Characteristics. This group of plants, Phylum Tracheophyta, are characterized by vascular tissues. Vascular tissues are somewhat analogous to the circulatory system of some of the more advanced animals. It is through the cells of this system of tissues that the plants are able to obtain the supply of water and the mineral matter carried in solution in that water that they need for life processes. A vascular system is not very important for plants that live in the seas or in low areas where there is always an abundant supply of water. In such places almost every cell of the plant can be in direct contact with the necessary solutions. However, before plants could advance far onto the land surfaces it was necessary that they develop a system better than osmosis and diffusion for the transfer of these solutions. Most of the land plants that have a vascular system also possess other specialized organs to help satisfy the needs of the plant.

Fig. 10-45. Three stages in the development of modern plants. The early plants reproduced by alternate sexless and sexual generations. Sexless plant spores generated gametophytes which made sperms and eggs. The second stage was reached with the development of gametophytes which made only eggs or only sperm. In water the sperm could swim to fertilize the egg. In the last stage seeds developed permitting reproduction out of water. The seed holds the female spore until the eggs are born. Then the sperm is obtained from pollen, a male spore. The seed protects the eggs and provides it with the necessary food for the early part of its growth. ·(Adapted from *The World We Live In.*) (Courtesy of James Lewicki.)

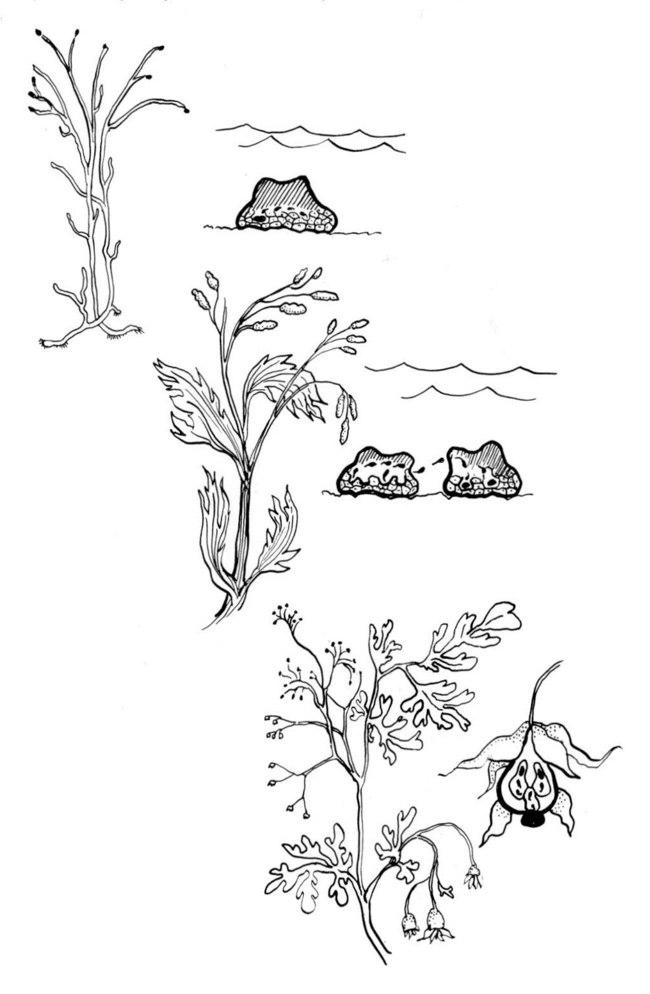

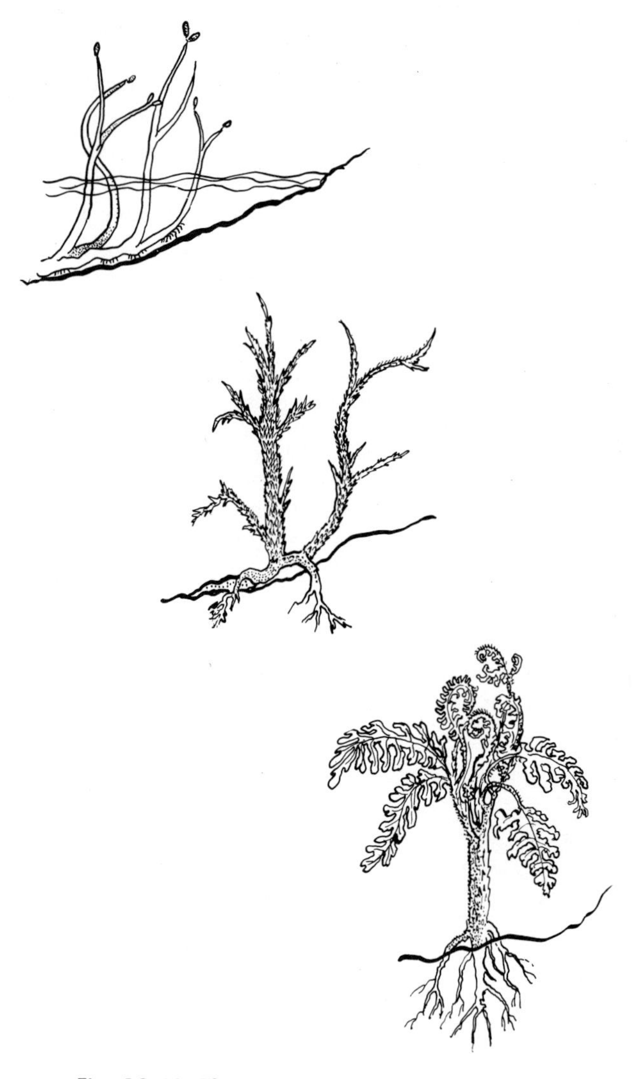

Fig. 10-46. Three stages in the evolution of modern root, leaf, and stem systems. The first plants did not have either roots or stems. In the intermediate stage the plant has very simple leaves and an elemental root system. The last stage shows the modern plant. (Adapted from *The World We Live In.*) (Courtesy of James Lewicki.)

These needs include the need for water and mineral matter in solution that are obtained from the soil, and sunlight and carbon dioxide that are needed from the air. In general these needs are satisfied by the development of a root system designed to absorb solutions from the ground, and leaves or specialized stems that can obtain sunlight and carbon dioxide.

Two other problems are encountered by plants that live out of water. The first of these is the need for some sort of supporting tissue. Plants that live in water simply float. They do not require any special features that will hold them up, but the land plants that grow high into the air must be strong enough to hold up their own weight. Thus all the true land plants have a specialized tissue designed to support the plant. The second major problem that is encountered by plants living on land is the mechanism of reproduction. In water the problem is simple because the gametes that must combine are suspended in a liquid that is favorable to their survival. In air they tend to dry out rapidly and die. Consequently specialized mechanisms of sexual reproduction had to evolve. The solutions to these problems provide the main means of classification used for the plants.

Subphyla

The vascular plants are subdivided into four main subphyla: Psilopsida, Lycopsida, Sphenopsida, and Pteropsida. Of these the Pteropsida are by far the most abundant group at the present time although others have been in the past geologic ages. A few of the main characteristics of each of these are given below. You should refer to any text on botany for more detailed descriptions.

Psilopsida. This nearly extinct group of plants included almost certainly the first plants that had a true vascular system. That system is the ultimate in simplicity. There are no roots in the true sense of the word. A part of the stem of the plant runs along underground and is somewhat specialized to serve the same function as a root. There are also no large leaves. A few have very small leaves, but in most the stems carry on the photosynthesis necessary to the life of the plant.

Lycopsida. Lycopods are sometimes known as club mosses. Like so many other plants they apparently reached the peak of their development during the later part of the Paleozoic Era, the Carboniferous. At that time lycopods grew to heights that are comparable to the present-day sequoias of the Western United States. Today these once magnificent plants are represented by a relatively small number of herbs. Lycopods possess true roots, and the stem is differentiated into stems and leaves. Their most remarkable characteristic is the development of two different kinds of spores. These are called microspores and macrospores. They develop into male and female gametes. Some of the ancient lycopods developed a mode of reproduction that was very much like the seeds of most modern plants. The eggs developed in a hard protected case and remained there even after fertilization.

Sphenopsida. You probably know this group as the modern horsetails that grow in profusion around many bogs and near streams. They are also known as the scouring rushes. They are different from the lycopods in that they produce neither seeds nor anything similar to seeds. Their stems are rather distinctive in that they are vertically ribbed and jointed. The leaves grow as a whorl at each joint.

Class Filicineae. *Pteropsida*. These plants are known as ferns. Probably the most distinctive feature of the ferns is the nature of the leaves. These range in size from a fraction of an inch to as much as 60 to 100 feet. In some these leaves are simple, but most of them are divided into leaflets. So a single large leaf may be subdivided into many smaller leaves giving the whole a lacy appearance. The ferns have a well-developed vascular system and although they are most commonly relatively small plants they grow to great heights as tree ferns in New Zealand today, and such plants were common in the coal swamps of the Carboniferous. Such trees grow where the climates are warm throughout the year and where there is moisture. Thus ferns are most abundant where there is warmth, moisture, and shade. Fertilization of the ferns depends on the presence of a thin film of water through which the sperms may move as they encounter and fertilize eggs.

Class Gymnospermae. The pines and other cone-bearing plants are the most prominent present-day representatives of this class, but others have been equally important in the past. Gymnosperms and angiosperms are both seed-bearing plants. In this they are distinguished from the other groups. The male gametophyte is a pollen grain which is usually able to drift in the air for long periods of time. It is resistant to drying. Once the egg is fertilized it develops into a seed, and finally the seed is dropped to the ground or in water where it

Fig. 10-47. Four important fossil plants: Lepidodendron, Cordaites, Sigillaria, and Calamites. All of these were abundant in the coal-forming swamps which covered the eastern interior of North America during the Carboniferous. Illustrated: Sigillaria (two forms), Lepidodendron, Calamites, and Cordaites.

may grow. The most primitive members of the gymnosperms are seed ferns of which there is a hangover from past times known as the ginkgo, or maidenhair tree. Other extinct or nearly extinct gymnosperms are the cycads, cordaites, and cycadeoids.

The conifers are by far the most common living gymnosperms. These are the cone-bearing trees such as pines, firs, spruces, cedars, hemlocks, cypresses, redwoods, and junipers. They are usually known as the evergreens, and most have narrow, needle-like or scale-shaped leaves. Some of them are deciduous and shed their leaves at the beginning of the cold or dry season. It is interesting to note that conifers now occupy environments that are somewhat less favorable for plant growth. The angiosperms have taken over the warm moist and temperate climates. Conifers grow in abundance over much of the temperate zone, but they grow in dry, cold, and windy regions as well. The male and female cones of the conifers are separate. Pollen usually has small winglike projections. The pollen is dispersed by the wind. Some of it eventually reaches a female cone where fertilization of the egg may take place.

Class Angiospermae. The angiosperms are flowering plants. They are the most important plants to man and most other vertebrates. Almost all of our fruits, vegetables, and cereals come from these plants. They are by far the most successfully adapted plants for life on the continents. They have a vascular system and seeds like the gymnosperms, but differ in the mode of reproduction in that they have flowering seed. It is this group of plants that is so closely tied in with insects which transfer the pollen from one flower to another, making fertilization possible.

The angiosperms are divided into two major groups based on the nature of the seed. Most of an angiosperm seed is made up of one or two leaflike structures that are packed with food. This food is used by the young plant as it begins to grow. If the seed has one such organ it is called a monocot; if there are two it is called a dicot. The monocots include: onions, grasses, sedges, tulips, lilies, and palms. Some familiar dicots are: carrots, peas, potatoes, squashes, sunflowers, spinach, blackberries, and almost all of the broad-leafed trees such as the oaks, fruit trees, magnolias, elms, maples, and peaches.

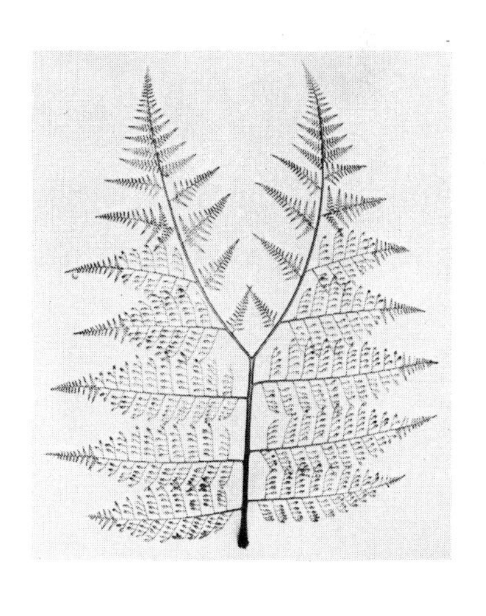

V EXPLORING THE PAST

11 A Pattern Is Set

The Continental Framework of North America

THE CONTINENTAL MARGINS

Beginning at least in the early part of the Cambrian and probably at some time in the Precambrian a pattern of sedimentation and diastrophism began in North America which continued throughout the Paleozoic Era. There were many variations in the pattern from time to time. There were transgressions and regressions of the sea across the interior of the continent. Several major orogenies took place, altering the pattern, but it continued recognizably until the end of the era. All geologists agree on certain parts of that pattern. It is agreed that the North American continent consisted of a central region, called a craton, which occupied the interior areas of most of North America. This area exhibited remarkable stability throughout the Paleozoic. Most of it was low-lying, and during most of the time it was near sea level. Shallow seas spread over parts of the craton, covering all of it at

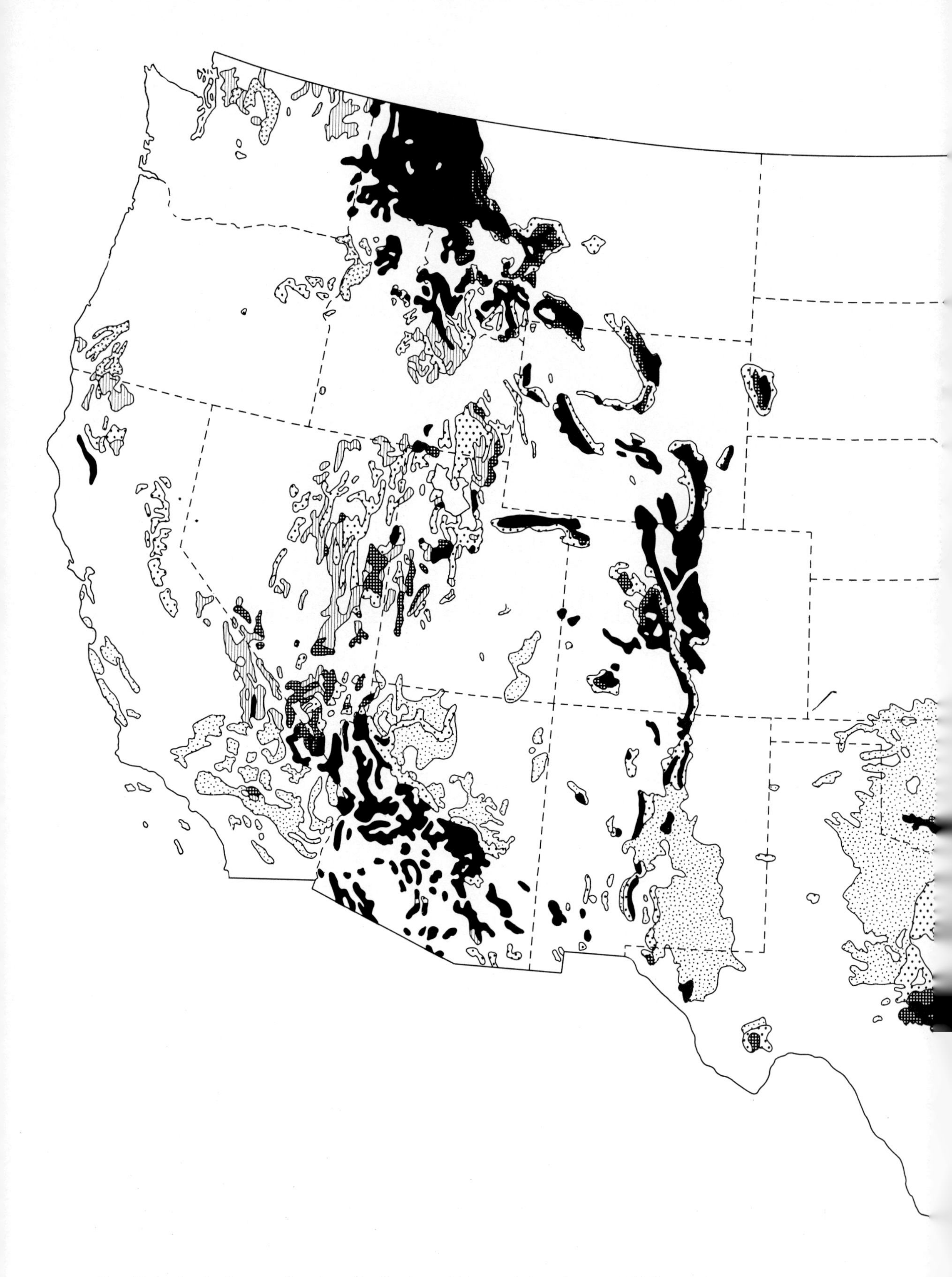

Fig. 11-1. Geologic map showing distribution of Precambrian, Lower, Middle, and Upper Paleozoic strata, and

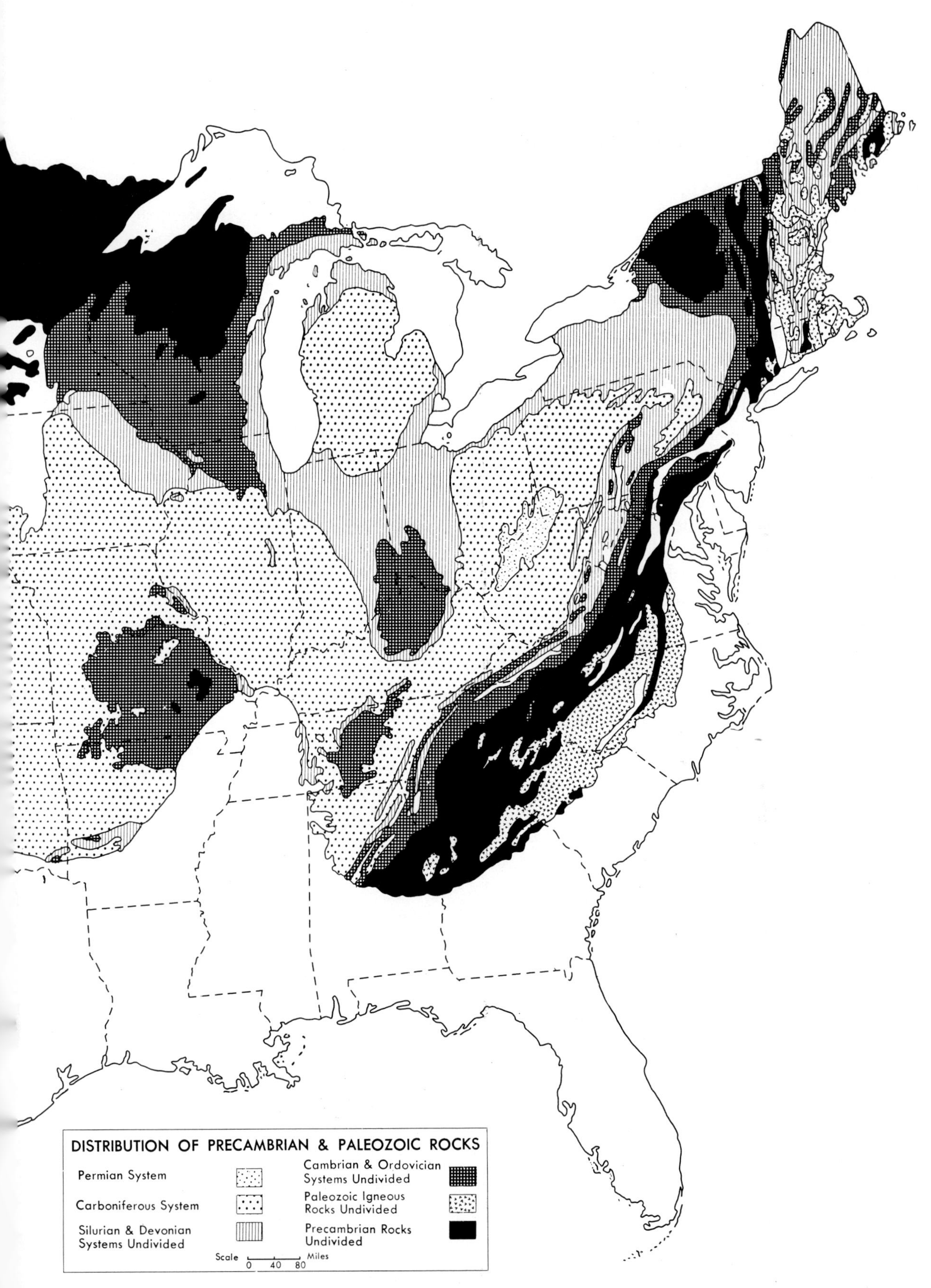

Paleozoic igneous rocks undivided. (Modified after *The Geologic Map of North America*, 1946).

times. Because the seas were shallow and the craton had low relief a slight change in sea level or a slight warping of the continent affected the shape of the seas. These slow changes went on almost continuously. A few areas in the craton tended to rise and stood higher than the surrounding plains most of the time. These areas include regions of the Adirondacks, the Cincinnati arch, the Wisconsin Upland, the Ozark Mountains, and probably a large part of the Canadian Shield. The boundary of this stable region extends along a line from eastern Labrador through Quebec, just east of the Adirondacks, and from there southward along the Appalachian upland. It swings westward about Birmingham, Alabama, and goes north of the Ouachita Mountains of Arkansas and Oklahoma. At the Rocky Mountain front it turns northward and follows the eastern front of the mountain system.

Long, narrow, troughlike depressions called geosynclines existed in the areas now occupied by the Appalachian Highlands and its northern extension into Newfoundland, by the Ouachita Mountains, and by the Rocky Mountains. Great thicknesses of sediments accumulated within these geosynclinal belts as compared with those deposited on the craton. But most of the sediments in the geosynclines were shallow-water sediments. The geosynclines were belts of mobility in the crust, and the bottom of these troughs must have become depressed as new sediments were deposited; so the sea bottom stayed relatively shallow in spite of the thick accumulation.

At this point general agreement as to the nature of the pattern ends, and controversy begins. Several views are held regarding the nature of the continental margins during the Paleozoic. The two hypotheses which are most commonly held are:

1. That the continental margins outside the geosynclines consisted of crystalline continental borderlands.
2. That the geosyncline consisted of two parts, a shallow trough near the craton and a more deeply subsiding trough on the oceanward side of the continent in which chains of volcanic islands stood. These are thought to be very similar to the island-arc systems that characterize the margin of the Pacific Ocean today.

Why there are two hypotheses

Before going into the evidence that supports each of these hypotheses let us examine the circumstances that allow two such strikingly different concepts, each supported by leading authorities, to exist. Usually controversies come about as a result of insufficient data or inconclusive facts. Such is the case regarding the Paleozoic continental margins. There are few places where Paleozoic strata are exposed near the present continental margins. In the eastern and southern United States the margins are covered by wide expanses of sedimentary rocks of Mesozoic and Cenozoic ages. These sediments are so thick along the Gulf Coast that no wells have penetrated deep enough to hit the lower part of the Paleozoic sections. In the southeastern United States the Mesozoic section is underlain by rocks similar to those of the Piedmont of Virginia. These are crystalline metamorphic and igneous rocks of Precambrian and Paleozoic age which contain no fossils. Farther north along the eastern coast the Paleozoic sections are exposed near the ocean, but unfortunately for the purposes of solving this problem they have been complexly folded and deformed in several orogenies that occurred during the Paleozoic. The section in that part of the country is further complicated by the scarcity of fossils in the exposed units of the early Paleozoic. Along the western coast of North America very few Paleozoic sedimentary rocks are exposed in the areas that would have been located in the crystalline land mass or in the geosyncline or island-arc system during the Paleozoic. Those areas are either covered by thick sections of younger sediments and lava flows or by the Pacific Ocean, or they have been eroded away as a result of post-Paleozoic uplift and erosion.

The borderland hypothesis

The pattern or framework of the North American continent as postulated by Professor

Charles Schuchert is sketched in Fig. 11-2. The main elements include the central stable region; the two major geosynclines, the Appalachian in the east and Cordilleran of the west; two embayments, the Ouachita and Sonoran; and a number of continental land masses, Appalachia, Llanoria, Cascadia, and others.

Schuchert's borderland hypothesis followed the failure of two earlier concepts of the continental margins devised by J. D. Dana to explain all the facts known at that time about the stratigraphy of the margins.

Marginal reefs. The first of Dana's ideas, presented in 1856, was that a great reef or sand bank lay off the eastern shore of the main North American continent separating the Atlantic Ocean from a vast lagoon along the edge of the continent. He suggested that the southward-flowing Labrador current carried most of the sediment deposited along the shores of the continent during the Paleozoic. When the structure and stratigraphy of the eastern United States had been studied in sufficient detail it became apparent that the Green Mountains of Vermont had been formed during the Paleozoic. These lie exactly in the

Fig. 11-2. Borderland hypothesis. This theory is schematically represented in this outline map of North America during the Paleozoic showing the geosynclines and borderlands postulated by Schuchert. (Modified after Charles Schuchert.)

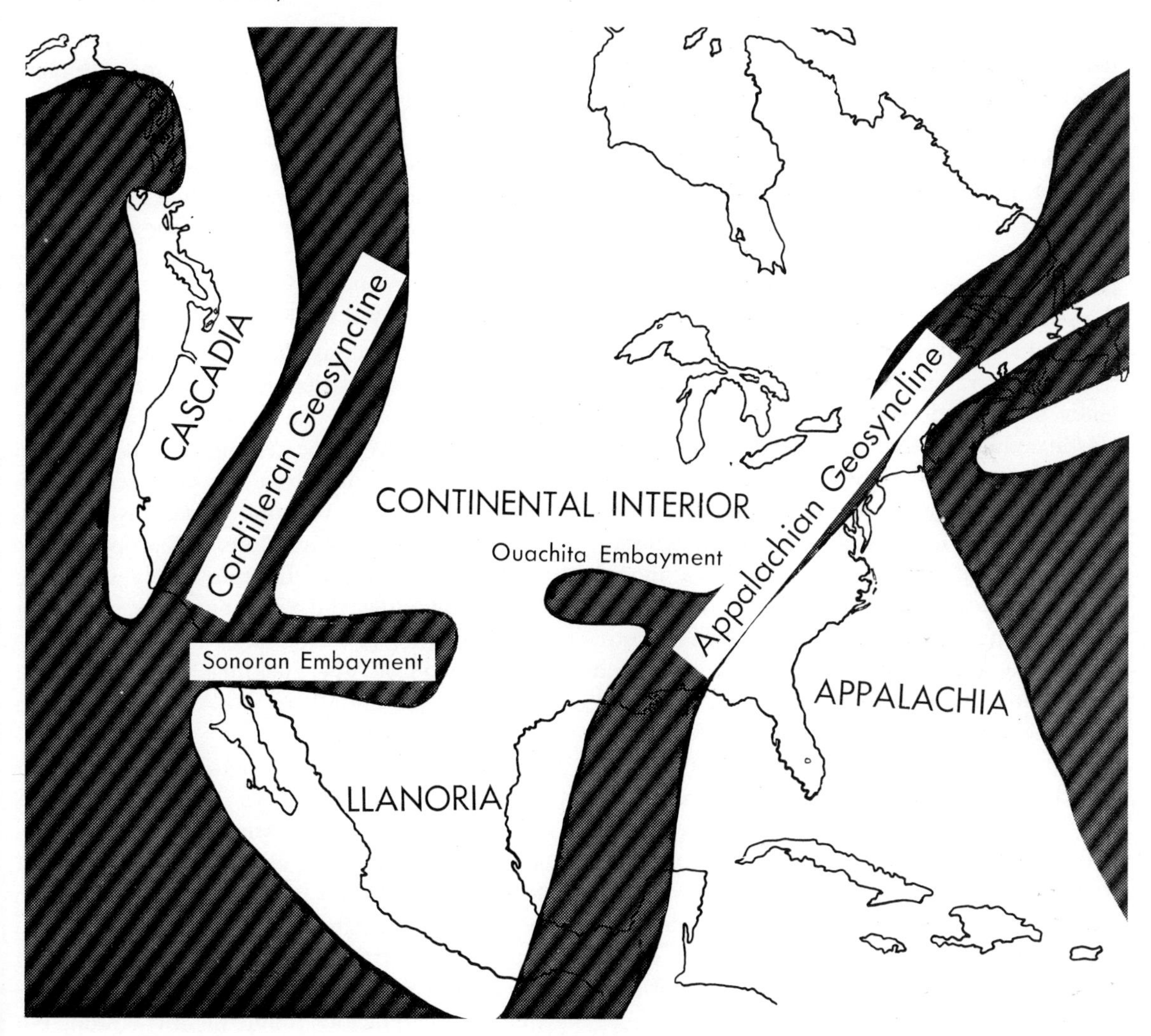

path Dana postulated for the Labrador current. The current had to be in that position to bring in the sediments now exposed in the region south and west of New England. Recognizing that his earlier theory was wrong Dana formulated a new hypothesis.

Marginal crystalline ridges. In place of the marginal reefs Dana postulated that marginal crystalline ridges of Precambrian rocks rose before the start of the Paleozoic Era. He suggested that these occupied the position of the large exposures of crystalline rocks now exposed in the Sierra Nevada and Rocky Mountains in the west and in the Blue Ridge and Piedmont along the east coast. These old uplifted areas were supposed to be the source of the sedimentary rocks that are now found on the continental margins. Unfortunately this theory met with failure also. It turns out that most of these crystalline rocks are not even Precambrian in age, that Dana's marginal ridge on the eastern coast did not rise until the end of the Paleozoic, and that the ridge on the west coast was not uplifted until late in the Mesozoic Era.

Borderlands. It was at this time that the borderlands were first postulated. They were postulated in order to provide a source area for the sediments that are definitely known to have been laid down in the geosynclines that bordered the craton. Why should such borderlands be located off the coasts? Many of the clastic sediments that are found in these geosynclinal accumulations thicken toward the east along the east coast. Such eastward coarsening is found in beds of Ordovician, Silurian, and Devonian age at various places in the eastern United States. In 1897, to account for these sediments, Dr. H. S. Williams first postulated a now lost land mass which he called Appalachia. Appalachia was located in a very convenient position off the eastern coast out on the continental shelf. In this position Appalachia could easily provide an explanation for the observed gradation in size of sediment. The absence of a comparable land mass in that position today was accounted for by the conjecture that the continent had subsided into the ocean. Modern geophysical studies of the nature of the continental margins do not support this view of a sunken continent.

One of the leading proponents of borderlands was Charles Schuchert. His concepts of these lands have been widely accepted. The eastern borderland, Appalachia, occupied the area of the present Piedmont and coastal plains and extended out into the Atlantic Ocean an indeterminate distance. Cascadia occupied the area of the modern coast ranges and extended out into the present Pacific Ocean. A third major borderland occupied the present site of the Gulf Coast and Gulf of Mexico. According to Schuchert these elements persisted as dominant features of the continental framework throughout all of the Paleozoic Era.

Theory of marginal volcanic geosynclines and island arcs

For many years the concept of marginal borderlands had few vocal critics, although even as early as 1856 Dana rejected the idea:

> . . . On the idea that the rocks of our continent have been supplied sands and gravel from a continent now sunk in the ocean . . . the whole system of progress . . . is opposed to it. The existence of an Amazon on any such Atlantic continent in Silurian, Devonian, or Carboniferous times is too wild an hypothesis for a moment's indulgence.

Hans Stille was the first to recognize the existence of two belts along each of the North American coasts, one of which contains primarily nonvolcanic sediments and a second located farther out from the continent which was the loci for volcanic intrusions and extrusions of great magnitude. He proposed the term "eugeosyncline" for the deeply subsiding belts containing the volcanic rocks. Professor Marshall Kay and Professor A. J. Eardley have been two of the leading proponents of this concept, and their works form the basis for this discussion.

Fig. 11-3 shows a generalized location for the two early Paleozoic geosynclinal belts which bordered North America during the era according to this hypothesis. The position of these belts changed later in the Paleozoic. On both coasts the inner belts are characterized as long, narrow troughlike depressions containing thicker accumulations of marine sediments than those typically found on the craton, but

Fig. 11-3. Island-arc hypothesis. The alternative to the borderland hypothesis is a theory that the craton, stable continental interior, was separated from the deep ocean basins by miogeosynclinal belts in which sandstones and limestones accumulated. Further from shore in the eugeosynclinal belt great thicknesses of graywacke, sandstones, lavas, limestones, and shales accumulated. Island arcs similar to those of the Pacific and Caribbean occupied these outer belts. (After Marshall Kay and E. Raisz.)

not so thick as those sections deposited farther out in the eugeosynclines. These inner belts, called miogeosynclines, are further distinguished by the absence of volcanic sediments in them. They contain thick sections of sandstone, shale, and limestone. The eugeosynclines are located farther out from the craton. They more or less parallel the miogeosynclines but are much more active belts in which subsidence is more pronounced allowing more sediments to accumulate. These belts are distinguished by the presence of igneous intrusions and extrusions yielding layers of lava flows, volcanic ash mixed with clastic sediments, and graywacke. The paleogeography of the North American continental borders in the Paleozoic Era resembles that of one of the island-arc systems of the Pacific Ocean today. Perhaps deep-sea trenches extended along the eastern margin of a festoon of volcanic islands, such as the Aleutians or Japanese islands, and were separated from the main continent by a relatively shallow sea.

Evidence. Before accepting such a theory we should examine at least a part of the evidence advanced to support this increasingly popular concept. It is unnecessary to detail the evidence for the miogeosyncline since there is little controversy as to the nature, location, or age of these units most of which are highly fossiliferous.

Kay (1951) points out that there are thick

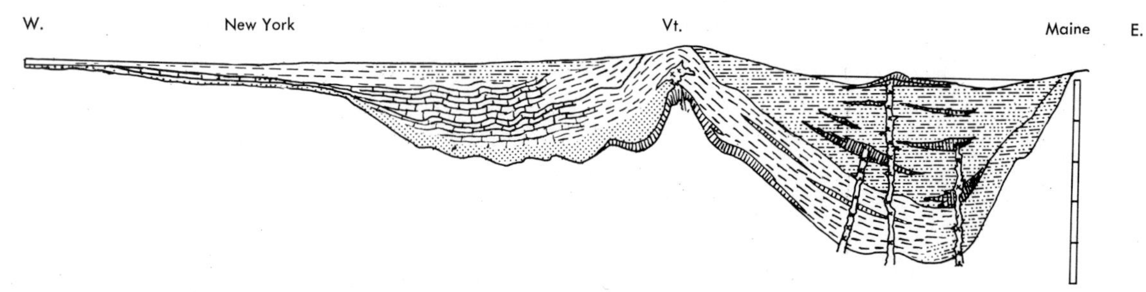

Fig. 11-4. New York to Maine. Section across the eugeosynclinal and miogeosynclinal belts from New York to Maine in the middle of the Ordovician Period, according to Kay. (After Marshall Kay).

sections of sedimentary rocks which contain volcanic rocks in Newfoundland and in New England. These sections include rocks of Cambrian, Ordovician, Silurian, and Lower Devonian series. Similar sequences which are of unknown age because they lack fossils are found in the Piedmont region of the eastern United States. It is likely that these rocks are also of Early Paleozoic age.

Evidence from the Cambrian System. The general nature of the evidence has already been summarized in the foregoing passages. These generalizations are here documented by quotations from two of the men who have carried on a large part of the research on this problem. The quotations below show the nature of their argument and the reason for their decisions.

The oldest volcanic-bearing sequences lie conformably or unconformably below fossiliferous Cambrian rocks and have been variously classified as late Pre-Cambrian or Lower Cambrian. . . . In eastern Newfoundland, thousands of feet of sediments with associated basalt and rhyolitic flows

Fig. 11-5. Cross sections across North America. The top section depicts the present topography. The second profile is drawn to represent a section during the Cambrian Period according to the theory of borderlands. The bottom section represents a profile in the Cambrian according to the island-arc hypothesis. (After Marshall Kay and Schuchert and Dunbar.)

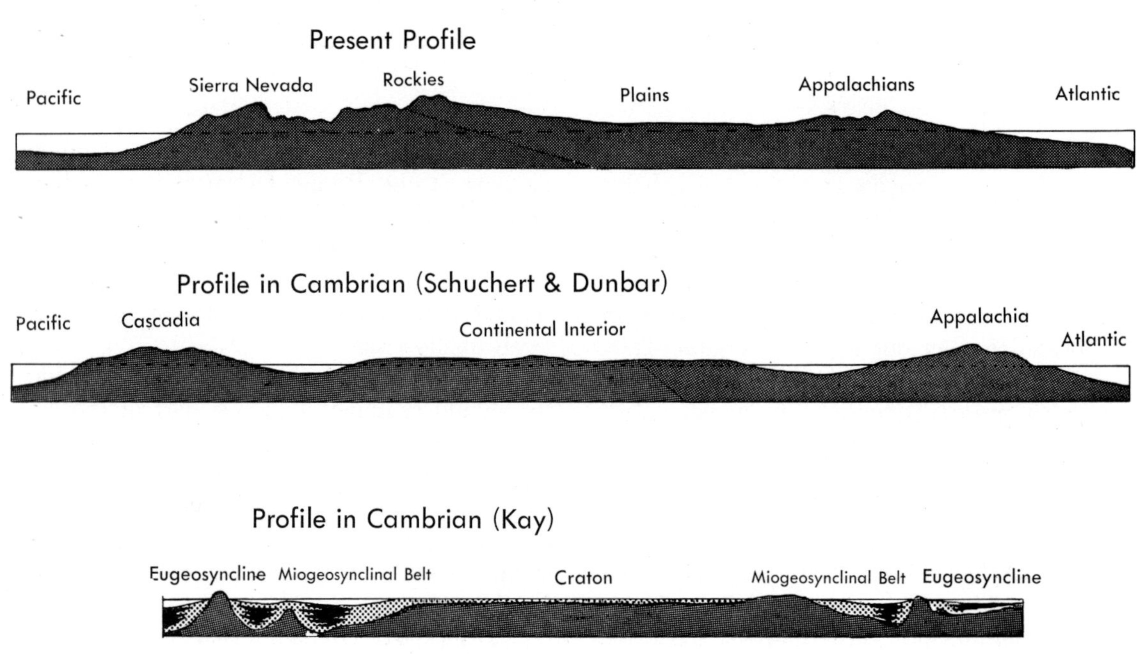

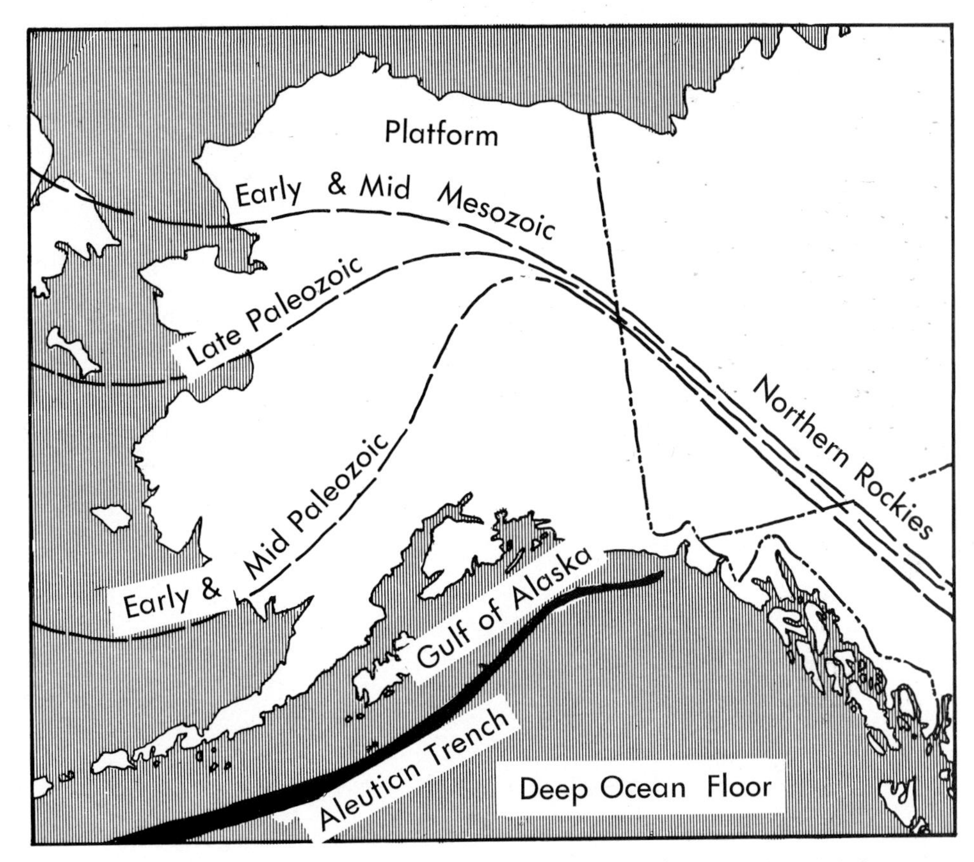

Fig. 11-6. Deformation affecting Alaska. The black lines show the belts of deformation that have affected Alaska during the Paleozoic and Mesozoic Eras. In this region successively younger deformed belts lie to the north and east.

and fragmentals lie unconformably below fossiliferous Lower Cambrian. Lower Cambrian fossiliferous arenites and argillites of Cape Breton, Nova Scotia, contain and overlie felsite lavas and granite pebble-bearing conglomerates overlapping plutonic rocks. . . . Far to the southwest along the east side of the Appalachian Valley, basalt flows are in quartz arenaceous sediments (unicoi) in southwestern Virginia and eastern Tennessee. . . . In the Appalachian Piedmont from Pennsylvania southward, the Glenarm Series is folded, intruded, and unconformably overlapped by conglomerate beneath argillite (shale) bearing late Ordovician fossils; the Glenarm is Pre-Cambrian, early Cambrian, or even Ordovician. The Glenarm has lava and pyroclastic rocks.

These quotes serve to illustrate how Kay (1951) has documented the stratigraphic evidence which supports the concept of chains of volcanoes in eugeosynclinal belts off the North American coasts. Fig. 11-4 shows a section from New York to Maine across the miogeosynclinal and eugeosynclinal belts at the middle of the Ordovician.

Eardley (1947) summarizes his views on the nature of the Paleozoic Cordilleran geosyncline as follows:

The Cordilleran geosyncline in Paleozoic time consisted of two main troughs—a western, the Pacific, and an eastern, the Rocky Mountain. The sediments of the western trough from California to Alaska are characterized by a large amount of volcanic material and graywacke in every system. Phyllites, slates, argillites, schists, gneisses, recrystallized chert, marble, metaconglomerate, meta-andesite, and various metamorphosed pyroclastics make up the thick sequences. Great batholiths of Mesozoic age invaded the sediments of the Pacific trough; but in only one place, the Idaho batholith, did they reach the Rocky Mountain trough. . . .

The volcanic materials are nearly all andesites and came from the west. Since the sites of extensive accumulation of andesitic flows and debris today are in troughs adjacent to island archipelagos, it is suggested that a volcanic archipelago flanked the Pacific trough on the west. The Paleozoic graywackes and conglomerates also came from the west. . . . Several angular unconformities indicate orogeny in the belt to the west. The island archipelago was therefore a site of continuing orogeny during the Paleozoic.

Instead of a land of continental proportions, with a shore in western Montana, a volcanic orogenic archipelago is believed to have existed, which for the most part lay west of our modern coast.

REFERENCES

EARDLEY, A. J., 1947, Paleozoic Cordilleran geosyncline and related orogeny: Jour. Geol., v. 55, p. 309-342

KAY, MARSHALL, 1951, North American geosynclines: Geol. Soc. America Mem. 48, 143 p.

SCHUCHERT, CHARLES, 1910, Paleogeography of North America: Geol. Soc. America Bull., v. 20, p. 427-606

———, 1923, Sites and natures of the North American geosynclines: Geol. Soc. America Bull., v. 34, p. 151-229

12 The Cambrian Period

CLASSIC LOCALITIES OF LOWER PALEOZOIC STRATA

The Cambrian, Ordovician, and Silurian systems were first recognized in England between 1830 and 1879. The controversy leading to their recognition is here used to illustrate a type of problem that is frequently encountered in stratigraphic work. In the early 1800's the oldest system of rocks which had been recognized was the "Old Red" sandstone (Devonian age) which underlies the coal measures (Carboniferous age). Below the "Old Red" sandstone the rocks appear in places to be extremely complex. In some places they are complexly deformed and contain few fossils. These rocks were known as the "Primitive Series."

Sir Roderick Murchison was the first to recognize the Silurian System in the "Primitive Series." He is an unusual figure in geology for many reasons. He went to fight in the Napoleonic wars at the age of 15. After the wars he retired to his estate in Scotland to become

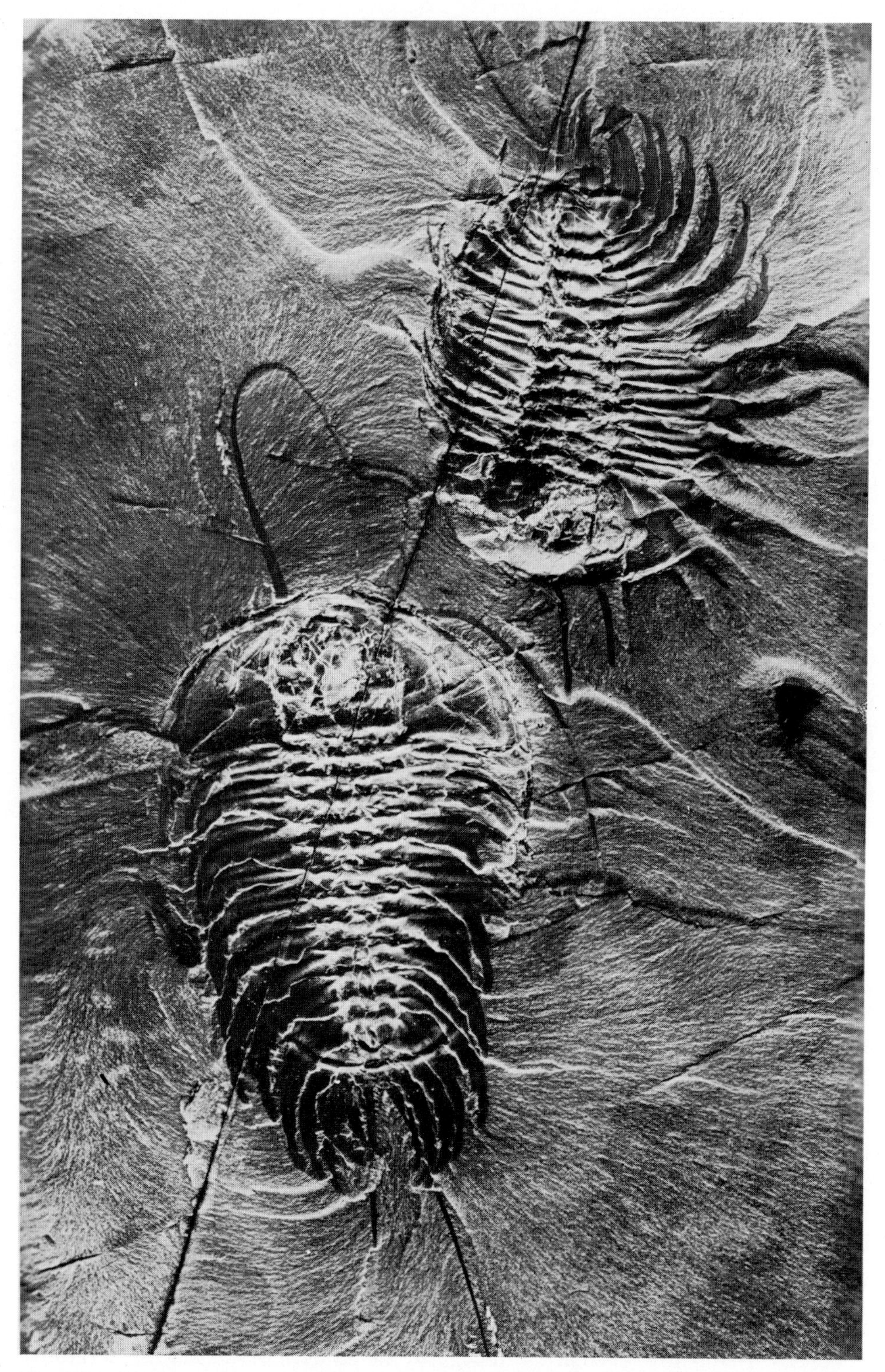

Fig. 12-1. Trilobites. These fossils of the species *Olenoides serratus* were collected from the Burgess shale which is of Middle Cambrian age. They are typical of the near perfect preservation of fossils in this famous collecting locality in British Columbia. (Photo by courtesy of U.S. National Museum.)

a gentleman of leisure, but was soon persuaded by Sir Humphrey Davy to go to school in London. There he came to know a prominent geologist, Adam Sedgwick, of Cambridge. Murchison was 32 years old when he became interested in geology, and he was largely self-educated in the subject. He spent much time with Sedgwick and in 1830 they decided to try to unravel the geology of the "Primitive Series." Sedgwick began work in the complex deformed area of northwest Wales, and Murchison started at the base of the "Old Red" sandstone in slightly deformed and fossil-bearing rocks (Fig. 12-2). About 4 years later the two men defined two systems of rocks in the two areas. Murchison published a volume, *The Silurian System*, 1838, describing the sequence immediately below the "Old Red" sandstone which he named for the Silures, a Celtic tribe found in the area during the Roman conquest. Sedgwick named the sequence he had studied in Wales the Cambrian System. It was assumed that the Cambrian System would be found to underlie the Silurian when the work

Fig. 12-2. Geologic map of North Wales. This region is the classic locality for Lower Paleozoic strata. The Harlech Dome in the center of the map is surrounded by Ordovician strata. To the east less deformed Silurian, Devonian (Old Red), Carboniferous (Carboniferous limestone, millstone grit, and coal measures are grouped together), and Trias strata are exposed. Northwest of the Harlech Dome and around the margins of the dome the geology is much more complicated. Note the metamorphic complex, and the igneous intrusions. (Modified after *British Regional Geology of North Wales* by Bernard Smith and T. N. George.)

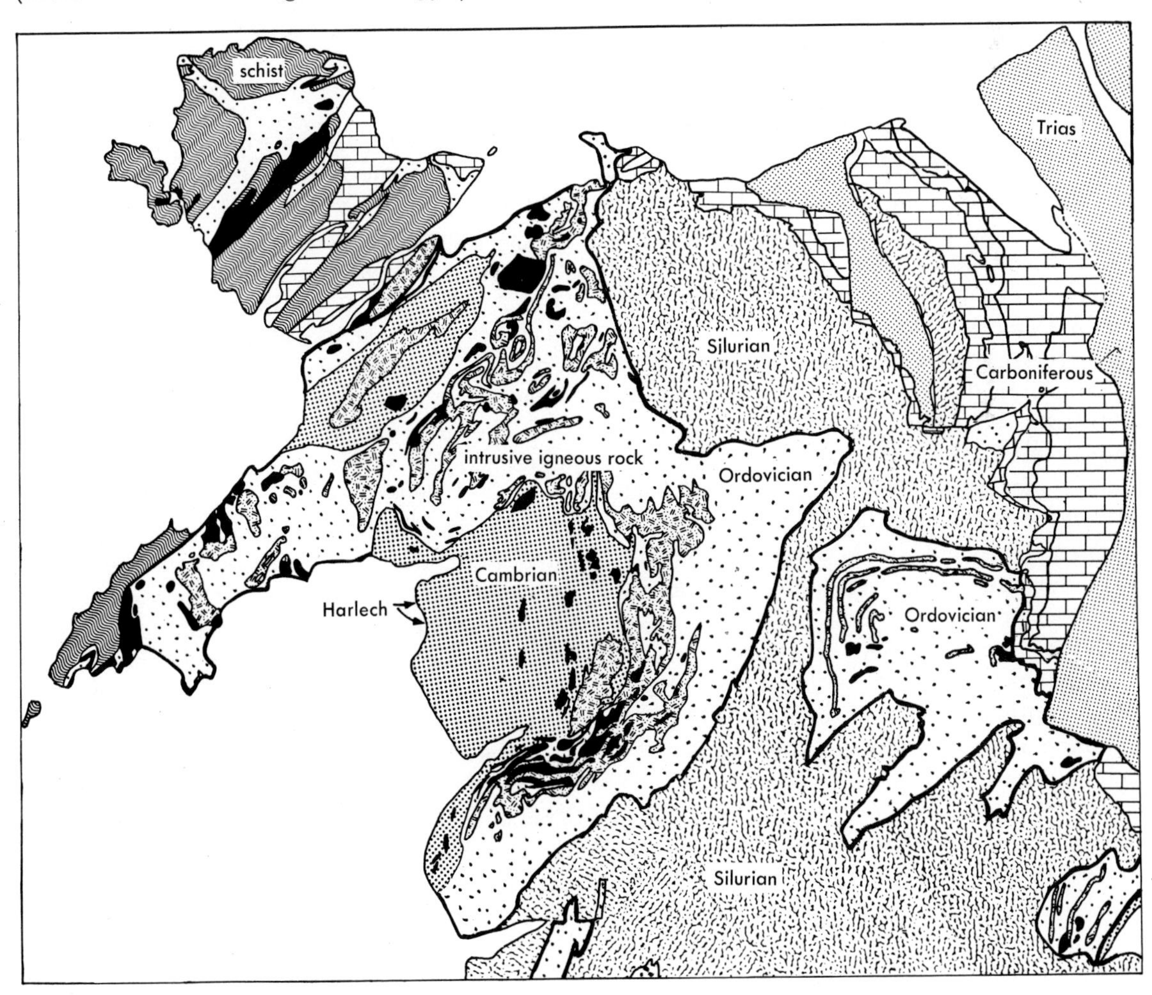

was completed. But as the two men continued their studies in areas closer to one another they found that the two systems overlapped. The lower part of the Silurian System was part of the Upper Cambrian. A bitter dispute followed with neither Murchison nor Sedgwick being willing to yield. Later Sedgwick discovered an unconformity in the Silurian which eventually became the basis for a solution in 1879 when Lapworth proposed a new system name for the rocks of the Lower Silurian. That name, Ordovician, is now almost universally accepted. Unfortunately it never resolved the dispute raging between Murchison and Sedgwick.

Geology of Harlech Dome, North Wales

Sedgwick chose the Harlech Dome as the place where he would begin his study of the "Primitive Series." The area has proven to be the best exposure of the Cambrian System in Wales. It is located in a high, rugged, and sparsely populated part of Wales. The section here is the type locality for the Cambrian System. It serves as a standard with which every other Cambrian section in the world is compared. Fossil fauna from the units near the Harlech Dome provides the key to identification of Cambrian rocks of the same ages in other areas. For these reasons the locality is important. In the following discussion the details of this section are given not as a memory exercise but to illustrate what a typical Cambrian stratigraphic section may be like. Then we proceed to see how the fossils found in this section may be used to locate rocks that are of the same age but of very different lithology in another area.

Harlech Dome Section. There are no Precambrian rocks exposed in the center of the dome, so it is possible that there are still older Cambrian units than those exposed near the center of the dome.

ORDOVICIAN STRATA: These overlie the Cambrian System unconformably around the edge of the dome.

TREMADOC: This forms a thick section of gray and blue mudstones and shales which are partially altered to slate. The section is several thousand feet thick.

LINGULA: These beds consist of two groups: one possesses rhythmically alternating layers of dark shale and compact fine-grained sandstone, probably of shallow-water origin, and the second group is made up of a thick sequence of black shales, slates, and bands of volcanic ash and lava. The whole sequence is about 4200 feet thick.

MENEVIAN BEDS: These are made up of very fine-grained black mudstone 300 feet thick.

HARLECH BEDS: These units display a rhythmic oscillatory nature of the sedimentation somewhat like that of the Lingula units. The sequence is composed largely of grits and shales. It is 6500 feet thick.

Gamlan shales		b
Barmouth grits	a	
Manganese shales		b
Rhinog grits	a	
Llanbedr slate		b
Dolwen grits	a	

Guide fossils. The fossil zones are the best indicators of time lines that we have in these sections. Thus for purposes of correlation they are extremely important. Without some way of relating sections in different places our history would consist of thousands of disconnected stories that would have little meaning. Trilobites, the highest form of life of the Cambrian, serve as the zonal indices.

The grits of the Harlech beds are unfossiliferous, and the only fossils in the series of slates and shales are worm borings, which are of little value for purposes of correlation. The Menevian beds are the earliest on the dome to yield many fossils. Most of these are trilobites. The one that appears in the lowest part of the sequence is *Paradoxides.* Higher in the section *Paradoxides* is accompanied by *Agnostus, Menevia,* and horny brachiopods. In the Lingula flags which overlie the Menevian beds the principal trilobite is *Olenus.* The overlying Tremadoc beds contain the trilobites *Shumardia* and *Angelina,* and the earliest graptolite remains found in Britain.

Discovery of the Lower Cambrian fauna. At the Harlech Dome no fossils were found in the lowest beds, the grits and shales; therefore we cannot obtain a guide fossil from that area for correlation. Later, however, it was discovered that there is an earlier fauna below the *Paradoxides* zone of the Menevian beds. That was found in the St. David's district of South Wales. Unlike the Harlech Dome area the Cambrian System at St. David's is in direct contact with the Precambrian rocks. Here the Precambrian is largely composed of volcanic tuffs. Over these tuffs we find the basal Cambrian unit, a conglomerate composed of quartz, quartzite, and tuffs that are unfossiliferous. The section is given below:

LINGULA SERIES: similar to those at the Harlech Dome: contain the same fauna as at Harlech Dome.

MENEVIAN SERIES: similar to those at the Harlech Dome: contain the same fauna as at Harlech Dome.

SOLVA SERIES:
- Gray flagstones: contain *Paradoxides aurora.*
- Green and purple mudstone and sandstones: contain *Ctenocephalus solvensis.*

GREEN PEBBLY SANDSTONES: contain *Paradoxides harknessi.*

CAERFAI SERIES:
- Red shales and purple sandstones: contain *Olenellus.*
- Green fine-grained sandstones; no fossils.
- Basal conglomerate: quartz, quartzite, tuffs.

PRECAMBRIAN:
- Volcanic tuffs: no fossils.

By combining the section at St. David's with that at the Harlech Dome it is possible to establish the index fossils for the time before the first *Paradoxides* found at the Harlech Dome. Using the same methods at other areas of outcrop of Precambrian, Cambrian, and Ordovician rocks the fossil assemblages characteristic of each part of the Cambrian System were gradually worked out for northern Europe.

Summary: technique of using type section

This technique of making use of the type locality and other sections to obtain a complete stratigraphic section may be summarized:

Strata at the type locality may contain some fossiliferous and some unfossiliferous units. These units are defined and described. The zones of each unit containing particular index fossils are described in detail, and take their names from those fossils which characterize them. At every new locality the stratigraphic section is studied and compared with the type section. It may be found to contain faunal zones above the highest or below the lowest of the type section. It may also reveal the existence of other zones within those at the type section, and it may contain other fossils that are not present in a zone already defined at the type section. And, of course, the new section may be less complete than the type section. Even an entirely different fauna may be found in rocks of the same age in another locality. Why is there so much possibility for variation? Remember that the fossil assemblages are like living assemblages; not all animals inhabit the same environment. Likewise not all parts of the world's seas are receiving the same type of sediment at the same time. We must remember that only a part of the surface of the earth is not subjected to deposition of sediment simultaneously.

Thus it is not particularly surprising to find that for the Cambrian the assemblages of fossils in Northern Scotland are very different from those found in Wales. Fortunately there are enough of the same trilobites in the two sections to make possible identification of the Cambrian System in Northern Scotland. Once this is accomplished it is possible to study the fauna there and establish new guides that are useful for correlation in that region.

Connecting the Cambrian System of North America with that of Europe. The Cambrian units in North America were first recognized on the basis of their position with reference to the Precambrian, and by use of faunal zones that contain fossil assemblages similar to those of England and Europe. In general, Precambrian rocks are described as "complex, highly metamorphosed, intensely deformed, or pri-

CAMBRIAN SYSTEM	HIGHLAND RANGE NEVADA	MONT.-WYO.	ARBUCKLE AND WICHITA MTNS.	VALLEY OF PENN., MD., AND VA.
CROIXIAN SERIES	Mendha limestone	Pilgrim limestone	Butterly dolomite Signal Mountain fm. Royer dolomite Fort Sill limestone Honey Creek fm. Reagan sandstone	Conococheague limestone
ALBERTAN SERIES	Highland Peak limestone Burrows dolomite Peasley limestone Chisholm shale Lyndon limestone Comet shale	Park fm. Meagher fm. Wolsey shale Flathead sandstone		Elbrook fm.
WAUCOBAN SERIES	Pioche shale Prospect Mountain quartzite			Waynesboro fm. Tomstown dolomite Antietam quartzite

Fig. 12-3. Correlation chart for the Cambrian System. Cambrian stratigraphic sections from four important areas in the United States are shown. Generalized lithologies are indicated by symbols (see chart on inside back cover). Blank parts of the section indicate that no strata corresponding to that part of the Cambrian time are found. They may never have been deposited, or they may have been eroded away. The vertical coordinate on this chart is time, not distance. Thus the chart does not indicate the thickness of the various units. (After Geological Society of America Correlation Charts.)

Fig. 12-4. Guide fossils for the Cambrian Period. The fossils depicted on this illustration are common guide fossils for the Cambrian. Those on the bottom row are guides to the Lower Cambrian, etc. While these are guide fossils the range of some of them far exceeded the part of the period they are here related to.

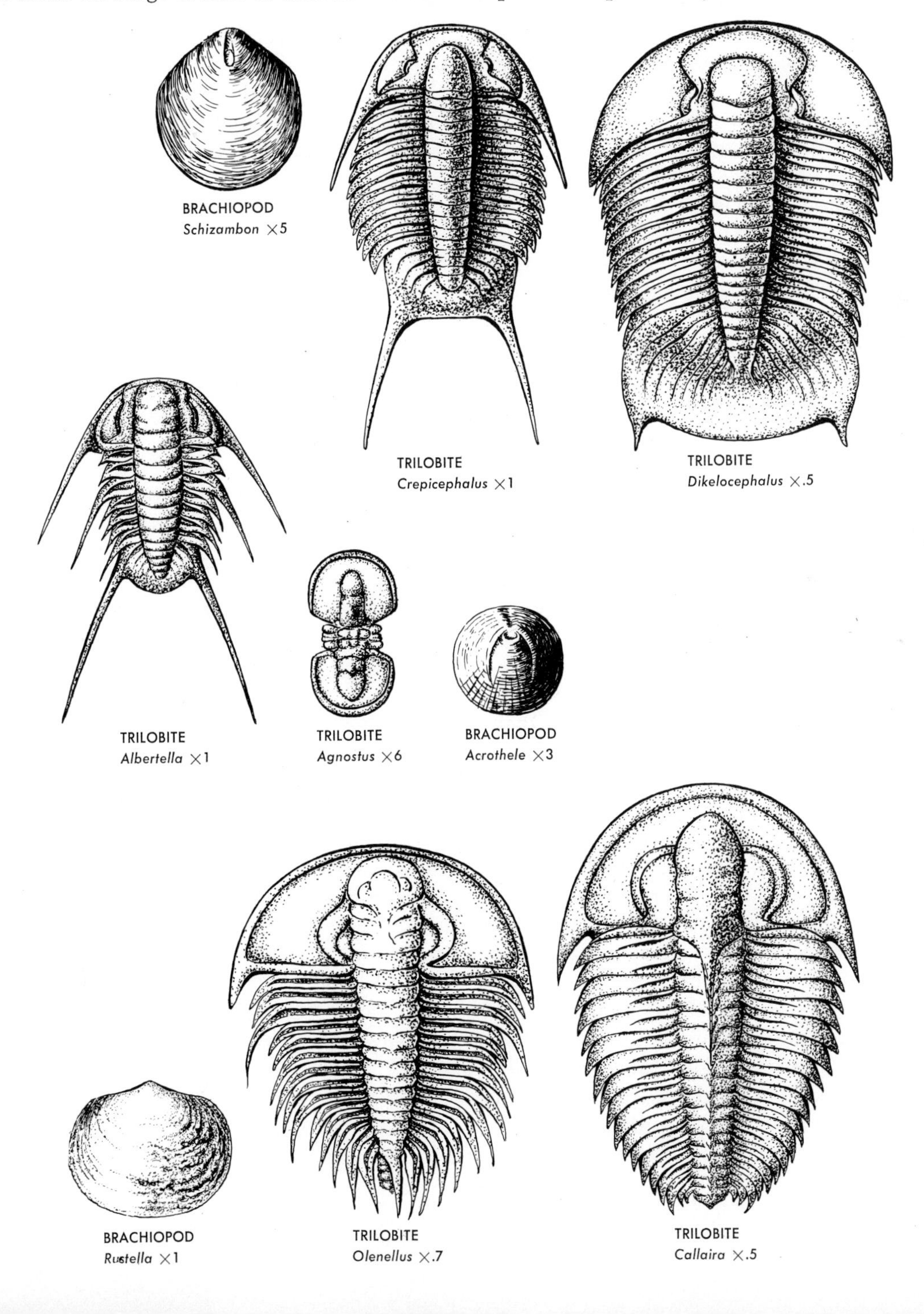

marily crystalline rocks." All of these terms do apply in one place or another; however, about the only valid generalization that can be made is that they contain few if any distinguishable fossil remains. In this respect they do not differ from most Cambrian rocks. There are in fact many unfossiliferous sedimentary and metasedimentary rock units which lie above igneous and metamorphic complexes which are dated by radioactive means as Precambrian. These are overlain by fossiliferous Cambrian or Ordovician rocks. The age of these rock units is still an open question awaiting the discovery of a fossil or a refinement of technique which will make it possible to correlate them with either Cambrian or Precambrian units. Their existence points out one important fact: that rock units dated by their stratigraphic position relative to the Precambrian are at best of questionable age. The use of faunal zones is much more reliable.

Cambrian rocks are well exposed in many parts of eastern North America where they were first correlated with the type section at the Harlech Dome.

DISTRIBUTION OF CAMBRIAN ROCKS IN NORTH AMERICA

Fig. 11-1 shows the distribution of Cambrian and Ordovician rocks in America. These lower Paleozoic rocks are exposed at the surface in areas which have been uplifted and eroded since they were deposited. More than 440 million years have elapsed since the Cambrian units were deposited in seas off the land areas of the world. In that time sea level has changed relative to the land masses many times bringing about submergence of parts of the continents and the deposition of other younger sediments. In places the thickness of these later sedimentary rocks amounts to many thousands of feet. At other times areas have been warped up, and the Cambrian and younger rocks have been eroded away. All of the United States has at one time or another been submerged beneath the sea and collected sediment. We now see Cambrian rocks exposed at the surface only where the area has been uplifted and eroded deeply enough to expose these lower units of rock. For this reason we should look for the Cambrian rocks in mountain belts around domes, and in deeply dissected regions. Exposures are found in the folded mountain upland which extends from Alabama to Newfoundland in the eastern part of North America and in the Rocky Mountain region in the folded belts and on the margins of the uplifted block-faulted mountains. Cambrian units are exposed around structural domes in the Adirondacks of New York, the Wisconsin Upland, the Ozark dome, the Black Hills, the Llano Uplift of Texas, and, in the Grand Canyon, the deeply dissected Colorado Plateau.

Cambrian rocks are often found in wells drilled for water and oil and in mines. The extent of their subsurface distribution is much less definite than surface outcrops. In many areas little drilling has been done, and other areas are covered by such great thicknesses of younger rocks that drills have not penetrated more than a part of the way to any existing Cambrian units. Other large areas such as the Piedmont in the eastern United States and most of the Canadian Shield have been stripped of any existing Cambrian rocks.

PALEOGEOGRAPHY OF THE CAMBRIAN

Any picture of the paleogeography of the early part of the Paleozoic will of necessity reflect the writer's views of the nature of the continental margins. Figs. 12-5 and 12-7 are restorations of the early Paleozoic reflecting different ideas regarding the continental framework. The concept of bordering volcanic islands will be presented here. The borderland hypothesis is documented in other Historical texts. There is little variation in the two theories in so far as the miogeosyncline and continental interior are concerned.

Lower Cambrian paleogeography

In the Early Cambrian time shallow seas occupied the eastern United States and Canada. The strand line extended from Labrador

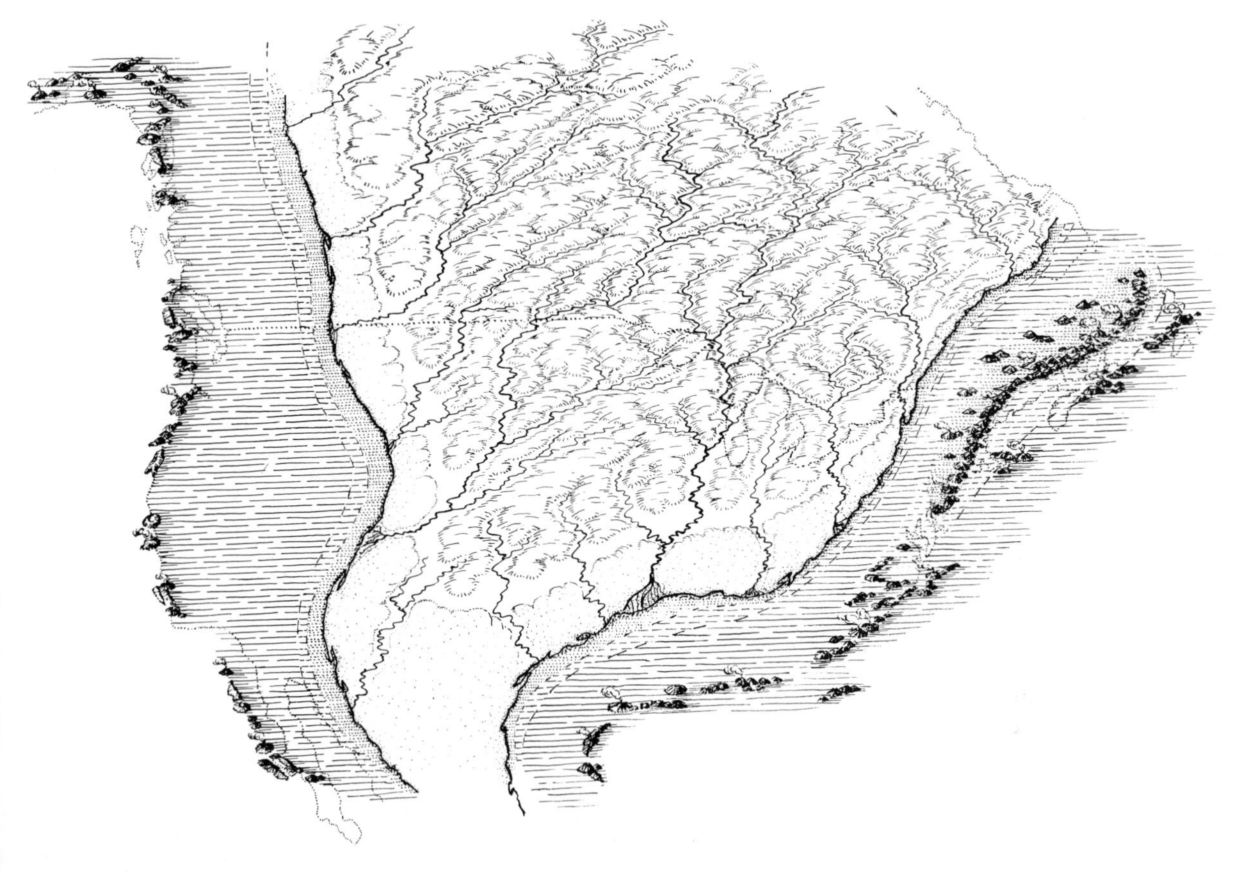

Fig. 12-5. Early Cambrian paleogeography. This drawing is a hypothetical representation of the North American continent in the Early Cambrian. Compare this drawing with the map showing distribution of Cambrian and Ordovician strata, Fig. 11-1. Such comparison will show that the detail both east and west of the continental margins is hypothetical. Volcanic islands are represented in the regions occupied by Appalachia and Cascadia according to Schuchert's theory.

southward along the St. Lawrence and east of the Adirondacks across central Pennsylvania, West Virginia, and eastern Tennessee. Its course from there southward is questionable. Along the coast, sediments were supplied from the low-lying continental interior. The waves reworked the weathered debris supplied from rivers and wave erosion and dropped out sand and clays. Further eastward limy sediments accumulated from the shells of marine animals, and calcium carbonate was precipitated in the sea. Further out from the continent a land mass stood which may have had southern extensions not shown here (Fig. 12-5). This extensive land area probably consisted of a large group of islands made up mostly of dormant volcanoes on the western side and more active volcanoes to the east. These supplied volcanic debris and lavas to that part of the eugeosynclinal belt in which they were located.

On the western coast the strand line ran approximately along the eastern side of the present Canadian Rockies, along the western border of Montana into Wyoming, across the eastern part of Utah and the western part of Arizona. As the sea moved inland, sands and pebble conglomerates were deposited near the shore, muds were deposited farther offshore, and limestones formed in the deeper waters. Some shales reappeared in the west, perhaps signifying another emerged area, but there is little detailed knowledge of this land.

Middle Cambrian paleogeography

The position of the eastern shore had changed little by the Middle Cambrian, but the land mass offshore probably had been worn

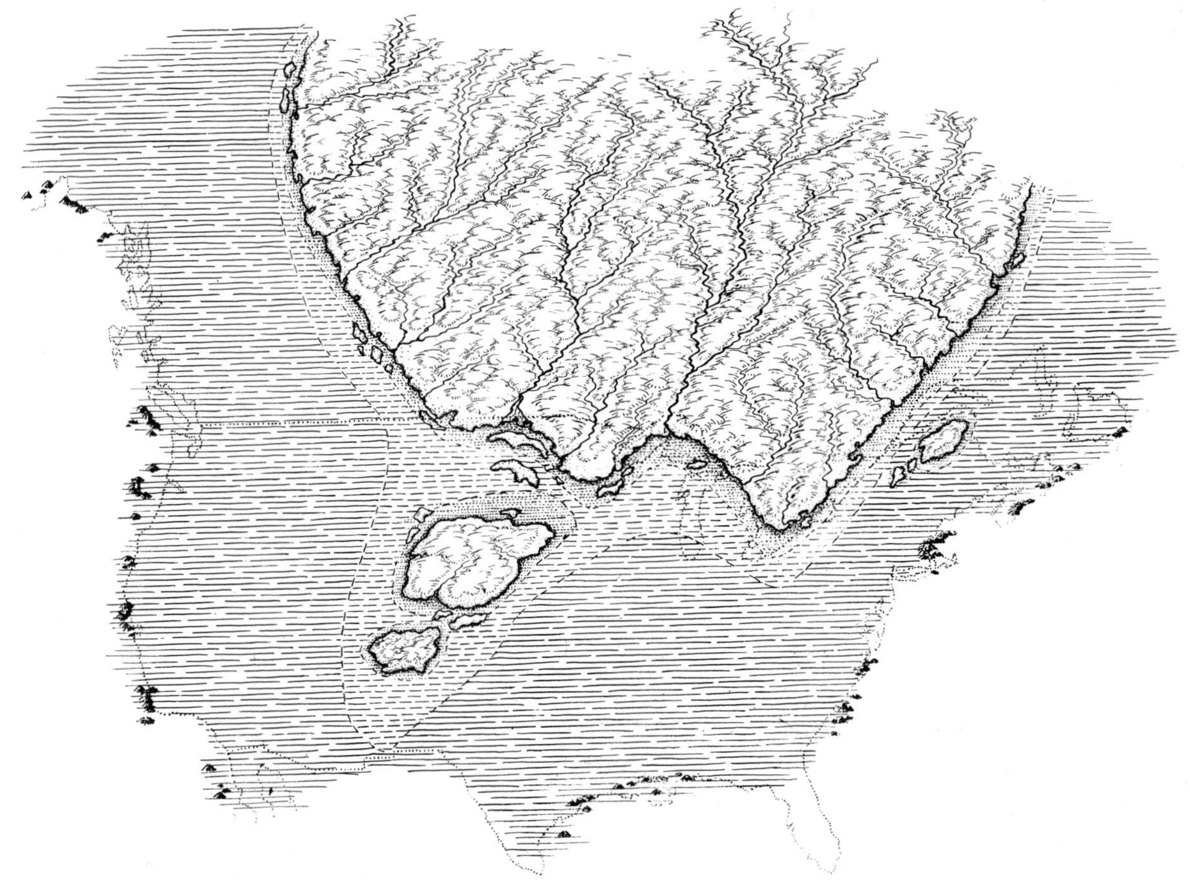

Fig. 12-6. Late Cambrian paleogeography (hypothetical). By the Late Cambrian, marine waters covered most of the United States. The transgression of the seas started much earlier, but by the time depicted here only a few areas remained above water. The land areas were located in northern New Mexico and southern Colorado, in northern Colorado, Wyoming, and Nebraska.

quite low, and little if any volcanic activity was going on in the area.

In the west the sea was encroaching on the continental interior. The shore line had shifted eastward into central Montana, extended across the middle of Wyoming and eastern Utah, and covered most of Arizona. The near-shore deposits were still sands and silts, and limestones were being deposited farther from shore over the Lower Cambrian sands.

Late Cambrian paleogeography

The seas continued to encroach on the continental interior through the Middle Cambrian and in the Late Cambrian. By the time of the Trempealeauian stage the sea had advanced over most of the United States leaving only a few isolated areas above water in northern New Mexico-Southern Colorado and the land called Siouxia by Schuchert, located in Colorado, Wyoming, and Nebraska. At the close of the period the seas withdrew from most of the continent in what appears to have been a world-wide lowering of sea level.

THE MEANING OF LAND BARRIERS

An example from the Cambrian of North America

Note the thin land mass which extends northeast from Appalachia on Schuchert's outline of North America in the Cambrian, Fig.

12-7. Compare this with the paleogeographic map of the Early Cambrian, Fig. 12-5. Regardless of the basis for other differences there is agreement about the position of this barrier. It is a land or island chain that stood out above water half a billion years ago, and vanished almost 400 million or more years ago, yet its presence and approximate position have been determined. It occupied an area which is largely covered by water today, and only a very small remnant of the area is now above water, and this present configuration is in no way connected to the ancient geography of the region. This leads us to ask how it is possible to know that any such land ever existed.

If you examine the outcrop map you will see that Cambrian units are well exposed in Newfoundland, Nova Scotia, New Brunswick,

Fig. 12-7. Early Cambrian seas. This drawing is based on Schuchert's work in which continental borderlands are assumed to lie off the coasts. Notice how the seas on the eastern coast are separated by a land barrier, just as they are in Fig. 12-5, which is based on the theory of island arcs. See the text for the significance of this similarity.

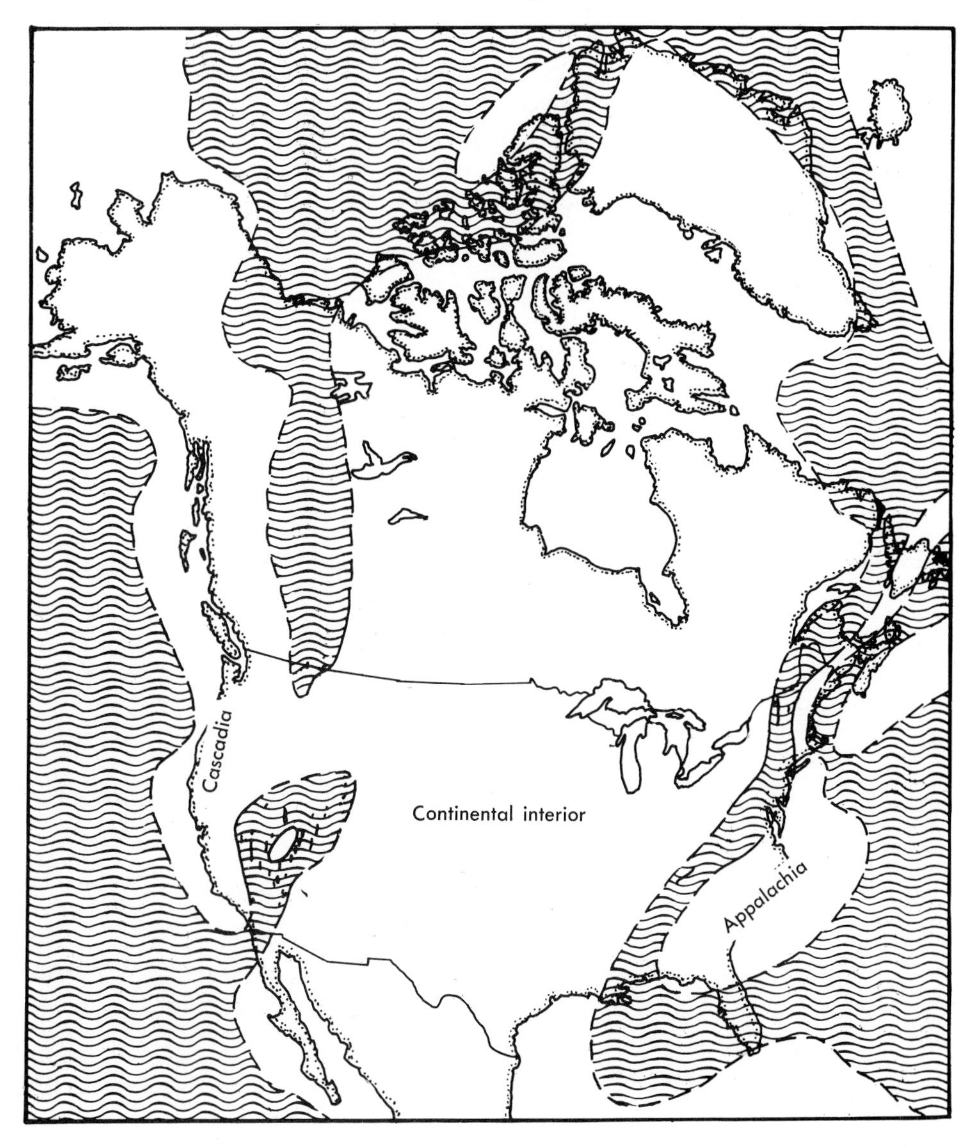

at Gaspé Bay, and at Boston and in the Green Mountains farther south in New England. Although these areas are close together a striking difference is found in the fossil content of the Cambrian beds in different parts of the area. It is seen, for example, that the assemblage of fossils found in the eastern part of Newfoundland is more nearly identical with that of the Harlech Dome in Wales than with the fossils in the western part of Newfoundland. The western Newfoundland fauna is like that found in the Cambrian of the Pacific coast of North America, in Scotland, and in most of the other Cambrian units in the Appalachian region of the United States. Because of this distribution the two faunas are sometimes referred to as the Atlantic and Pacific faunas. As in Scotland a few of the same fossils are found in some units of both provinces making correlation possible. For example, in New England a patch of St. Albans shale containing Middle Cambrian Atlantic faunas is found in an otherwise Pacific province.

The interpretation that is put on the distribution of these faunas is simple. The faunas must have been prevented from moving from the eastern area of Newfoundland to the west. Certainly no one can question their ability to move, since the same groups that are found in Wales occur in the eastern belt of North America, and the same groups are found in western Newfoundland and in the Pacific. What could have prevented their movement? A land barrier. Of course the type of land barrier cannot be determined from the fossil distribution. It could have been a large continental land mass or it could have been a row of interconnected volcanic islands. That the two faunas do mix in a place or two suggests that the barrier was not always continuous, but it did prevent large-scale migration of the faunas. The nature of the land mass is best determined from the nature of the lithology of the Cambrian units.

The possibility that Atlantic province faunas might have lived in the area of the Ouachita Mountains region in Arkansas and

Fig. 12-8. Temporal transgression and the Bright Angel group. This triangular diagram is a schematic representation of the variations in space and time of the Bright Angel group. Sections are shown at three different localities. Note the lithologies vary from one of these places to another. The rock unit lines cut across the time lines (black).

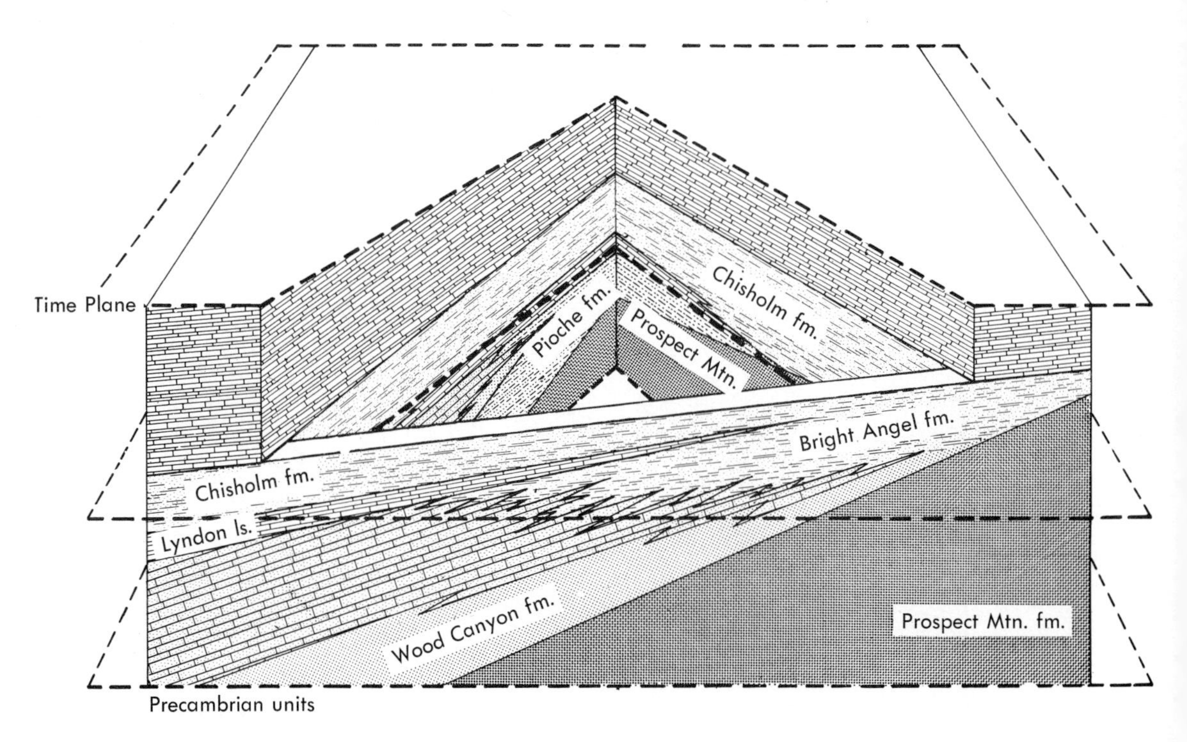

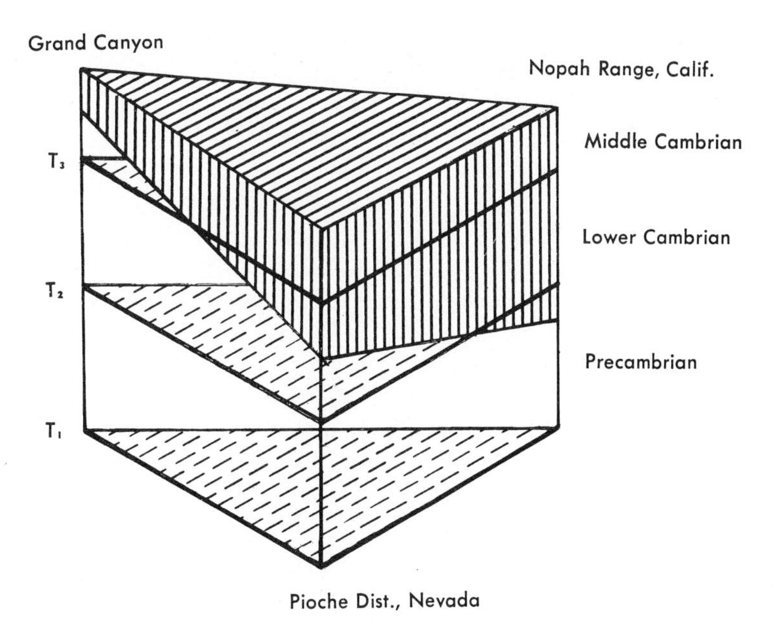

Fig. 12-9. Simplified representation of the data shown in Fig. 12-8. The time lines or planes are indicated as T1, T2, T3. The Bright Angel group is shown undivided by the striped pattern. (After H. E. Wheeler and E. M. Beesley.)

Oklahoma is suggested by the presence of Atlantic province faunas in the Ordovician of that region.

PRINCIPLE OF TEMPORAL TRANSGRESSION

The following study of the stratigraphy of the Cambrian units of the southern part of the Great Basin region in the southwestern United States is an excellent illustration of the reason for using a three-fold system of stratigraphic nomenclature, time, time stratigraphic, and rock units. The rock units involved are those of the Bright Angel shale and its equivalents in an area of more than 12,000 square miles over a triangular section of northern Arizona, southwestern Nevada, and southeastern California. The Bright Angel group of formations is underlain by the Prospect Mountain quartzite (also designated Tapeats and Sterling) and is overlain by the Middle Cambrian limestones (variously named in different localities).

The Bright Angel group is continuous throughout this area and is consistently in contact with the Prospect Mountain quartzite and overlying limestones. The type locality for the Bright Angel group is in the Grand Canyon of Arizona. Here it is above the lower part of the Middle Cambrian time line (Fig. 12-8). This is established by the presence of Middle Cambrian fossil fauna in the unit. (The fauna includes the genera *Clavispidella, Ehmaniella, Elrathia, Kootenia, Nisusia, Anoria, Glossopleua,* and others.)

At Pioche, Nevada, the Bright Angel group consists of the Pioche shale, Lyndon limestone, and Chisholm shale. Here the Bright Angel group lies within both the Lower and Middle Cambrian series. The lower boundary is indicated by the thickness of the zone containing the Lower Cambrian trilobite, *Olenellus,* and the upper boundary by the fauna of the Chisholm shale.

In the Nopah Mountain range of southeastern California the Bright Angel group is equivalent to the Wood Canyon and Cadiz formations. The top part of the Cadiz formation consists of 330 feet of Chisholm shale underlain by 30 feet of Lyndon limestone and 1200 feet of shaly and limy sediments overlying the Wood Canyon formation. The Lower Cambrian boundary, as established by the lowest occurrence of the *Olenellus* zone, is about 340 feet above the base of the Wood Canyon, making the lower part of the Bright Angel group Precambrian in age here.

Thus the different parts of a mappable rock unit, in this case the Bright Angel group, may have been deposited at very different

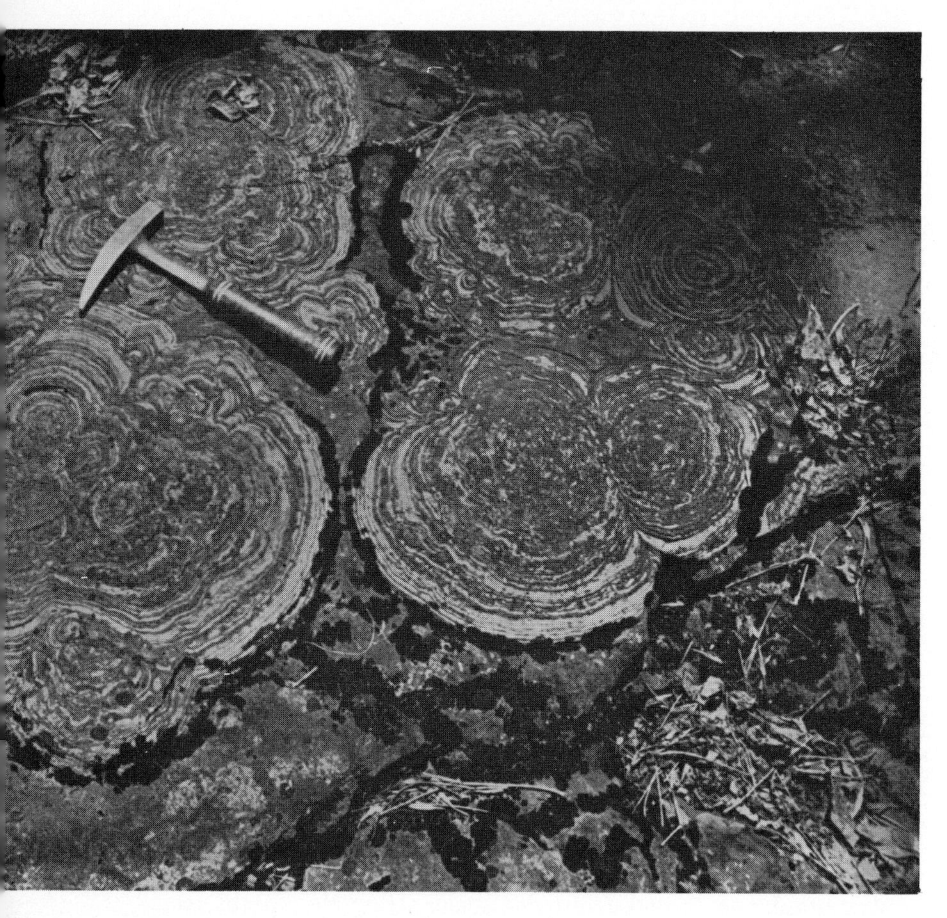

Fig. 12-10. Calcareous alga, *Cryptozoon proliferum*. This reef of alga is exposed near Saratoga, New York. The surface of the reef has been scoured by continental glaciers providing a beautiful cross-sectional view of the reef. (Photo by Edgar W. Spencer.)

times. The time span represented by deposition of various parts of this unit may exceed 50 million years. How can this happen? The Prospect Mountain quartzite was originally a sandstone probably formed in the shallow water along the margin of the land masses in the Precambrian and early Cambrian time. This sea gradually encroached on the land, transgressed the land, as a result of a downward warping of the land or a rise in sea level. In this sea finer weathering products from the land were washed farther out and deposited as clays and silts (which eventually became the Bright Angel group when it was consolidated). In some areas, California and Nevada, for instance, greater thicknesses accumulated over longer periods of time than in the area which was to become the site of the Grand Canyon. So the same rock unit can be different ages in different places. This is an important concept in historical geology. Most rock units do not span as great a time as the Bright Angel group, but few are laid down at the same time throughout their extent.

LIFE OF THE CAMBRIAN PERIOD

Notable aspects of the life

The Cambrian is known as the "Age of Trilobites." These early arthropods make up more than half of the assemblages of fossils. They appeared in abundance in the Early Cambrian and continued to prosper throughout the period. They swam and burrowed through the sea-floor sediments in the shallow- and medium-depth waters in the seas and on the continental shelves. Some of the most important of the trilobites are illustrated, Fig. 12-4.

One of the most interesting aspects of the life of the Cambrian is the great diversity of organisms that lived at that time. This is not so surprising when we remember the amount of time that is involved in the Precambrian. In the 3 1/2 billion years that preceded the beginning of the Cambrian there was ample time for life to begin through synthesis of inorganic matter and for it to pass through the initial stages of differentiation and the development of complex structures. What is most surprising about the Cambrian fauna is the tremendous difference between the fossils we find in the Cambrian System and those in the Precambrian units immediately below. Precambrian fossils are virtually unknown for all but a very few of the simplest organisms. Yet in the Cambrian we find almost every invertebrate phylum represented among the fossils. To be sure some of these are very minor constituents of the Cambrian populations, and many of them are relatively primitive organisms by comparison with later members of their groups, but nevertheless the initial diversification into many different structural groups had already taken place before or at least during the Cambrian. We expect to find that the chordates also lived during the Cambrian. The first known fossil chordates appear in the Ordovician, but the first remains are those of a highly developed animal. There must have been more primitive forms earlier.

Fig. 12-11. Burgess shale restoration. Some of the plant and animal life of the Middle Cambrian which has been preserved in detail in the Burgess shale are shown. These animals lived on the shallow sea floor in British Columbia, an area which now stands thousands of feet above sea level. This view includes (1) colonies of branching sponges, (2) trilobites, (3) sea cucumbers, (4) jellyfishes, and (5) an arthropod somewhat like modern crustaceans. (Photo by courtesy of the U.S. National Museum.)

Important groups represented in the Cambrian fauna

1. TRILOBITES: The most important animal group in the Cambrian seas.

2. BRACHIOPODS: Next to the trilobites the most numerous animals in the Cambrian. The earliest of these had a chitino-phosphatic shell and were inarticulate and unhinged, but later the articulate brachiopods appeared.

3. SPONGES: The glass, siliceous spicules of sponges are abundant in the Cambrian. The pleosponges were the most abundant sponges. Large reefs of these are found in California and New York as well as in other parts of the world.

4. CALCAREOUS ALGAE: Forms of calcareous algae similar to those of the Precambrian are found in abundance in the limestones of the Cambrian.

Minor groups represented

1. PROTOZOANS: Almost certainly were present although fossils have not been absolutely identified.

2. ECHINODERMS: One group of these bottom dwellers, the cystoids, was present in parts of the Cambrian seas.

3. GASTROPODS: A few small uncoiled and coiled shells.

4. CEPHALOPODS: These had uncoiled shells.

5. PELECYPODS: Very rare.

6. GRAPTOLITES: The first graptolites appeared before the end of the period.

7. COELENTERATES: Jellyfish have been found preserved in a remarkable fossil locality in British Columbia, the Burgess shale.

8. WORMS: These soft animals have been preserved at the same locality as the jellyfish.

Fig. 12-12. Restored Cambrian sea floor. (Photo by courtesy of the Chicago Natural History Museum.)

Fig. 12-13. Mount Assiniboine. Located south of Banff, Alberta, this mountain is composed of sedimentary rocks laid down in a Cambrian sea. The nearly flat-lying strata have been dissected by recent glaciation. Mount Assiniboine is a horn. Note also the cirques and other glacial features. (Photo by courtesy of the Royal Canadian Air Force.)

The Burgess shale

Dr. Charles D. Walcott made one of the most extraordinary and probably the most significant fossil discoveries in 1910 while he was on an expedition in the Canadian Rockies. Near Field, British Columbia, he found carbonized fossils in the black shales exposed on the face of Mt. Wapta. The fossils were part of the Burgess shale of Middle Cambrian age. Imprinted as a delicate carbon film on the bedding plane of these shales or near-slates he found 130 species of Cambrian organisms. Most of them have never been found at any other locality. Their preservation is most exceptional. Even the soft parts of the bodies are preserved. In some, even the internal organs can be distinguished. Here we find the soft bodies of jellyfishes and soft worms preserved in detail. The discovery of this fauna gives us an excellent insight into the true nature of the assemblages that were present. The discovery of such a locality makes us expect and hope that others like it will be found both in other parts of the Cambrian section and perhaps some day in the Precambrian as well.

Fig. 12-14. Restoration of two of the animals found in the Burgess shale. (C. Walcott)

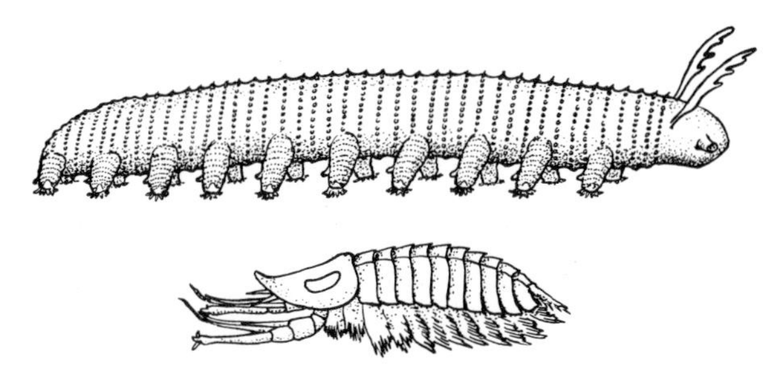

REFERENCES

DEISS, CHARLES, 1941, Cambrian geography and sedimentation in the central Cordilleran region: Geol. Soc. America Bull., v. 52, p. 1086-1114

KAY, MARSHALL, 1942, Development of northern Allegheny synclinorium and adjoining regions: Geol. Soc. America Bull., v. 53, p. 1601-1658

———, 1951, North American geosynclines: Geol. Soc. America Mem. 48, 143 p.

KING, P. B., 1950, Tectonic framework of southeastern United States: Am. Assoc. Petroleum Geologists Bull., v. 34, p. 635-671

———, 1951, *The Tectonics of Middle North America,* Princeton University Press, Princeton, 203 p.

WHEELER, H. E., and BEESLEY, E. M., 1948, Critique of time-stratigraphic concept: Geol. Soc. America Bull., v. 59, p. 75-86

13 The Ordovician Period

PHYSICAL HISTORY OF THE ORDOVICIAN

This period marks the most extensive known encroachment of the seas upon the land masses of the world. Seas receded from most of North America for a short time following the Cambrian, but soon returned, first to reoccupy the geogynclines, and then gradually to advance over the continent. The continent's low topography allowed the seas to cover large areas with slight relative shifts in sea level. During this period the seas did not maintain a single configuration very long. Slight movements of the continent raised some areas above the sea and lowered others. The bulk of the sedimentary rocks deposited in these seas were limestones, shales, and dolostones as would be expected since there were few large land masses to supply coarse debris.

A wealth of information is available about the stratigraphy of each of the periods of our time scale. Only a few of the more important aspects of each period are considered here. Three of the most interesting features of the Ordovician are:

1. The nature of the fossil records which have been used to correlate the Ordovician System throughout the world.
2. The nature of the origin of one of the most extensive rock units in the United States, the Saint Peter Sandstone.
3. The Taconian orogeny, which brought the Ordovician Period to a close, was one of the greatest periods of mountain formation in the history of the earth.

THE AGE OF GRAPTOLITES

The Ordovician Period is often called the age of graptolites:

1. They are the best-known guide fossils for the system.
2. They are widely distributed and abundant in rock units of the period.
3. Although they first appeared in the Cambrian they underwent a tremendous diversification in the Ordovician.

Fig. 13-1. Evolutionary trend among the graptolites. Early in the Ordovician the stipes of the graptolites hung down, but through time these tended to grow in positions that became progressively turned up. Another evolutionary trend among the graptolites was toward a reduction in the number of stipes. Early forms had as many as thirty-two or more stipes. (After Ruedemann.)

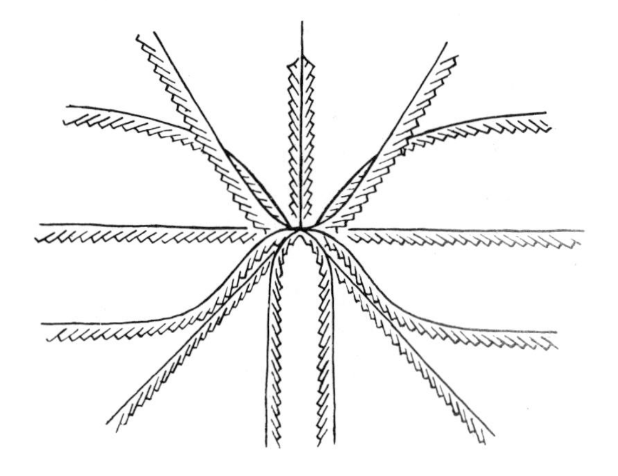

Graptolites are not very spectacular fossils. In fact for a great many years there has been uncertainty as to the phylum in which they belong. They have at one time or another been classed as bryozoans, coelenterates, or placed in a separate category by themselves. Most paleontologists are now convinced that they are hemichordates, a group that has some characteristics of chordates and others that are typical of the invertebrates. Most of the fossil graptolites are mere carbonized prints on shales and slates.

Very few fossils have been as useful as the graptolites for the purposes of correlation. Primary among the reasons for their usefulness is the nature of the organism. Graptolites lived in colonies. These colonies consisted of long stipes to which the individuals were attached. The stipes hung from a float, either one that they built or some other object such as sea weed or other animals or plants. Thus many of the graptolites were attached to free-floating bodies in the ocean. There could hardly be a better natural means of distributing animals throughout the world. They were carried everywhere the sea currents could carry them. The fact that they were particularly abundant during the Ordovician Period makes it all the more likely that they would be scattered throughout the seas of that time. It seems probable that land barriers were about the only thing that prevented them from being distributed even more widely. Not all of the graptolites were attached to floating bodies. Some were attached to the shells of other animals, and some were tied to the sea floor.

A second important reason why they are so important as guide fossils is that the organism underwent a series of changes during the 80 million years of the Ordovician. They first appeared in the Cambrian, but in the Ordovician Period several evolutionary trends began to bring about a diversification in the structure of the colony. We are not sure why these trends occurred, but by examining a sequence of graptolite-bearing shales we find that the first colonies had many more stipes than the succeedingly younger ones, and the position of the stipes changed. At first they hung down, but they became progressively turned upward.

The preservation of graptolites has been exceptional. The abundance of their remains is an indication of their wide distribution in the Ordovician. Yet they do not occur in very many different rock types. They are almost exclusively found in shales and shaly sedimentary rocks. It seems hard to imagine that a floating organism could be deposited in the muds of one environment only. Studies have been made of the assemblages associated with different rock types in the Ordovician System of England.

Large brachiopods are one of the few fossils found with the near-shore sediments such as conglomerate, sandstone, and sandy limestone. In greater depths of water where the sediments are finer we find three zones: (1) the inner one, containing trilobites and brachiopods, (2) the middle one, containing mainly trilobites, and (3) the third and outer one containing mainly trilobites and graptolites. These are in progressively finer sediments and probably deeper water. Farther out where the sediments are mainly muds or shales graptolites dominate the assemblages. The most likely explanation of this seems to be that the graptolites were preserved where they were dropped into reducing environments (where

Fig. 13-2. Fossil graptolite. The carbon film on this shale is typical of the preservation of graptolites. Shown here is a Tetragraptus. (Photo by courtesy of the U.S. National Museum.)

Fig. 13-3. Environments in which graptolites are found. This diagram depicts the association of certain animal assemblages with particular environments and sediment types. Both the lithology and the fossil content of a rock unit indicates the environment of deposition. (After G. L. Elles.)

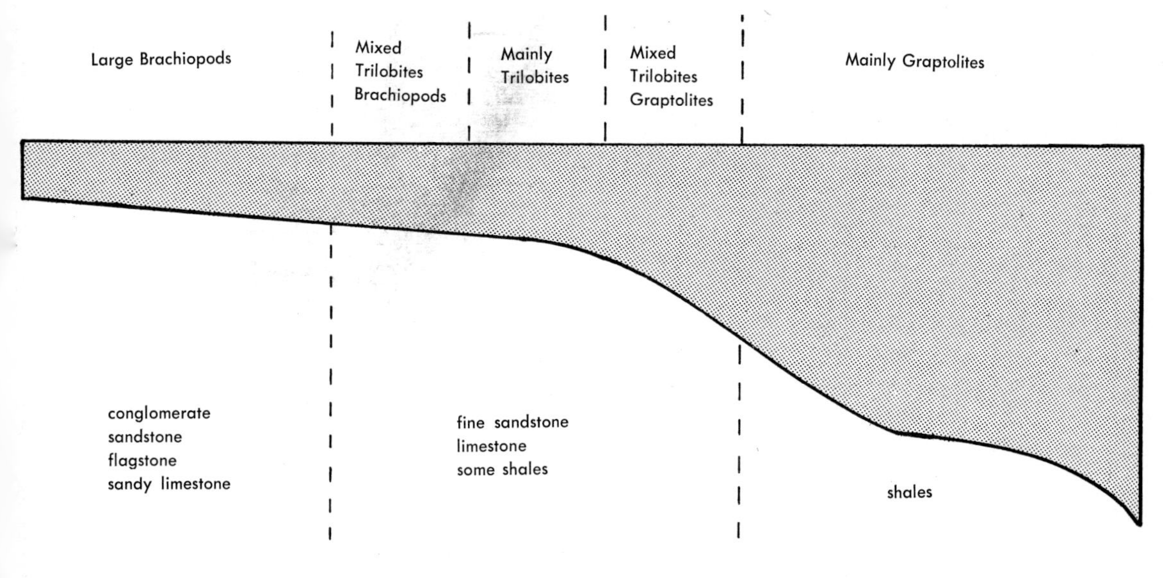

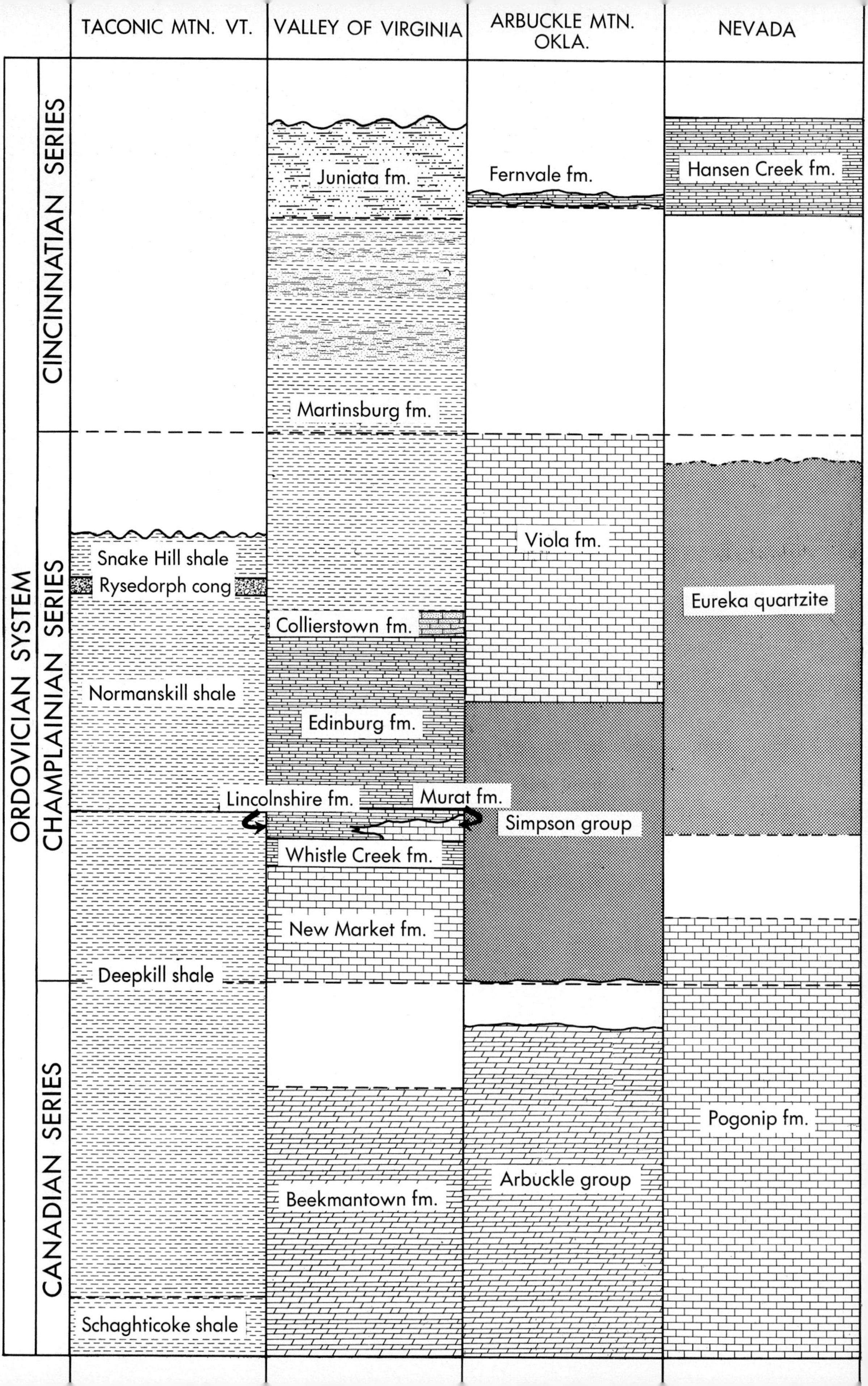

ORDOVICIAN SYSTEM

CINCINNATIAN SERIES

CHAMPLAINIAN SERIES

CANADIAN SERIES

TACONIC MTN. VT.

Snake Hill shale

Rysedorph cong

Normanskill shale

Deepkill shale

Schaghticoke shale

VALLEY OF VIRGINIA

Juniata fm.

Martinsburg fm.

Collierstown fm.

Edinburg fm.

Lincolnshire fm.

Murat fm.

Whistle Creek fm.

New Market fm.

Beekmantown fm.

ARBUCKLE MTN. OKLA.

Fernvale fm.

Viola fm.

Simpson group

Arbuckle group

NEVADA

Hansen Creek fm.

Eureka quartzite

Pogonip fm.

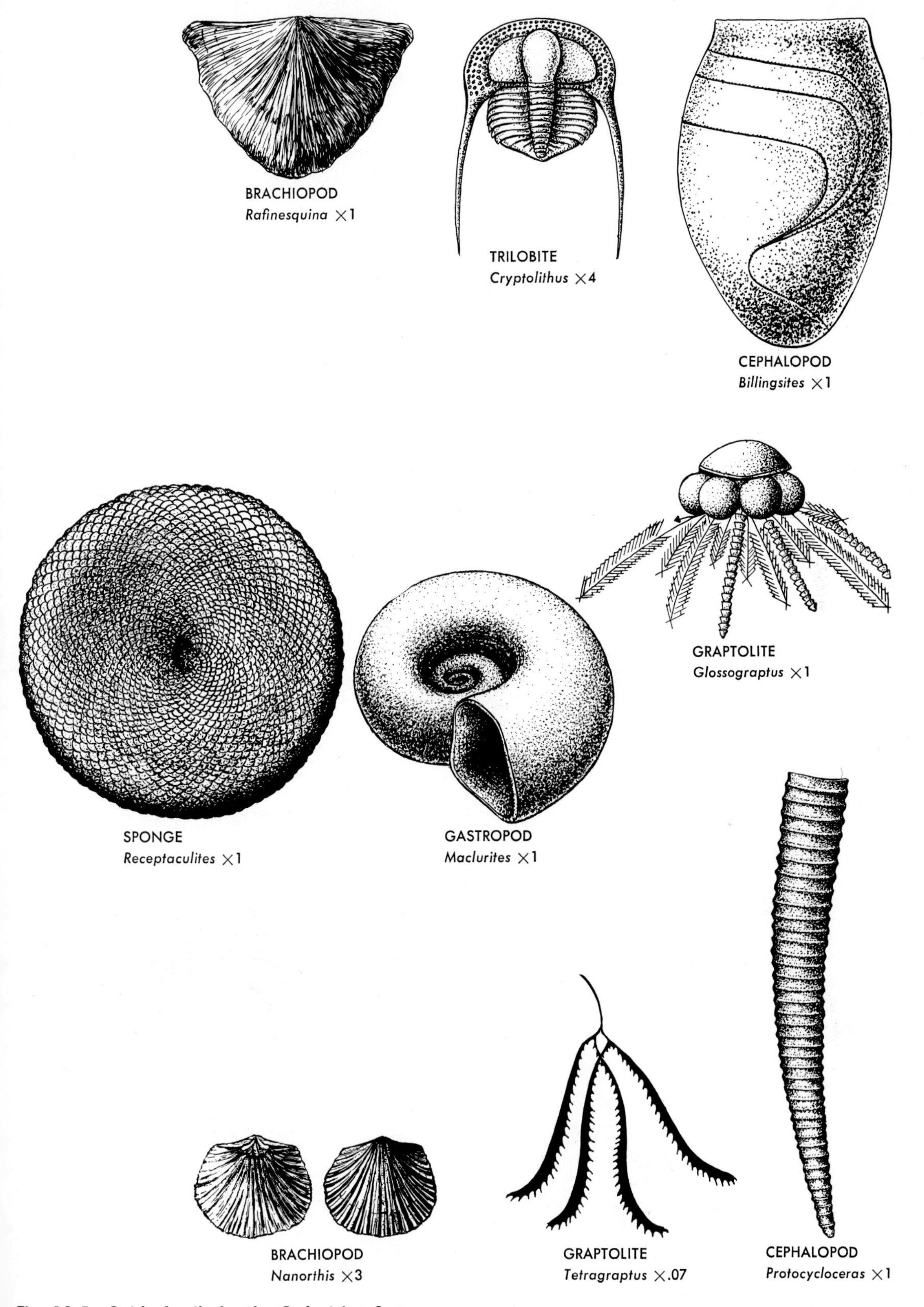

Fig. 13-5. Guide fossils for the Ordovician System.

Fig. 13-4. Correlation chart for the Ordovician System.

there is a scarcity of oxygen). The deeper and poorly circulated water in which most shales are deposited are of this nature. In such an environment there would be relatively few scavengers that would eat the graptolites before they could become buried.

ST. PETER SANDSTONE

It was noted in the introduction that the interior of the North American continent was low topographically during the Ordovician Period and that seas swept across the interior from time to time. The units formed in these shallow seas are lithologically simple. Carbonates, limestone, dolostones, shale, and sandstones are the most prominent types found in the Mid-continent. Each can usually be traced with ease over a large area. One of the most remarkable of these units is the St. Peter sandstone. It is unusual because of its great extent (it covers about a quarter of a million square miles and averages 57 feet in thickness), its

Fig. 13-6. Shorelines at five stages in the course of the deposition of the St. Peter Sandstone. The actual extent of outcrops is indicated by the shaded patterns. The wavy lines show progressive stages in the transgression of the sea in which the sandstone was deposited. Limestone mixed with sand characterizes the unit in southern Illinois. The blank area in the center of the outcrop pattern coincides with the Ozark Dome, a region from which the St. Peter has been eroded. It is thought to have extended as far west as the dark wavy line, a hypothetical shoreline. (After E. C. Dapples.)

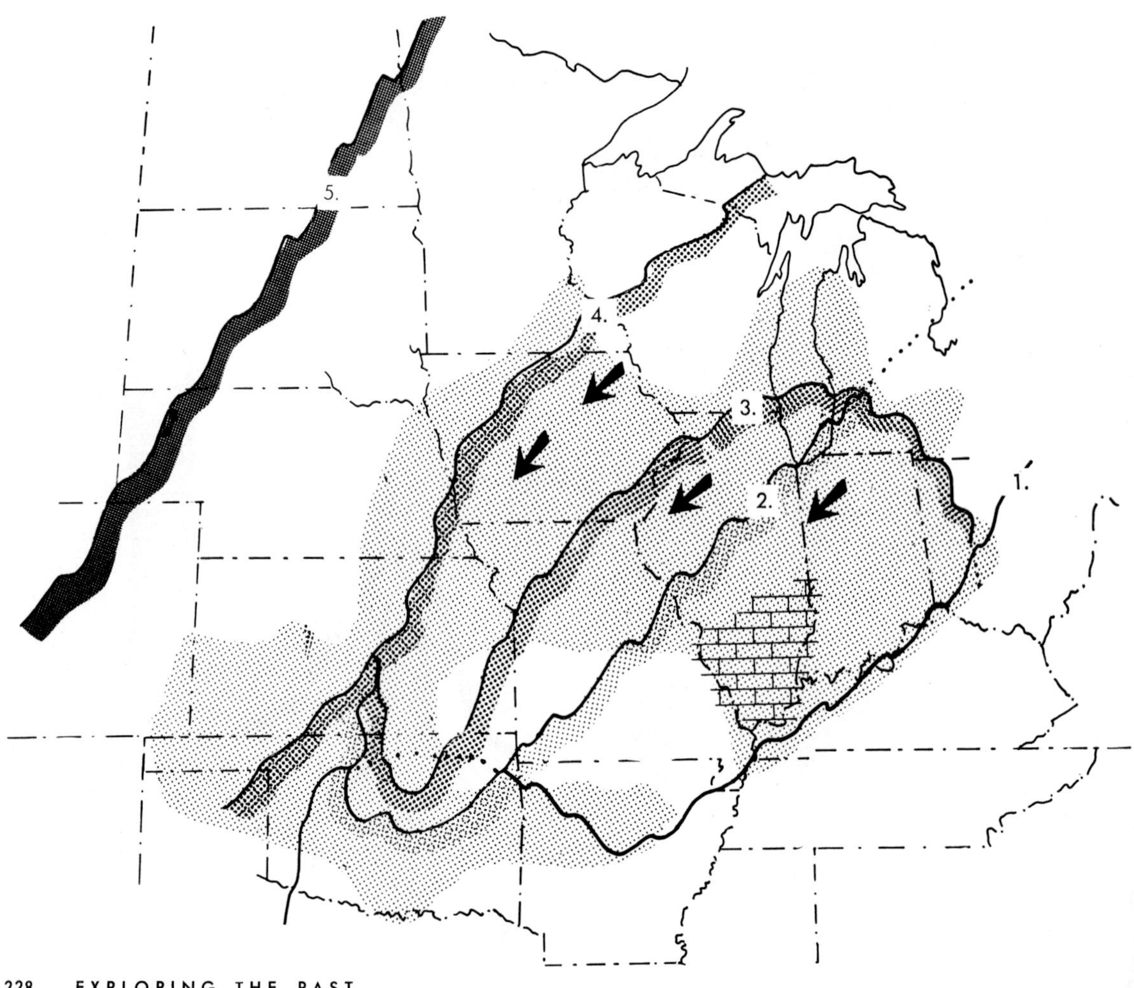

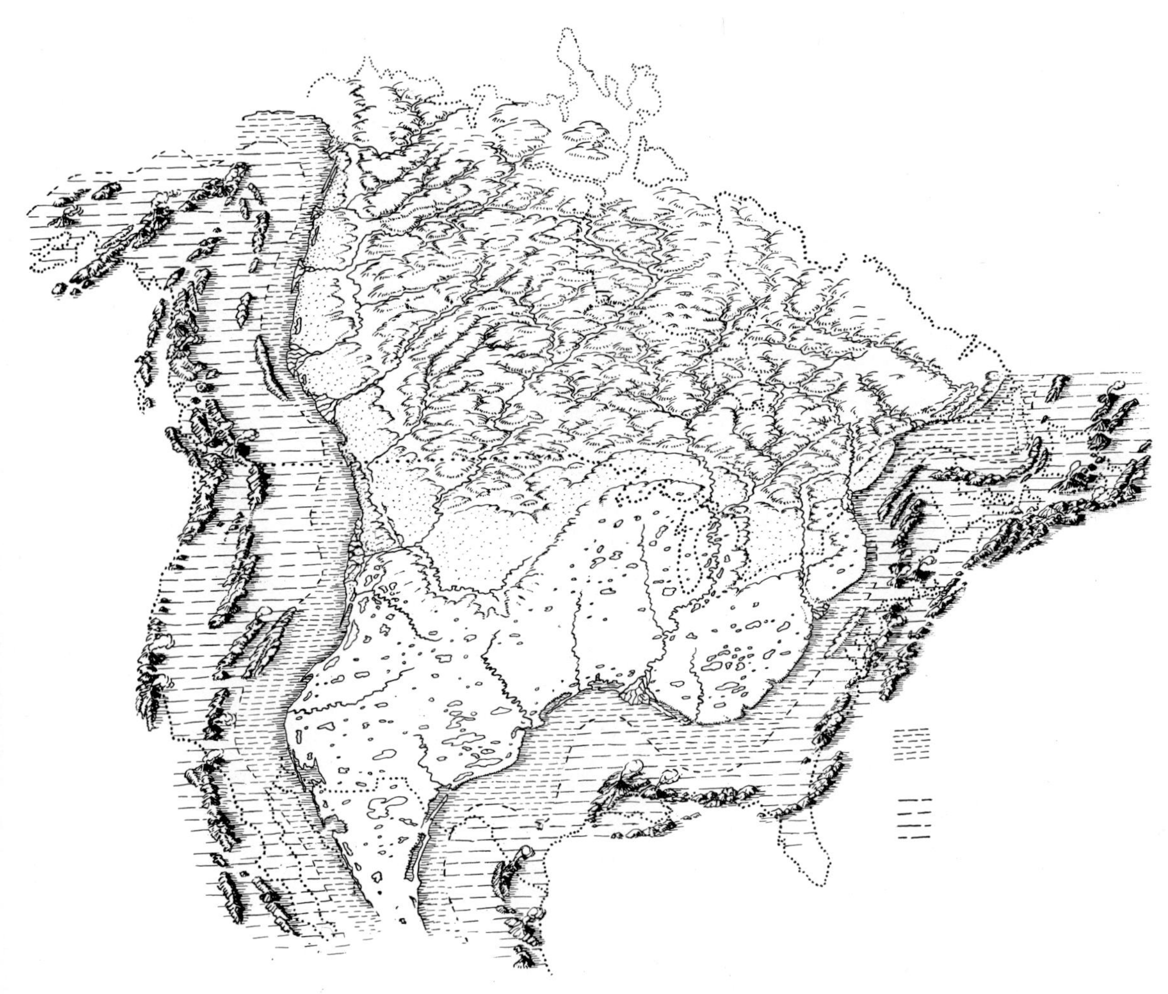

Fig. 13-7. Paleogeography of the Ordovician. This view of the paleogeography is drawn for the early part of the Middle Ordovician, Early Chazyan. The Taconic Mountains had not yet risen. (After Marshall Kay and E. Raisz.)

uniform mineralogic composition, and its characterizing physical properties. It is, for example, more than 99 per cent quartz, the grains of sand are nearly all the same size, they are exceptionally round, and the largest grains are pitted.

The St. Peter covers an area extending from western Kentucky and Ohio to Colorado and Wisconsin. Exact dating of the unit in different areas has gradually led to the conclusion that the St. Peter, like the Bright Angel group, has a transgressive character. It is oldest in the south and east and becomes progressively younger northward toward Minnesota.

Professor E. C. Dapples, in work at Northwestern University, has made one of the most comprehensive studies of the St. Peter sandstone. Formation of this sheet of sand began when the sea started to transgress the continental interior. The shore line occupied position 1 of Fig. 13-6 at an early stage. At that time the shore line extended around a subsiding basin in Oklahoma. There were some shifts of the shore line within the area of the basin – reflecting diastrophic movements that raised and lowered parts of the basin at different times. Outside the basin the shore line gradually migrated inland as the shelf became slightly depressed. By the time the shore line had reached position 3, carbonates were being

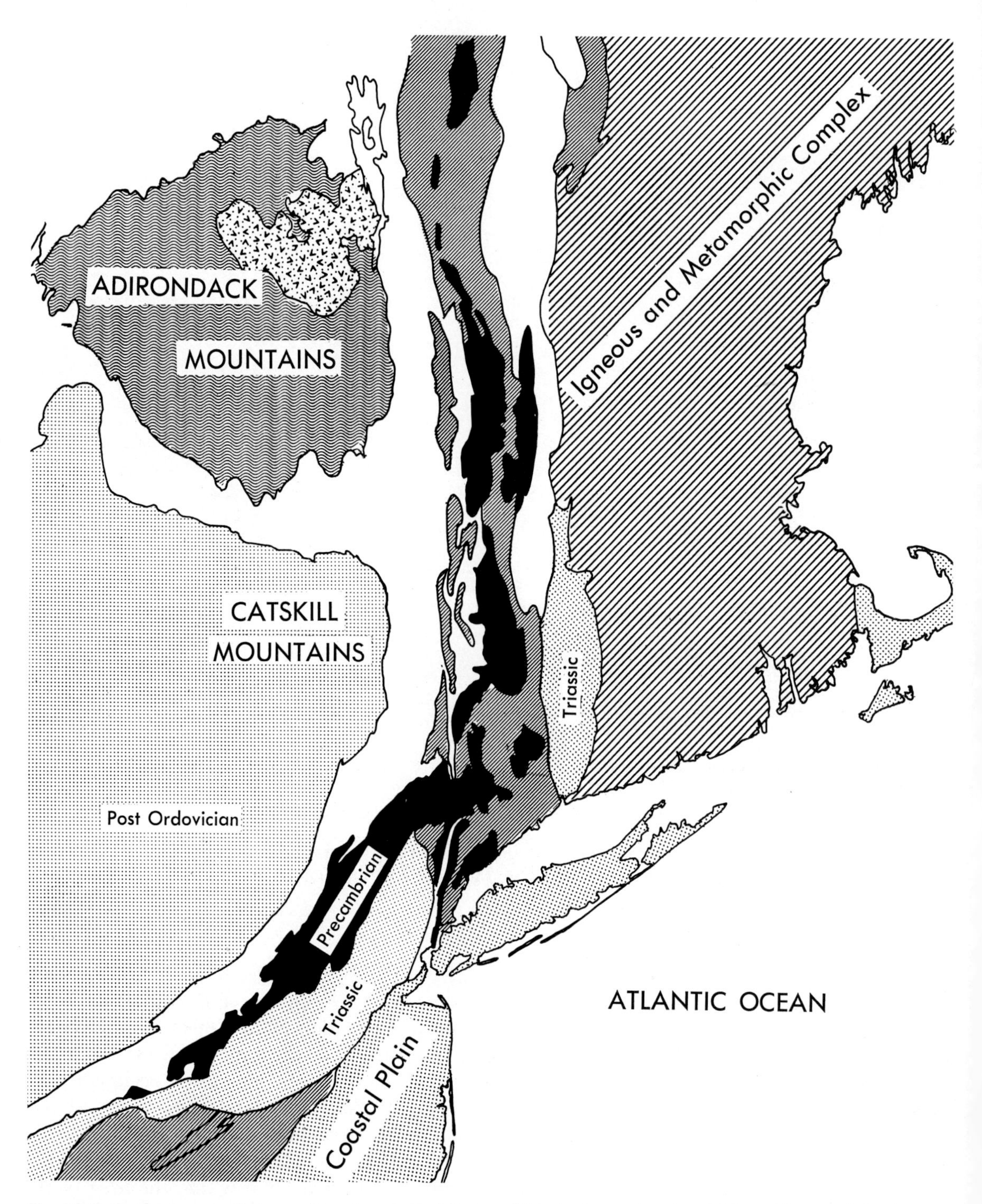

Fig. 13-8. Geologic map of the northeastern United States. This is the region in which evidence of the Taconian Orogeny is found. The structures of the Taconian Orogeny are found in the white area which extends northward from New York City. Black areas are Precambrian gneisses and granites within the deformed belt. Rock units that are younger than the orogeny are shaded in a dot pattern. The Adirondack Mountains are composed of older Precambrian units. The region shaded by diagonals was undoubtedly involved in the Taconian Orogeny but the rocks there are igneous and metamorphic units that are unfossiliferous. (After the Geologic Map of North America.)

deposited in southern Illinois and in the Oklahoma basin, and the seas were regressing from southeastern Michigan. This was followed by a general transgression of the sea as far inland as shore-line position 5.

Arrows on the maps indicate the directions of currents in the seas. These currents were primarily responsible for the transportation of the sand. The evidence of this is cited by Dapples.

Fig. 13-9. Tectonic sketch map of the northeastern United States. The heavy barbed lines are thrust faults formed during the Taconian Orogeny. Within the same belt the strata are complexly folded and faulted. To the southwest in Pennsylvania fold axes of a much later deformation are found. Likewise the down-dropped fault troughs are of Triassic age. The region affected by the deformation at the end of the Ordovician lies east of the Adirondacks and extends both northeastward and southwestward. (After the Tectonic Map of the U.S.)

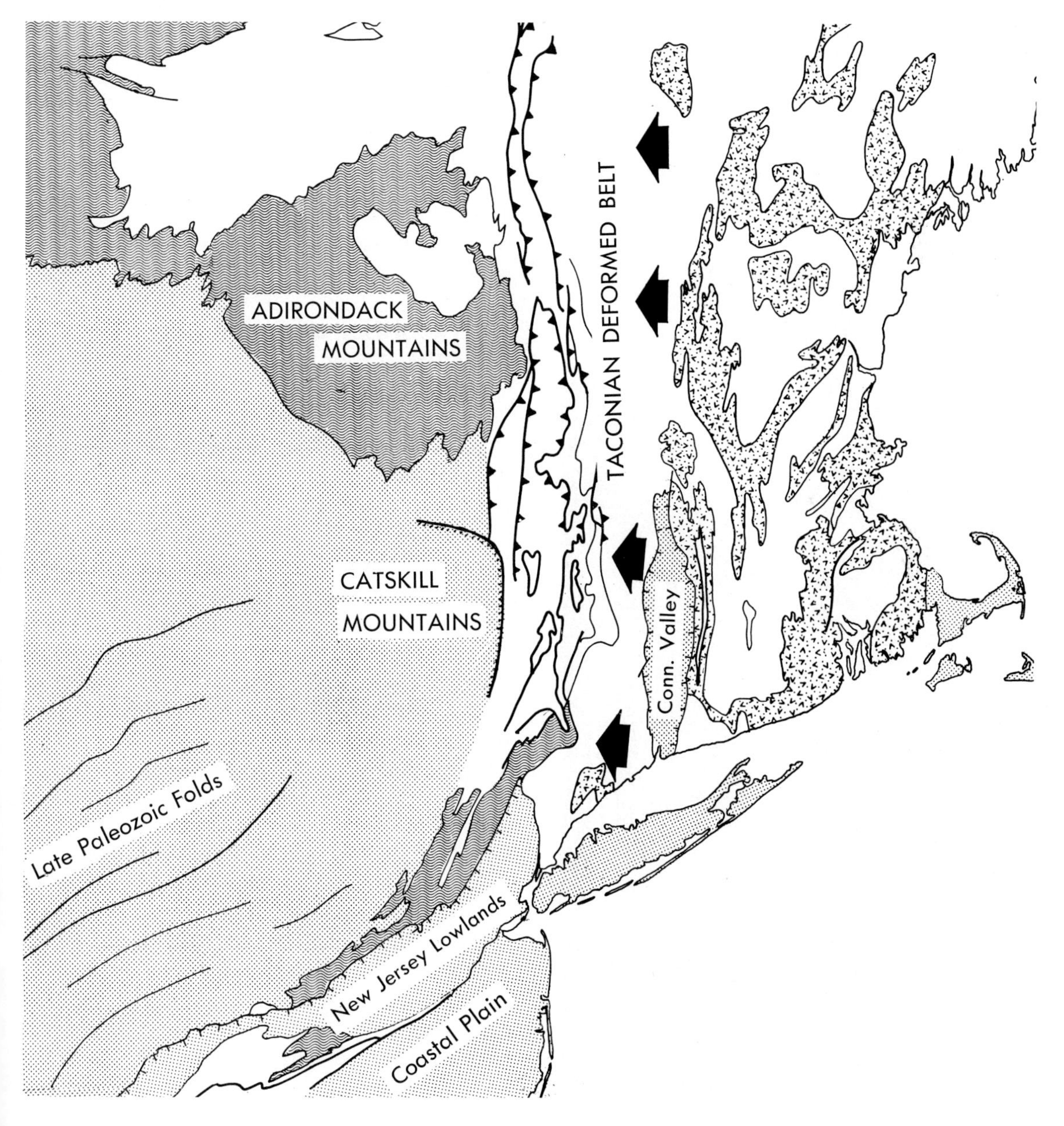

As the marine transgression proceeded, local lenses of shale accumulated near the shoreline. The presence of these individually small but widespread shale pockets indicates that clay-size material was being carried by the currents and deposited locally, but never as extensive beds except in the Simpson basin (Oklahoma). It appears that the summation of all current activity was shifting fine material in a southwesterly direction.

The source of supply of this sand was probably from the mouths of a number of large streams that flowed off the land masses of the west into the sea north of the area of deposition. These sands would have been carried down to the south by the longshore currents. It is also possible that some of these sands came from ancient beach sands, or even from wind-blown deposits. The nearly perfect rounding and sorting that is so typical of these sands make us suspect that they are reworked deposits of some sort. As the sea continued to transgress, the deposits of the earlier shores were reworked until they formed an almost continuous sheet over the entire stable shelf. In the Simpson basin, a structural basin that existed in Oklahoma at that time, the units which are contemporaneous with the St. Peter sandstone are not nearly so homogeneous. These differences reflect the differences in the two types of environments. Where the St. Peter was laid down there was little diastrophism, but in the basin there was tectonic disturbance that caused a greater variety of sediments and greater thickness than characterized those spread over most of the continental interior.

Fig. 13-10. Taconian thrust sheets. The blocks shaded in black are the positions occupied by thrust sheets now found in the deformed belt before the orogeny started. (After A. J. Eardley.)

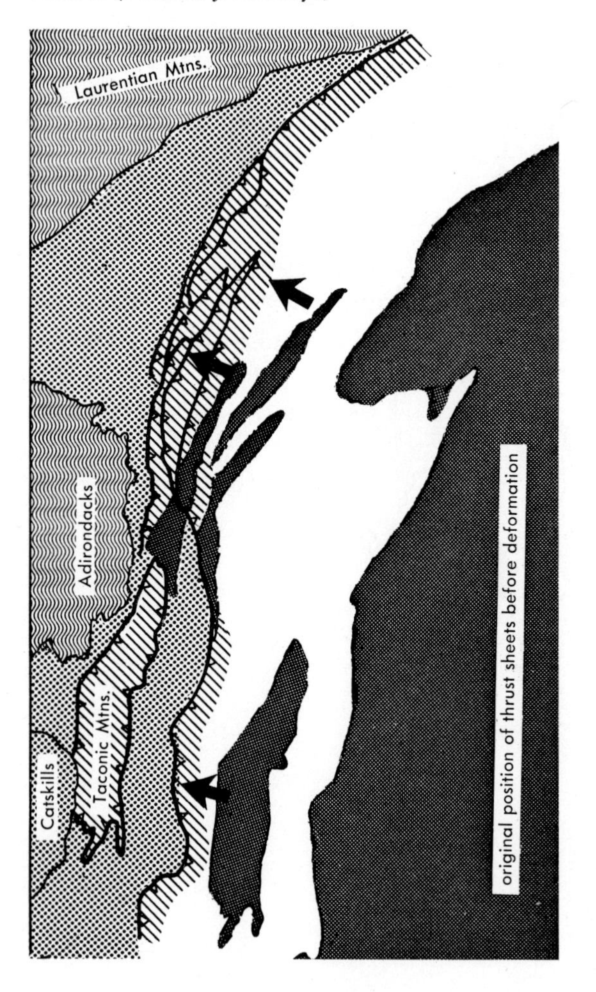

THE TACONIAN OROGENY AND THE QUEENSTON DELTA

Toward the end of the Ordovician Period a major mountain system began to rise along the eastern coast of North America. This was the Taconic Mountain Range, the ancestor of the present-day Taconic Mountains of western Vermont. Most of the evidence of this great upheaval is found in New England and farther north in eastern Canada. The range formed might very well have resembled the modern Rockies or the Alps. This mountain range rose in the easternmost part of New England and was thrust and folded toward the continental interior. Before it started to rise North America was probably more nearly a featureless continent than it ever has been since. It was a land of shallow seas and low land areas. As the mountains rose in the east sediments were eroded and transported off into these seas, and a huge deltaic deposit, the Queenston delta, was built across the eastern United States.

The classic area for the study of the Taconian orogeny is illustrated on the general tectonic and geologic maps of New England, Figs. 13-8 and 13-9. All of the sedimentary rock units that had been deposited in the seas of the Cambrian and earlier Ordovician were involved in the diastrophism. These are now exposed in a narrow belt extending down the Hudson River valley and southwestward. Northwest of this belt we now find metamorphic and igneous Precambrian rocks of the Grenville Province exposed in the Adirondacks. In the south and west of this belt the Cambrian and Ordovician systems are overlain by Silurian, Devonian, and younger sedimentary units. East of this belt in New England we find a large area that is made up of complex igneous and metamorphic rocks. Some of these are certainly Precambrian in age; others are intrusives of Paleozoic age. Other parts of the belt are covered by long troughs of Triassic rocks that lie on the side of the belt.

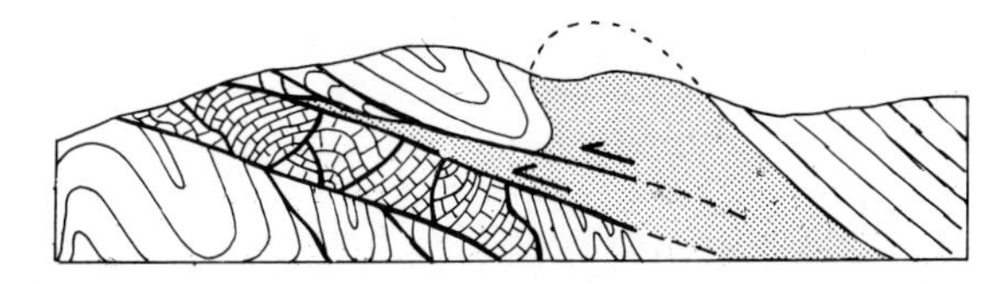

Fig. 13-11. Details of the margin of one of the thrust sheets. Notice how the units have been folded and thrust. In one zone a limestone unit is broken and individual blocks have been rotated by the deformation. Here Lower Cambrian units are thrust on top of Ordovician units. (After Cushing and Ruedemann.)

Structures

The most prominent structures of the Taconian orogeny are extensive thrust sheets, shown in Fig. 13-10. Several large sheets of Cambrian and Ordovician rocks were thrust westward and brought to lie on top of younger formations. The details of the front of one of these sheets, the Taconic thrust sheet, is illustrated in Fig. 13-11. In this view the Lower Cambrian formations are thrust over Middle Ordovician strata. Note the crush zone and the complex nature of the thrust. Other sheets of the thrust are shown with their restored positions before the thrusting occurred. Some of these sheets are completely isolated from their roots, the area from which they came. These are completely surrounded by formations that are younger than they are. Such a thrust sheet is called a klippe.

The Queenston Delta

As soon as the mountains began to be uplifted in eastern North America they were subjected to increased erosion. Consequently, these erosion products were carried out into the seas that lay on either side of the mountains. Those that were carried to the west and deposited in the eastern United States are still preserved. These deltaic deposits began to be built toward the end of the Middle Ordovician Epoch. At that time sedimentation in the eastern United States changed from predominantly

Fig. 13-12. Cross section drawn from the Adirondack Mountains eastward across the Taconian deformed belt. The diagram has been simplified to show the Taconic Klippe, and its relations to the Adirondack and Green Mountains. Cambrian and Ordovician rock units were involved in the deformation. Silurian units lie unconformably over part of this deformed belt. (After Brace.)

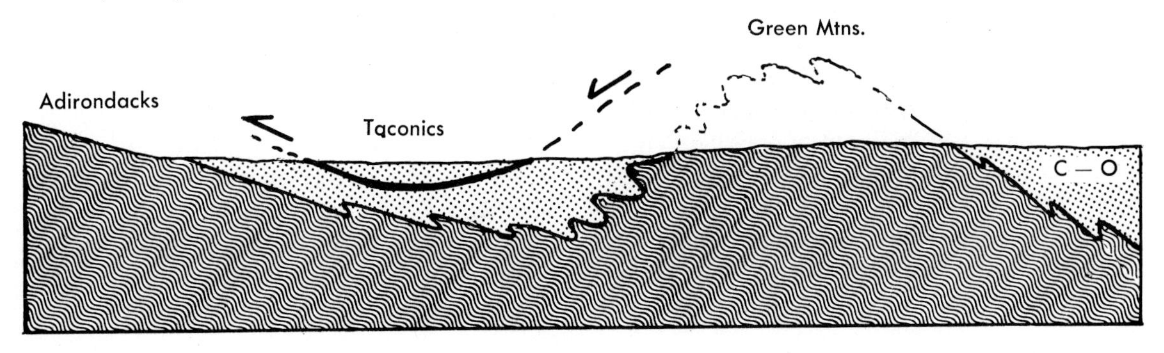

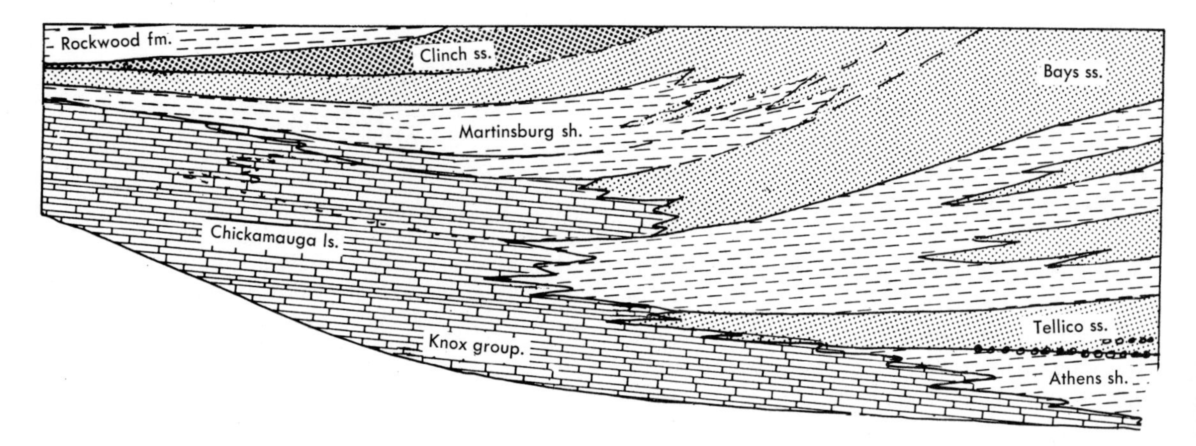

Fig. 13-13. Cross section across eastern Tennessee. Notice that the coarser sediments of the east grade westward into finer sediments. Limestones were laid down across the entire section early in the Middle Ordovician, but by the end of the period coarse sediments were laid almost to the westernmost end. The section is a little over thirty miles long. It shows that the Taconic Mountains extended far enough south to exert a strong influence on the sedimentary pattern. Middle and Upper Ordovician sections are shown here. (After P. B. King.)

limestone as it had been throughout most of the earlier part of the period. Instead of limestone, shales and clastic sediments began to be deposited. By the start of the Late Ordovician, muds were being distributed over most of the eastern seaways. The source lay to the east in the mobile belt, the eugeosyncline of Cambrian time. This was situated in parts of eastern New England, eastern New Jersey, and on the continental shelf farther south. The muds derived from this land were spread westward as far as the vicinity of Cincinnati, Ohio. Running through Cincinnati both northward and southward a broad arch, called the Cincinnati arch, may have been primarily responsible for preventing the spread of these muds farther westward. Black muds lay east of the arch, and limestones were formed beyond, over the interior of the continent.

Through the Late Ordovician the sediments in the east became increasingly coarser. Finally the coarse clastic sands gave way to conglomerates and finally to nonmarine debris. Thus as mountains rose, areas farther west were being brought closer to the source. As the mountains got higher, coarser sediment was eroded off. The distances between the mountains and the seas were not great enough for the debris to become well sorted and broken down into smaller sizes. At first the landward part of the delta was small, but as the land continued to rise more debris was brought down by streams than the seas could distribute, and the delta expanded. It forced the shore line to retreat westward eventually as far as Niagara in New York.

Dating the Taconian orogeny

The eastern border of North America was involved in three orogenies in the Paleozoic Era, one at the end of the Ordovician, one toward the close of the Devonian, and a third near the end of the Permian. The structures formed in each of the later of these deformations are superimposed on those of the earlier in at least part of the eastern United States. The question therefore arises as to how we are going to determine the relative ages of the structures. In other words, how can we be sure that the structures we see in the Taconic Mountain Range were formed in the Ordovician? The effects of the Taconian orogeny are most evident in the northern Appalachians. Several independent lines of evidence are available to indicate the late Ordovician age of the Taconian orogeny there. Those lines of evidence are:

a. Sediments produced by the mountains formed the Queenston Delta.
b. Angular unconformities between Ordovician and Silurian units.

Examples of these relations are found at the following places:

1. Along the Hudson River, south of Albany, New York, folded and faulted Cambrian and Ordovician formations are overlain by relatively flat-lying Silurian units.
2. At Beecraft in New York a corner of a large

rian rocks.

3. In northern New Jersey, a Silurian unit, the Green Pond conglomerate, lies on Precambrian rocks which were eroded bare of Cambrian and Ordovician units prior to the Silurian.
4. In New Hampshire there are exposures of Silurian units on an eroded intrusive that cuts Ordovician but not Silurian units. This is the Highlandcroft magma series.

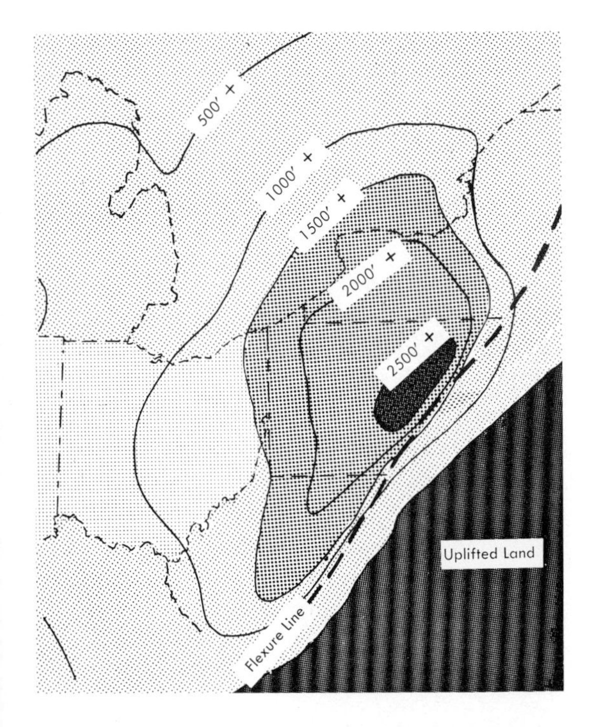

Fig. 13-14. Isopach map of the Upper Ordovician Queenston delta. The mountain range stood in the position indicated by the dark shaded portion. From it, eroded debris spread westward to form a huge delta. The thickest part of the delta was located in central Pennsylvania as indicated by the 2500 foot isopach line. (After Marshall Kay.)

Fig. 13-15. Restored sections for the Silurian and Upper Ordovician from New England to Ontario. Units deposited in the Queenston Delta are shown in the east end of the lower section. Note the thickness of the units in the geosynclinal belts.

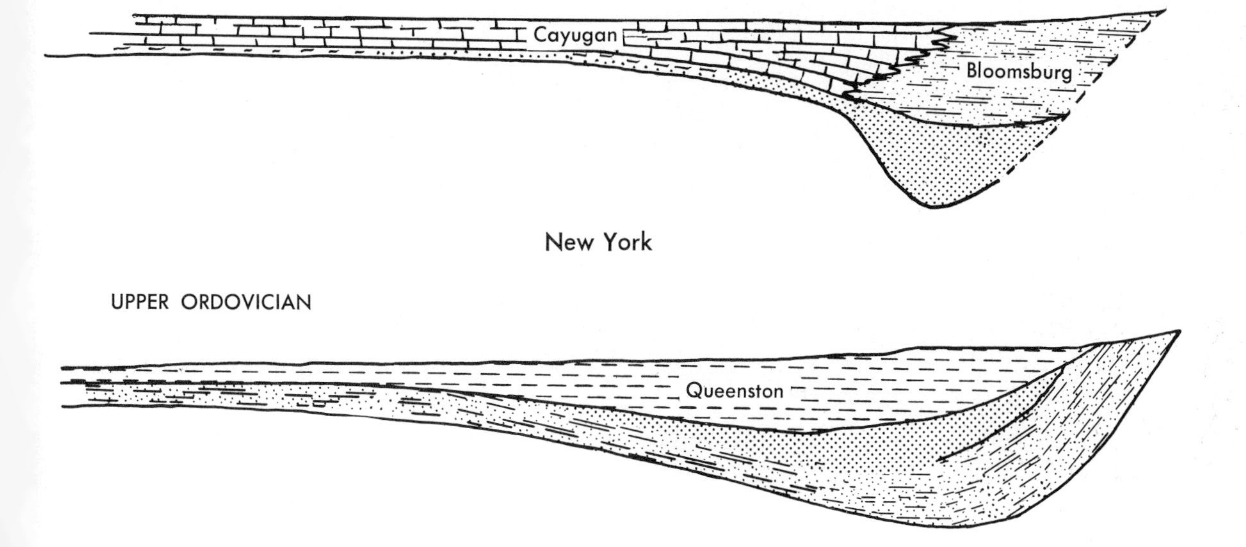

What principles are used in each of these examples? Such techniques are used elsewhere to establish ages of other periods of deformation.

LIFE OF THE ORDOVICIAN

I. NEW FORMS

1. Remains of the earliest fish, ostracoderms, are found in the Ordovician rocks.
2. First true corals, the honeycomb corals and horn corals, appeared early in the Ordovician for the first time.
3. Several new echinoderms appeared. These included the first crinoids, sea lilies, the first blastoids, and the first starfishes.
4. Bryozoans appeared in the early part of the Ordovician.
5. Several arthropods were present in the Cambrian, but the first ostracods came in the Ordovician. These are small crustaceans that look like shrimps, but they have two shells which give them an external appearance something like a clam.

II. ADVANCEMENT

None of the major groups found in the Cambrian formations are known to have become extinct in the Ordovician. The brachiopods and trilobites continued to be very numerous and underwent further diversification with the appearance of many new genera for the first time in the Ordovician. Likewise calcareous algae were present as they had been ever since the Precambrian. Clams were very rare in the Cambrian, but they were fairly common in Ordovician seas.

Fig. 13-16. Restoration of an Ordovician sea floor in the vicinity of Chicago. The seas which occupied the central United States contained the fauna and flora depicted here. They include (1) trilobites, (2) seaweeds, (3) straight shelled cephalopods, (4) "honeycomb" corals, (5) gastropods, and (6) nautiloids (swimming), (Courtesy of the Chicago Natural History Museum.)

Fig. 13-17. Vermont marble being quarried from Ordovician units. These units were folded and metamorphosed during the Taconian orogeny.

III. PEAK OF DEVELOPMENT

1. Age of graptolites: The importance of these marine animals has already been stressed. They reached the peak of their development before the end of the period.
2. Cephalopods were much more numerous in the Ordovician than in the Cambrian. One particular species was the largest animal in the Ordovician world. It had a straight uncoiled shell that was 15 feet long.

IV. NOTABLE ASPECTS OF ORDOVICIAN LIFE

The most important development in the fauna is the appearance of the first fossil fish. Only scales and a few fragments of bony plates have been found. These first fish were covered by a hard bony armor plate, the reason for calling them ostracoderms, armor-skin. Their remains have been found in several localities in the Rocky Mountains. It appears from the nature of the sediments in which they are found that the fish inhabited fresh water. These fish are the first vertebrates known to have lived on the earth. They were soon followed by a great array of animals adapted to life on the continents and in the air as well as in the seas.

There is still no evidence of plant life on land. It is entirely possible that such life has not been preserved even if it were abundant. Almost certainly low parts of the continents must have supported some simpler forms of plants such as lichens. These could have lived where there was plenty of water nearby as around lakes or near quiet waters.

REFERENCES

KAY, MARSHALL, 1951, North American geosynclines: Geol. Soc. America Mem. 48, 143 p.

STOSE, G. W., 1946, The Taconic sequence in Pennsylvania: Am. Jour. Sci., v. 244, p. 665-696

WOODWARD, H. P., 1957, Chronology of Appalachian folding: Am. Assoc. Petroleum Geologists Bull., v. 41, p. 2312-2327

14 The Silurian Period

DISTRIBUTION OF SILURIAN FORMATIONS

The most extensive outcrops of Silurian strata are found around the Great Lakes. These form an almost perfectly continuous ring of outcrops around the State of Michigan. In this area they come to the surface around a large basin known as the Michigan basin. Other large exposures are found in the Mohawk Valley of New York. These may be traced eastward into the Hudson River valley. The Silurian System is exposed almost continuously from near Albany, New York, to Birmingham, Alabama, on the western side of the Appalachian Highlands. In the central United States there are exposures around the margins of the Nashville dome and the Ozark dome. Extensive exposures occur in the Ouachita Mountains in Arkansas. There are no exposures across the Great Plains. In the Rockies the Silurian is sporadically exposed on the flanks of a few mountains, but the largest exposures in the west are found in the Basin and Range province of Idaho, western Utah, and Nevada, and in central eastern California near Death Valley.

PHYSICAL HISTORY OF THE SILURIAN

History of the Early Silurian

Early in the Silurian Period the eastern part of the United States was submerged by a shallow sea. This sea spread around the southern end of a large land mass that had risen to the north in the geosynclinal belt, the Taconic Highlands. The sea gradually spread from the Gulf of Mexico northward, almost over the area of the Great Lakes. To the west it inundated everything as far as western Oklahoma and central Texas. About the same time a second body of water moved into the central part of the country from the northeast. It covered the southeastern part of Canada and almost reached the southern inundation. That the two never did actually connect during the Early Silurian or Medinan Epoch is borne out by the fossil assemblages. The two groups, although geographically close to one another, are very different, indicating that a land barrier persisted and separated them throughout the epoch.

Sedimentation in the Appalachian geosyncline at this time was very much like that of the Cambrian and Ordovician. Near the uplifted mountains streams brought coarse sediment that was dropped near the land areas. This debris was spread as far to the west as the Cincinnati arch, but beyond that the sediments were largely clear-water deposits of limestone. Along the western side of the Appalachian land mass an extensive band of sands and gravels was deposited. This band extended all the way from New York to Alabama and included the Clinch sandstone formation and the Tuscarora sandstone formation. These are between 500 and 1000 feet thick. Much of this accumulation was deposited above sea level as alluvial fans very similar to the deposits of the Queenston delta. These formations are particularly notable because they now stand up as ridges in the folded belt of the Appalachian Mountains. Because they are composed of sandstone they are more resistant to chemical weathering than are the limestones that occur with them. It is through this section and the resistant ridges composed of these sandstones that a number of the famous water gaps in the Appalachians are cut.

In the far west there is little evidence of Early Silurian sedimentation. Presumably the region was above sea level and undergoing erosion.

Middle Silurian

By the Middle Silurian the Taconian land mass had been worn to a low plain. The evidence of this is the absence of coarse sediments in the continental interior even near the margins of the former mountains. Instead we find that the sediments are largely fine muds, which became compacted to form shales. One unit of the series, the Clinton formation, contains a mixture of sandstone, limestone, and shale. This unit is particularly important because it contains hematite. The hematite is locally concentrated sufficiently to make it a satisfactory ore, and it has long been used as the principal ore source for the Birmingham, Alabama steel industry. It has been mined at other places in the past when there were severe ore shortages. Gradually the Middle Silurian, Niagaran, seas spread out farther eastward and finally covered the region that had been occupied by the major mountain system of the Taconian orogeny. These seas were very extensive, reaching across southern and western Canada and even into Alaska.

In the west about the same time a seaway developed in southern California. This sea spread northward as far as Idaho and eastward into New Mexico and Texas. This epoch marks one of the greatest encroachments of the sea upon the North American continent. It is almost as extensive as the late Ordovician submergence. As you might expect at a time when there were very few land masses of any size, conditions were very favorable for the formation of limestone in the Niagaran seas. The lime-secreting organisms are favored by clear water, and they must have been very abundant in this epoch for there are vast beds of limestone and the magnesium-rich lime rock known as dolostone. This unit covered the northeastern United States and Canada. Probably the best exposures of it are found in the gorge of

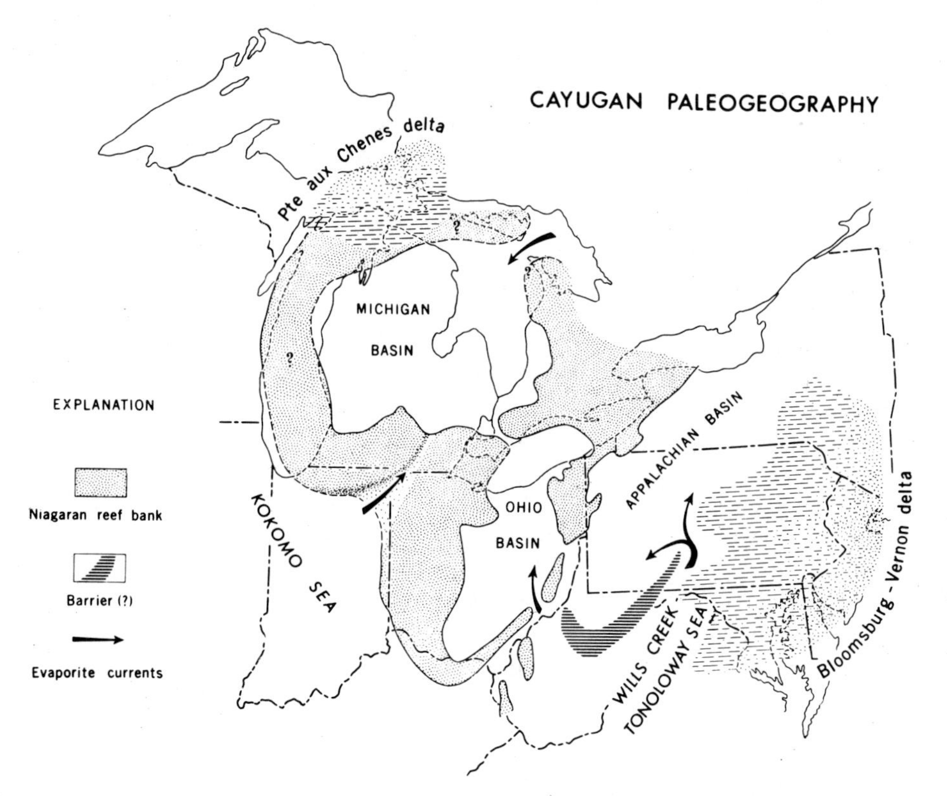

Fig. 14-1. Paleogeography during the Cayugan. The limits of the reconstruction are governed by the extent of Silurian outcrops. See Fig. 14-2. Through well-cutting within the region of Silurian outcrop, it has been possible to reconstruct the position of extensive Niagaran reef banks, possible land barriers, and inlets through which marine waters entered the evaporite basins. This reconstruction has been based on the data given in Fig. 14-2. (From L. I. Briggs.)

the Niagara Falls which is the type locality for this series.

Not all of the Niagaran limestone formations are stratified limes. Many of them consist of large moundlike masses of the skeletons of corals, bryozoans, and other marine organisms. Such a reef is called a *bioherm,* indicating that it is composed of a mixture of animals and plant remains and not solely corals. These reefs encircled a topographic basin that occupied the State of Michigan. They are most common in Wisconsin, Iowa, northern Illinois, Indiana, northern Michigan, and southern Ontario.

In the eugeosynclinal belt of the eastern part of North America there was considerable volcanic activity. A section of nearly 4000 feet of volcanic rocks is found in the Niagaran Series along the Gulf of St. Lawrence. Many of these lava flows were extruded under water, as evidenced by fossil fragments in the lower few inches of lava. To the south, even greater thicknesses of ash and lava flows are found in Maine.

Fig. 14-2. Cayugan clastic ratio and evaporite facies. These two maps are the result of lithologic studies of Cayugan rocks from outcrops and well cuttings throughout the region shown. At the top the per cent of clastic sediment in the Cayugan rocks is shown, and the edge of present outcrops is indicated. Note the absence of clastic sediments in the center of the Michigan basin and in eastern Ohio. Eastward the amount of mud and sand increases until the units are entirely composed of sands and muds. At the bottom is a map showing the amount of halite in Cayugan sedimentary rocks. Where the amount of halite in the evaporite facies drops below 25 per cent, anhydrite becomes the most important constituent. This grades into carbonate rocks, dolostone. (From L. I. Briggs.)

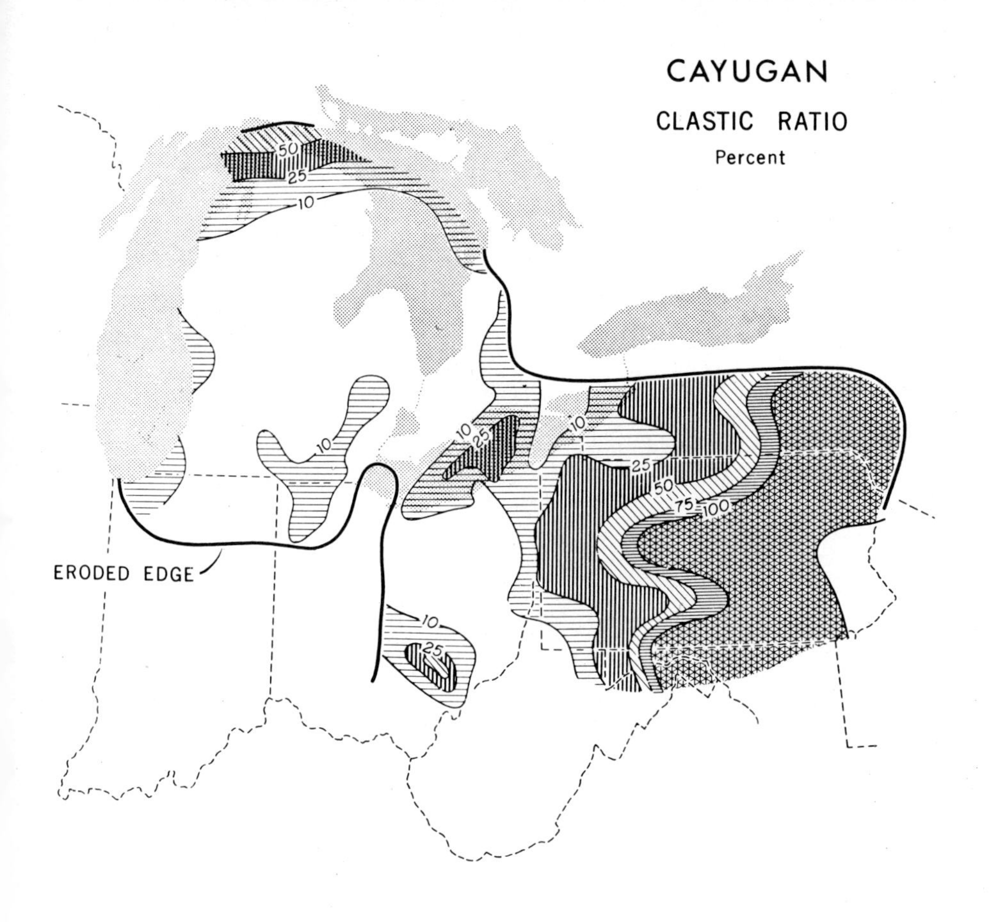
CAYUGAN
CLASTIC RATIO
Percent
50
25
10
10
10
25
10
25
50
75
100
10
25
ERODED EDGE

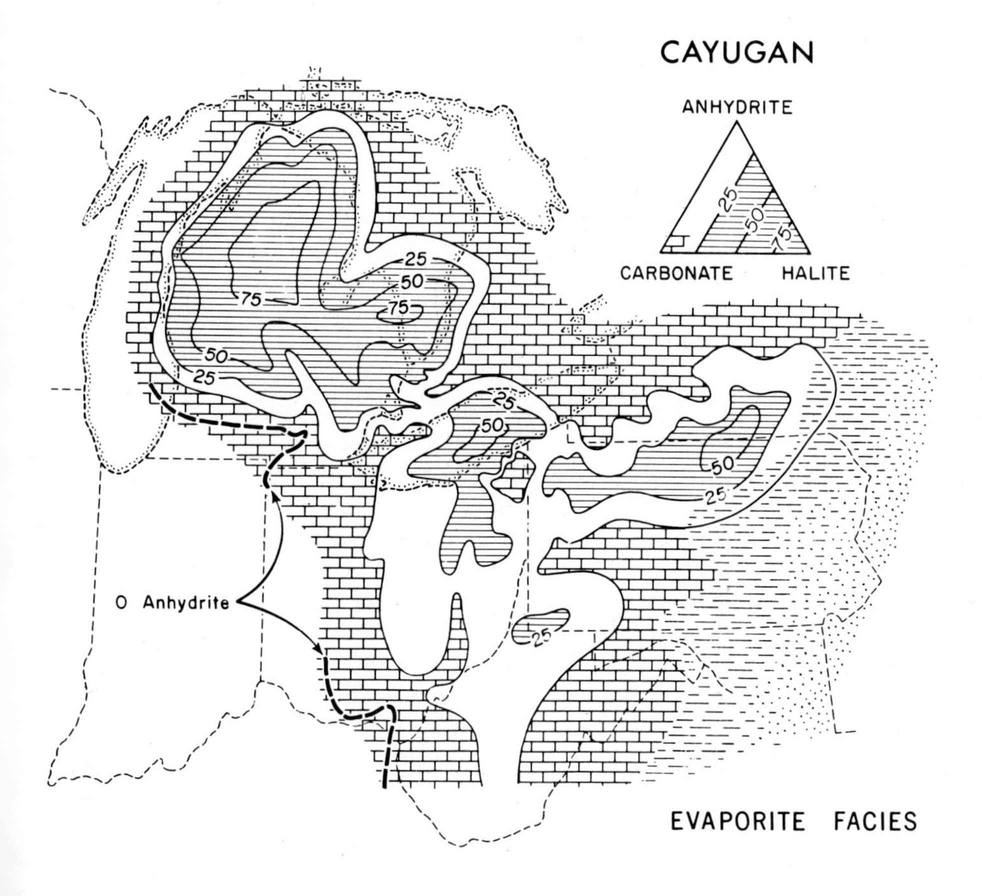
CAYUGAN
ANHYDRITE
25
50
75
CARBONATE
HALITE
25
50
75
75
50
25
25
50
50
25
0 Anhydrite
25
EVAPORITE FACIES

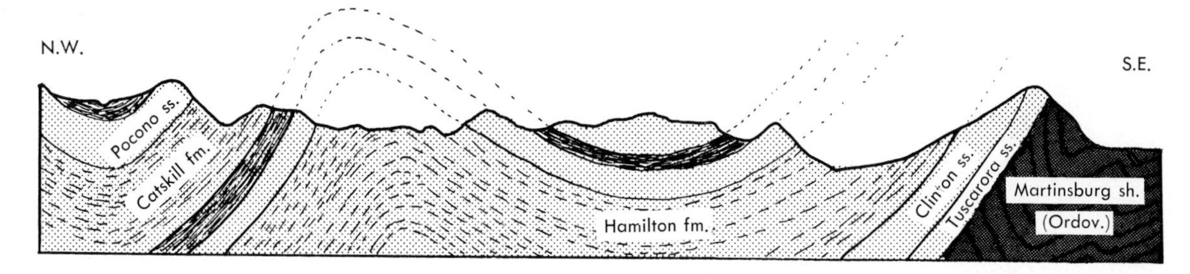

Fig. 14-3. Cross-sectional view of the Delaware River Water Gap. The Martinsburg Shale of Ordovician age is exposed at the right (SE). It is strongly folded, turned up, and truncated by an erosion surface. The Clinton and Tuscarora sandstones lie unconformably above the Martinsburg Shale. Notice that the sandstones hold up the ridges in this section as is characteristic of the Appalachian Valley and Ridge province. The folds in the units above the Martinsburg were formed near the end of the Paleozoic Era.

Late Silurian

Finally the seas that had become so extensive across North America began to recede. This took place during the Cayugan Epoch. As withdrawal took place seas were severely restricted, and inland seas were left without connections to the open seas. In these restricted bodies evaporation reduced the volume of water, and the remaining waters became supersaturated with salts. Finally salts began to be precipitated. The group of formations that contains this salt is known as the Salina Group. The section is 4500 feet thick in Michigan where the topographic basin earlier in the period had become the site of one of these inland seas. About 1000 feet of salts was left in New York State. The quantities of salt are so great that it seems probable that the climate was arid and that there were at least temporary connections or perhaps continual shallow connections with the oceans through which sea water could enter the seas.

Toward the end of the period the arid climate gave way to more normal conditions. Marine waters of what seems to have been ordinary salinity extended over the area, and thin limestones and dolostones were laid down.

In western North America in the inner miogeosynclinal belt there is a moderately thick section of limestones and dolostones in this slightly subsiding belt. Farther west in the eugeosynclinal belt there was volcanism. Graptolite-bearing volcanic rocks and shale were deposited. To the north in southeastern Alaska the subsidence in this belt was great. About 11,000 feet of sediments was deposited including nearly 5000 feet of limestone.

EVAPORITES OF THE SILURIAN

When the Niagaran seas began to retreat from the continental interior of North America several partially enclosed basins retained waters. Two of these are notable, the Michigan basin and the Ohio-New York basin. The Michigan basin at this time was a tectonically formed basin. It was an area of subsidence and it was also a physiographic basin. The general shape and positions of these basins may be seen in Fig. 14-1. Salina time was not entirely dominated by evaporite deposition. There are thick fossilferous limestones in the section. When these were formed the circulation of water throughout the basins was relatively free. At these times waters moved through the basins between the Arctic seaways of Canada into the Appalachian trough in Ohio, Kentucky, and southeastward.

Three major evaporite cycles have been recognized in the Salina formation of the Michigan basin. A generalized stratigraphic column of the Salina formation is given in Fig. 14-6. Note the repetition of this sequence:

Limestone—Anhydrite—Salt—Anhydrite.
Limestone—Anhydrite—Salt—Anhydrite—Dolomitic Shale.
Limestone—Anhydrite—Salt—Anhydrite—Dolomitic Shale.

The limestones are normal marine sediments. Salt and gypsum are sediments formed when the salinity of sea waters becomes concentrated to the point that the water is supersaturated with these salts. Gypsum, calcium sulfate, contains water. No gypsum is shown in the section given above. Instead we find anhydrite, a calcium sulfate that does not have any water with it. Salt, which has an affinity for water, pulls the water out of the gypsum deposited near it and therefore transforms the gypsum into anhydrite.

Some very interesting deductions have been made about the conditions within these basins at the time of the deposition of the Salina formation. The Salina formation outcrops at the surface in places around the edge of the Michigan basin, but more than 150 wells have penetrated the formation. Samples collected from these well cuttings have been analyzed by L. I. Briggs. Each sample collected was broken down into its constituents, and the relative amounts of halite, anhydrite, and limestone or dolostone were recorded. Once this is done for all the wells it becomes possible to see that there is a systematic distribution of these predominant rock types. It is possible to see clearly defined differences between the basin in Michigan and Ontario and the one in Ohio, Pennsylvania, and New York. The Michigan basin was relatively more saline. Furthermore it is possible to establish where the inlets were that fed normal marine waters into the basins. One of them was probably the principal connection to the open ocean during the entire Salina time. This is deduced from the relative abundance of limestone through this section leading into the Michigan basin from the north. The second connection at the southern entrance to the basin-fed marine waters

Fig. 14-4. Niagara Falls. The falls have formed where the river flowing from Lake Erie into Lake Ontario has cut across a cuesta. The strata are slightly tilted to the north. The falls are gradually retreating and will one day be eliminated entirely. Niagara Falls is one of the best exposures of Silurian strata in the United States.

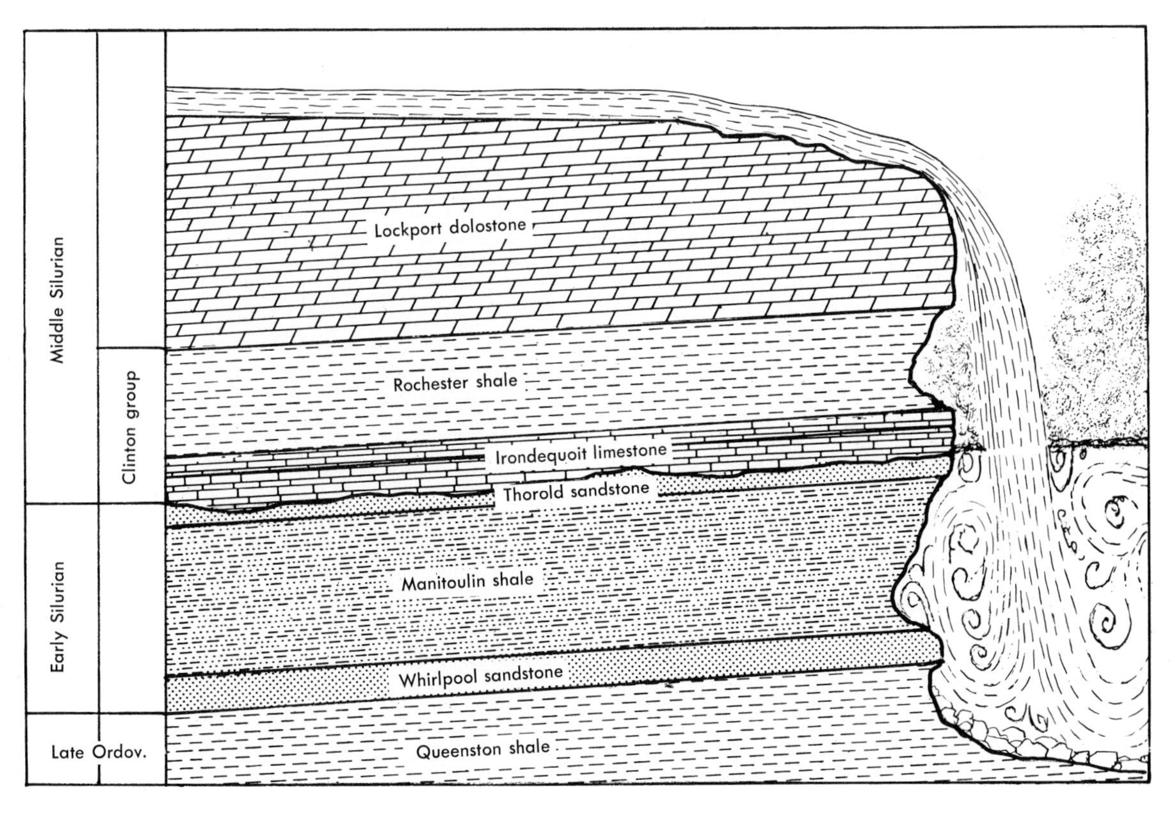

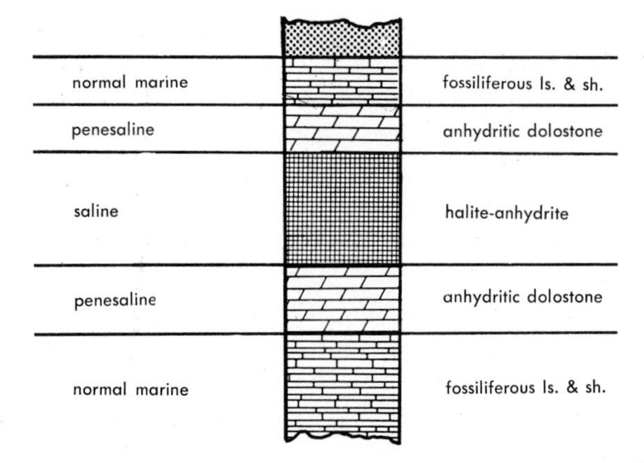

Fig. 14-5. An evaporite cycle, schematically represented. The salinity, rock types associated with it and the presence of fossil assemblages, if any, are indicated. In the hypothetical case shown here normal marine waters occupy a shallow sea in which limestone is being deposited. As the sea becomes restricted supplies of normal marine waters are cut off and the salt content of the water rises. The first part of the saline sequence to be formed is anhydrite or gypsum and dolostone. Then when concentration of salts becomes excessive, halite and anhydrite are deposited. As conditions return to normal the sequence is reversed. (After L. L. Sloss.)

from the Appalachian seas into the basin from time to time when it was open. This entrance appears to have been larger and to have carried more flow during the second cycle of evaporite formation, for limestone characterizes that part of the Salina formation in that region. The third entrance led from the Michigan basin into the Ohio-New York basin. This entrance allowed brine from the Michigan basin to flow into the adjoining areas.

Evaporation was brought on in all these basins by the effects of poor circulation, and probably arid climates.

The two basins were separated by a northeast-southwest trending ridge. The ridge was composed of reefs covered by very shallow water. At times it was almost continuous, at other times it consisted of widely separated reefs, but during most of the period it was effective in restricting the circulation of water between the two basins. Sedimentary rocks deposited during this period are very thin over the ridge, but they are thousands of feet thick in the basins.

LIFE OF THE SILURIAN

I. NEW FORMS

1. Eurypterids: Arthropods, with jointed legs. These strange-looking marine animals called sea scorpions were numerous toward the end of the period. Some of them were up to 9 feet long making them the largest arthropods ever known.
2. Fossils of lycopsid land plants are the first of the club mosses. They had poorly developed roots, but possessed leaves and stems and represent a marked advance over the nonvascular plants.

Fig. 14-6. Schematic representation of the three major evaporite cycles that are recognized in the Salina formation. (After L. I. Briggs.)

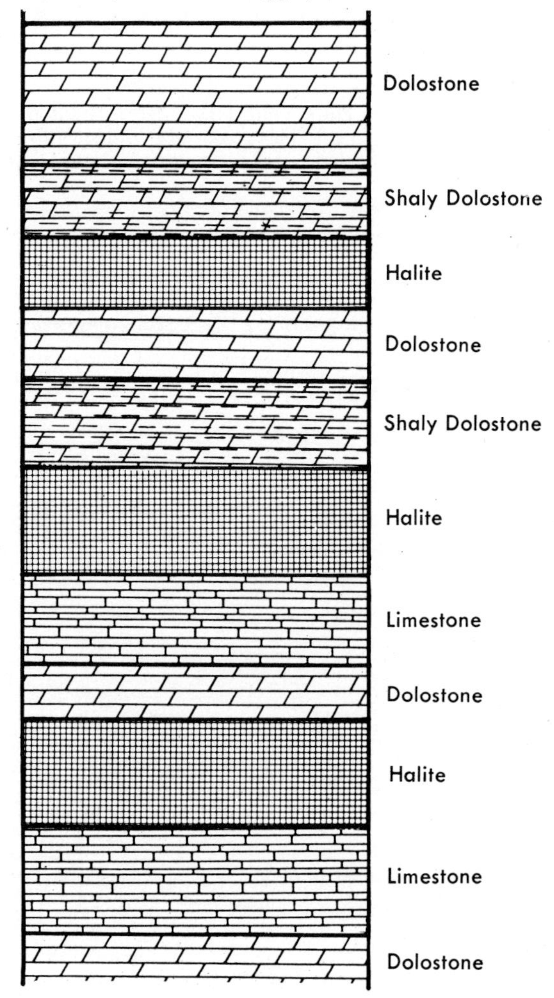

Fig. 14-7. Restored eurypterids. These are the largest arthropods which have ever lived on earth. Some of them grew to be 9 feet long. They were among the most prominent creatures of the Silurian seas which occupied the continental interior. Note also the gastropods carrying coiled shells on their backs in the background. (Courtesy of the N.Y. State Museum and Science Service.)

3. Fossil scorpions and millipeds are known from the Upper Silurian. These are most significant because they may well be the first animals to become adapted to breathing air.

II. PEAKS, ADVANCEMENT, AND DECLINE

1. Tabulate corals reached the peak of their development and were important in the Silurian reefs of the central United States.
2. Crinoids, the echinoderm sea lilies, also attained their maximum development. They were abundant and widely distributed. These are important guide fossils for the system.
3. Graptolites were beginning to decline from their peak in the Ordovician.
4. Corals became even more important. They expanded, and the honeycomb, chain, cup, and compound corals thrived in the shallow warm waters of the Silurian seas of central North America.
5. Bryozoans were still present.
6. Brachiopods underwent continued expansion. Many new forms appeared during the Silurian and in the following periods.
7. All of the major groups of mollusks were present: gastropods, cephalopods, and pelecypods.
8. Trilobites that had been so important in the earlier periods began to decline. Many strange specialized forms appeared. They tended to become increasingly ornamented.

III. NOTABLE ASPECTS OF SILURIAN LIFE

There were relatively few major changes in the general aspects of the fauna from those of the Ordovician. The invertebrates continued to be the most important groups

Silurian System	Penn. to Tenn.	W. New York	Arkansas	Northern Calif.
Cayugan Series	Keyser limestone Tonoloway limestone Wills Creek shale Bloomsburg red beds	Cobleskill (Akron) dolomite Salina group	Missouri Mountain slate	
Niagaran Series	McKenzie fm. Clinton group	Lockport-Guelph group Decew limestone Clinton group	Lafferty limestone St. Clair limestone Blaylock sandstone	Montgomery limestone
Albion Series	Castanea sandstone Tuscarora (Clinch) sandstone	Albion group	Brassfield limestone	Grizzly fm.

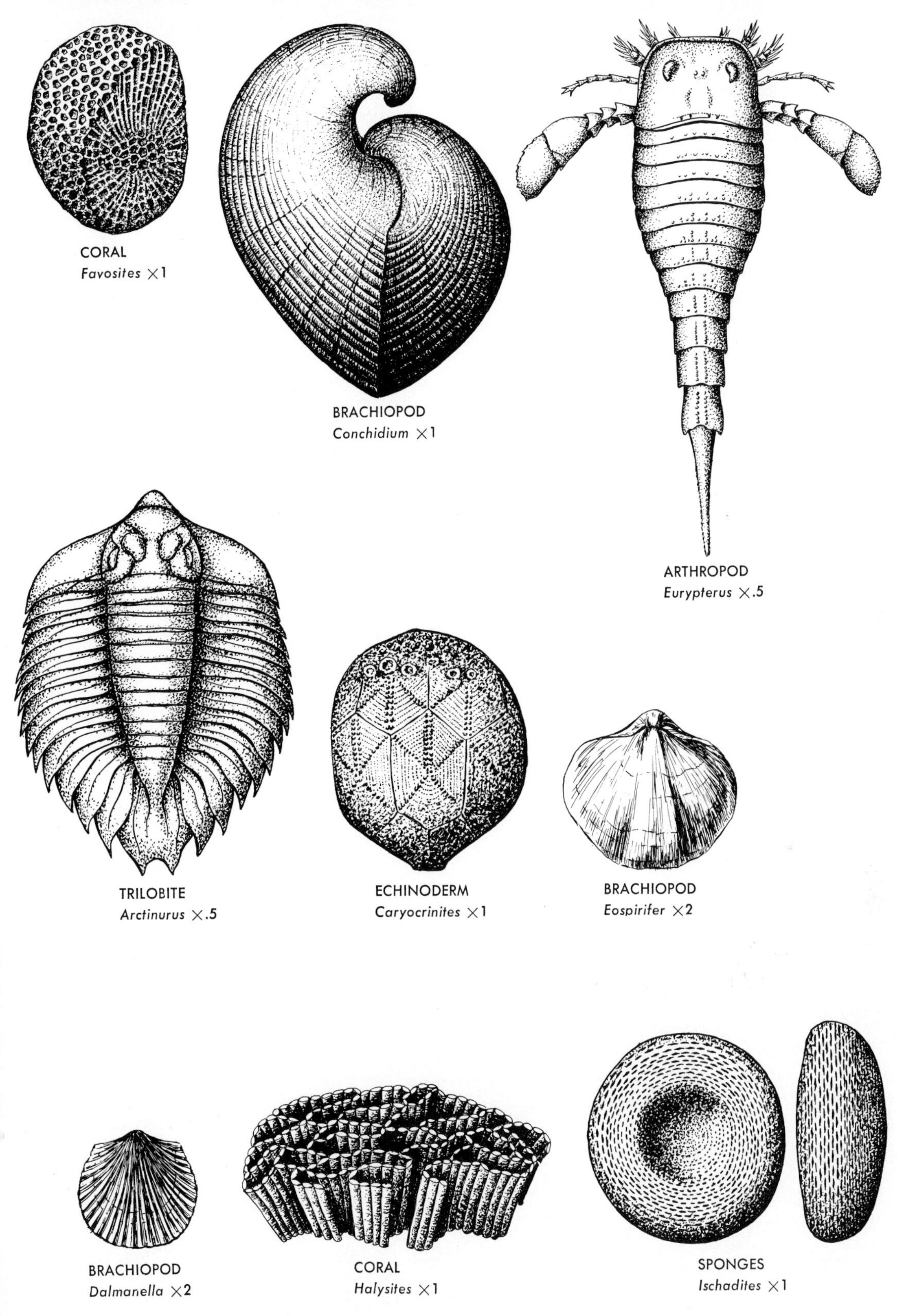

Fig. 14-9. Guide fossils for the Silurian.

Fig. 14-8. Correlation chart for the Silurian.

of animals, and plants were very scarce on the land masses. The first definite evidence of relatively large land plants is found in this system. These remains almost certainly do not represent the first plants to live on land, but they are the first that have been preserved in much detail. The lands of the Cambrian, Ordovician, and most of those of the Silurian were barren wastes. Only the lowlands had much in the way of a vegetative cover, but the plants that appeared at this time were the forerunners of the greatest forest of all time that came in the Carboniferous.

A second noteworthy occurrence is the presence of the scorpions and millipeds. Both of these arthropods, as we now know them, are capable of breathing air. The soft parts of those found in the Silurian are not well enough preserved to reveal lungs or lunglike organs that might have been used to breathe air, but if the animals did have such organs they are probably the first animals to obtain their oxygen supply directly from the air.

Fig. 14-10. Restored Silurian sea floor. The assemblages shown here were found on the Silurian reefs. Tall graceful sea lilies, crinoids, stand up from the floor which is inhabited by trilobites, brachiopods, coiled cephalopods, and a variety of corals (honeycomb coral, *Favosites*, tube coral, *Syringopora*, chain coral, *Halysites*, and a solitary coral). Middle Silurian. (Courtesy of the Chicago Natural History Museum.)

REFERENCES

BRIGGS, L. I., 1957, Quantitative aspects of evaporite deposition: Michigan Academy of Science, Arts, and Letters, v. XLII, p. 115-123

EARDLEY, A. J., 1947, Paleozoic Cordilleran geosyncline and related orogeny: Jour. Geology, v. 55, p. 309-342

KINDLE, E. M., and TAYLOR, F. B., 1913, Geology of the Niagara Falls quadrangle, New York: U. S. Geol. Survey Geol. Folio 190

LOWENSTAM, H. A., 1957, Niagaran reefs in the Great Lakes area: Geol. Soc. America Mem. 67, v. 2, p. 215-248

15 The Devonian Period

DISTRIBUTION OF OUTCROPS

Devonian rocks are best exposed in the northeastern and north-central parts of the United States. Other extensive outcrops are found in New England, and from southern New York they extend south along the eastern margin of the Appalachian Plateau. From New York they also extend west to form rims around the Michigan basin and the Cincinnati arch. Devonian rocks are well exposed around the Ozark dome, in the Ouachita Mountains, and along the flanks of many mountain uplifts in the Rockies.

PHYSICAL HISTORY OF THE DEVONIAN

Devonian in the eastern United States

Only a few outcrops of rocks deposited in the eugeosynclinal belt of the eastern North American coast have survived the erosion of post-Devonian time. Those remaining prove that a section of more than 6000 feet of terrigenous material was deposited in the Early Devonian time alone. This sequence is intruded by igneous rocks and in overlain by Upper Devonian sandstone. The missing Middle Devonian signifies an epoch of nondeposition and erosion during the Middle Devonian orogeny, the Acadian orogeny. This region was uplifted and was the source of sediment that is still preserved in the rocks of the Catskill Mountains in New York.

Early Devonian seas were at first restricted to a narrow belt trending northeast into New York. Carbonate rocks, limestones, and dolostones, were deposited in this trough. Then the sea began to advance, flooding more of the eastern coast and leaving a thin veneer of beach sands, the Oriskany sandstone, spread as far west as Michigan. By the Middle Devonian the nature of the sedimentation began to show the marked influence of a rising land area to the east. The Middle Devonian Hamilton group contains considerable amounts of shale. Other units are conglomerate and red beds found in the eastern part of the Appalachian Plateau. The Catskill delta had begun to form by the beginning of the Late Devonian, and it continued to grow until it had accumulated a 12,000-foot thick section of sediments from the high mountains east of it. These sediments resemble those of the Queenston delta of Late Ordovician age, but are much better exposed. A similar delta formed as a result of the Acadian orogeny (also known as the Schickshockian orogeny) is found in Gaspe, Canada.

Devonian in the central United States

In the central part of the United States, Lower Devonian limestones filled some of the reef-rimmed basins which had formed in the Silurian, such as the embayment in southern Illinois. The Michigan basin continued to be active in the Early Devonian. More than 2000 feet of limestone accumulated as the basin subsided. Slight subsidence continued into the Middle and Late Devonian epochs, but the most active phases of the downwarping were over by that time. A large number of minor unconformities are found in the Middle Devonian of the Mid-continent. Most of the units are lensing limestones with occasional beach sands. These create a picture of a low continental region periodically inundated by slight fluctuations of sea level or warping of the crust. The Devonian closed with the deposition of a westward-spreading sheet of black shale that continued to form during Late Devonian and Early Mississippian time.

Devonian in the western United States

The Lower Devonian is missing from the west, and only a few areas contain Middle Devonian units. In the western eugeosynclinal belt volcanic activity continued. Small welts or rising land areas of igneous and volcanic material rose within the belt, were eroded, and supplied more sediment to the immediately surrounding regions.

The sporadic occurrence of Devonian outcrops over such a large area as the western United States makes it difficult to correlate events throughout the whole region. The miogeosyncline received thick sections of carbonate rocks in British Columbia, the Yukon, and in Nevada.

THE ACADIAN OROGENY AND THE CATSKILL DELTA

The classic area for the study of the Devonian in the eastern United States is located just west of the Hudson River in New York State in the Catskill Mountains. The Hudson River now flows through a valley of Cambrian and Ordovician limestones and shales. West of the valley rises the escarpment of the Catskill Mountains. Along this escarpment and in the valleys cut into the mountains the sediments of Devonian time are beautifully exposed. These sediments, like those of the Ordovician-Silurian Queenston delta, are the erosional products from a high mountain range which lay east of the present Devonian outcrops. How the sediments of the Catskill Mountains have survived removal by erosion in the time since the end of the Devonian, while the higher central core of the Acadian Mountains has been removed down to the Cambrian-Ordovician units, is a puzzling question. This range must have been a very prominent mountain range to supply enough sediment to build a delta more than 12,000 feet thick on its flanks.

System	Series	WEST VIRGINIA	SCHOHARIE VALLEY NEW YORK	MICHIGAN	N. W. WYOMING
DEVONIAN SYSTEM	UPPER DEVONIAN SERIES	Catskill red beds		Ellsworth shale	
		Chemung sandstone		Antrim black shale	
			Catawissa red beds		Darby fm.
		Portage fm.	Katsberg red beds	Antrim black shale	Jefferson limestone
			Oneonta red beds		
	MIDDLE DEVONIAN SERIES	Genesee sh., Londes ls.	Gilboa sandstone	Potter Farm fm.	
		Hamilton shale	Hamilton group	Norway Point fm.	
				Alpena limestone	
				Genshaw limestone	
				Ferron Point shale	
				Rockport Quarry fm.	
				Bell shale	
				Rogers City limestone	
		Marcellus shale		Dundee limestone	
	LOWER DEVONIAN SERIES	Onondaga limestone	Onondaga limestone		
		Huntersville chert	Schoharie fm. Esopus shale	Mackinac limestone	Beartooth Butte limestone
		Ridgeley sandstone	Oriskany sandstone		
			Port Ewen limestone		
			Becraft limestone		
		New Scotland fm.	New Scotland fm.		
			Kalkberg limestone		
		Coeymans limestone	Coeymans limestone		

Fig. 15-1. Devonian correlation chart.

Fig. 15-2. Devonian guide fossils.

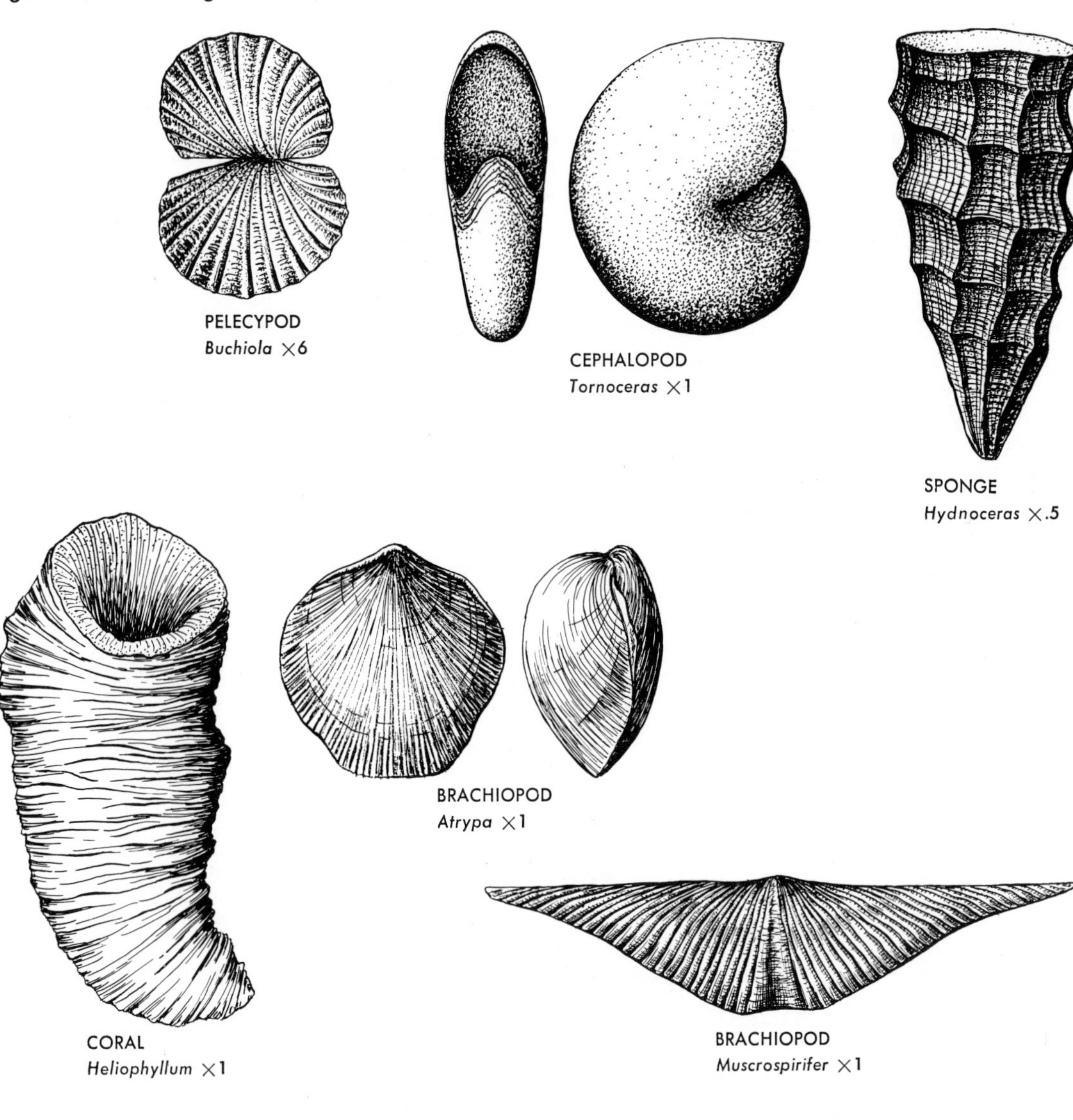

BRACHIOPOD
Eospirifer ×2

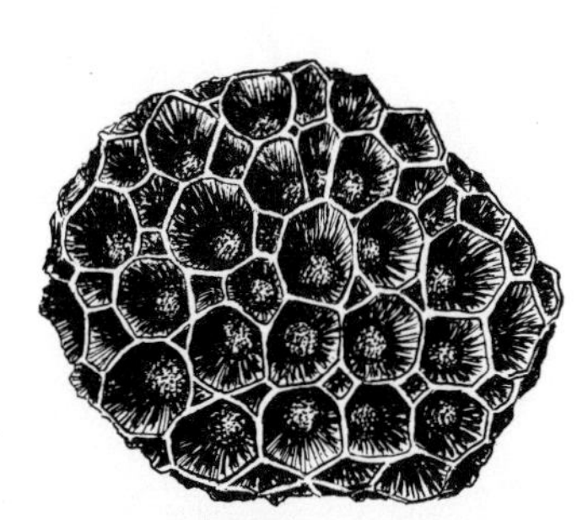

CORAL
Pleurodictyum ×.5

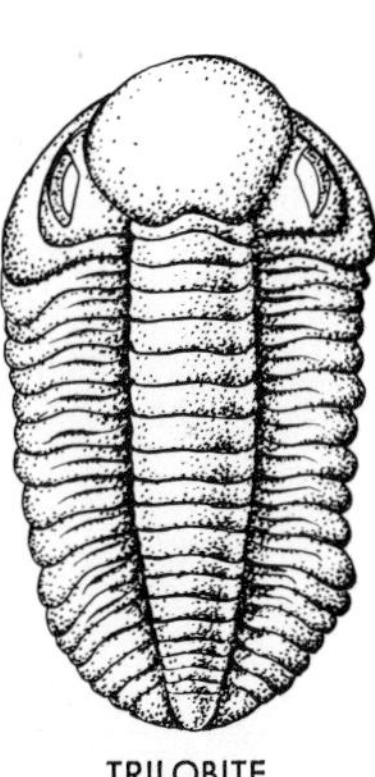

TRILOBITE
Phacops ×.5

Middle Devonian rock units gave first notice of the rising land in the Acadian Mountains, but the uplift culminated later in the Devonian, at which time the Catskill delta was formed. The following, based on the work of Dr. George H. Chadwick, New York State Museum Bulletin 336, outlines the history of the development of thought on the nature of the Catskill delta.

It was formerly supposed that the Upper Devonian strata of New York consisted of four successive formations each with a characteristic lithology and fauna or flora. These are the Genesee, a black shale; the Portage, an olive shale containing thin sandstone layers; the Chemung, a unit of sandy shales and sandstones; and the Catskill formation, composed of red shales and interbedded sandstones. A unit of white sandstone and conglomerate, the Pocono formation, was thought to lie over the above strata. In some places these five units can be seen in succession one above the other, but in other localities each can be seen to grade laterally into one of the others. After much field work and long years of disagreement it was finally established that all five of these types of sediments were laid down contemporaneously on a large alluvial fan and its deltaic extension into the shallow sea that covered the eastern interior United States. The white sands and conglomerates, the Pocono formation, were deposited high in the alluvial fan. The red muds that were washed down from the high parts of the fan covered the lower slopes of sand, forming the Catskill beds. Debris that was carried into the marine waters soon lost its red color as a result of reduction in the shallow warm waters of the littoral zone in which the Chemung formation was formed. The finest debris remained in suspension and was carried farther

Fig. 15-3. Geologic map of Silurian and Devonian exposures in the northern United States. The exposures of Devonian strata here are the most extensive in the United States. Many of the units are richly fossiliferous. The Catskill Mountains are composed largely of debris eroded from a mountain range which stood along the eastern coast during the Middle Devonian. The debris was deposited in a large delta, part of which is still preserved as the now deeply dissected Catskill Mountains. (After the Geologic Map of the United States.)

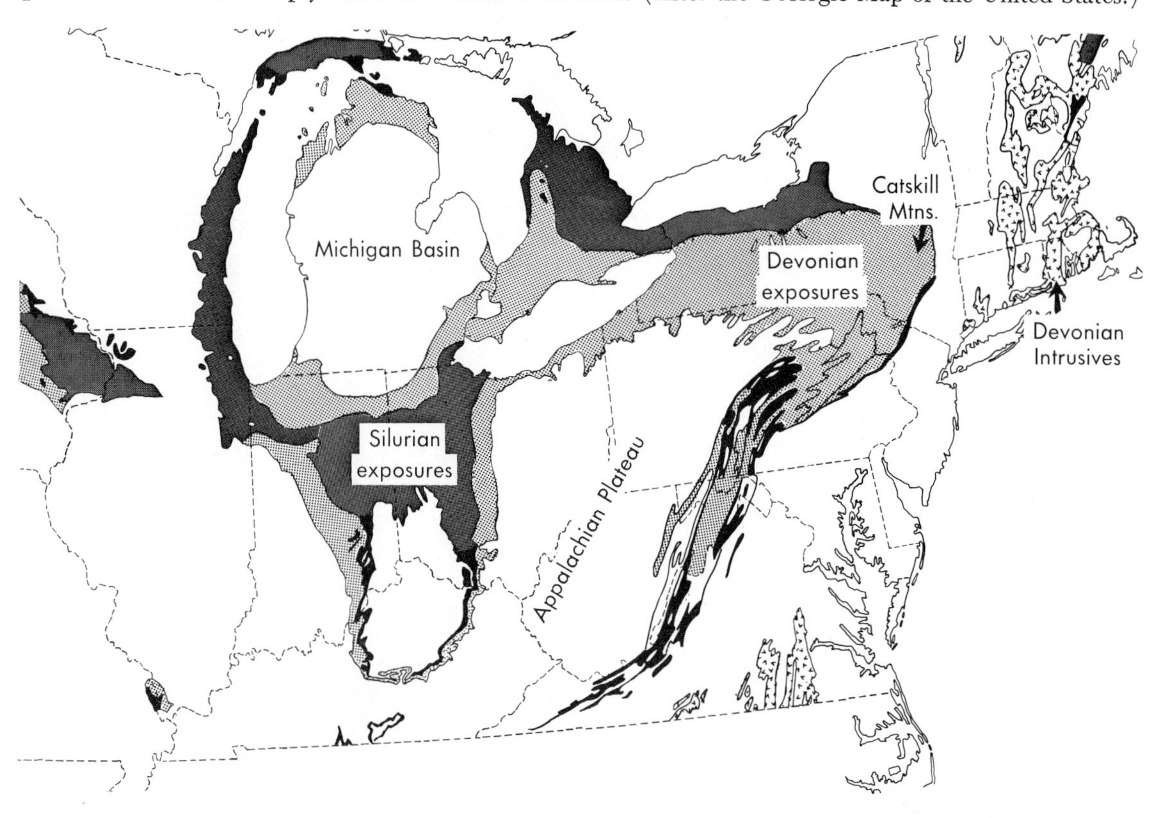

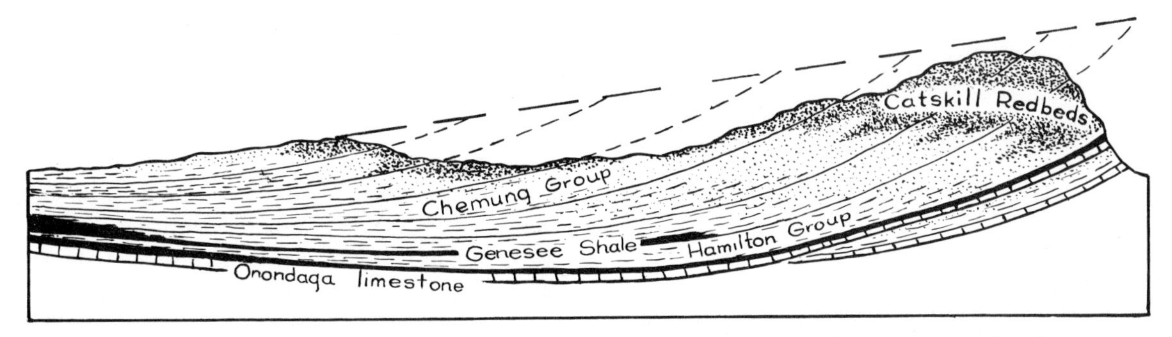

Fig. 15-4. Cross section across the Catskill Mountains. Notice how the units grade into one another. It was once thought that each unit was of a different age from the others. More detailed study has shown that they were laid down almost simultaneously.

westward into deeper waters where it was deposited as the Portage formation. Far out where the main source of sediment was organic material, the Genesee formation, a shale, was formed.

The apparent superposition of these deposits was brought about by long-continued uplift in the Acadian Mountains and consequent building westward of the alluvial fan and delta. As the delta built westward each zone or facies of sediment overlapped the one next to it. Eventually the Pocono was being deposited over the first-formed Genesee.

TRANSGRESSIVE AND REGRESSIVE BIOHERM GROWTH*

The Leduc oil field in Alberta, Canada, is one of the most prolific oil-producing areas in Devonian rocks. The oil in the Leduc field is produced from buried coral reefs or complex reefs composed of the remains of many other types of marine organisms called bioherms. The oil probably came initially from the shale units that are adjacent to the reefs, but it has become trapped in the porous bioherms. The main reservoir is the talus of the reef debris, broken fragments of the reef which form a pile of loose debris on the seaward side of the living parts of the reef. The reef itself is porous and also contains some oil and gas. As a result of the petroleum exploration we have learned much about the history of the seas in which these reefs grew. By mapping the position and depths of the bioherms at different times it is possible to trace the transgression and regression of shore lines in this region in the Devonian Period.

The bioherms are made up of corals, bryo-

*T. A. Link, 1949, Leduc Oil Field, Alberta, Canada, G.S.A. Bull., v. 60, p. 381-402

Fig. 15-5. The Catskill Mountains. This is an oblique view of a relief map of southern New York State. The Catskills are separated from the Adirondack Mountains by the Mohawk Valley on the north. The Hudson River valley forms the eastern boundary. The escarpment along the eastern edge is a prominent topographic feature. The relief map is by the U.S. Army Map Service. (Photo by E. W. Spencer.)

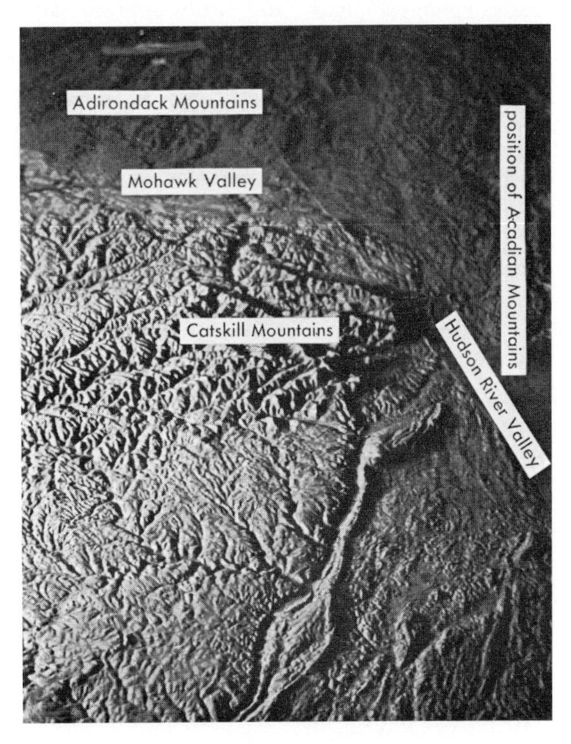

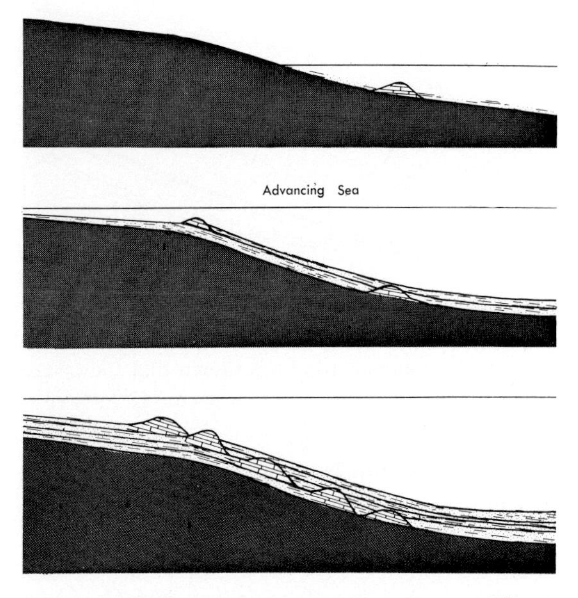

Fig. 15-6. Reefs growing in an advancing sea. This is a schematic section showing types of reef growth found in the Devonian of Alberta. In this case the sea moves inland rapidly between the top and middle stages causing the first reef to die. In the bottom stage the reefs are shown as growing just fast enough to maintain a position just below sea level. (After T. A. Link.)

zoans, sponges, algae, and other aquatic animals and plants. Many of them lived attached by stalks to the bottom of the sea. Such animals and plants are said to be sessile benthos, attached bottom dwellers. They are much better adapted to life in shallow water, and will not survive long in deeper water. Some of the most important of the reef-forming organisms propagate by a process of budding by which the young form on the side of the adult. The young are not generally free to move through the water, but must remain attached to the colony. For this reason they are not likely to survive if there is a relatively rapid increase in the depth of water. They will survive if the colony can grow upward at a rate equal to the increase in water depth. The distribution of bioherms in the Leduc field shows evidence of both transgressions and regressions of the seas. When the movements of sea level were rapid the reefs died out, and new reefs became established in a new position in water of a favorable depth. At other times the rate of deepening of the water was gradual, and the reef gradually grew upward and inland just fast enough to keep the top of the reef at the most favorable depth continually.

Fig. 15-6 shows three stages in a transgressing sea. Stage I shows a reef located off shore. As the water gradually deepens the reef grows almost straight upward. In stage II there has been a sudden rise in sea level, and the first reef has ceased to live. A new reef has started from the sea bottom in shallow water. In stage III a gradual rise in sea level finds the reef moving landward as the sea transgresses, but remaining in about the same depth of water.

Along the fore reef, debris broken off by wave action accumulates. Back of the reef, circulation of the water becomes restricted, and evaporites and clastic sediments from the shore begin to fill in the shallow water. Muds are formed in front of the reef farther out. If the sea suddenly withdraws, the reef re-establishes itself farther out, and evaporites are deposited on top of the earlier fore reef sediments of mud. If the sea withdraws gradually, the reef moves progressively seaward.

In the case of transgression the older reefs are covered by shales, whereas in the case of regression the older reefs become surrounded

Fig. 15-7. Phacops. This Devonian trilobite is one of the most abundant trilobites for the Devonian. (Photo by courtesy of the U.S. National Museum.)

Fig. 15-8. Devonian fossil fish locality. Beartooth Butte is an erosion remnant of early Paleozoic strata which remains atop the Beartooth Mountains, an uplifted block composed primarily of Precambrian gneisses. Near the top of the butte you can see a cross section of a Devonian stream channel which was cut into Ordovician limestones. The stream channel is filled with red, oxidized, Devonian fresh water deposits of sandstone in which fossil ostracoderms are found. The channel which once flowed at a much lower elevation is now about 10,000 feet above sea level. (Photo by E. W. Spencer.)

and covered by back-reef sediments such as salt, anhydrite, red beds, and gypsum. Both transgression and regression may produce reefs which

a. Are blanket-like in their coverage, or
b. Extend laterally for great lengths.

The rate of change of sea level will determine the form produced.

LIFE OF THE DEVONIAN

I. NEW FORMS

1. The first land vertebrates, amphibians, which belong to a group known as labyrinthodonts, appeared late in the Devonian.
2. The first air-breathing fish are found early in the period.
3. The first wingless insects appear.
4. The first evergreen trees, scale trees, and seed ferns appeared in the Gilboa Forest of western New York. This forest grew on the Catskill delta.
5. A group of cephalopods, known as the ammonoids, appeared. They are characterized by the unusual design of the suture pattern of their shells.

II. OLDER GROUPS THAT WERE STILL PRESENT

1. Corals were still abundant. Some of them reached huge sizes. The largest cup corals grew to be more than 2 feet high. One of the most important groups was the stromatoporoids.

Fig. 15-9. A fossil colony of bryozoans from the Hamilton Group of New York. Such colonies are one of the important constituents of Silurian and Devonian bioherms. (Photo by courtesy of the U.S. National Museum, R. S. Boardman.)

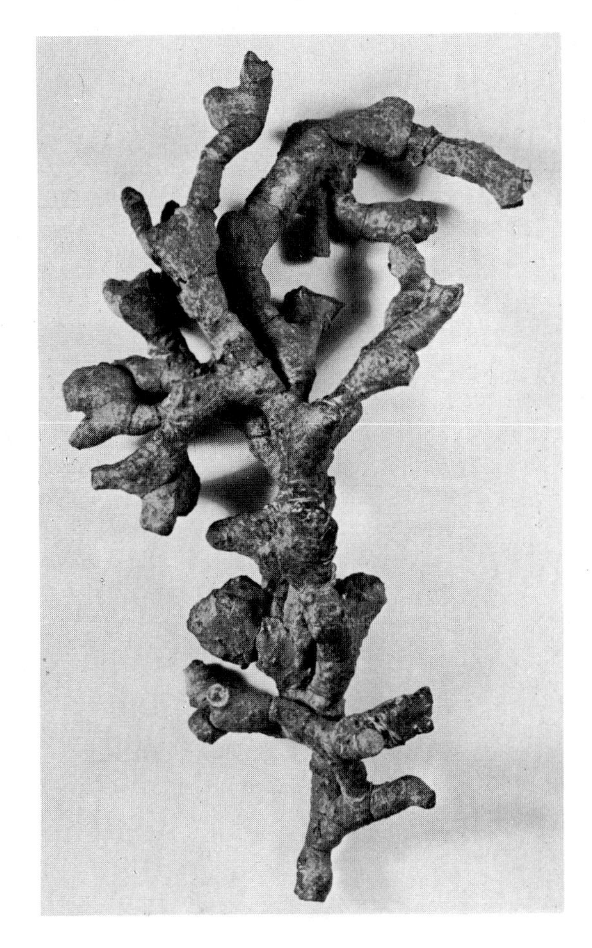

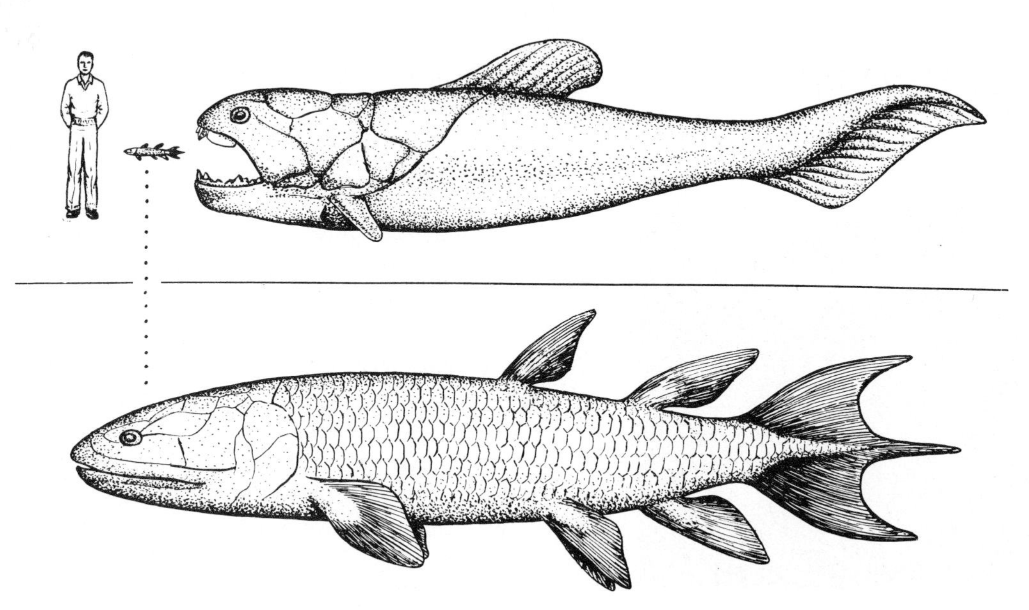

Fig. 15-10. Devonian fishes. At the top is a restored placoderm, *Dinichthys*, which grew to lengths of 30 feet. The head region was heavily armored with external bony plates that were jointed. Below is a Devonian crossopterygian. This fish was only about 2 feet long. The crossopterygians were probably the connecting link between the fishes and the first four-legged, air-breathing vertebrates. The basal lobe is the forerunner of the limb of the tetrapods. Other fish did not have such a lobe.

Fig. 15-11. Early land plants. Abundant and widespread land plants are found first in rocks of the Devonian Period, dating from about 350 million years ago. They set the stage for the invasion of the land by animals, which are ultimately dependent upon plants for food. Shown here are (1) one of the first ferns, a tree that grew 30 to 40 feet high; (2) horsetail rushes; (3) one of the most primitive plants, *Psilophyton,* which had no leaves; and (4) a lycopod, the tall tree without leaves which is covered by short spikelike projections which served as leaves. (From a mural by C. R. Knight, courtesy of Chicago Natural History Museum.)

Fig. 15-12. Restoration of a Devonian sea floor. This assemblage of animals would have been found on the Devonian sea-floor from New York westward to the Mississippi valley. Most of the animals shown are corals, a solitary coral (1), and several colonial corals (2). In addition there are a frilled nautiloid cephalopod (3), several trilobites (4), a gastropod (5), a crinoid (6), a straight shelled cephalopod (7), and brachiopods (8). (Photo by courtesy of the Museum of Paleontology, University of Michigan.)

2. Bryozoans.
3. Mollusca: Pelecypods, gastropods, and cephalopods were present. The pelecypods had become more abundant and diversified than ever before.
4. Trilobites were on the decline, but the largest ones ever found lived at this time. They are nearly 3 feet long.
5. Echinoderms: Blastoids, starfishes, and echinoids are all well represented in the Devonian, but the crinoids were particularly abundant.
6. Eurypterids were still present in the fresh-water deposits such as those of the Old Red sandstone of England.

III. EXTINCTION

1. The last of the ostracoderms probably died before the end of the Devonian. These, the first fish, had survived for more than 100 million years.

IV. PEAK OF DEVELOPMENT

1. Climax of the brachiopods was reached during the Devonian. More than 700 species have been described. They are extremely varied. Two of the most notable of these are *Spirifer* and *Stringocephalus*.
2. The Devonian is known as the "*Age of Fishes.*"

V. NOTABLE ASPECTS OF THE FAUNA AND FLORA

The first fish, the ostracoderms, appeared in the Early Ordovician. More than 120 million years later the fishes reached the climax of their development. The jawless ostracoderms were still abundant in the fresh-water streams of the Devonian, but there were many other fishes. One notable variety, which was known as the placoderm, contained platelike pieces of bone in its skin.

One of the giants of the fish world was the arthrodire, a joint-neck placoderm that grew to be 30 feet long. These may well have been the most feared predators of the period. Sharks were one of the most abundant groups. Many of them were considerably smaller than those we know today.

The first bony fishes, forerunners of many modern fishes, also lived in the early Devonian. One of the bony fishes to evolve in the Devonian was an ancestor of the African lung fish. We can learn a great deal about these early fish from the habits of the lung fish, which now live in upper parts of the Nile River valley. The climate is highly variable in this region. There are warm humid winters and very dry summers. In the winter the lung fish live in the water, breathing through gills like other fish, but in the summer, as the swamps begin to dry out, they embed themselves in the mud. Each fashions a chamber in the mud and rests there until the next humid season. During this period it makes use of a swim-bladder, which is connected to the throat, and functions just like a lung.

The main group of Devonian lung fish are known as crossopterygians. They possessed a lobe-shaped fin for which they are named. They are important because they are the connecting link between fish and the first amphibians, called labyrinthodonts, which appeared late in this same period of time. The difference between these groups is relatively minor. Both breathe air through lungs. Amphibians, like fish, must lay their eggs in water, and both are closely linked to the aqueous environment in other ways. Most of them spend their lives very near lakes, seas, or at least swampy lands. The strong muscular fins of the crossopterygian fishes are very similar in structure to the legs and webbed feet of the labyrinthodonts.

Fig. 15-13. Restoration of a Devonian sea floor. (Photo by courtesy of the N.Y. State Museum and Science Service.)

Fig. 15-14. Devonian forest group including *Lyginopterid*, center, and *Archaeosigillaria*, at left. The first record of a large forest comes from the Devonian System.

REFERENCES

COOPER, G. A., 1957, Paleoecology of Middle Devonian of eastern and central United States: Geol. Soc. America Mem. 67, v. 2, p. 249-277

WOODWARD, H. P., 1957, Chronology of Appalachian folding: Am. Assoc. Petroleum Geologists Bull., v. 41, p. 2312-2327

16 The Carboniferous: Mississippian and Pennsylvanian Periods

Extensive warm, humid swamps covered large parts of the continents during this time. The period is named for the carbonaceous, carbon-bearing sediments formed during the period. These formations lie unconformably over units of the Devonian System in England where the famous Coal Measures were deposited. The system has been divided into Lower and Upper Carboniferous in Europe where the lower system contains much less coal than the upper. In the United States the divisions are so marked that the Carboniferous is divided into two separate periods, the Mississippian and Pennsylvanian. The classic localities for the Mississippian are in the Mississippi Valley region, while the type sections of Pennsylvanian units are found in central and western Pennsylvania.

PHYSICAL HISTORY OF THE MISSISSIPPIAN PERIOD

Eastern and Central United States

Kinderhookian sediments in the eastern United States represent the gradual wearing away of the Acadian (Shickshockian) Mountains which formed toward the end of the Devonian time. That these mountains were still moderately elevated at the beginning of Mississippian time is shown by the Kinderhookian and Osagian series which contain large quantities of gravel, sand, silt, and clay. The basal part of the Mississippian is the Pocono formation, which reaches westward from the Catskill delta and Pocono Mountains of Pennsylvania to eastern Michigan and southward into Kentucky. In the central part of the continent a shale unit was deposited widely, except around the Ozark dome in Missouri, Oklahoma, and Arkansas where sandstone is present.

Osagian time has a history somewhat similar to that of the Kinderhookian except that the land mass of the Acadian Mountains in New England was lower, and smaller amounts of clastic debris were being carried westward from them. Instead limestone and fine muds were formed across the eastern interior seas. These units grade into one another, with the coarsest still in eastern Pennsylvania. All of the units of the Lower and Middle Mississippian thin over the Cincinnati arch, indicating its persistence as an unwarped unit.

Meramecian strata provide little or no evidence for the continued existence of the Acadian Mountains. Carbonaceous sediments were deposited in the Mid-continent and as far east as the eastern part of West Virginia, which probably was slightly emergent. At this time restricted seas returned to the Michigan basin depositing shales, salt, and gypsum under conditions somewhat similar to those which had existed there in the Silurian.

Chesterian time, the later part of the Mississippian, shows the spread of coal swamps into the eastern interior basins. Rhythmic alternation of sea and land occurred over a broad area. The land stood near sea level and became emergent or submergent by slight relative movements of sea level. Chesterian time began with limestone deposition. Overlying these

Fig. 16-1. The Age of Crinoids. Because crinoids are preserved in such abundance in rocks of Mississippian age it is often called "the age of crinoids." This garden of "sea lilies" represents one that lived on the sea floor in the Mississippi Valley during the Osagian Epoch. In addition to crinoids the restoration shows a blastoid (1), and a starfish (2). (Photo by courtesy of the Museum of Paleontology, University of Michigan.)

MISSISSIPPIAN SYSTEM	NEVADA	N. W. WYOMING	WEST KENTUCKY	WEST VIRGINIA
CHESTERIAN SERIES	Bailey spring limestone	Lower Amsden fm.	Buffalo Wallow fm. Tar Spring sandstone Glen Dean limestone Hardinsburg sandstone Golconda fm. Cypress sandstone Girkin limestone fm.	Mauch Chunk series Greenbrier series
MERAMECIAN	Scotty Wash quartzite	Sacajawea fm.	Ste. Genevieve fm. St. Louis limestone Salem limestone Warsaw limestone	Maccrady series
OSAGIAN	Peers Spring fm.		Muldraugh fm. Floyds Knob fm. Brodhead fm. New Providence shale	
KINDERHOOKIAN	Bristol Pass limestone	Madison limestone	New Albany shale	Pocono series

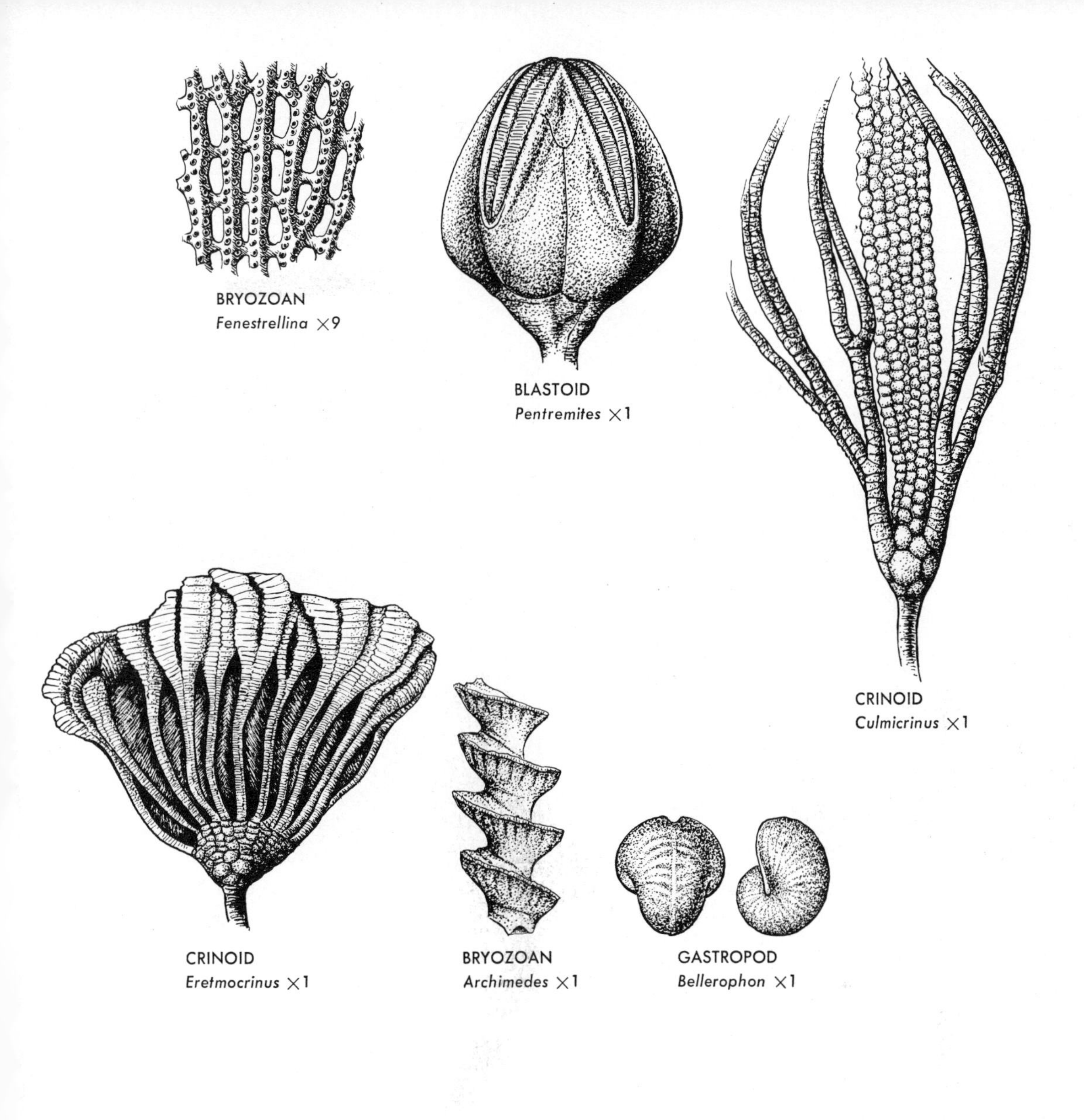

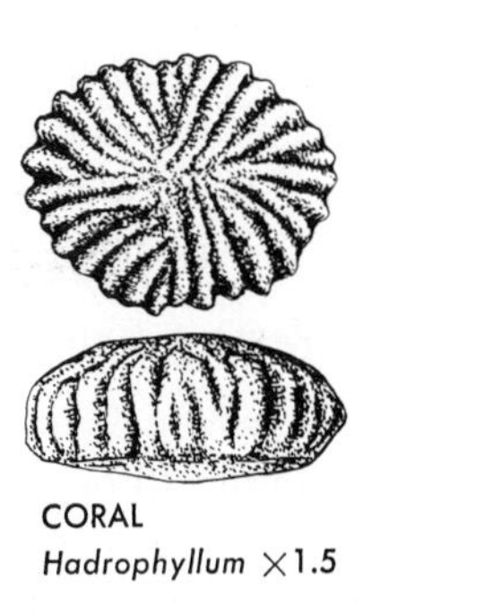

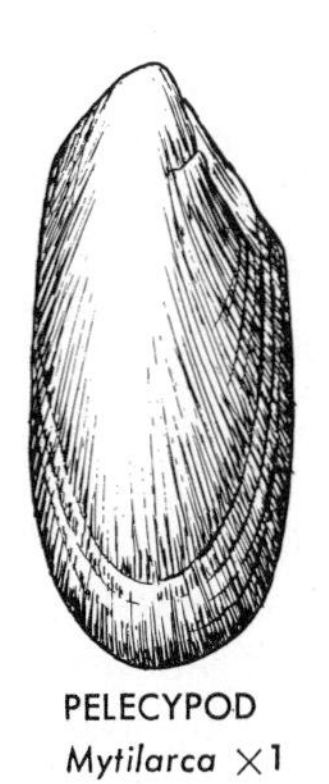

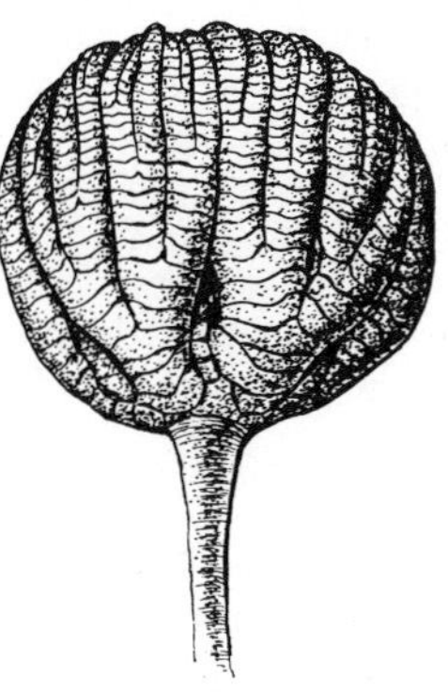

Fig. 16-3. Mississippian guide fossils.

Fig. 16-2. Mississippian correlation chart.

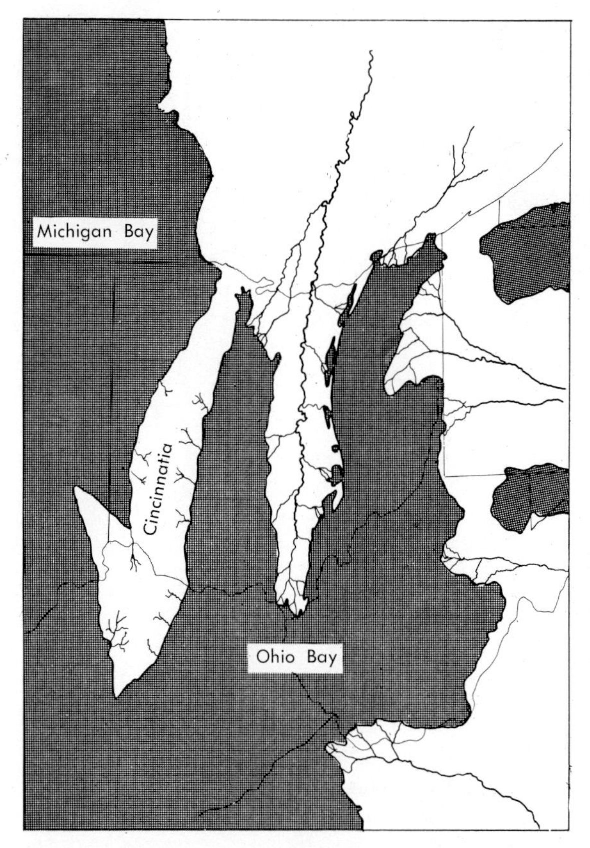

Fig. 16-4. Paleogeography of part of the Mississippian. Figs. 16-4, 16-5, and 16-6 show the distributions of Mississippian seas over all of Ohio, and parts of Virginia, West Virginia, Pennsylvania, Kentucky, Illinois, and Michigan. It is immediately apparent that the seas were transgressing the continent in these progressively later periods of the Mississippian. During the Mississippian and Pennsylvanian Periods seas occupied a large part of the continental interior which stood just about at sea level and was inundated by slight shifts in the level of the seas. The position of these ancient seas has been made possible by studies of the types of sediments formed in them. In some instances the shoreline features can be found and traced. Others are identified by the locations of swampy, littoral zone, and shallow water sediments. Paleogeography of Early Bedford time. (After Pepper, de Witt, and Demarest.)

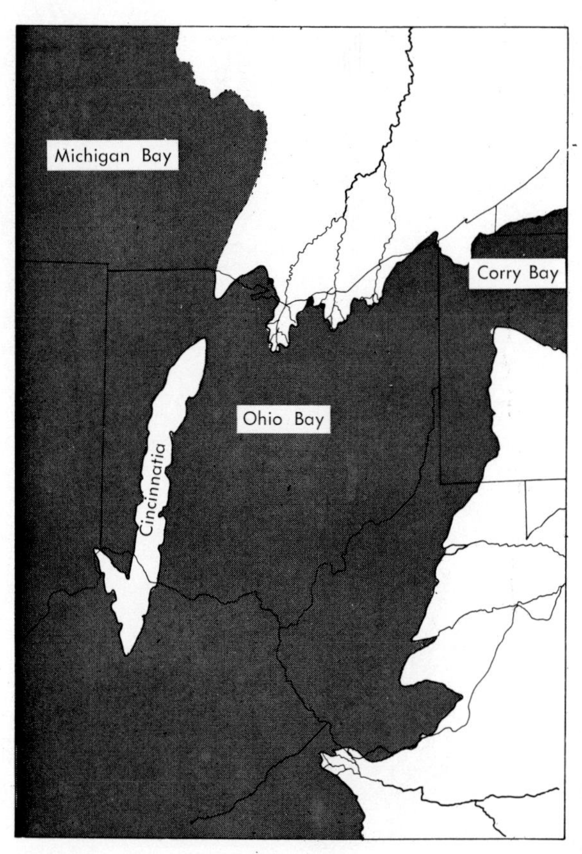

Fig. 16-5. Paleogeography of Late Berea time.

limestones is the Mauch Chunk formation (1600-3500 feet thick), which consists of alternating sandstone conglomerate, red shales, and coal. At the type section of the Mauch Chunk there are eight of the rhythmic changes, called cyclothems. In Arkansas, Upper Mississippian deposits are coarse, indicating the beginning of a disturbance which culminated in the formation of the Ouachita Mountains in the Pennsylvanian Period.

More than 3600 feet of sediment accumulated in the Illinois basin during the Mississippian. The basin began to form along a north-south axis in the Kinderhookian and continued to be warped downward into the Pennsylvanian. Each unit deposited in the basin is thickened toward the center of the basin. The sediments deposited in this basin have become an important source of coal and oil.

Western United States

A synclinal trough extended eastward onto the craton through central Montana. In the miogeosynclinal belt of the western United States exposures are scattered, and most of them are located along the flanks of mountains and uplifted toward the end of the Meso-

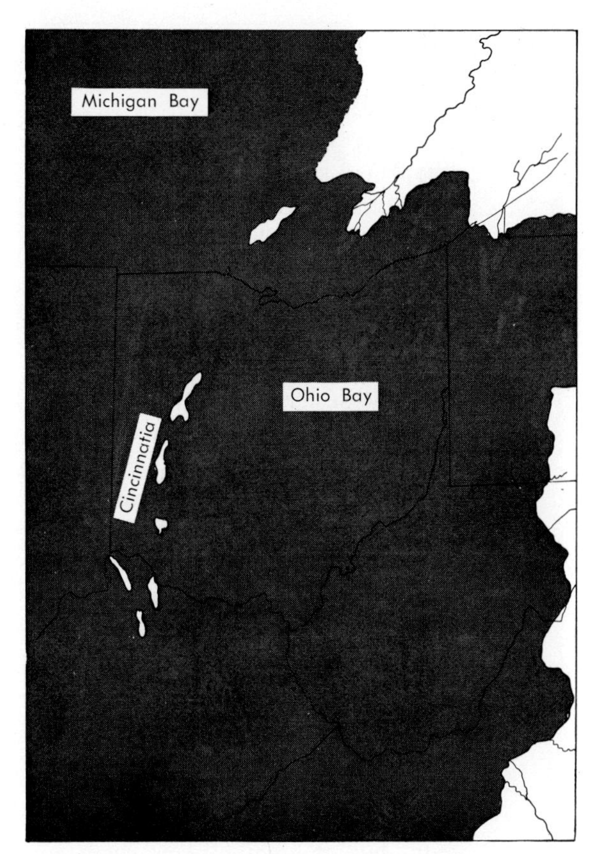

Fig. 16-6. Paleogeography of Sunbury time.

zoic. Thick limestone deposits mark most of the exposures. These units are as much as a mile or more thick in some areas. The Mississippian is not generally found directly on Devonian sediments. This indicates a pre-Mississippian period of uplift, erosion and nondeposition. In Utah the Mississippian is on Ordovician formations; in the Grand Canyon the Red Wall limestone of Mississippian age is laid on Cambrian sediments.

In the eugeosynclinal belt of the far west the sections are very thick and composed of muds, chert, and volcanic rocks. In the Klamath Mountains of northern California close to 7000 feet of muds and volcanic deposits were laid down. This region had been a nearly flat platform in Silurian and Devonian time. One of the most important aspects of the geosynclinal belts of the west is the instability they have exhibited over long periods of time. This instability continues to the present.

LIFE OF THE MISSISSIPPIAN

I. NEW FORMS

By the beginning of the Carboniferous all of the major phyla and a great many of the most important classes of animals were present. We have seen that amphibians appeared before the Mississippian. Reptiles are found in the overlying system. Thus it is probable that reptiles lived in the Mississippian and that we will some day find their remains.

Fusulinids appeared for the first time in the Mississippian. These microscopic-sized protozoans that belong to the group known as the Foraminifera have been exceptionally good guide fossils for the Carboniferous. In places they are so abundant that whole limestone units are made up of their tiny shells shaped like grains of wheat.

Fig. 16-7. Courses of sand-filled channels of the Bedford sandstone in northern Ohio. This diagram illustrates how uniformitarianism is used to reconstruct the past. On the right are the courses of channels of part of the Mississippi River near Natchez, Mississippi at the present time. On the left are sand filled channels that date back to the Mississippian time. It appears very likely that the conditions of the formation of these two have been very similar. The ancient river that flowed across Ohio 300 million years ago must have had a low gradient and probably flowed across nearly flat land. (After Pepper, de Witt, and Demarest.)

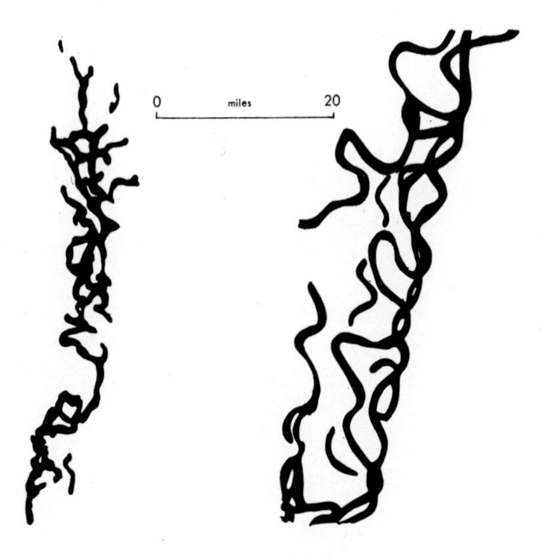

II. PEAKS AND ADVANCEMENT

1. *Age of crinoids:* Fragments of crinoids are found widely distributed in Mississippian limestones, and in a few the limestones are composed almost entirely of crinoid stems and brachiopods. The crinoids, sometimes known as sea lilies, had reached the peak of their development. They were abundant and highly diversified. In fact they are one of the most highly organized and diversified groups of the invertebrates.
2. *Brachiopods:* This group continued to be one of the abundant groups of shallow-water marine invertebrates. Several new groups became important in the Mississippian. The productid brachiopods, which have spiny projections from their shells, were one of these. They continued to be important throughout the Carboniferous. The second group were the spirifers. The distinguishing feature of these is the shape of the internal support that held up the soft part of the animal, the lophophore. You will remember that this is used to set up currents directed toward the mouth of the animals. The lophophore supports of the spirifers are spirals.
3. *Blastoids:* They were probably never as abundant as they were during the Mississippian. Before the end of the Carboniferous, however, they became extinct. The blastoids lived a life somewhat similar to that of the crinoids and were attached to the sea floors.
4. *Sharks:* This group of fish was the most important vertebrate of the Mississippian seas. Their teeth are particularly well preserved. Some of them had teeth especially designed for crushing shells of marine invertebrates. These short rounded teeth lined the jaws, giving them the appearance of a stone pavement; hence the name "pavement teeth." Several hundred species of sharks are known to have lived during this time, as compared with less than 100 species of sharks in the periods which preceded and followed the Carboniferous.
5. *Amphibians:* There are few remains of amphibians left since most of the deposits from this period are marine sediments, but the amphibians were undoubtedly undergoing diversification, since they are much expanded in the Pennsylvanian.

Fig. 16-8. Mississippian limestones, exposed in the distance on the face of these mountains in the Canadian Rockies. (Photo by courtesy of Canadian Pacific Railway.)

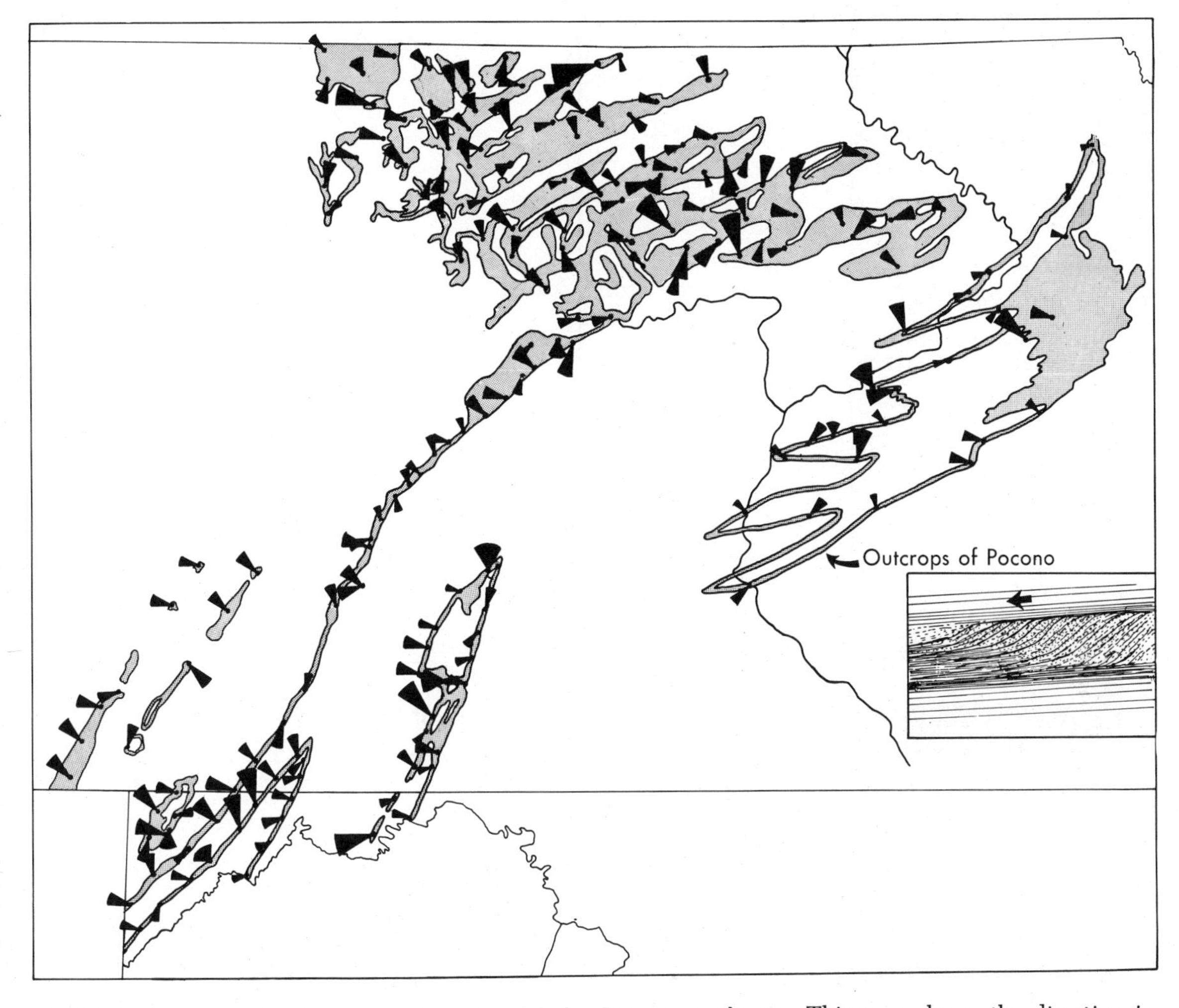

Fig. 16-9. Paleocurrents during the formation of the Pocono sandstone. This map shows the direction in which currents moved the sandy sediments which became the Pocono sandstone of the Lower Mississippian age. These directions were obtained by measurement of the direction of cross bedding in the unit. Inset: a cross bedded sandstone in cross section. The top set beds are truncated. (Modified after B. R. Pelletier.)

III. DECLINE AMONG MARINE INVERTEBRATES

Among the marine invertebrates several groups that had been particularly prominent during earlier periods began to show a marked decline. The rugose and honeycomb corals declined during the Carboniferous and finally became extinct in the Permian. Trilobites also gradually declined during the Carboniferous; the last survivors of this magnificent race vanished during the Permian. They may have become the prey of some of the more advanced animals such as the sharks, but the cause of extinction is still unknown.

Fig. 16-10. Permian fusulinids. (Photo by courtesy of the U.S. National Museum.)

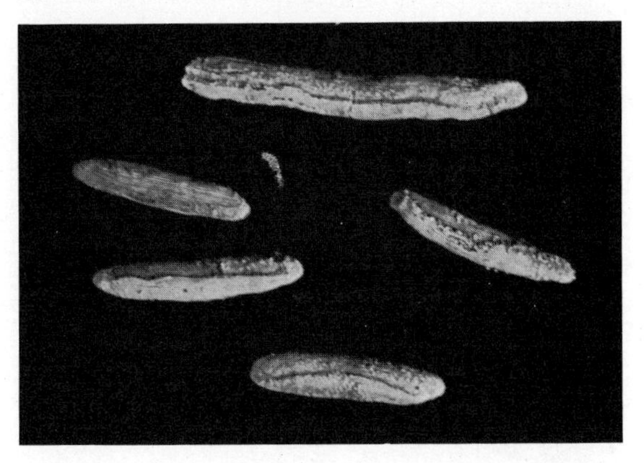

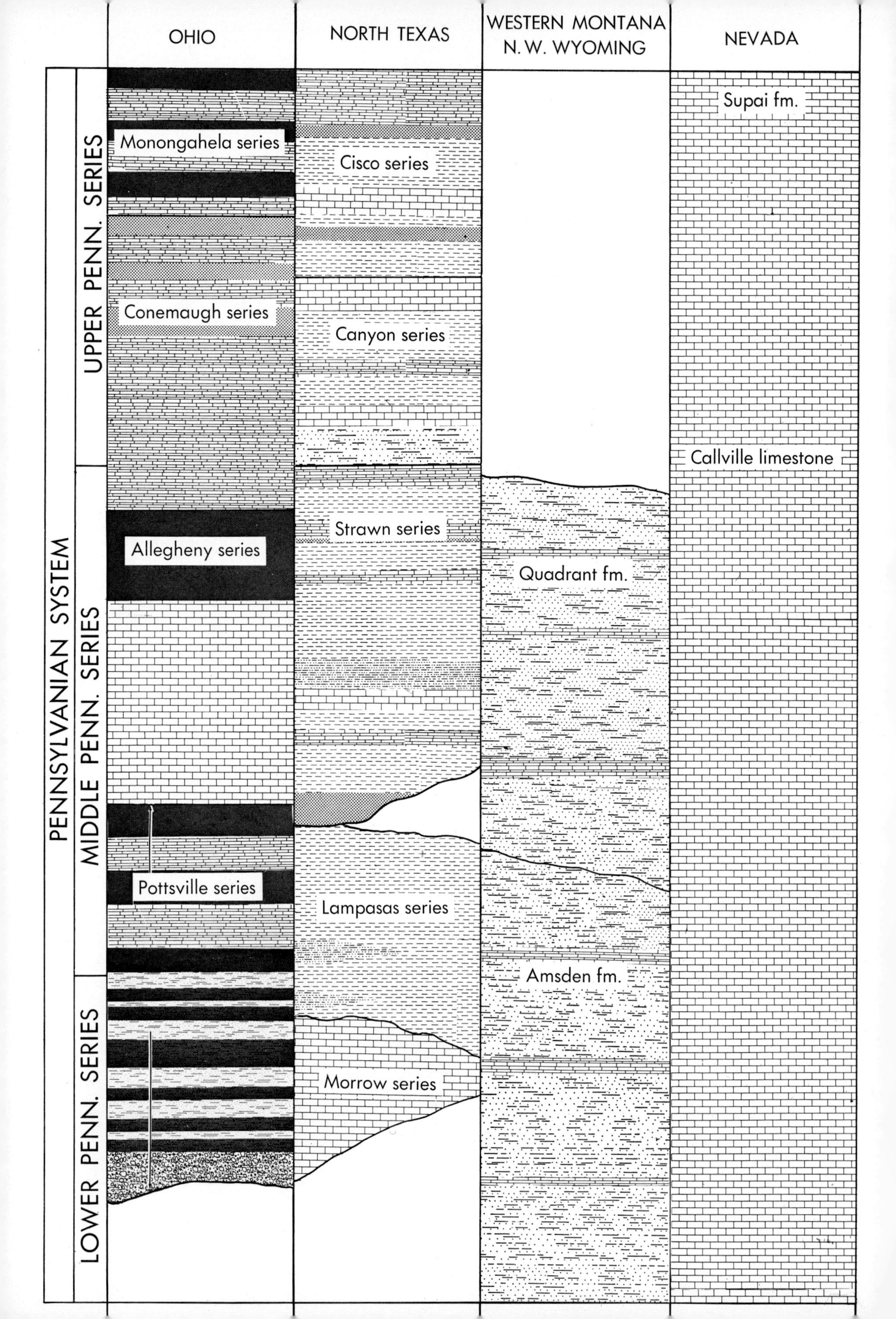
OHIO
NORTH TEXAS
WESTERN MONTANA
N. W. WYOMING
NEVADA
PENNSYLVANIAN SYSTEM
UPPER PENN. SERIES
MIDDLE PENN. SERIES
LOWER PENN. SERIES
Monongahela series
Conemaugh series
Allegheny series
Pottsville series
Cisco series
Canyon series
Strawn series
Lampasas series
Morrow series
Quadrant fm.
Amsden fm.
Supai fm.
Callville limestone

Fig. 16-11. Pennsylvanian correlation chart.

Fig. 16-12. Guide Fossils.

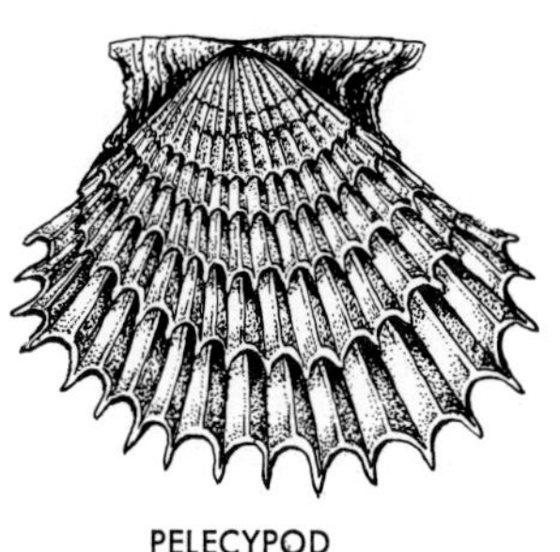

PELECYPOD
Acanthopecten ×2

GASTROPOD
Euconospira ×2

BRACHIOPOD
Dictyoclostus ×1

PELECYPOD
Monopteria ×1

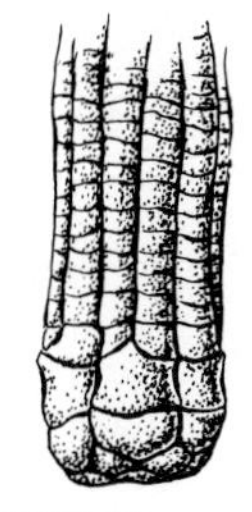

CRINOID
Graphiocrinus ×1

CORAL
Lophophyllidium ×1.5

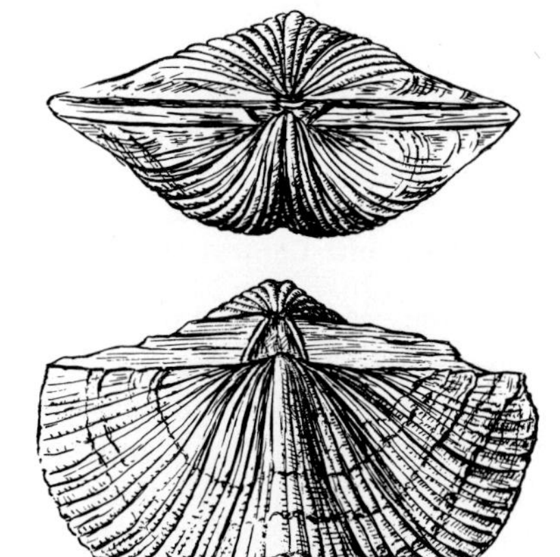

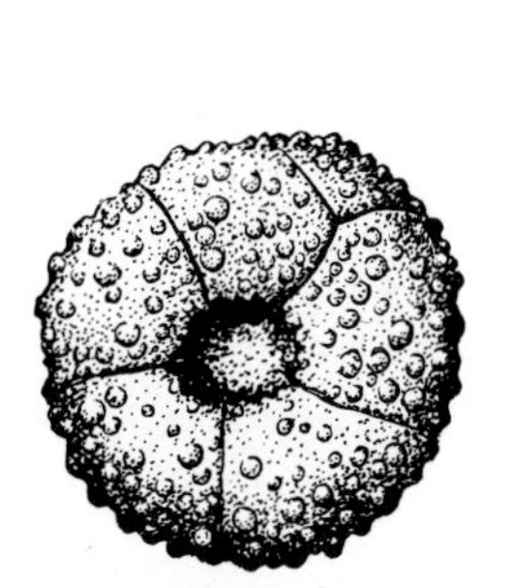

CRINOID
Ethelocrinus ×1

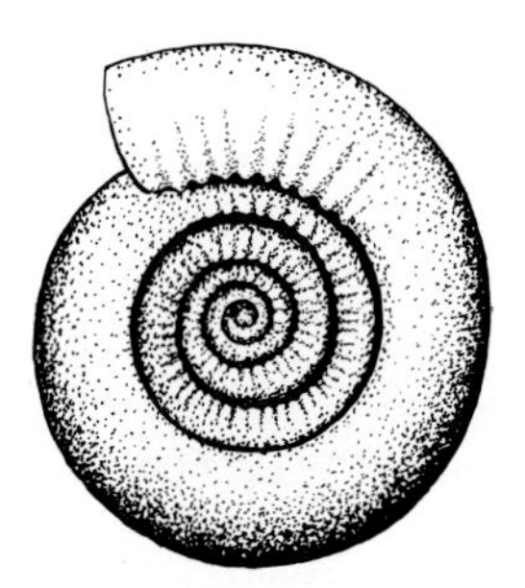

CEPHALOPOD
Gastrioceras ×2

BRACHIOPOD
Neospirifer ×1

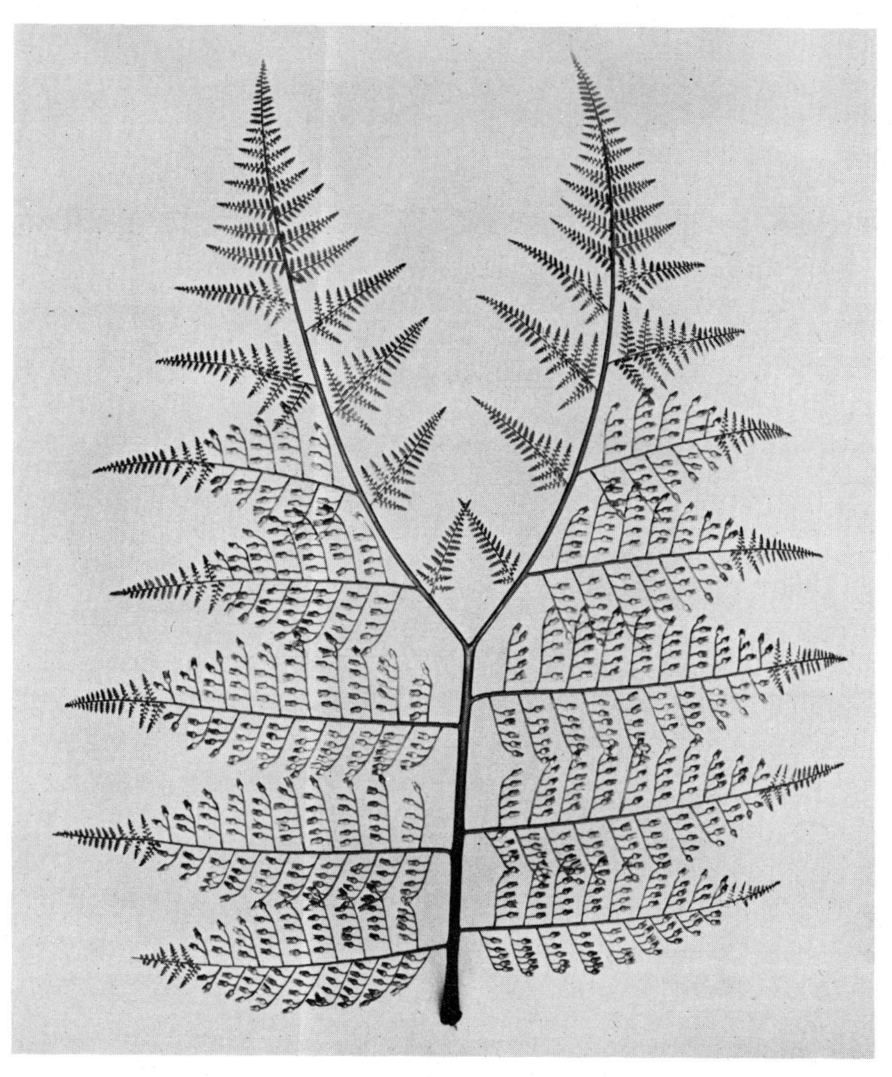

Fig. 16-13. Seed fern of the genus *Neuropteris*. This is one of the plants which lived in the coal forest of the Pennsylvanian. (Photo by courtesy of the Chicago Natural History Museum.)

PHYSICAL HISTORY OF THE PENNSYLVANIAN PERIOD

Eastern and Central United States

In the Maritime Provinces of Canada eugeosynclinal troughs contain over 15,000 feet of coarse Pennsylvanian clastic sediments, boulders of igneous rocks, and volcanic rocks. Within the geosynclines there were locally welts and troughs. Southward in New England, basins of Carboniferous age, filled with coarse conglomerates, lie on a rugged granitic topography. The area apparently had high relief and subsided considerably during the Carboniferous. The Boston basin and the Narragansett basin of Rhode Island are two of these Carboniferous infolded areas. The Narragansett basin contains over 10,000 feet of Carboniferous sediments including some anthracite coal and graphite.

In the Appalachian miogeosyncline, deposits thicken southward to a maximum of over 12,000 feet in Alabama. Coarse sedimentary rocks in the southern part were supplied from the southeast during the Pennsylvanian, suggesting that an area in the southeastern United States was emergent at that time.

In the continental interior, the pattern of deposition which started with the Mauch Chunk in the Mississippian continued into and through most of the Pennsylvanian. Rhythmic deposition characterized sedimentation from Kansas to Virginia. The number and thickness of cyclothems in different areas vary, suggesting local subsidence and warping of the continental interior. In the west the cyclothems are dominantly marine. Farther east the alternations are between fresh water and continental deposition.

South-central United States

The Pennsylvanian (and perhaps part of the Permian) was a time of prolonged and complex deformation in this region. The sites of the orogenies were geosynclinal belts in which there had been long-term subsidence and accumulation of sediments during earlier parts of the Paleozoic. The location of these belts included the areas now occupied by the Ouachita Mountains of Arkansas and Oklahoma and the Marathon Mountain region of Texas which were parts of a marginal geosynclinal system, and an east-west trending geosyncline which extended west from the Ouachita Mountains through Oklahoma. The Ouachita-Marathon belt is only partially exposed. Most of it is covered by Mesozoic and Cenozoic sedimentary rocks. The east-west trending geosyncline is known as the Wichita geosyncline. Deformation during the Pennsylvanian has divided it into a number of major elements the histories of which are treated separately. These elements and other major structural features of this region are illustrated.

There were three major phases of deformation in the region. The first, the Wichita orogeny, occurred in early Pennsylvanian time and affected the Wichita geosyncline. This has been dated by the shales deposited in the geosyncline at the time of the deformation. They contain large boulders of rocks ranging in age from Cambrian through Mississippian. Thus rocks of this age must have been exposed in the mountains that rose within and along the margin of the geosyncline. Accompanying this deformation a mountain range known as the Nemaha Mountains rose in eastern Oklahoma

Fig. 16-14. Cyclothems, depicted in this illustration of rhythmic sedimentation. Seas slowly transgressed and retreated from the shallow swampy continental interior, giving rise to systematic variations in the type of sediment forming. Starting with the erosion surface at the bottom, three complete cycles are shown. During the first part of the cycle continental deposits of conglomerate, sands, and muds cover the lowland regions. When this land is close to sea level, swamps form in which plant growth is abundant. The plant remains form a layer of peat which is covered by the first strata containing marine fossils, a shale. As the water becomes deeper some limestone becomes mixed with the shale and finally limestones deposited far from shore are laid down. These often contain fusulinids. When the sea begins to recede the character of the sediments change again back toward shaly limestone and shale. Then comes the next unconformity. During the interval of erosion part of the last shale and limestones may be removed. When the seas begin to advance again the cycle is repeated.

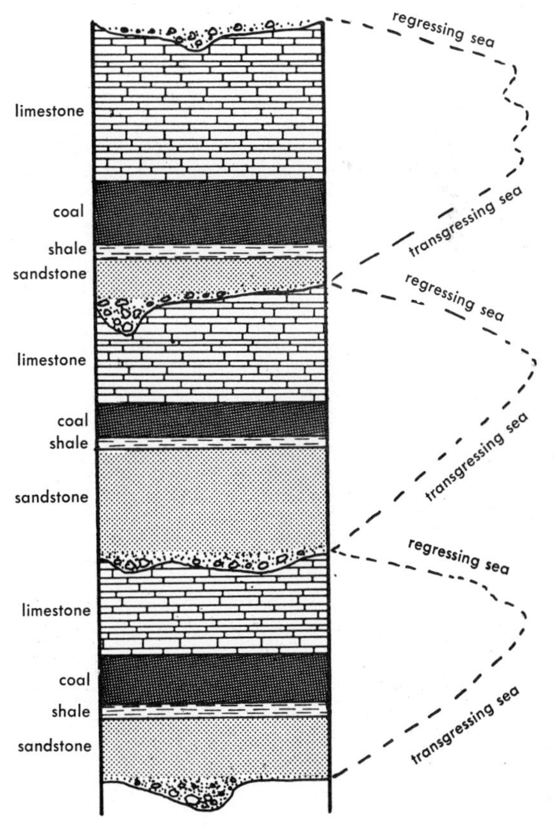

and Kansas. This range extended almost due north-south and it was not a part of the geosyncline. This mountain range is now completely buried under Pennsylvanian strata, and there is no surface evidence of its existence.

The second major phase of deformation came toward the end of the Pennsylvanian when the Arbuckle orogeny took place in southern Oklahoma. This orogeny was accompanied by great uplift and sharp folding of the earlier units in the geosyncline. Following this orogeny no more marine deposits were laid down in the newly uplifted region. Late Pennsylvanian and Early Permian deposits consists of continental debris which was eroded from the mountains and gradually filled in the basins and buried the flanks of the mountains which had been their source. These nonmarine deposits which consist of arkose are found to grade into and interfinger with marine sandstones and shales outside of the most intensely deformed region.

The third major phase of deformation affected the Marathon region and the Ouachita region of Arkansas and Oklahoma. This occurred after the Arbuckle orogeny. The age of these deformations is uncertain. They may be anything from Late Pennsylvanian to Jurassic. The reason for this uncertainty is due to the absence of Permian and Triassic sedimentary rocks in the region. They are considered by many geologists to be part of the orogeny which deformed the Appalachian Mountains toward the close of the Paleozoic. In both instances thick geosynclinal accumulations of sedimentary rocks were strongly folded, uplifted, and thrust to the west and northwest. A discussion of the Appalachian orogeny follows in the next chapter.

Western United States

In the far west a eugeosynclinal belt persisted through the Pennsylvanian, as did the miogeosynclinal belt in which thick sections of carbonates accumulated. In the southwest along the Nevada-California border an arch called the Manhattan geanticline stood above water. This is indicated by the presence of Pennsylvanian conglomerates in Nevada (To-

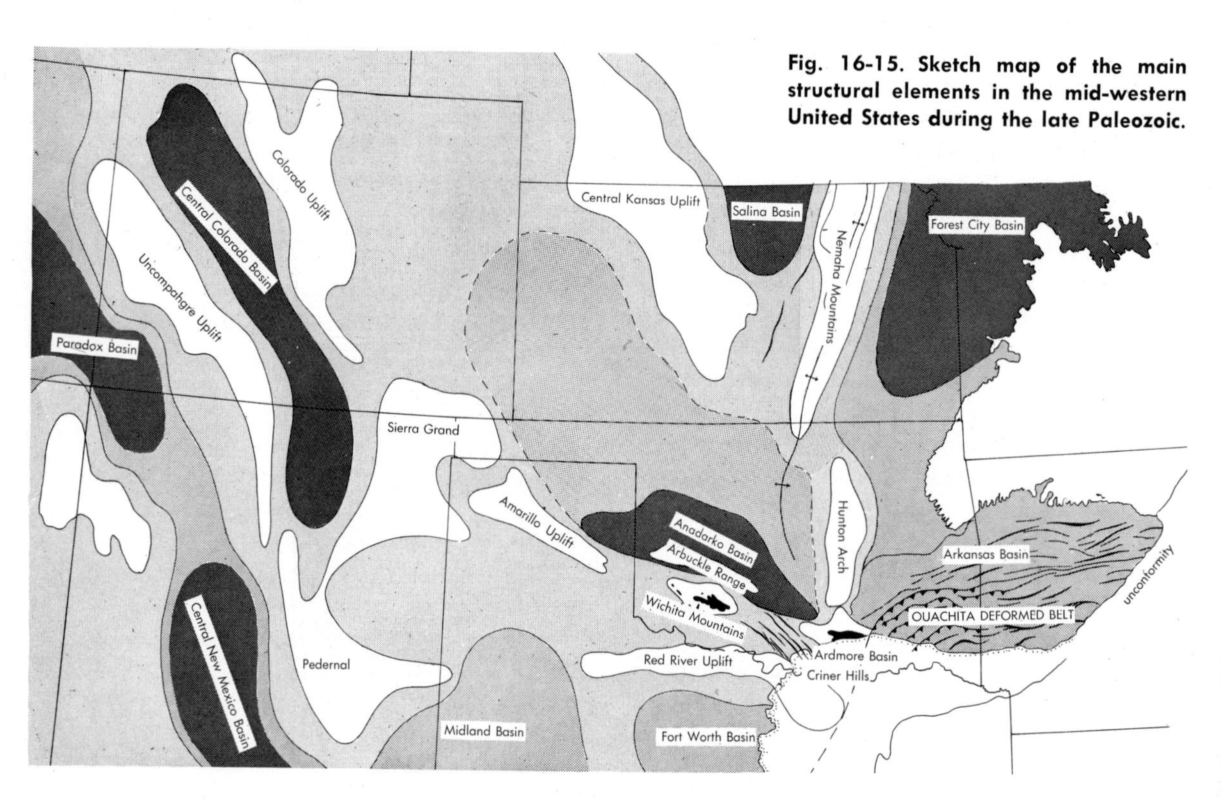

Fig. 16-15. Sketch map of the main structural elements in the mid-western United States during the late Paleozoic.

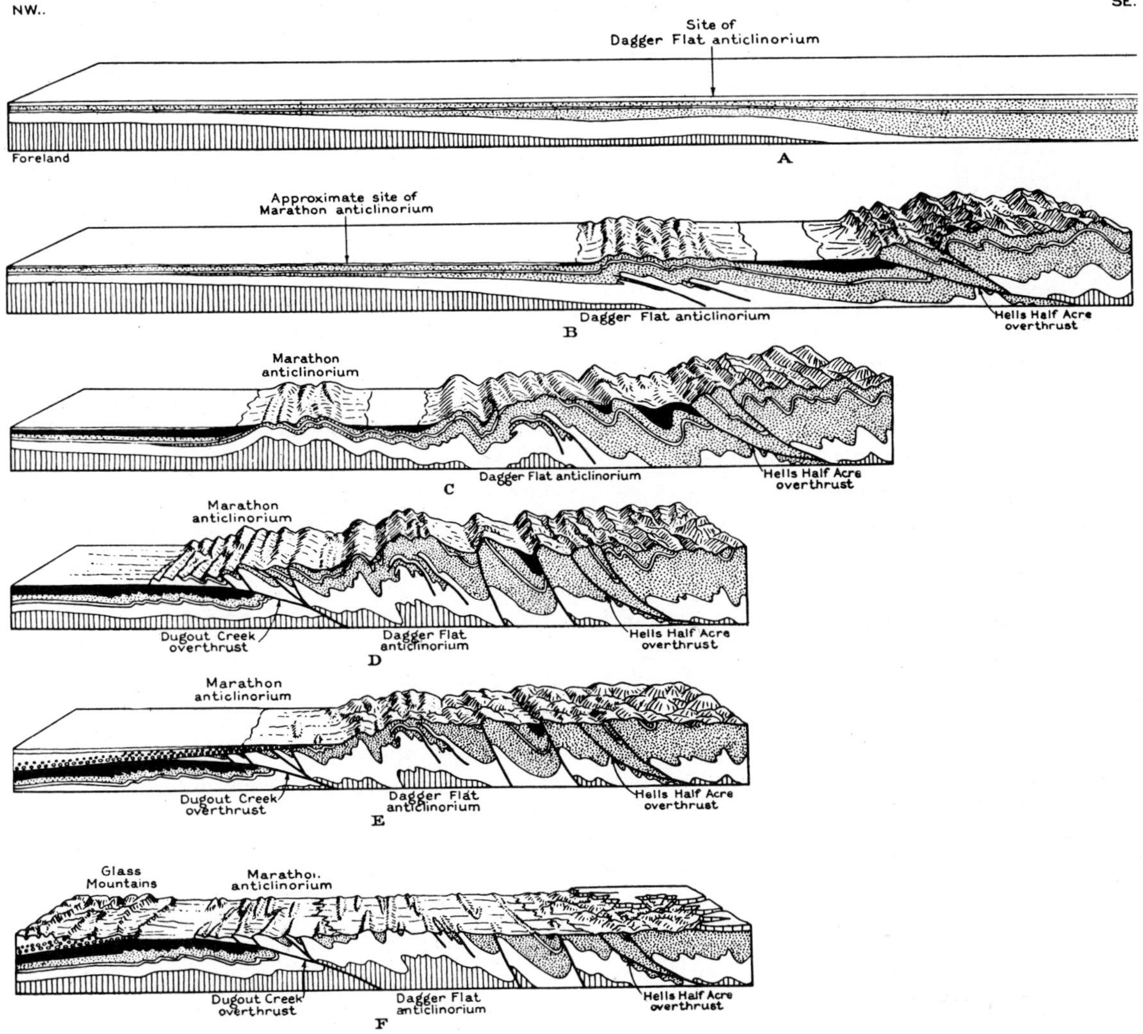

Fig. 16-16. Hypothetical block diagrams showing progressive development of structural features in the Marathon Region of Texas. (Modified after P. B. King.)

quima Range), and by the presence of an angular unconformity between Pennsylvanian and Permian units in the unlifted area. In the central Rocky Mountain states several uplifts and deeply subsiding basins formed during the Pennsylvanian. These included the Colorado Mountains, the Uncompahgre Range, the Central Colorado basin and the Paradox basin. The extent of the subsidence is indicated by the thickness of marine sedimentary rocks of Pennsylvanian age found within these basins. The two mentioned contain 10,000 and 18,000 feet respectively of limestone and shale.

The Wichita System

The history of this system is of interest not only for its importance as a major geosynclinal belt, but as an illustration of the complex nature of orogenic deformations. We can see here that different parts of this geosynclinal belt behaved differently, and that the deformation during an orogeny is not a simple uniform folding and thrusting of older geosynclinal sediments. This system also demonstrates that a number of events occurring at different times comprise an orogeny. The units deformed in

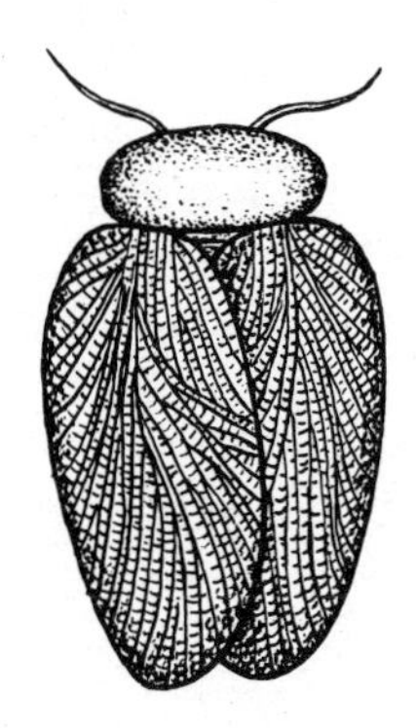

Fig. 16-17. Cockroach fossil. Cockroaches were so abundant during the Pennsylvanian that the period is sometimes known as the "Age of Cockroaches." This fossil is *Dictyomylacris* from an Upper Carboniferous coal swamp.

the Wichita system are also of particular economic importance, for this region is the source of large quantities of oil and gas.

The principal elements in the Wichita system are the Wichita Mountains, Amarillo Uplift, Arbuckle Mountains, Criner Hills, Hunton arch, the Anadarko geosyncline, and the Ardmore basin (Fig. 16-15). These elements are all remnants of a system of mountains and basins initially formed in the Pennsylvanian Period. The mountains rose from a geosynclinal belt, called the Wichita geosyncline, which extended from southeastern Oklahoma into the Texas Panhandle. Unlike the Appalachian and Cordilleran geosynclines this trough did not take shape until the later part of the Cambrian, but in the succeeding periods it accumulated a thick section of rocks not unlike those of the miogeosynclinal belts on the eastern and western continental margins. Even at the beginning of the Pennsylvanian Period there was evidence of crustal unrest south of the Wichita geosyncline. The units deposited there were sands and shales. Following the deposition of these units the southern side of the geosyncline became the site of orogenic movements, and an elongate land mass of folded geosynclinal sediments rose As it rose the geosyncline was restricted, and the Hunton arch formed at the southeastern end. This left a narrow, deeply subsiding trough called the Anadarko geosyncline and a southeastern basin known as the Ardmore basin. These depressions received the sediments eroded from the uplifted lands. These amount to over 15,000 feet of sands, shales, and conglomerates in the Ardmore basin.

Deformation in the system was completed in the late part of the Pennsylvanian when the Arbuckle orogeny elevated the Arbuckle Mountains and deformed the sediments that were laid down in the Anadarko geosyncline after the earlier phases of the Wichita orogeny. The Upper Pennsylvanian beds (Pontotoc group) lie unconformably on all earlier units including the Middle Pennsylvanian units in the basins. These late beds are continental deposits—conglomerates, arkoses, and sands. These red beds grade into marine sandstones and shales both to the north and south of the Wichita system. They cover all but the topmost parts of the Wichita mountain ranges. This then is a mountain system almost completely buried in the erosion products of its own decay.

LIFE OF THE PENNSYLVANIAN

I. NEW FORMS

1. *Reptiles:* The remains of true reptiles first appear in this period. Most of these early specimens were only about a foot long and had an elongate, slender body. Because their skin could retain moisture it was possible for them to travel great distances away from streams and swamps.
2. *Snails:* The first gastropods to live out of the marine environment were snails, which began to crawl through the swamps and then over land during this period.

II. PEAKS AND ADVANCEMENT

1. *Age of cockroaches:* Insects swarmed through the swamps of this period. Of these the cockroaches were notable not only because of their great number but also because of their variety. Almost 1000 different species of cockroaches have been described from this system. Some of these grew to be as long as 3 inches.
2. *Insects:* Besides the cockroaches almost 2000 other species of insects lived in the Pennsylvanian. It was during this time that some of these species attained the

largest sizes ever known for insects. Dragonflies with a wing spread of nearly 30 inches were abundant, and several other kinds grew to be a foot long.

3. *Amphibians:* The labyrinthodonts were particularly abundant. Several subdivisions of the amphibians were common. The giants were approximately 15 feet long. They had large bodies with strong tails, but relatively small legs. There were others whose general appearance was very similar to that of modern snakes. One of the smallest of the amphibians grew no larger than angle worms. The ability of several

Fig. 16-18. A restored Pennsylvanian coal swamp. It was from such forests as these that the coal fields of the continental interior of the United States originated. The ferns are similar to many living plants, but the lycopods, *Sigillaria* (1) and *Lepidodendron* (2) are unlike any living trees. Notice also the small amphibian at the base of the largest trees. A large cockroach is in the foreground on a fallen lepidodendron. (Photo by courtesy of the Chicago Natural History Museum.)

forms to lay their eggs in soft sand instead of in water was perhaps the most outstanding advancement of this group as a whole. This adaptation was a big step toward occupation of the continents.

4. *Fusulinids*: These Foraminifera appeared in the Mississippian, but did not become extremely abundant until the Pennsylvanian, when they became a major constituent of some marine limestones.

Fig. 16-19. The bark of a lepidodendron. The markings are leaf scars. These scars are arranged in vertical rows on *Sigillaria,* but in a rhombic pattern on *Lepidodendron.* (Photo by courtesy of the Chicago Natural History Museum.)

III. DECLINE AND EXTINCTION

1. Blastoids became extinct in the Early Pennsylvanian.

IV. NOTABLE ASPECTS OF LIFE: THE SWAMPS

No feature of the life of the Pennsylvanian is as outstanding as the swampland forest that covered large areas in almost every part of the world. We have little record of the life that may have thrived on the higher lands, but from the swamps there is a record of profuse vegetation unlike any before or since the end of the period. These forests were unlike modern swamps, for there were no flowering plants such as those that make up most of the modern vegetation in lowland regions. These Pennsylvanian forests were dominated by seed ferns and giant scale trees. The scale trees, *Lepidodendron* and *Sigillaria,* were the largest trees of the time. They rival the modern sequoias in height; the largest was more than 100 feet high. The majority, however, were smaller—under 5 feet in diameter. The name "scale tree" is given to these groups because the bark looks as though it is covered by scales. Actually these are scars left after leaves were shed from the branches and trunk. The lepidodendron bark is easily distinguished by the diamond-shaped leaf scars that are arranged spirally around the branches. Their leaves were very similar to pine needles and ranged around 8 to 10 inches in length. The sigillaria leaf scars are oval in shape and arranged in vertical rows, creating an easily distinguished pattern.

Under these higher trees grew a thick luxuriant growth of seed ferns and true ferns. Scouring rushes grew in dense thickets like modern cane brakes. The largest of these rushes was *Calamites.* This genus grew as tall as 30 feet and was almost a foot in diameter. Rushes are recognized by the vertical ribs and regularly spaced joints in the stems. A whorl of simple leaves grew at the joints of these plants. Like the larger scale trees they contained a pithy center surrounded by a thick layer of woody matter.

Fig. 16-20. Coal forest restoration. A large dragonfly with a wing span of nearly three feet dominates the center of this view into a Carboniferous coal swamp. Also present are ferns: (1) *Sigillaria,* (2) *Lepidodendron,* (3) *Calamites,* a large rush that grew to be as much as thirty feet tall, and (4) smaller rushes, *Sphenophyllum.* (Photo by courtesy of the Chicago Natural History Museum.)

In the slightly drier portions of the swamps we would have found a tree similar to the modern conifers. These trees are known as *Cordaites* and were 20 to 30 feet high. The main difference between these and true conifers, which also existed in the Carboniferous, is found in the nature of the leaves. The *Cordaites* had bladelike leaves that grew to be 6 or more feet long.

COAL AND ITS FORMATION IN THE CARBONIFEROUS PERIOD

Coal is vegetable matter which has undergone a number of changes in its physical and chemical properties. It is formed from the remains of plants. The woody substances of the plants, called anthraxylon, make up most of the coal. The anthraxylon consists of plant

Fig. 16-21. Restoration of a *Sphenophyllum*. This is one of the small plants that thrived in the Carboniferous swamps. The arrangement of leaves in whorls and jointed stems bearing longitudinal ribs is characteristic of rushes. (Photo by courtesv of the Chicago Natural History Museum.)

stems, limbs, branches, twigs, roots, and spores and the husk or shell-like spore or seed coverings. This part of the coal is usually bright, shiny, and black. It is harder and has a higher luster than the impurities in coal beds. The impurities, called attritus, are a dull gray or black, composed of charred matter, waxes, oils, fats, resinous materials, and mineral matter.

Chemically, coal is composed of hydrocarbons, the name applied to compounds composed of carbon and hydrogen, but unlike minerals, coal does not have a definite chemical composition. Great variations may occur in the types and quantities of the hydrocarbons in a given coal unit. Coals differ in the extent to which the physical and chemical changes have altered the original plant matter and in the amounts and types of impurities present. All but the most highly altered coals contain gases derived from the decayed organic matter. The gases include methane, carbon dioxide, nitrogen, and carbon monoxide. These gases account for many of the disastrous fires and explosions that have occurred in coal mines. Mineral constituents make up a small but often important part of the coal. Pyrite, gypsum, some phosphorus, salt, sand, limestone, and iron also occur in coal. A high sulfur content makes the coal unsuitable for metallurgical uses, such as the manufacture of steel, because it may form sulfuric acid. Phosphorus content is also important because it has the effect of making metals brittle.

Conditions under which coal formation begins

The best clues to the environment in which coal is formed come from the plant remains preserved in the coal, from the sedimentary sequences in which the coal is found, and from observations of present-day conditions under which peat, the initial stage in coal formation, accumulates. Two types of environments seem most favorable for the initiation of coal formation: (1) swamps located above sea level, such as the high moors, and (2) low or tidal swamps. The former are usually glacial swamps such as those which presently exist in New Jersey, northern New York, Wisconsin, and in the basin of Michigan. In northern Russia mastodons have been preserved in peat deposits of one of these swamps that is frozen over during the winter. The tidal swamp is flooded by marine waters twice daily in some cases; other low swamps may stand only slightly above tides and receive water only during unusually high tides. These two types of deposits can usually be distinguished with ease by the marked difference in the character of the cyclothems with which they are associated. The high-swamp deposits contain no marine fossils and very little if any limestone. Sands, gravels, arkoses, and shales are more likely in high swamps, while the tidal swamp is likely to be covered by marine waters and become associated with marine fossils and marine limestones. It is probable that carboniferous coals of the State of Pennsylvania were laid down in high swamps, for such coals are associated with sands dominantly, but the coals found in Illinois are overlain by marine deposits.

One of the most interesting aspects of coal formation is the climatic condition under which peat accumulates. Many lines of evidence point to widespread uniform climatic conditions throughout most parts of the world during the Carboniferous. Limestones similar to those now being deposited off the coast of Florida were formed in high northern latitudes. Trees grow more rapidly during the warm moist periods of the year than they do in the winter. Such seasonal variations in growth cause growth rings consisting of a dark (winter) ring and lighter, thicker summer rings. No growth rings are found in the plants and trees of the Pennsylvanian Period, suggesting that the plants grew at a constant rate throughout the year. This helps to explain the exceptional abundance of plants necessary for the formation of the extensive coal units which are found in the Carboniferous System throughout the world.

Most coals were formed in place (*in situ*), while the evidence suggests that other deposits accumulated only after the plants had been transported some distance. The *in situ* mode of origin is most widely accepted for the following reasons:

1. Large quantities of peat are being formed *in situ* today.
2. Many Carboniferous coal units contain the remains of trees standing vertically with their roots embedded in the clays beneath the coal.
3. Most coals are pure. If the plant material had been transported, more of a mixture might be expected.

That coal may also be formed after transportation of the plant matter is borne out by the presence of peat in some deltaic deposits where plants rafted down streams become incorporated in the sediments of the delta.

One of the best examples of a swamp in which peat is presently being formed is the Dismal Swamp of Virginia and North Carolina which has already been described. The vegetation in most swamps is abundant around the margins of the swamp or lake. As more and more vegetation grows and dies, it gradually fills the lake. The remains of weeds, water lilies, rushes, algae, and higher plants gradually form a matlike mass covering the swamp. If the peat remains exposed to the air, oxidation and bacteria will destroy it, but once it is buried it becomes a potential coal bed. The rate at which peat accumulates varies considerably, depending on the amount and rate of plant growth and peat formation relative to the amount and rate of decay. As much as 1 or 2 feet may form within a period of 10 years at the present time. It is estimated that about 20 feet of peat is required for the eventual formation of 1 foot of coal; thus the thickest coal seams (over 250 feet thick) may represent former peat deposits nearly a mile thick.

Transformation of peat to coal

The transformation of vegetable matter into coal involves physical and chemical changes:

1. Moisture and volatile components are lost.

2. Molecules in the remaining matter are rearranged.
3. The amount of fixed carbon and ash increases relative to the other constituents.
4. The matter changes to a darker color.
5. There is an increase in hardness and compactness.

These changes are brought about by several processes. Each of these processes must have some effect, although their relative importance in the transformation still needs further clarification. The first requisite is submergence and burial of the peat to remove it from oxygen and thus oxidation. Oxygen will combine with carbon to form carbon dioxide and heat. Among the first stages in the alteration of the peat are biochemical changes brought about by bacteria (such as *Micrococcus* and *Streptococcus*). These are most active in the upper part of the peat, because, as they break down the carbohydrates in the plants, they form acids in which they cannot live. The action of the bacteria is to weaken and break down the vegetable matter. As more sediments are deposited above the peat the weight of the overburden becomes great, causing load metamorphism. This compacts the peat and accelerates the release of gases.

Some of the additional factors which may be important in determining the eventual type or rank of coal to be formed are:

1. Time.
2. Depth of burial.
3. Heat generated by frictional movement during diastrophic movements or near igneous intrusions.
4. Dynamic metamorphism during compression. This is suggested by the location of higher ranks of coal in more intensely deformed belts of the Appalachian Highlands in eastern Pennsylvania.

Ranks of coal

Peat: An accumulation of matted plant matter in various stages of decomposition. It may be distinctly fibrous, woody, or a dark jelly-like substance. It has a high water content and makes a poor fuel.

Lignite (brown coal): A brownish-black coal in which the alteration of vegetable material has proceeded further than in peat. Plant matter contained in this coal is readily identified.

Sub-bituminous coal: Grades down into lignite and up into bituminous. It is more compact than lignite, darker, and glossy in luster. It parts along surfaces parallel to the bedding of the unit.

Bituminous coal: It usually shows a laminated structure, with the layers having different lusters. It is black, and soft enough to leave a black streak on paper. The fracture is roughly cubical.

Coking coal: A special type of bituminous coal used in the manufacture of steel. Coking coal forms a pasty mass when it is heated to the point of decomposition. While at high temperature it gives off gases that leave it as a cellular mass of hard, grayish-black material called coke. Sometimes two bituminous coals may be mixed to make coke.

Cannel Coal: A special type of coal formed from the spores of plants and small plant remains which were deposited in the open areas of water in the coal swamp. It is a dull black, has a conchoidal fracture, and a very fine-grained texture. It burns rapidly, is easy to light, and makes a good domestic fuel.

Anthracite Coal: Two ranks of coal are recognized as gradational between bituminous and anthracite—semibituminous and semianthracite. The variations are only in degree. Anthracite is dark black, has a brilliant luster, is hard, and will not mark paper. It resembles obsidian, natural glass. It burns with a short blue flame and gives off little odor or smoke. Anthracite breaks with a smooth conchoidal fracture.

This sequence demonstrates what is generally accepted as a progressive change in physical and chemical properties. The next step in the metamorphism of coal would be the formation of graphite, pure carbon. The anthracite of Rhode Island is in places graphitic.

RHYTHMIC DEPOSITION IN THE CARBONIFEROUS

The Pennsylvanian strata in most parts of the continental interior of the United States are characterized by cyclic recurrence of sequences of lithologic units, called cyclothems. These rhythmic deposits may be absent, or they may be represented by anywhere from 1 to 90 cycles. The cycles are not confined to any particular sequence of sedimentary units or rock types. They may record the recurrence of diastrophic movements or climatic fluctuations. The local variations in them are due to such local conditions as sedimentary environments, sources of sediments, and local climatic and diastrophic movements.

The ideal cyclothem in the Pennsylvanian of Illinois would contain 10 units as follows:

1. Sandstone.
2. Sandy and micaceous shale.
3. Fresh-water limestone.
4. Underclay.
5. Coal.
6. Gray nonmarine shale.
7. Marine limestone.
8. Black slaty shale.
9. Marine limestone and calcareous shale.
10. Shale containing ironstone bands or nodules in the upper part and thin limestone layers in the lower part.

These cyclothems are separated by disconformities, which mark periods of emergence and erosion. During these periods of erosion part or all of the last cyclothem may be removed, but as the next cycle begins the erosion surface is covered by cross-bedded nonmarine sandstones and pebble lenses laid down along the strand line. A sandy shale deposit follows; muds are from the slightly higher land. Between the time of emergence and erosion and before submergence and marine sedimentation a swampy condition similar to the present-day Dismal Swamp of Virginia and North Carolina prevailed. In these swamps the Carboniferous plant life flourished, and the remains of plants accumulated in the waters of the swamp. In some places the thickness of accumulation was not great, but some of the swamps must have contained hundreds of feet of peat which accumulated as the swamp persisted in spite of gradual submergence. When the water in the swamp became too deep for most plant life, the swamps ceased to grow and were gradually covered by muds deposited in the marine water. The first muds and limy sed-

Fig. 16-22. Underground coal mining operation. When the coal has not been too deformed by folding or faulting it is possible to carry out a large part of the mining with machinery. However, much of the coal from the anthracite coal mines is so completely deformed that it must still be mined by hand.

iments above the coal contain shallow-water fossil faunas. In the deeper water, pure and more massive limestones were laid down. At this point the relative levels of land and sea began to swing back, and the sea began to regress. As the water became shallower, shaly limes and then shale were formed. The next thing in the stratigraphic section is another erosion surface indicating that the area was emergent again.

The cyclothems in different parts of the continental interior vary greatly in thickness and lithology. In spite of these variations some units in the Pennsylvanian have been traced extensively throughout large areas. A parting known as the Blue Band in the Herrin coal of Illinois is known at places in Illinois, Indiana, Kentucky, Iowa, and Missouri and may be equivalent to partings in Ohio, Pennsylvania, and West Virginia.

REFERENCES

BERRY, E. W., 1920, Paleobotany, a sketch of the origin and evolution of floras: *Smithsonian Inst. Ann. Report, 1918-1920,* p. 289-407

CHENEY, M. G., *et. al.*, 1945, Classification of Mississippian and Pennsylvanian rocks of North America: Am. Assoc. Petroleum Geologists Bull., v. 29, p. 125-269

MOORE, R. C., 1935, Late Paleozoic crustal movements of Europe and North America: Am. Assoc. Petroleum Geologists Bull., v. 19, p. 1253-1325

WANLESS, H. R., 1955, Pennsylvanian rocks of Eastern Interior Basin: Am. Assoc. Petroleum Geologists Bull., v. 39, p. 1753-1820

WHITE, DAVID, and THIESSEN, REINHARDT, 1913, The origin of coal: U. S. Bur. Mines Bull. 38, p. 67-75

WILLIAMS, J. S., 1957, Paleoecology of the Upper Mississippi Valley region: Geol. Soc. America Mem. 67, v. 2, p. 279-324

17 The Permian Period

Classic locality for the Permian

The type section of the Permian system is located in the province of Perm, Russia. The stages of the Permian have been defined on the basis of the stratigraphic section there. Permian rock units underlie the vast plains between the Moscow Basin and the Ural Mountains. Before the Early Permian a geosyncline extended along the present belt of the Ural Mountains. During the Early Permian this geosynclinal accumulation was folded, and a mountain range rose from the trough, spreading sediments out into the adjacent shallow seas and low land areas. A second pulse of folding came in the Middle Permian, and finally toward the end of the Permian all of Russia emerged, and continuous land extended across the continent of Asia—which up to that time had been divided by the waters occupying the geosynclinal trough.

PHYSICAL HISTORY OF THE PERMIAN

Eastern United States

The only Permian rocks exposed in the eastern part of the United States are found along the axis of the broad synclinal structure that constitutes the Appalachian Plateau. The Permian Dunkard group is found in West Virginia, western Pennsylvania, and eastern Ohio. This small area of Permian may well be all that remains of a formerly extensive sequence of Permian sediments. The orogeny that elevated and folded the miogeosynclinal belts along the eastern coast of North America from Pennsylvania to Alabama, and probably farther southward, occurred in the late part of the Paleozoic about the same time the Ouachita Mountains were folded and raised. The early movements may have begun in the Pennsylvanian Period and extended through the Permian. The scarcity of Permian units makes precise dating impossible, but most of this orogeny, named the Appalachian orogeny, is thought to have taken place in Permian time.

Texas-Kansas

The most extensive outcropping of Permian units in the United States is found in a belt extending from northern Texas through western Oklahoma and into Kansas. The second most extensive belt is farther west in west Texas and New Mexico. Other Permian exposures are scattered through the Rocky Mountain states. In the central part of the belt, running from the west Texas basin through Kansas, about 1000 feet of limestones were deposited in the Early Permian time. On either side debris from the continents was washed into the seas. The seas became restricted, particularly in Kansas, and, as the waters evapo-

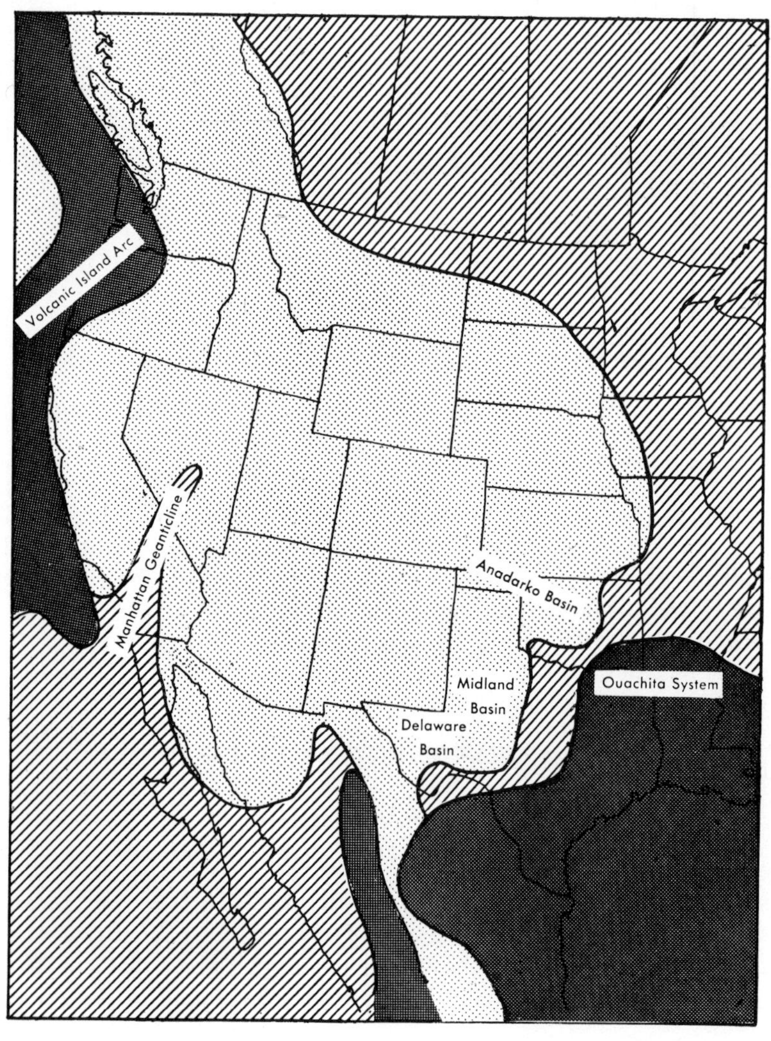

Fig. 17-1. Framework of western United States in the Permian. The dark belts were orogenic belts, geosynclinal belts in which deformation was most strong. The areas covered by diagonals were above sea level and yielded sediments which were carried into the shallow marine waters which covered the region marked with the fine dot pattern. (After A. J. Eardley.)

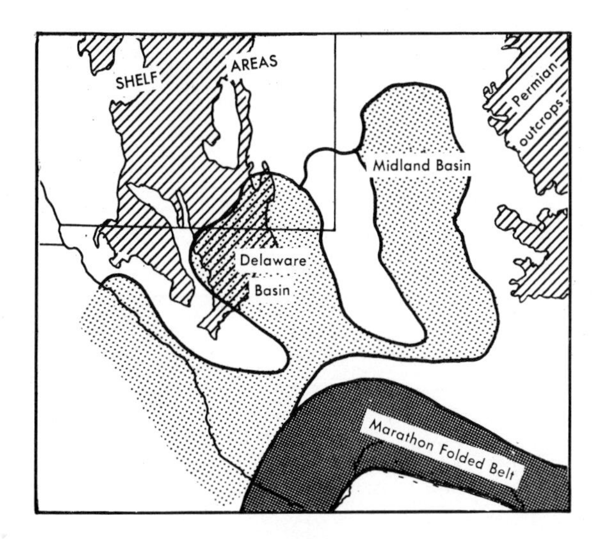

Fig. 17-2. Basins and shelf areas of western Texas during the Permian. The Marathon belt was subjected to deformation during the Pennsylvanian and stood high during the Permian to furnish coarse sediments to the basins north of it. Around the rim of these basins reefs flourished in the Permian. In front of them debris accumulated from the reef. Behind them on the shelf evaporites accumulated. Toward the end of the Permian the seas began to recede from this region and the reefs were covered by red beds. (After N. D. Newell.)

rated in the shallow sea, evaporites (especially gypsum) were deposited. In the Middle or Guadalupian Stage several basins subsided in the west Texas region. These include the Delaware and Midland basins, which are currently important oil-producing areas. These basins subsided rapidly as limestone was deposited in the central parts of the basins. Reefs grew in abundance around the basin rims, giving rise to restricted circulation of the waters back of the reef and consequently to the formation of evaporites and red shales. By Late Permian time deposition was restricted to the Delaware basin. Within this basin almost 5000 feet of evaporites, made up mainly of anhydrite and salt, was deposited. These units were then covered by variegated shales and dolomites, and finally marine red beds, as the seas gradually withdrew from the area.

Western part of the craton

On the western edge of the craton, local conditions dominated the nature of the deposits. Over wide areas there was no deposition during part or all of the Permian, while in others many thousands of feet of sediments accumulated. In the Paradox basin of Utah 10,000 feet (Oquirrh Formation) was deposited. In Arizona the Mississippian units are overlain by sandstones and shales of Permian age. In the miogeosynclines of the western United States thick marine beds were deposited. Some of these are locally made up of conglomerate, particularly near the active belts in the eugeo-

Fig. 17-3. Cross section across the Guadalupe Mountains. These mountains including the famous El Capitan are composed of the reefs which existed along the borders of the Permian basins. In front of the reef fragments broken off by wave action accumulated and graded into finer sediments which were being laid down in the basins. Behind the reef water circulation became restricted and the rate of evaporation was great resulting in deposition of quantities of dolostone and evaporites. (After N. D. Newell.)

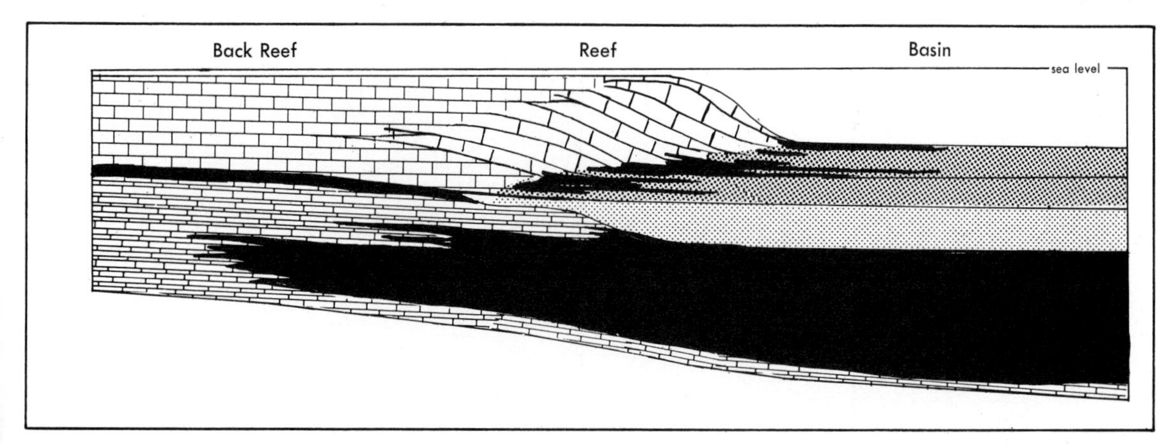

PERMIAN SYSTEM	NORTHERN CALIF.	WYOMING	OKLAHOMA	GLASS MOUNTAIN TEXAS
OCHOAN SERIES				
GUADALUPIAN SERIES	Dekkas andesite Nosoni formation	Phosphoria formation	Quartermaster fm. Whitehorse group El Reno group	Capitan limestone Altuda fm. Word fm. Vidrio formation
LEONARDIAN SERIES	McCloud limestone	Phosphoria formation	El Reno group Hennessey shale Garber sandstone Wellington fm.	Leonard fm. Hess formation
WOLFCAMPIAN SERIES	McCloud limestone		Chase group Council Grove group Admire group	Wolfcamp formation

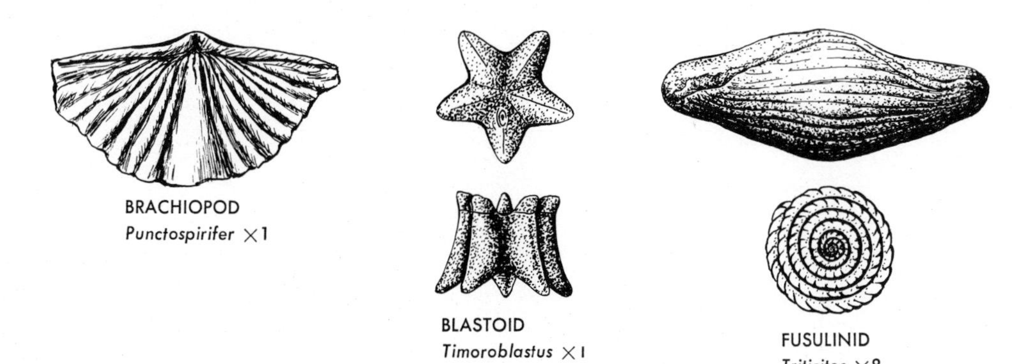

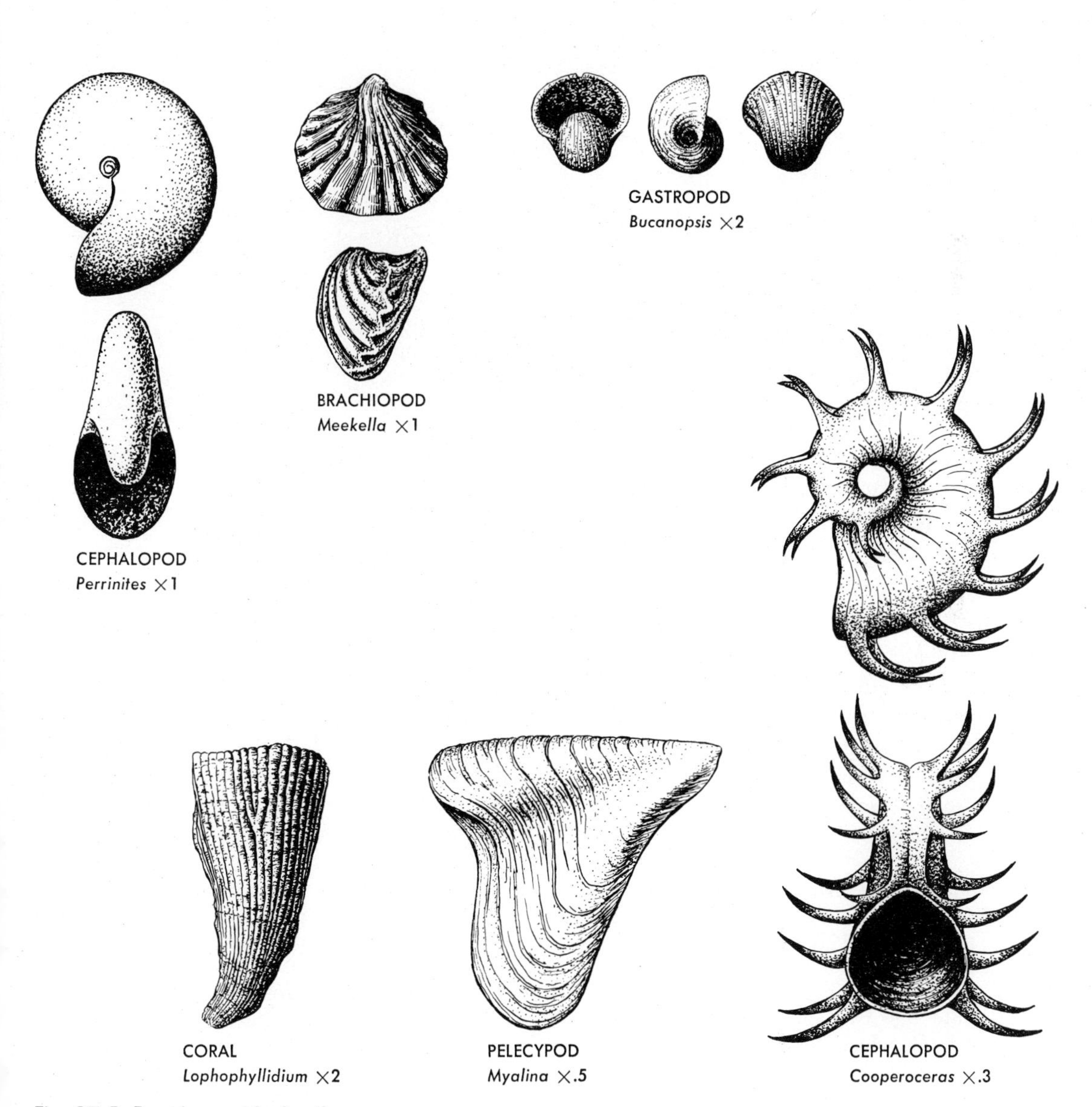

Fig. 17-5. Permian guide fossils.

Fig. 17-4. Permian correlation chart.

Fig. 17-6. Southern end of the Guadalupe Mountains. El Capitan is seen here covered by a cloud. The peak is a limestone formed of reef-making organisms. Judging from the elevation of the reef above th basin sediments, the basin that stood here in Permian time must have been a couple of thousand feet deep. (Photo by courtesy of Muldrow Aerial Surveys Corp.)

syncline. In the eugeosyncline great quantities of marine volcanic deposits associated with carbonates are present. In western Nevada and Idaho, Permian volcanic rocks several miles thick lie with angular unconformity over earlier Paleozoic sediments marking a Pennsylvanian disturbance in that area.

APPALACHIAN OROGENY

The region known to have been affected by the diastrophism at the end of the Paleozoic extends from central Alabama northeast into northern Pennsylvania, a distance of more than 1000 miles. The name "Appalachian Highlands"

Fig. 17-7. Appalachian Provinces. The Coastal Plain is underlain by extensive sheets of semi-consolidated sediments laid down as wedges during the Mesozoic and Cenozoic Eras after the Appalachian orogeny had ended. The Piedmont and New England areas are covered by complexly deformed igneous and metamorphic rocks of Precambrian and early Paleozoic age. The Blue Ridge is partly composed of the rocks of the Piedmont and partly of Cambrian rocks. The northern extension of the Blue Ridge is known as the Reading Prong of the New England Highlands. In the Valley and Ridge Province, Paleozoic strata are folded and cut by thrust faults which have moved the sections northwestward. The most intense zones of folding and faulting are along the Blue Ridge. Farther to the northwest the folded strata are less deformed and in the Appalachian Plateau they are gently tilted westward. The Black areas are basins bordered by normal faults which were dropped down on one or both sides during the Triassic after the Appalachian orogeny was over. Continental deposits are found in the Triassic basins. (After the Tectonic Map of the United States.)

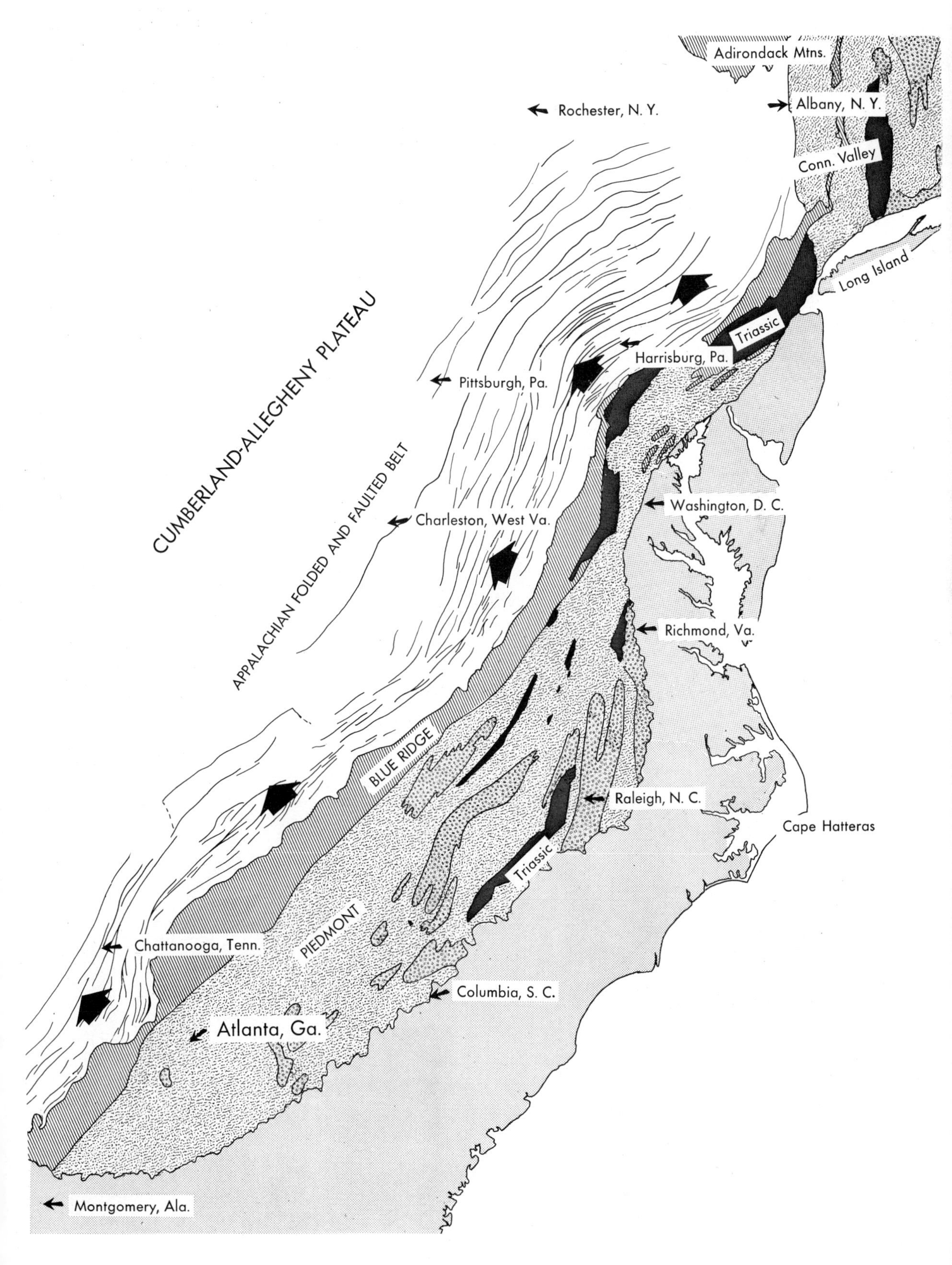
Adirondack Mtns.
Rochester, N. Y.
Albany, N. Y.
Conn. Valley
Long Island
CUMBERLAND-ALLEGHENY PLATEAU
Triassic
Harrisburg, Pa.
Pittsburgh, Pa.
APPALACHIAN FOLDED AND FAULTED BELT
Washington, D. C.
Charleston, West Va.
Richmond, Va.
BLUE RIDGE
Raleigh, N. C.
Cape Hatteras
Triassic
Chattanooga, Tenn.
PIEDMONT
Columbia, S. C.
Atlanta, Ga.
Montgomery, Ala.

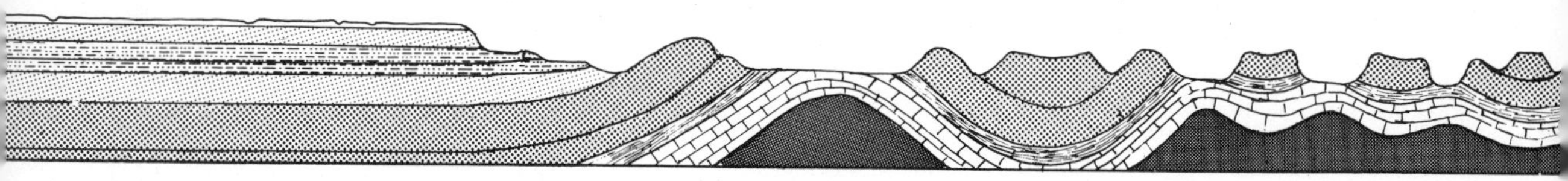

Fig. 17-8. Cross section of the Appalachians from the New Jersey Highlands to the Appalachian Plateau. This section does not cross the Triassic basins, the Blue Ridge, or the coastal plain. (After A. K. Lobeck's *Physi-*

is usually applied to this area. It contains four distinct physiographic divisions, the Piedmont, the Blue Ridge, the Valley and Ridge, and the Appalachian Plateau. The eastern and southern margins of the Appalachian Highlands are covered by Mesozoic sediments of the Coastal Plain. The Piedmont makes up the southeastern edge of the Appalachian Highlands. It is a complex zone of Precambrian and Paleozoic igneous and metamorphic rocks characterized

Fig. 17-9. View of the topography of the Appalachian Plateau and the folded and faulted belt of the Valley and Ridge Province. The folds which have been etched out of Early Paleozoic strata were deformed at the end of the Paleozoic, but the topography which is shown here did not originate until many millions of years later. The topography is Neogene in age. From this view it is easy to pick out plunging anticlines and synclines in the province. In general the folds are tightest in the east and broad in the northwest. (Photo of relief maps of the U.S. Army Map Service by E. W. Spencer.)

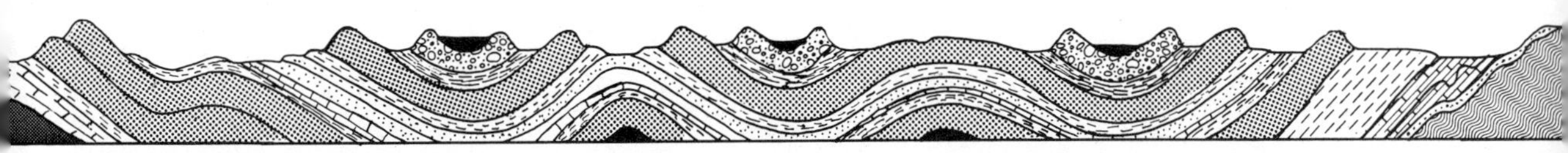

ographic Diagram of North America, copyright by A. K. Lobeck. Reproduced with permission from the publisher, The Geographical Press, a division of C. S. Hammond and Company, Maplewood, New Jersey.)

by complex structures. The Blue Ridge, composed of highly resistant quartzites of early Cambrian age and Precambrian units, is a long, almost continuous ridge along the northwestern edge of the Piedmont. At the southwestern end of the Blue Ridge lie the Smoky Mountains. The northwestern flanks of the Blue Ridge and Smoky Mountains are covered by folded and faulted Lower Paleozoic sediments. Limestones and shales exposed there have weathered and eroded more readily than the sandstones, quartzites, and the igneous and metamorphic rocks. The less resistant units are valleys, and the harder formations hold up as ridges of the Valley and Ridge Province. Farther northwest folded Silurian and Devonian sandstones and shales outcrop. These are more resistant than limestones and form ridges. West of this belt of valleys and ridges the eastern escarpment of the slightly deformed Appalachian Plateau is found. From this escarpment north and west the Mississippian and Pennsylvanian units outcrop. They surround the single large Permian deposit in the eastern United States.

Dating the Appalachian orogeny

We have seen that parts of the eastern United States were involved in two major orogenies before the Permian. A third orogeny took place in the Permian. In an area that has undergone several periods of deformation, certain problems arise in trying to interpret the structures found at the conclusion of all three deformations. This section deals with these problems and their solutions.

The first orogeny occurred at the end of the Ordovician when the Taconic orogeny uplifted, folded, and faulted the sedimentary sequences which had been deposited in the northern part of the Appalachian geosyncline in the Early Paleozoic. The erosion products from these mountains were spread westward and are preserved; they make up the Queenston delta. A second period of intense deformation affected the northern Appalachian geosyncline about the middle of the Devonian Period. This, the Acadian orogeny, also produced high mountains whose history has been similar to the mountains of the Taconic orogeny. In the millions of years following their elevation they were eroded down, leaving large quantities of the debris eroded from them in the Catskill delta. Finally, the eastern United States experienced a third orogeny, and the last up to the present, known as the Appalachian orogeny. The absence of great thicknesses of alluvial and deltaic deposits from the mountains formed in the Appalachian orogeny leads many geologists to the conclusion that this orogeny was somewhat less intense than the earlier ones, but the structures formed during it are much better preserved and better exposed than those of the earlier orogenies. Most of the evidence of the Appalachian orogeny lies in the Appalachian Highlands, extending from northern Pennsylvania to Alabama. If the earlier orogenies were more intense and affected more of the Appalachian geosyncline, then it is likely that they are responsible for some of the structures now exposed in the southern Appalachians, and generally described as results of the Appalachian orogeny.

Orogenies may be dated by determining the age of the youngest strata that are affected by the deformation (within the deformed area). Where an area has been involved in two or more periods of deformation the effects of the second deformation can be accurately determined only if strata younger than the first

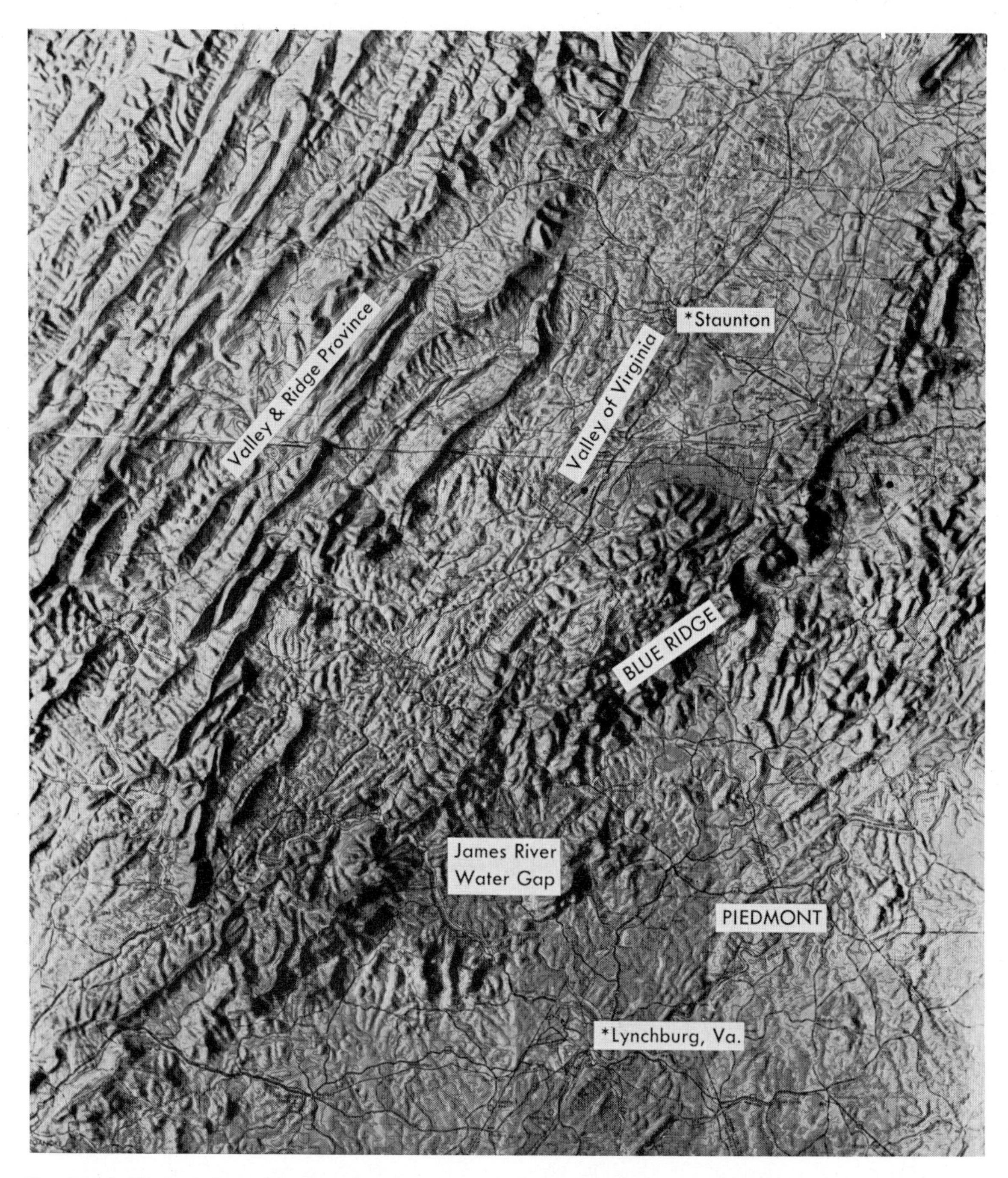

Fig. 17-10. Vertical view of topography of a segment of the Appalachian Highlands north of Roanoke, Va.

deformation are preserved in the same area as strata that predate both deformations (i.e., strata affected by the two orogenies and also sediments that were affected only by the second orogeny). Unfortunately the strata that have remained after the millions of years of erosion since the Appalachian orogeny are not distributed in such a manner as to make it easy to demonstrate the effects of the three Paleozoic orogenies throughout the Appalachian mountain systems. In eastern New York and western New England, the classic areas for

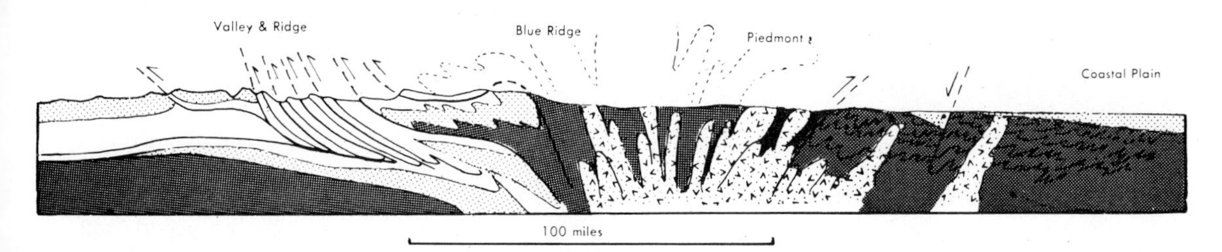

Fig. 17-11. Schematic section across the Appalachian Mountain belt. This view suggests the nature of the origin of many Appalachian structures. The center of the diagram is in the position of the Piedmont and the Coastal Plain which were probably in the most intensely deformed portion of the mountain system. The folds and faults of the Valley and Ridge were formed on the margins of the belt. (After P. B. King.)

study of the Taconic and Acadian deformations, Upper Paleozoic sediments are absent—thus making it impossible to show what the effects of the Appalachian orogeny were in this region. In the southern Appalachian Highlands, from northern Pennsylvania to Alabama, the sediments of the Carboniferous Period are folded and faulted, as is the entire Paleozoic section. It is difficult to evaluate the effect of Early Paleozoic orogenies in this belt because no strata younger than Ordovician are exposed from the Piedmont to the Valley and Ridge Province. Thus there is a long belt in the southern Appalachian Highlands in which some structures may be older than the Appalachian orogeny. Angular unconformities in the sediments of the Paleozoic section (particularly toward the southern end of the Appalachians) prove the existence of welts, or small uplifts, within the Appalachian geosyncline during the Paleozoic, but no structural features can be directly related to these rather localized uplifts.

The date of the Appalachian orogeny cannot be pinpointed. Even in the southern part of the Appalachians, where Carboniferous sediments are present, the Permian is absent except for an area in the Appalachian Plateau in West Virginia, Ohio, and Pennsylvania. The Permian Dunkard group is slightly deformed. Thus the orogeny is most probably of Middle to Late Permian age, although it could have begun much earlier in the eastern parts of the Appalachian geosyncline.

The effects of the Appalachian orogeny

Many and varied structures were formed during the Late Paleozoic deformation. The thick sedimentary sections of the Paleozoic, which had been deposited within the southern part of the Appalachian geosynclinal belt, were strongly uplifted, folded, and faulted. We cannot say exactly what happened to sediments that had been deposited in the postulated eugeosynclinal belt, for they are eroded off the

Fig. 17-12. Section of thrust fault. A thrust fault in southern Virginia has carried a slab of Cambrian strata out to the northwest more than twenty miles over Cambrian and Ordovician strata. This sheet is one of several similar though not quite so extensive sheets in the Appalachians. This section is taken along the Virginia–Tennessee state line and shows the structure of the Pine Mountain thrust. (After P. B. King.)

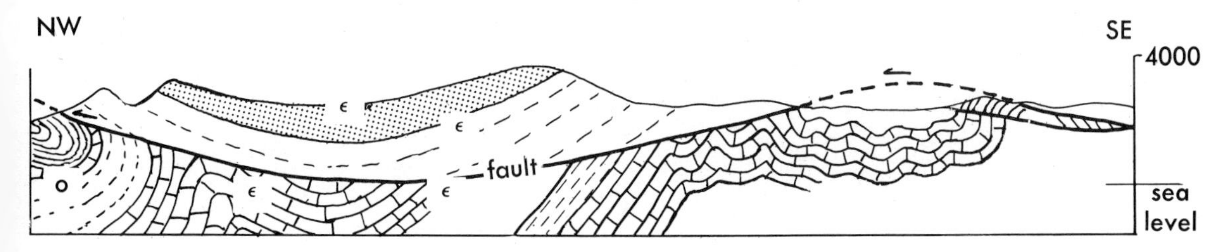

Fig. 17-13. Ammonite suture patterns.

Piedmont and are overlain by the younger sediments of the Mesozoic and Cenozoic in the Coastal Plain. Beginning with the western edge of the Piedmont, the sediments are strongly folded and thrust-faulted. The folds are asymmetric toward the northwest, and the low-angle thrusts are inclined toward the southeast, suggesting that the whole geosyncline was moved toward the stable continental interior from the southeast toward the northwest. The intensity of folding dies out toward the northwest across the Appalachian Highlands until we reach the Appalachian Plateau, which is only slightly warped into a broad open syncline. The eastern edge of this syncline makes the escarpments of the Allegheny and Cumberland Plateaus.

What happened to the deformed belt to the south

In central Alabama the deformed belt of the Appalachians disappears under the Coastal Plain sediments. What happens to it from there is debatable. Many geologists think this belt is directly continued in the Ouachita Mountains of Arkansas and Oklahoma. If so, the belt of deformation must swing around sharply to the west in southern Alabama, even more sharply than it swings southward in Pennsylvania. Such a swing is a definite possibility. The trends of some folds in the Paleozoic have been discovered through drilling in Mississippi. These demonstrate at least an eastward continuation of the Ouachita folded belt. The age and structure of the deformed belts in the Ouachita and Appalachian Mountains are in harmony with the idea of a single continuous deformed geosynclinal belt.

Fig. 17-14. "Sail-lizard," *Edaphosaurus*, from Permian strata exposed near Geraldine, Archer County, Texas. The purpose of this sail-like structure on the back of the animal is not known. The structure of the teeth indicates that they lived on plant matter. They lived in the Late Pennsylvanian and Early Permian (Photo by courtesy of the U.S. National Museum.)

Fig. 17-15. Permian reptiles and amphibians. The remarkable fin-backed Dimetrodon and Edaphosaurus and the more lizard-shaped Casea were characteristic reptiles of the Permian period, 240 million years ago. By this time, the reptiles had displaced their ancestors, the amphibians, as the dominant land vertebrates. (From a mural by Charles Knight, by courtesy of the Chicago Natural History Museum.)

LIFE OF THE PERMIAN

I. NEW FORMS

1. *Theriodonts:* This group of carnivorous reptiles were the first animals to have teeth like those of the mammals. Their teeth were differentiated into incisors, canines, and molars. Their remains have been found in the Karro formations of South Africa.

II. PEAKS AND ADVANCEMENT

1. The true conifers, *Walchia,* rapidly expanded to replace scale trees and other types of forest in Permian time. It is likely that these were better adapted to the colder climates that seem to have existed through this period.
2. *Ammonoids:* This group of cephalopods began to become more important and diversified than ever before.
3. *Reptiles:* They spread and became more specialized.

III. DECLINE AND EXTINCTION

The close of the Permian Period found many groups that had been important in earlier parts of the Paleozoic begin to die out. Among these were:

1. Trilobites.
2. Fusulinids.
3. Honeycomb and tetra corals.
4. Most crinoids died out before the end of the period.
5. Many groups of bryozoans died out.
6. The trees of the coal swamps of the Carboniferous began to decline. Many of them dwindled almost to extinction.

IV. NOTABLE ASPECTS OF PERMIAN LIFE

The specialization of the reptiles is especially interesting. One of these groups, the theriodonts, developed teeth like those of the mammals. One group of primitive reptiles characterized by a solid-roofed skull had become diversified so that some of them, carnivores, ate meat; others fed on insects, and still others, herbivores, lived on plants. One of the most peculiar looking reptiles of the period was the Dimetrodon, which possessed a series of spines connected by skin that stood up on its back, giving it the appearance of a sail.

The amphibians were also abundant during the Permian. *Seymouria* was a group that possessed characteristics intermediate between those of reptiles and amphibians. They were about 2 feet long and looked somewhat like the giant of the Permian amphibians, eryops. One of the strangest of the amphibians had a wedge-shaped head. These animals, named *Diplocaulus*, lived in fresh water.

Glossopteris flora: Two of the most characteristic plants of the Permian of the southern hemisphere are *Glossopteris* and *Gangamopteris.* Both of these have small, thick leaves that give them the names "tongue ferns." The remains of these plants occur frequently with sediments deposited near the margins of Permian glaciers. Apparently they lived under the frigid conditions near ice sheets. The interesting thing about this assemblage of plants is that they are found on continents that today are separated by thousands of miles of ocean water. The problem they raise is how could such an otherwise restricted group suddenly appear in such widely separated regions as Africa, South America, and India. Several answers have been offered, and none can be totally discounted or definitely proven.

1. The spores of *Glossopteris,* which have a broad double-wing shape, might have been blown for long distances and might possibly have gotten across the oceans in this way or in ocean currents.

2. There may have been land bridges connecting the southern tip of South America with the Antarctica continent and another connect-

Fig. 17-16. Monument Valley. (Courtesy Esther Henderson Photo, Tucson, Arizona.)

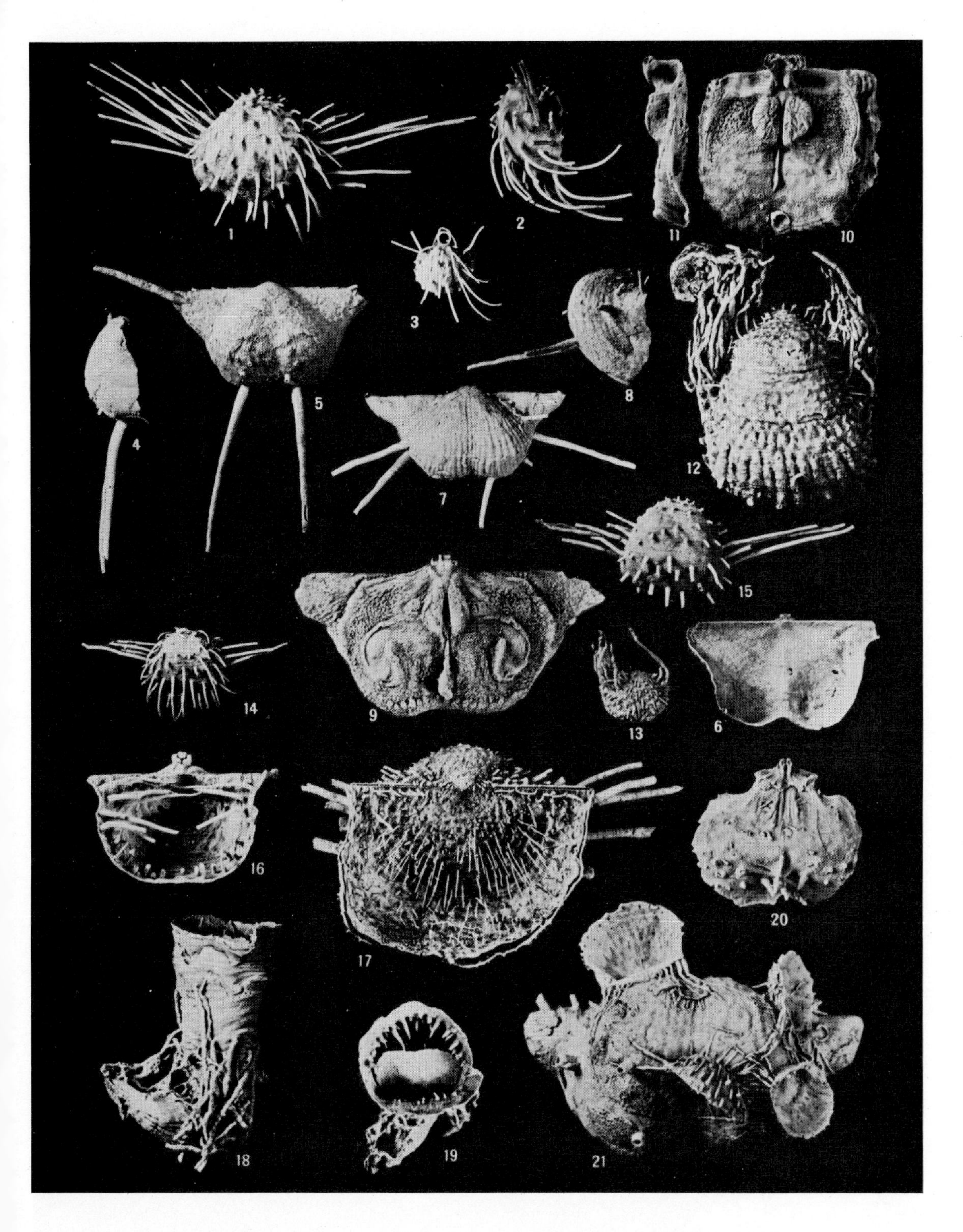

Fig. 17-17. Permian brachiopods. This remarkable collection of fossil brachiopods has been recovered from the Glass Mountains, Brewster County, Texas. The shells have been replaced by silica and thus can be etched out of the limestone in which they occur by use of acid. Even the small spines which project from the shells have been preserved. (Photo by courtesy of G. S. Cooper, U.S. National Museum.)

ing Antarctica with South Africa. Such a bridge between South America and Antarctica seems possible since there are a number of islands between the two land masses, but the distance between South Africa and Antarctica is great. It has even been suggested that there were continental lands that simply sank away between then and now, but geophysical studies reveal no sign of a true continental-type crust anywhere in the region.

3. India and the continents of South America and Africa were once all together. Since the Permian they have split and drifted apart to their present positions. This theory, which is known as the theory of continental drift, has been long debated. The outlines of the lands on either side of the ocean are quite suggestive of this possibility, but it is difficult to explain why the split took place and how the continents were moved.

Fig. 17-18. Fauna of the western Texas Permian seas. This close-up of a Permian reef shows brachiopods hanging attached to the reef (1), gastropods (2), nautiloid cephalopod (3), gastropods (4), and seaweed (5). (Photo by courtesy of the Museum of Paleontology, University of Michigan.)

Fig. 17-19. Restoration of a Permian sea floor. This reef is inhabited by sponges (1), brachiopods (2), coiled cephalopods (3), and corals (4). (Photo by courtesy of U.S. National Museum.)

REFERENCES

JONES, T. S., 1953, Stratigraphy of the Permian Basin of West Texas: West Texas Geol. Soc. Guidebook, Midland, Texas, 63 p.

NEWELL, N. D., 1957, Paleoecology of the Permian reefs in the Guadalupe Mountain area: Geol. Soc. America Mem. 67, v. 2, p. 407-436

NEWELL, N. D., *et al.*, 1953, *The Permian Reef Complex of the Guadalupe Mountains Region, Texas and New Mexico:* W. H. Freeman and Company, San Francisco, 236 p.

SCHUCHERT, CHARLES, 1932, Gondwana land bridges: Geol. Soc. America Bull., v. 43, p. 875-915

18 The Triassic Period

PHYSICAL HISTORY OF THE TRIASSIC

The high mountains formed along the eastern United States during the Appalachian orogeny were being worn down through the Triassic. The resulting debris was carried eastward and westward down the slopes of the uplift, and some was trapped in graben-like basins along the axis of the uplifted mountain chain. Large dikes and sills were intruded within these down-dropped blocks. In the western part of the country volcanism dominated the Triassic in the eugeosynclinal belt, leaving great thicknesses of lava flows and ash from Alaska southward through California. Triassic strata are among the most colorful beds of the continental interior. Red beds and gypsum make up some sea-marginal deposits, and variegated deposits of volcanic dust, clays, and sands derived from older uplifts in the miogeosyncline cover the Colorado Plateau and surrounding areas.

Eastern United States

Triassic sediments in the eastern United States are nonmarine sands, gravels, and lake deposits trapped in down-faulted troughs along the Appalachian Highlands. Today these troughs are lower than their surroundings. They include the Connecticut Valley, the New Jersey lowlands, which are continuous with a valley in southeastern Pennsylvania, the Richmond basin, and numerous others southward into South Carolina. See Fig. 18-6. These troughs apparently subsided as sediments accumulated within them. The faulting and subsidence were accompanied by intrusion of basalt, which probably came up along the high-angle faults that form boundaries of the troughs on at least one side and spread out into the accumulated sediments as sills. The Palisades sill, which forms the scarp along the western edge of the Hudson River in New Jersey, is one of the thickest of these sills. The deformation that accompanied the faulting and intrusion is called the Palisades disturbance.

Western United States

In the far western United States and northward into Canada and along the coast of Alaska the Triassic is characterized by volcanic activity. The evidence of this is the great thickness of sediments, which include tuff (volcanic ash), lava flows, and pillow lavas that are interbedded with marine sediments. The most extensive sections of Triassic are found in Nevada where the sequence is about 25,000 feet thick. The Excelsior formation is one of the best known of these units. It was deposited in a trough that covered most of the western part of Nevada and extended northward through Oregon and Washington. Southward, this trough was cut off by a land barrier which separated it from a broad shallow sea that covered the area from North Dakota to Texas and westward to Idaho and California. The two water-covered areas collected quite different types of sediments. The deep trough in Nevada received much volcanic material from the west, but the broad shallow sea on the continental interior collected only a little volcanic dust. Most of the sediments within this sea were muds and sands from locally emergent areas in Colorado and Arizona. A widespread break appears in the Middle Triassic of the west. It appears that the continental interior rose above sea level for some time before the Late Triassic seas returned.

TRIASSIC LOWLANDS OF NEW JERSEY

There are only minor variations in the type of Triassic sediments of the various down-faulted troughs in the eastern United States. Although they are not connected, they underwent much the same sequence of events in the Triassic. Some of these troughs are bounded by high-angle normal faults on the one side only (usually the western side), but others are bounded by faults on both the western and eastern sides. The center blocks are dropped down, forming a graben. All of the sedimentary rocks in these troughs are continental deposits. No marine units of Triassic age are known east of the Rocky Mountains.

The Triassic in New Jersey is composed of three units known as the Newark group:

Brunswick formation: Soft red shale with sandstone beds, the latter more abundant toward the northeast; conglomerate beds composed of quartzite or limestone pebbles in a red matrix occur along the northwestern border. Maximum thickness: 10,000 feet.

Lockatong formation: Hard dark shale composed locally of thin beds of quartzite or limestone pebbles in a red matrix occur along the northwestern border. Maximum thickness: 3500 feet.

Stockton formation: Gray feldspathic sandstone and arkose, conglomerate, and red shale; conglomerate beds with quartzite and limestone pebbles in red matrix occur along the northwestern border. Maximum thickness: 3000 feet.

These sediments were laid down on the flanks of the Appalachian Mountains as broad coalescing alluvial fans. The distribution of sediments is similar to that of modern alluvial fans. The largest boulders and coarsest fragments in the rocks eroded from the higher mountains are dropped closest to the moun-

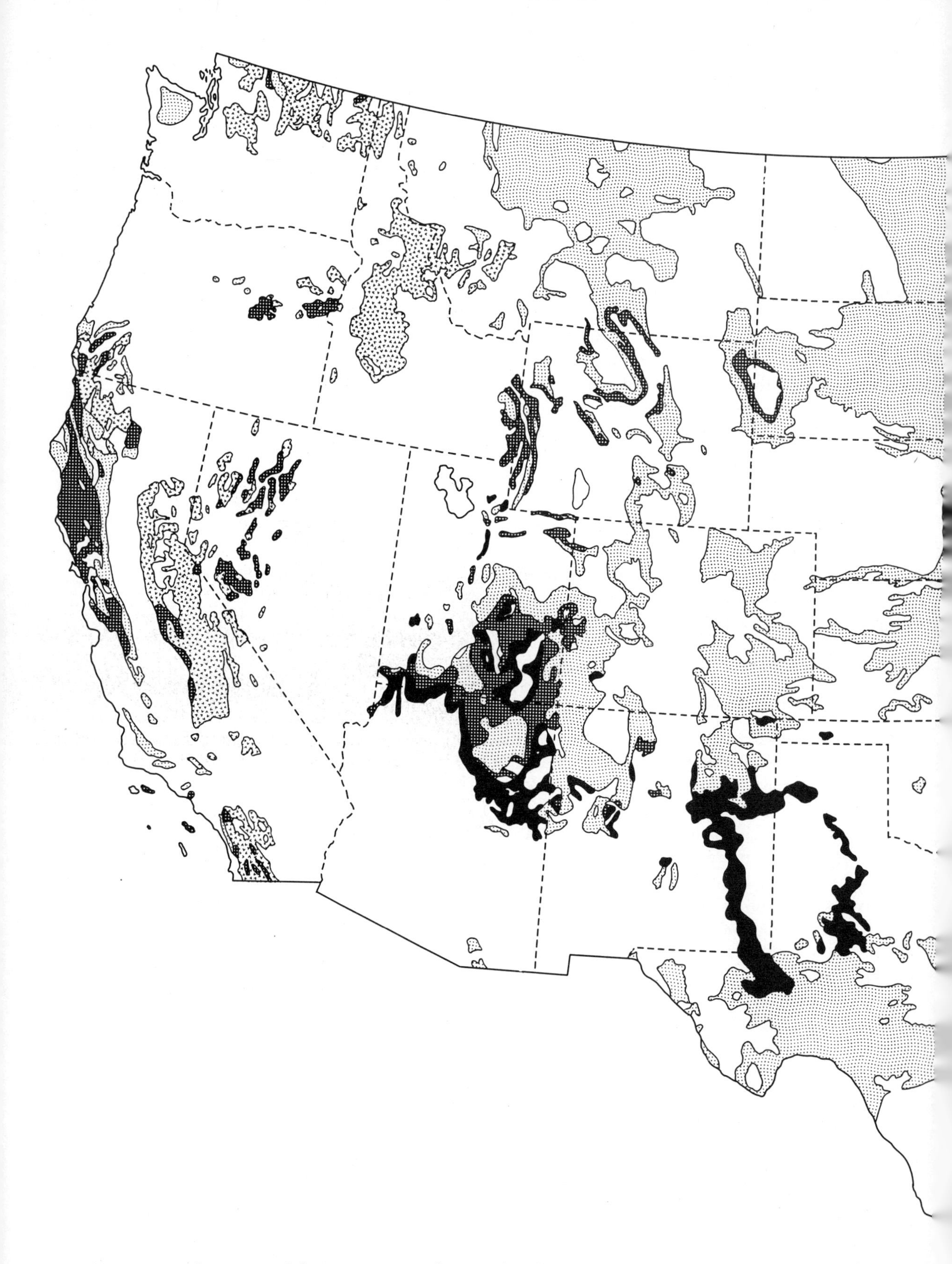

Mesozoic. Geologic map of the Mesozoic Era showing distribution of Triassic, Jurassic, and Cretaceous strata

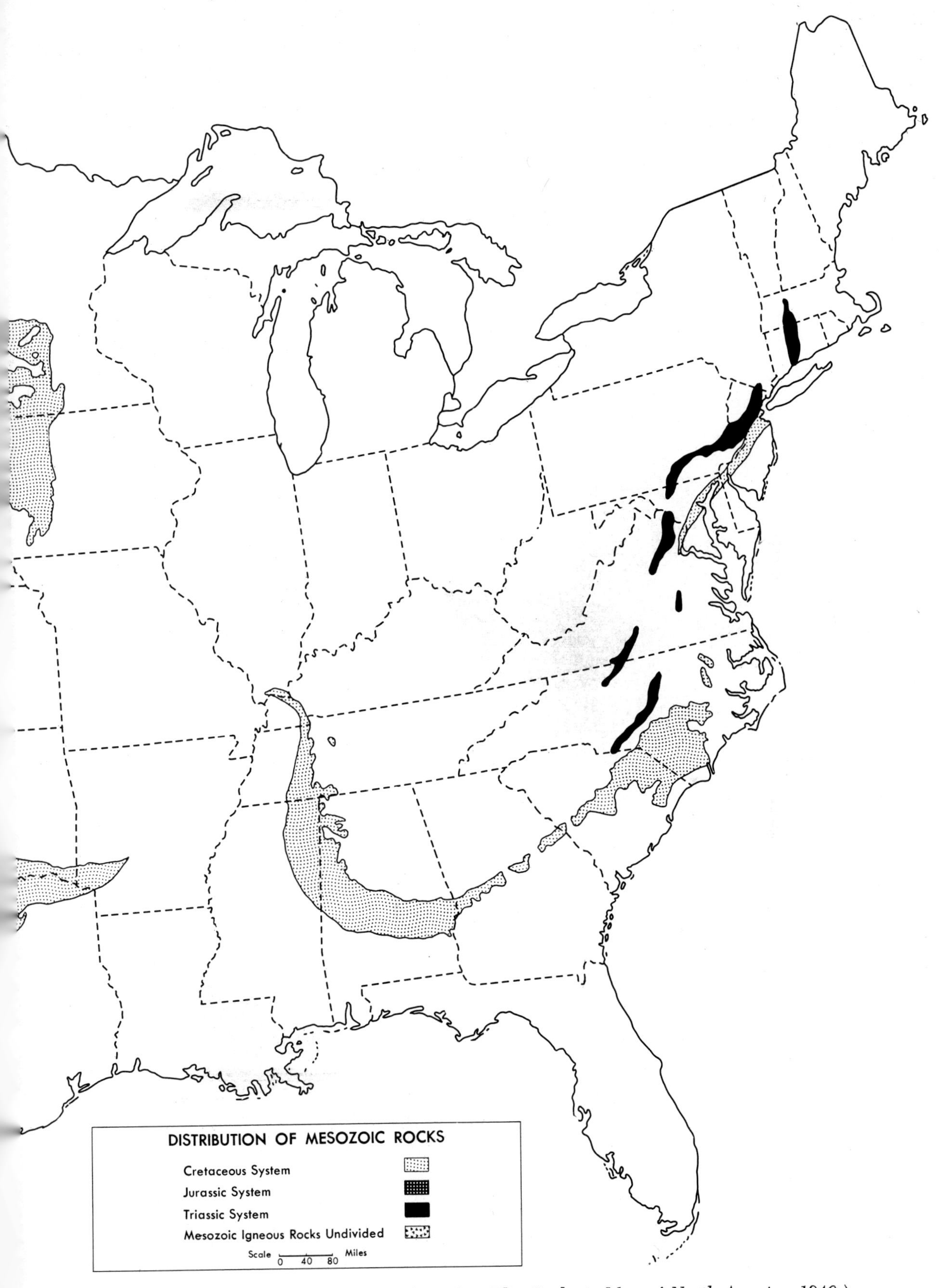

and Mesozoic igneous rocks undivided. (Modified after *The Geologic Map of North America*, 1946.)

TRIASSIC SYSTEM	CALIFORNIA	NEVADA	COLORADO PLATEAU	NEW JERSEY
UPPER TRIASSIC SERIES	Brock shale Hosselkus limestone	Gabbs formation Luning formation	Chinle formation Shinarump conglomerate	Newark group
MIDDLE TRIASSIC SERIES	Pit shale	Excelsior formation		
LOWER TRIASSIC SERIES		Candelaria formation	Moenkopi formation	

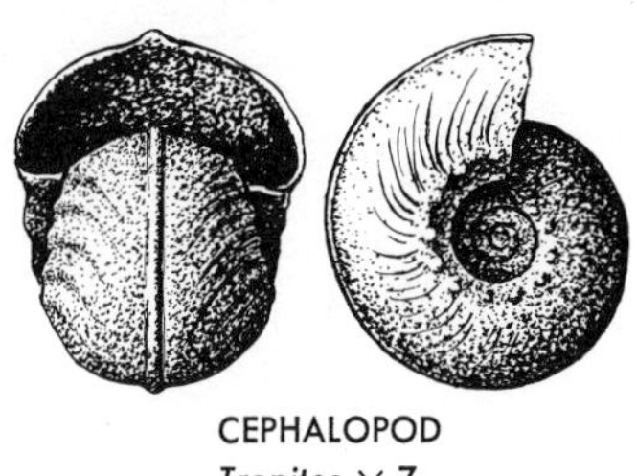

CEPHALOPOD
Tropites ×.7

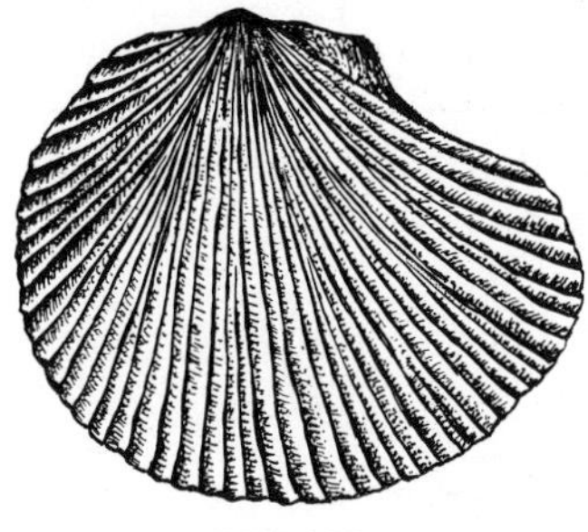

PELECYPOD
Monotis ×.8

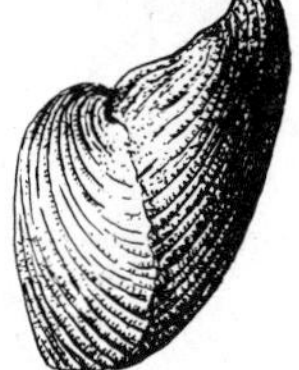

BRACHIOPOD
Spondylospira ×1

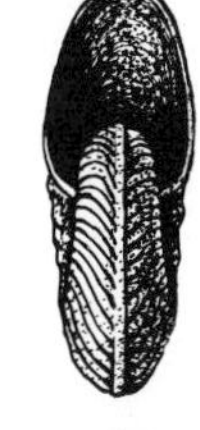

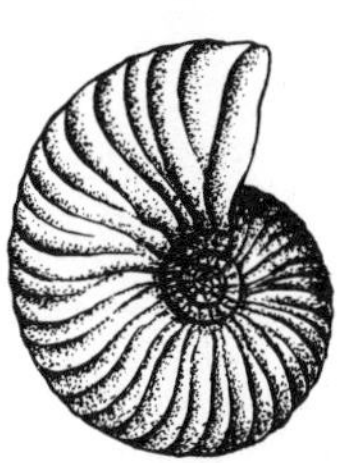

CEPHALOPOD
Ceratites ×1

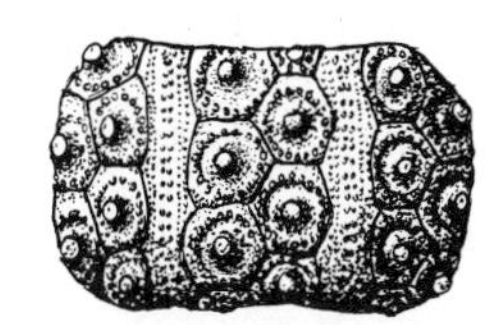

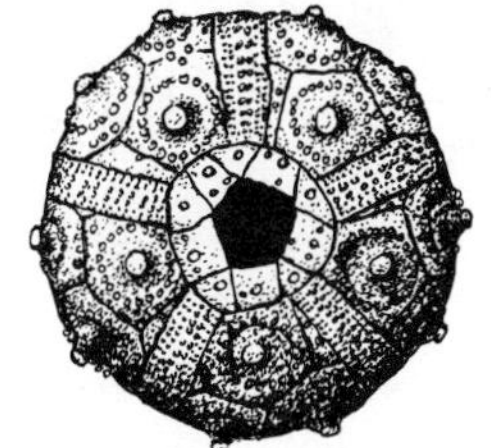

ECHINOID
Triadocidaris ×1

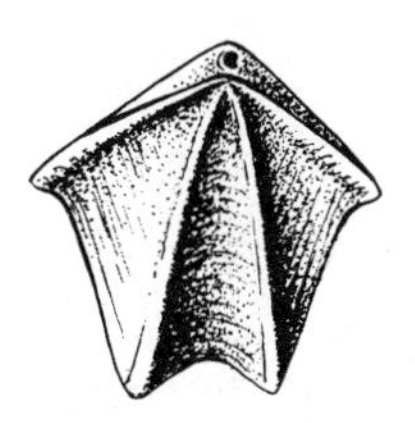

BRACHIOPOD
Tetractinella ×1.3

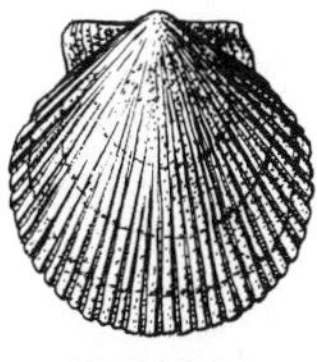

PELECYPOD
Chlamys ×1

CORAL
Margarosmilia ×10

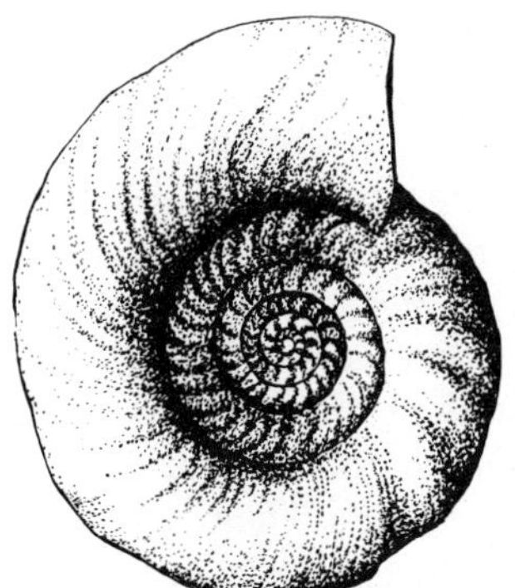

CEPHALOPOD
Columbites ×1

Fig. 18-2. Triassic guide fossils.

Fig. 18-1. Triassic correlation chart.

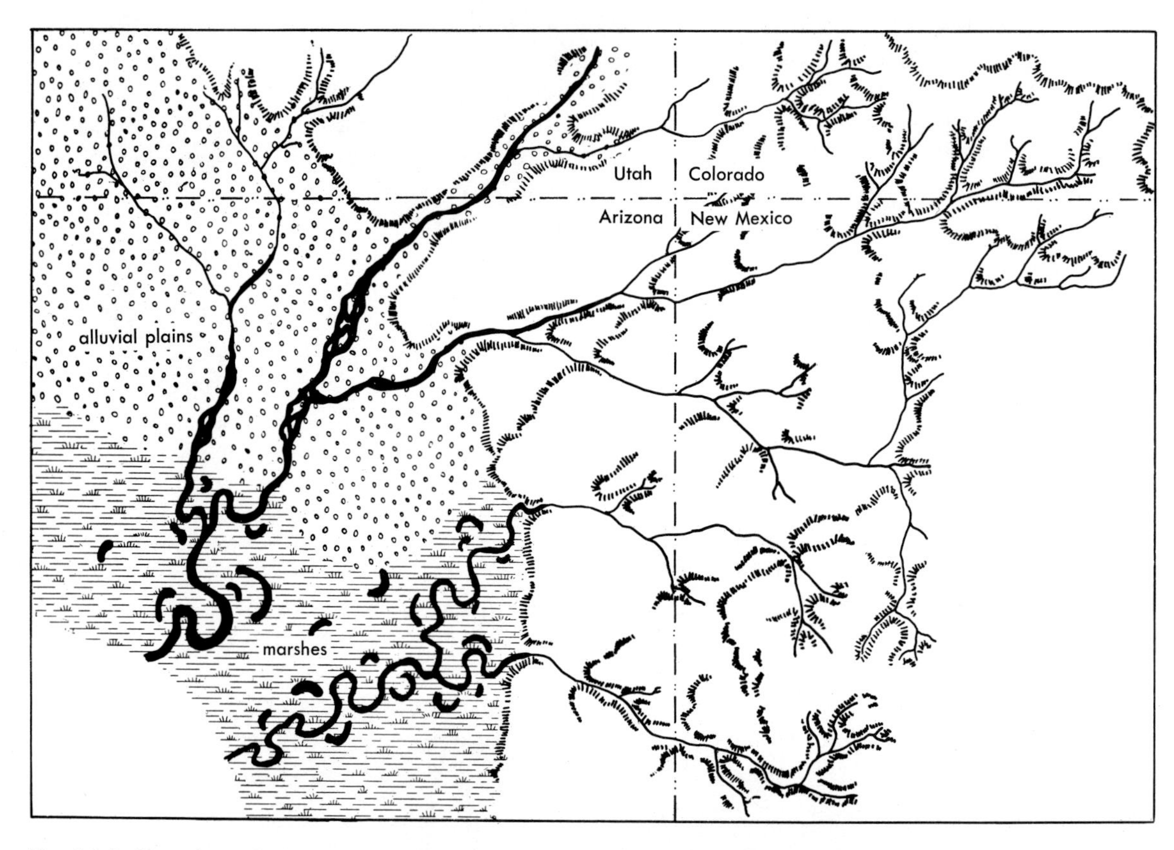

Fig. 18-3. Hypothetical physiography in the four corners district of Colorado, New Mexico, Arizona, and Utah during the time of the deposition of the Moenave Formation. This diagram and Fig. 18-4 show conditions at two times during the Triassic in this region which is famous for its colorful exposures of Mesozoic strata. Reconstruction of the physiograph in this region at a number of times during the Triassic have been made possible by careful analysis of the distribution of sediments bearing indications of depositions in particular types of environments. The types of sediment deposited in various environments have been outlined in Chapter 4. Characteristics of the marshes, alluvial plains, lagoons, and sand dunes are still preserved in these units. (After Harshbarger, Repenning, and Irwin.)

tains and finer sediments are carried out farther to the edge of the fan. At times the margins of these basins were occupied by lakes in which muds were deposited. Mud cracks can be seen in the now-consolidated Triassic muds. These mud cracks are most common in the eastern parts of the lowlands and are similar to mud cracks that we see in bottom sediments around the margins of lakes and along muddy shore lines where the bottom is periodically wetted and dried out. These same muds, now shales, contain the fossil remains of fresh-water fish.

When the first Triassic sediments were deposited (Stockton formation) the nearby mountains were higher than they were later in the Triassic, and thus more coarse debris was deposited in the trough. After the faults had become active, the side nearest the mountains went down in relation to the mountains, and sediments accumulated there were thicker than farther east. Today most of these sediments dip toward the northwest, the opposite direction from their initial dip. This has been brought about by faulting, which rotated the strata down on the west, and later by uplifts of the region.

Igneous activity took place several times in the New Jersey lowland during the Triassic. Three lava flows are found on the Triassic red sands and shales, and the Palisades sill was intruded into the sediments. This igneous activity, and the block faulting which accompanied it, are usually referred to as the Palisades disturbance.

The three extrusions have become weathered and eroded so they stand out today, forming ridges in the central part of the Triassic lowlands of New Jersey. The bottoms of these flows conform to the sediments on which they lie. The upper surfaces are very porous and irregular. Many of these large porous zones formed by escaping gases have later been filled with unusual mineral deposits (zeolite minerals) brought in and deposited by circulating ground water and hydrothermal solutions. In places the bottoms of the flows are porous as though the lava flowed out onto lakes or marshes, vaporizing the water. These flows range in thickness from 600 to 900 feet.

The largest igneous body within the Triassic is the Palisades sill which is 1000 feet thick. It extends more than 20 miles along the Hudson River. That this basaltic sill was intruded within the sedimentary sequence is substantiated by many facts. The top and bottom are very fine-grained rock, indicating rapid cooling and insufficient time for coarse crystals to develop. Heat lost from both the top and bottom of the sill has metamorphosed the sediments for distances up to 100 feet from the contact. Locally the sediments were melted by the heat of the molten rock, and in places fragments of the sediments are found trapped within the basalt of the sill. These blocks became dislodged and were partially altered by the heat and solutions.

The only later rock units laid on the Triassic of this area are Pleistocene glacial deposits which cover most of the northern United States. For the remainder of the Mesozoic our attention is directed to the west.

Fig. 18-4. Hypothetical physiography in the Colorado Plateau country during the deposition of the Wingate sandstone. See caption under Fig. 18-3. (After Harshbarger, Repenning, and Irwin.)

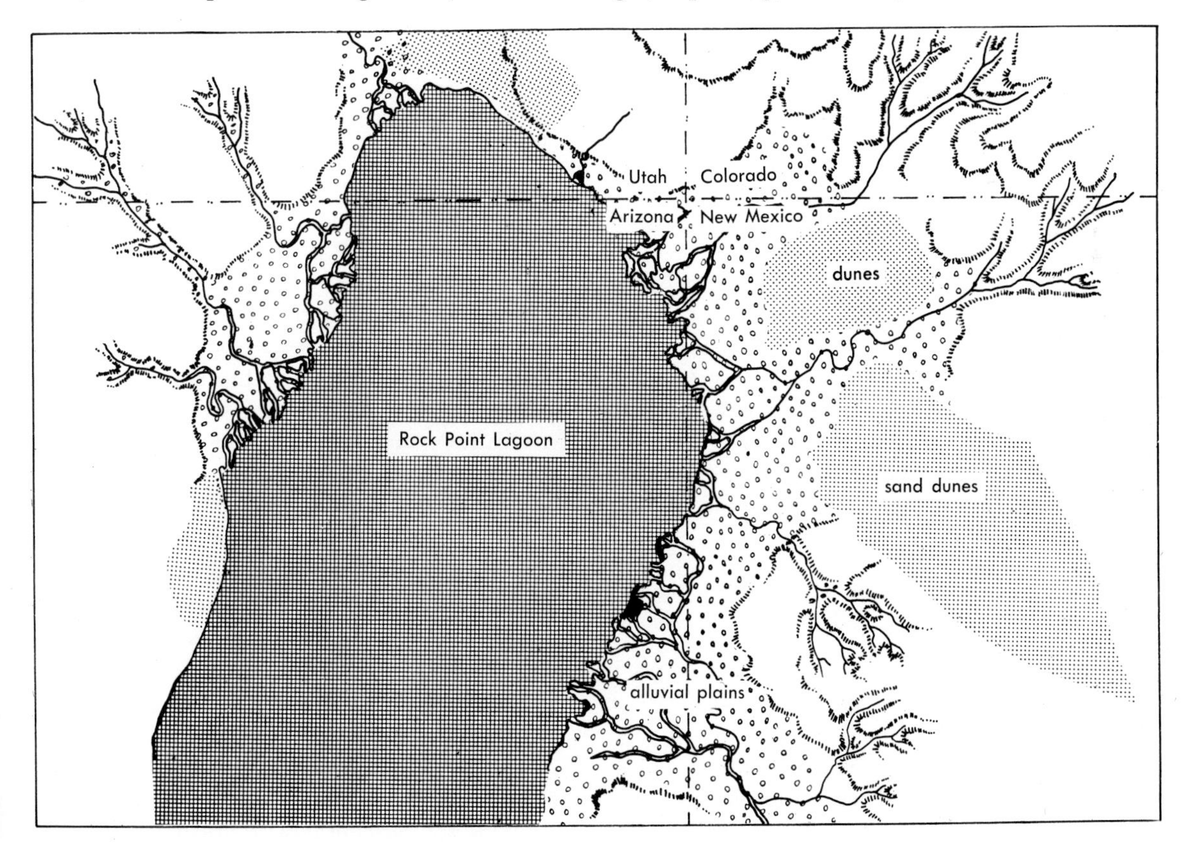

Fig. 18-5. Triassic strata exposed in the Colorado Plateau near the Arizona-Utah boundary. (Photo by E. W. Spencer.)

Triassic history of the Peace River area, Alberta, Canada

Triassic units in western Canada are restricted to the area near Peace River east of the Canadian Rocky Mountain foothills. This region was an eastern extension of a seaway that covered western Nevada, eastern Oregon, and Washington. Unlike the western side of this sea, no volcanic materials were deposited in the Peace River section. Description of the section there follows:

Pardonet formation: dark calcareous shales, dark calcareous siltstones, and smaller proportions of dark limestones.

Baldonnel formation: buff, brown to gray, fine, fossiliferous dolomite with some chert.

Charlie Lake formation: massive anhydrites, red dolomitic siltstones, microcrystalline, buff to gray dolomites, interbedded anhydrites, and small amounts of salt. Facies changes are caused by the transition from evaporite deposition in the east to a normal marine depositional environment in the west.

Halfway formation: marine, gray to light-gray, fine-grained quartz sandstone, in part dolomitic and calcareous, with some buff, finely crystalline dolomite and siltstones. Sharp changes in thickness have been observed, which are attributed to near-shore sand-bar deposits.

Liard formation: marine, gray, massive beds of fine, calcareous sandstone, arenaceous limestones, limestone, and minor amounts of siltstone and shale.

Toad Grayling formation: gray, calcareous and dolomitic siltstone, with minor beds of sandstone, dark-gray shale, and dark limestones. Toward its eastern extent the formation becomes relatively rich in sandstone, reflecting near-shore deposition of sand bars. Many of these sands have become filled with oil and gas.

Triassic history of this area as interpreted from the above stratigraphic data and field mapping follows. See how much of this interpretation you could make if you had nothing more than the formation descriptions and a map of their distribution (Figs. 18-8 and 18-9).

1. At the beginning of the Triassic there was an eastward transgression of the sea which resulted in onlap of the Toad Grayling formation on the land mass. At the height of this advance sand bars were formed along the eastern shore.
2. The Toad Grayling formation was deposited after a regression of the sea in the western part of the region.
3. The seas advanced a second time, and the sands of the Halfway formation were laid down.
4. Then came a sudden change in conditions within the environment, which initiated the deposition of evaporites of the Charlie Lake formation. On the western side perhaps some restrictive barrier cut off the sea from deeper waters with better circulation.
5. Many interruptions occurred in the conditions as normal marine sediments were deposited in the west, and fresh-water stream-laid sediments were de-

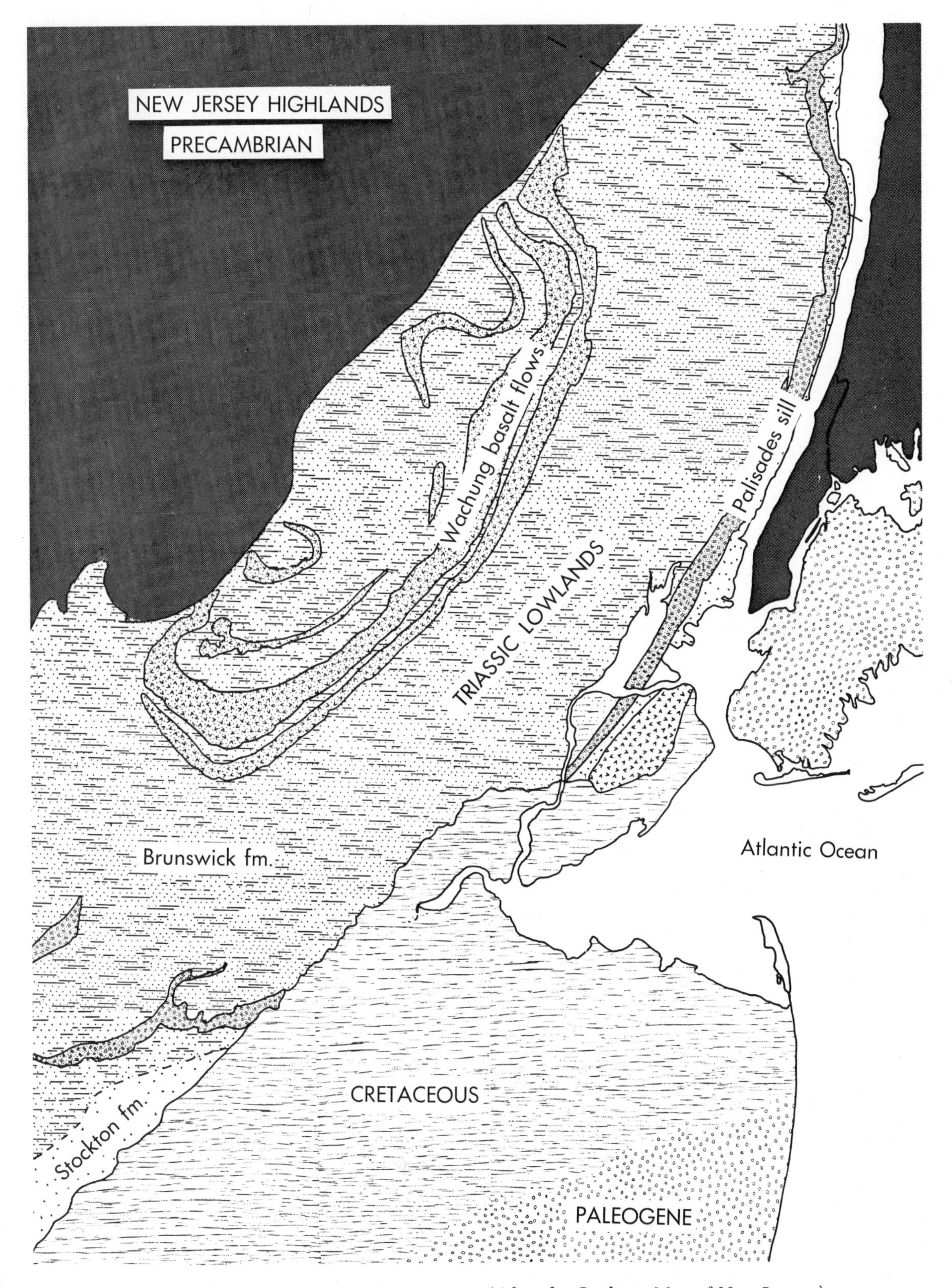

Fig. 18-6. Map of the Triassic lowlands of New Jersey. (After the Geologic Map of New Jersey.)

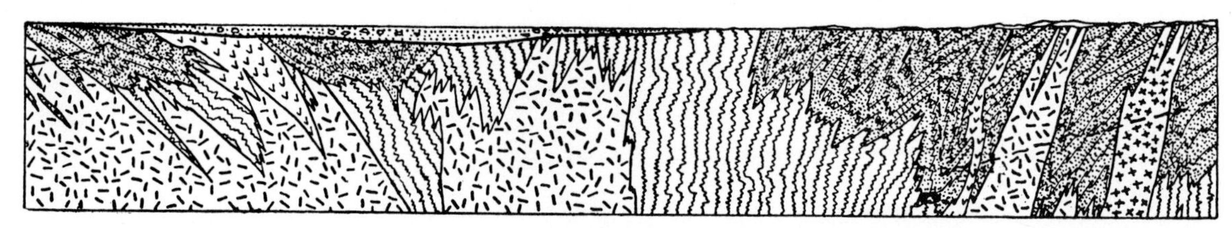

At the beginning of Triassic Sedimentation

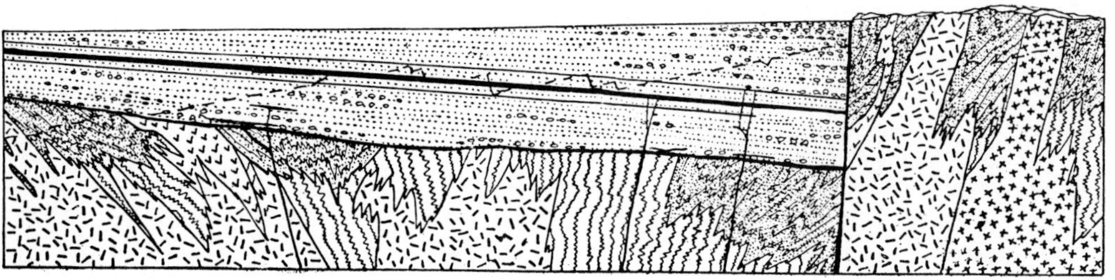

At the close of the Triassic

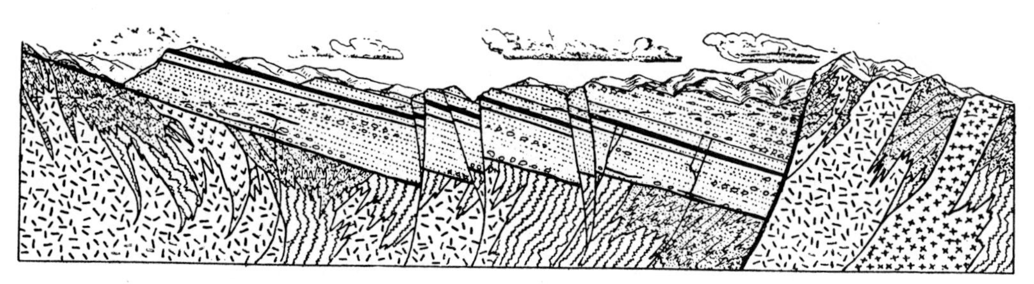

In the Jurassic

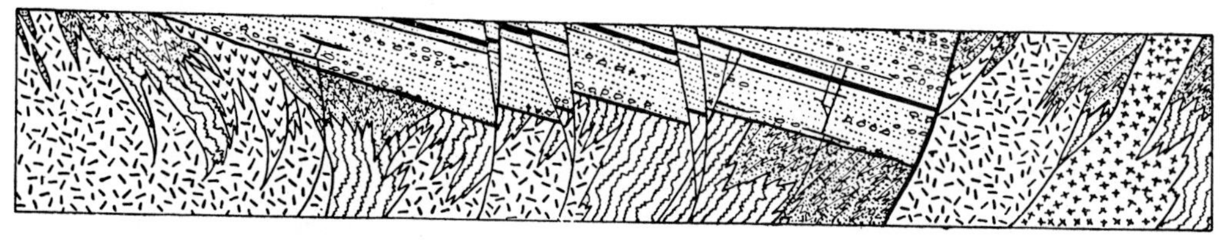

In the Cretaceous

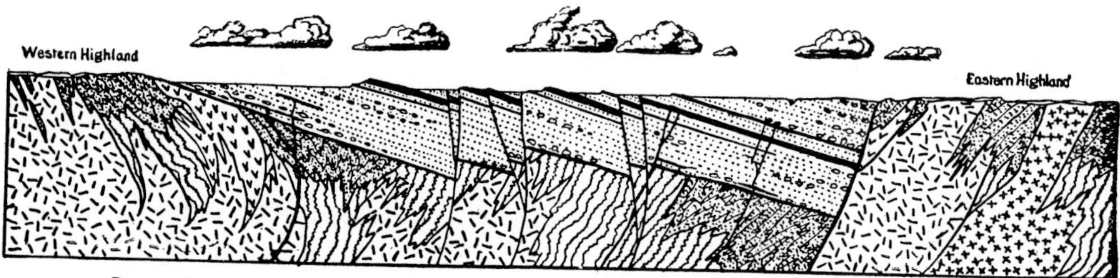

Present

Fig. 18-7. Evolution of the Connecticut lowland from the Late Paleozoic to the present. (After J. Barrell.)

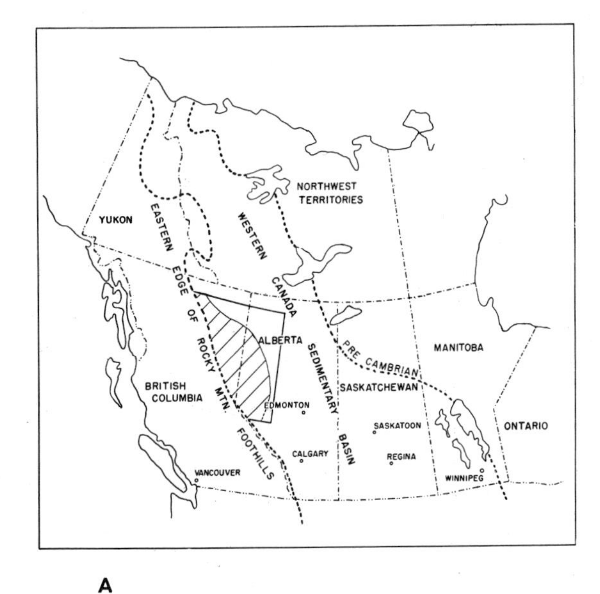

A

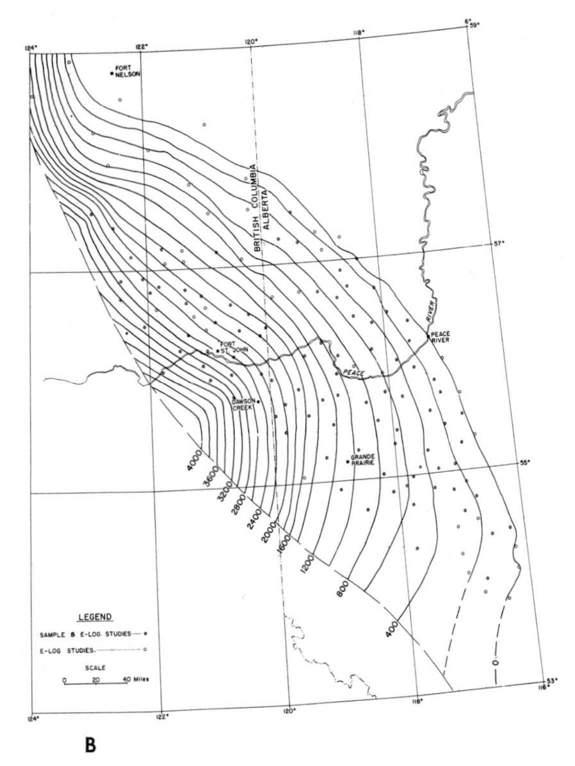

B

posited on the eastern shore of the evaporate basin. Occasionally these sediments flooded into the basin.

6. The evaporite environment shifted farther west until the barrier disappeared or was sufficiently submerged to restore circulation. When marine waters again circulated, dolostone was deposited to form the Baldonnel formation.
7. Finally the Pardonet beds were laid down in the small area next to the foothills of the Canadian Rockies.

LIFE OF THE TRIASSIC

I. NEW FORMS

1. *Dinosaurs:* Most spectacular of the reptiles, the dinosaurs evolved in the Triassic, and before the end of the period they had established themselves as the dominant animals in the world. They began a rule that lasted throughout the Mesozoic Era and was shared only with other reptiles.
2. *Hexacorals:* These corals, the scleractinians, belong to the same class as most modern corals. They supplanted the tetracorals and honeycomb corals that died out in the Permian.
3. The first lobsters and shrimplike animals appeared.

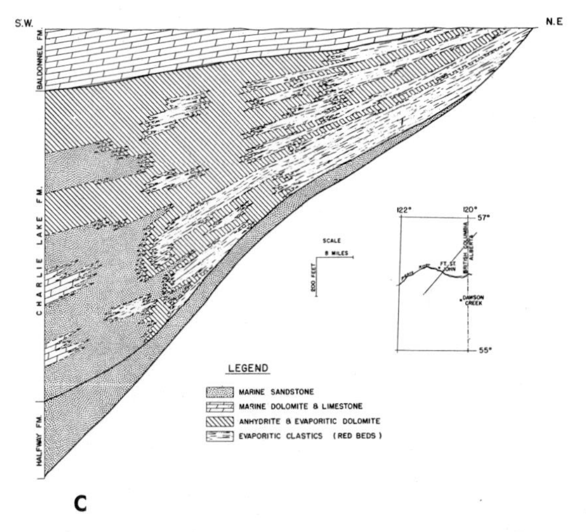

C

Fig. 18-8. Peace River district of Canada. This large region in which Triassic strata are located is east of the foot hills of the Canadian Rockies. It was part of the eastern margin of the geosynclinal belt which covered a large part of the western United States and Canada in the Triassic. (A) is an index map of western Canada showing the general location of the Triassic. The second diagram shows an isopach map of the entire Triassic section and the position of wells from which data related to the Triassic have been obtained. Section (C) is taken along a northeastward line across the region near Ft. St. John. (From A. D. Hunt and J. D. Ratcliffe.)

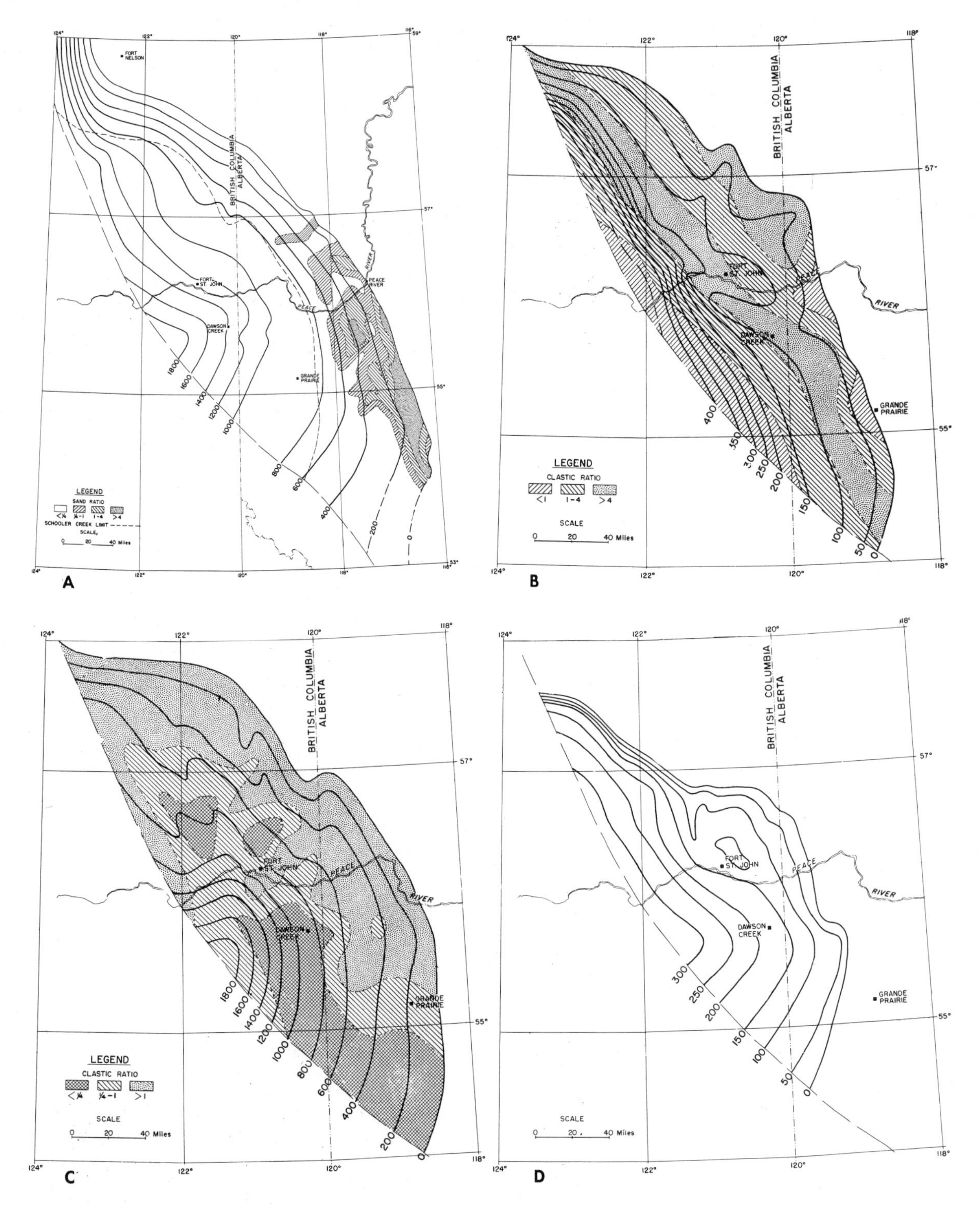

Fig. 18-9. Isopachs of units deposited during the Triassic in the Peace River district, Canada. Isopachs are drawn on the Toad Grayling formations (A) and the ratio of sand in the units is indicated. A similar diagram is given for the Halfway formation (B), and for the Charlie Lake formation (C). Isopachs are shown for the Baldonnel formation which is a dolostone (D). Study these diagrams and see if you can reconstruct conditions during the Triassic in this region. (From A. D. Hunt and J. D. Ratcliffe.)

Fig. 18-10. Mammal-like reptiles. Two hundred million years ago, reptiles of a kind destined to give rise to the mammals had come into existence. This scene, during the Triassic period in South Africa, shows a clumsy plant-eater (kannemeryeria) being attacked by a group of active flesh-eaters (Cynognathus) believed to be close to the actual ancestors of mammals. (From a mural by Charles Knight, photo by Chicago Natural History Museum.)

II. PEAK AND ADVANCEMENT

1. *Rule of the reptiles:* Discussion below.
2. *Ammonoids:* These cephalopods became the most important of the marine invertebrates. The suture patterns in the ammonites tended to become increasingly complex. Some of them could swim, but apparently others simply floated in the surface waters. Toward the end of the period the ammonoids almost became extinct, but one group of them survived into the Jurassic, when they underwent a second evolutionary burst. It may be that they were killed

Fig. 18-11. Petrified trees in Triassic sediments in the Chinle formation in the Petrified Forest, Arizona. These trees grew to heights of 100 feet and can be as much as 7 feet in diameter. These were conifers similar to our modern pines.

off at the end of the Triassic by the marine reptiles that might very well have fed on them.

III. DECLINE AND EXTINCTION

1. Scale trees and seed ferns were very rare in the Triassic. Most of the climates of this time were apparently too dry for these plants.

IV. NOTABLE ASPECTS OF TRIASSIC LIFE

Reptiles: The reptiles became exceedingly abundant and varied in their adaptations during the Triassic. One group, the phytosaurs, was similar in appearance and mode of life to the alligators. Two important groups of them returned to the seas from which their ancestors had come. These, the ichthyosaurs and plesiosaurs, were large, streamlined, and fishlike in appearance. They must have been very swift swimmers. The plesiosaurs were shaped something like a turtle with a long flexible neck. They were clumsy compared with the ichthyosaurs but used their long necks to good advantage in grabbing the fish they live on.

A number of mammal-like reptiles have been found in South Africa. Some of these are so similar to mammals that the only important differences appear to be in the number of bones in the lower jaw or in the feet. They may have had warm blood, hair, milk glands, and other mammalian characteristics. In general appearance these reptiles resemble modern opossums. Other mammal-like reptiles were much larger. They were heavy-boned animals with only two teeth in the upper jaws (Fig. 18-10).

Petrified forest: The petrified forest of northern Arizona contains the remains of a forest of huge trees that lived in the Triassic. These trees were preserved in the clays of the Chinle formation. Most of the trees we see in the petrified forest were conifers, similar to those that grow in the southwest today, except in size. Many of these tree trunks are over 100 feet long and up to 10 feet in diameter. Some of these cone-bearing trees may have been up to 200 feet high. A few ferns are found in the same area. They grew along the banks of streams.

REFERENCES

COLBERT, E. H., 1947, Little dinosaurs of Ghost Ranch: Natural History, v. 56, p. 392-399, 427-428

HARSHBARGER, J. W., REPENNING, C. A., and IRWIN, J. H., 1957, Stratigraphy of the uppermost Triassic and the Jurassic rocks of the Navajo Country: U. S. Geol. Survey Prof. Paper 291, 74 p.

HUNT, A. D., and RATCLIFFE, J. D., 1959, Triassic stratigraphy, Peace River area, Alberta and British Columbia, Canada: Am. Assoc. Petroleum Geologists, v. 43, p. 563-589

MC KEE, E. D., 1954, Stratigraphy and history of the Moenkopi formation of Triassic age: Geol. Soc. America Mem. 61, 133 p.

MULLER, S. W., 1949, Sedimentary facies and geologic structures in the Basin and Range province: Geol. Soc. America Mem. 39, p. 49-54

REESIDE, J. B., JR., *et al.*, 1957, Correlation of the Triassic formations of North America, exclusive of Canada: Geol. Soc. America Bull., v. 68, p. 1451-1514

19 The Jurassic Period

PHYSICAL HISTORY OF THE JURASSIC

In the United States, no Jurassic rock units are exposed east of the Great Plains. This was a time of erosion in the Appalachian Highlands, the erosion products being carried into the ocean and the Gulf of Mexico. Drilling in the Gulf Coast has revealed Upper Jurassic sediments beneath the Cretaceous as far north as southern Arkansas, and the core samples taken from these wells indicate that the Jurassic units may have formed under an arid climate in a sea supersaturated with salt. Jurassic beds are thought to be the source of the salt domes in the Gulf Coastal Plain.

Western United States

At the close of the Jurassic the eugeosynclinal belt of the western coast was involved

Fig. 19-1. An exposure of Jurassic strata near Gallup, New Mexico. (Courtesy of the New Mexico State Tourist Bureau.)

in an orogeny, the Nevadan orogeny, which marked the end of the western eugeosynclinal belt. This belt had been the site of much deposition and activity since the early Paleozoic. In the Early Jurassic a troughlike depression extended down from western Canada, across Washington, Oregon, and California into Mexico. This trough, in which volcanic debris accumulated, was separated by low land from an inland sea which occupied eastern Nevada, the site of the present Colorado Plateau, and extended up along the western Wyoming-Idaho border. The California trough collected over 30,000 feet of sediment in the Early and Middle Jurassic. The inland trough through Utah contains less than 3000 feet of much finer sediment. By the end of the Jurassic a belt from southern California northward along the California-Nevada border through Oregon and Washington had been uplifted as a result of the Nevadan orogeny. The western California trough had been narrowed by this orogenic deformation, but it continued to subside rapidly and collected over 20,000 more feet of sediment in the late Jurassic. Igneous activity was connected with the Nevadan orogeny. A huge batholith of granitic magma was intruded in the region of the Sierras of western Nevada. These mountains were then uplifted and have continued to stand as land ever since the Jurassic. They have been uplifted several times since the Jurassic.

In eastern Montana and in the Williston Basin a shallow sea covered a vast area during the Late Jurassic. The eastern part of it was a low marshy land, but farther westward shallow marine waters covered the area. This body of water has been named the Sundance Sea. It is famous for the dinosaur remains found in it.

Jurassic of the West Coast

The Pacific border of the United States is typical of the long narrow belt of deeply subsiding geosynclines that extended northward along the western coast of Canada in British Columbia and into Alaska. Probably similar features continued southward also. Within this belt deep subsidence, volcanic activity, and orogeny mark the Jurassic history. The Nevadan orogeny occurred in the Late Jurassic. It so altered the structure, depositional patterns, and physiography that it is a natural dividing line in the history of the Jurassic. Before the Nevadan orogeny a geosynclinal belt occupied the region of western California and eastern Nevada. This subsiding trough was continuous to the north into Oregon and Washington. It received sediments almost continuously through the Early Jurassic in California, but in Oregon there was deformation within the trough before the first Jurassic sediments were deposited. These preliminary movements of the orogeny which was to follow resulted in folding, faulting, and the formation of masses of coarse conglomerate on the flanks of the uplifts. Chains of island arcs stood off to the west of the geosyncline and supplied volcanic materials and debris for the sediments

Fig. 19-2. Distribution of Jurassic strata and their thickness indicated by isopachs. A large part of this chart is based on data obtained through drilling. There are no exposures of Jurassic strata in the Coastal Plain. (Modified after Paleotectonic maps, Jurassic system, E. D. McKee, *et al.*)

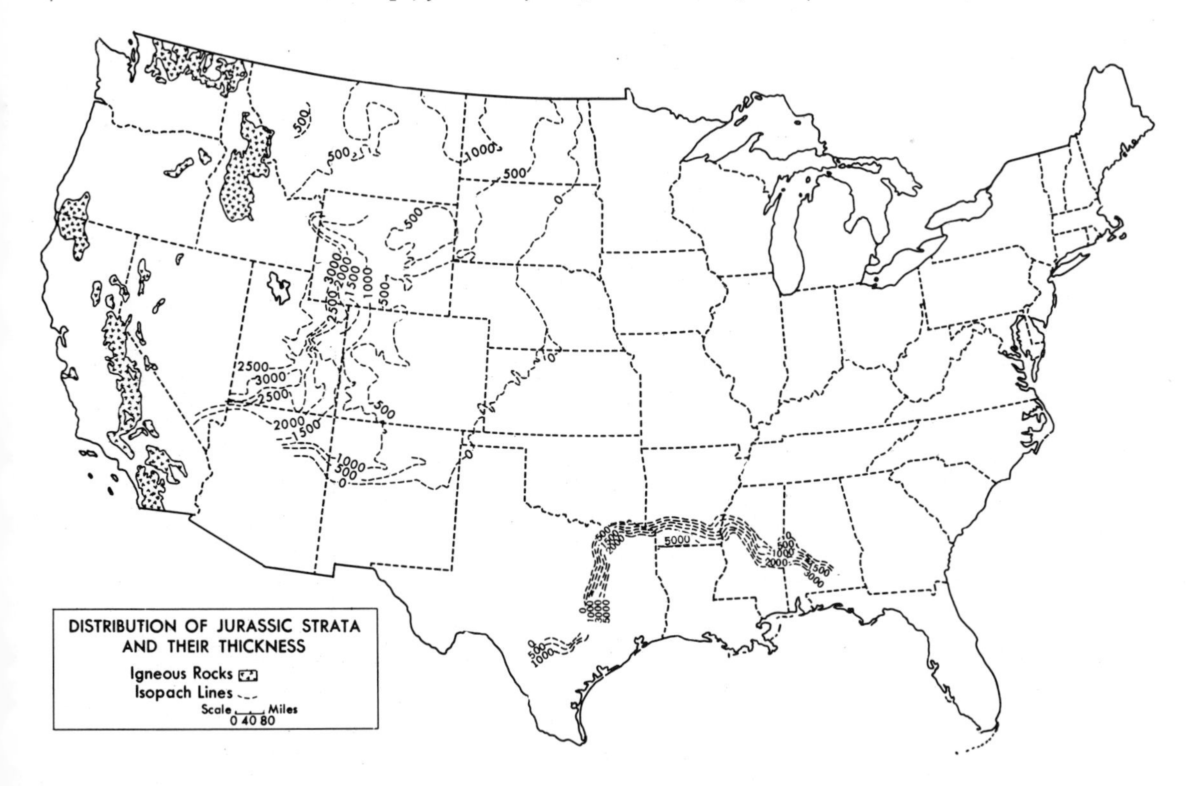

	UTAH	SOUTHERN WYOMING	EAST TEXAS	EASTERN CALIF.
UPPER JURASSIC SERIES	Morrison fm.	Morrison fm.	Cotton Valley group	
			Buckner fm.	
	Summerville fm.	Upper Sundance fm.	Smackover fm.	Mariposa slate
			Eagle Mills fm.	
	Entrada sandstone			
	Carmel fm.	Lower Sundance fm.		
MIDDLE JURASSIC		Gypsum Spring fm.		
LOWER JURASSIC SERIES	Navajo sandstone	Nugget sandstone		Milton fm.
	Kayenta fm.			
	Wingate sandstone			

Fig. 19-3. Jurassic correlation chart.

Fig. 19-4. Jurassic guide fossils

GASTROPOD
Eucyclus ×1

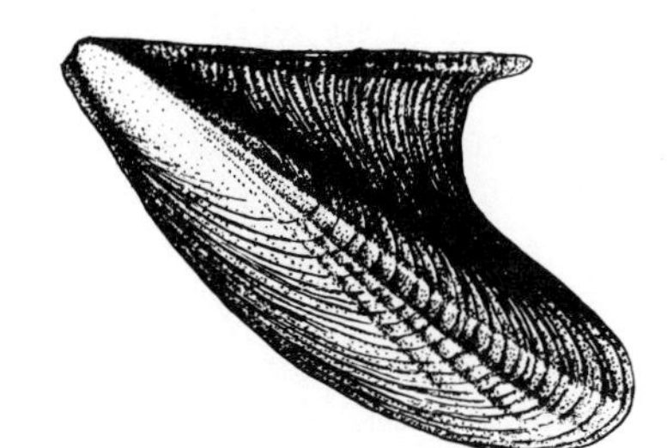

PELECYPOD
Gervillia ×1

CEPHALOPOD
Lytoceras ×.7

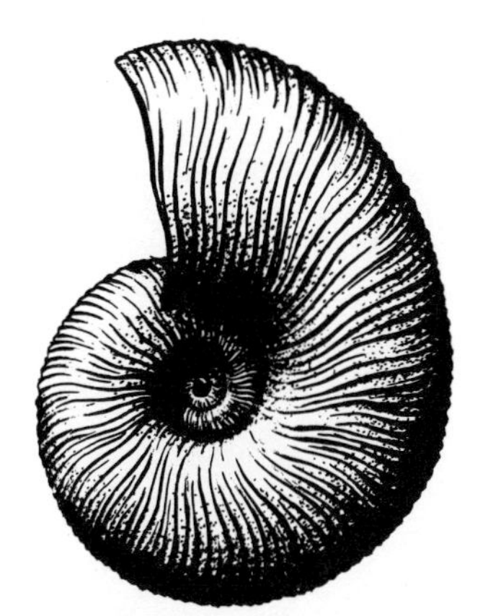

CEPHALOPOD
Substeneroceras ×.5

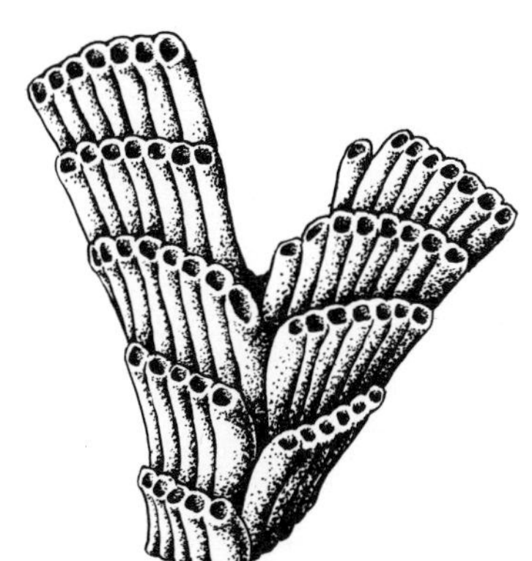

BRYOZOAN
Idmonea ×1

PELECYPOD
Pteria X0.51

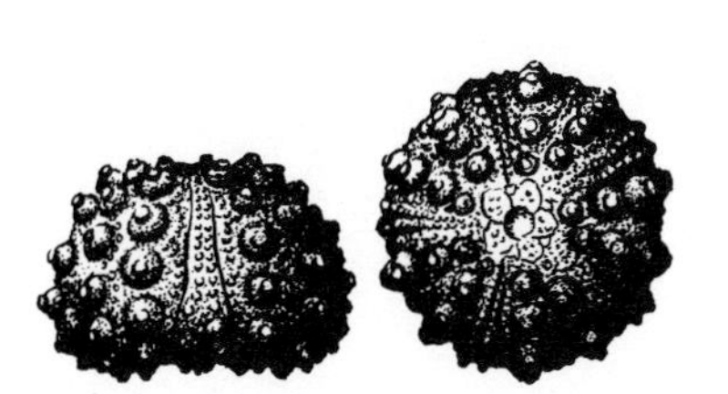

ECHINOID
Hemicidaris ×1

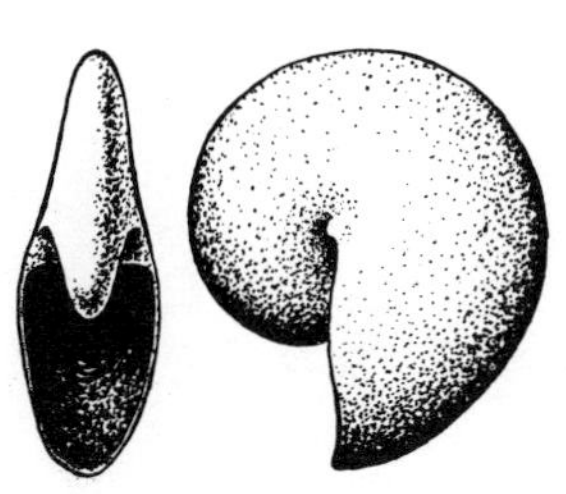

CEPHALOPOD
Phylloceras ×.3

FORAMINIFER
Frondicularia ×18

of the trough. The total thickness of these volcanic materials is over 12,000 feet in places. They are most abundant in California and southwestern Oregon. Most of the lavas were extruded under water, forming pillow lavas composed of all types of lava from acidic rhyolites to the dark mafic basaltic types. The centers of this volcanic activity can be recognized in places by preserved volcanic necks and by areas of unusually thick concentrations of flows and coarse agglomerates. In addition, large masses of molten rock were intruded into the geosynclinal accumulations and cooled below the surface. This volcanic activity was followed by a period of relative calm in which the Mariposa slate accumulated within the trough. This was a great thickness of muds, but some greenstones and volcanic dust were mixed with it.

The Nevadan orogeny uplifted and violently deformed the Jurassic sediment that, as we have seen, had accumulated within the geosyncline. The rocks formed in the preceding periods of time were folded into overturned and even recumbent folds. Major thrust faults moved the folded Paleozoic rocks in the western part of the syncline over the Jurassic units on the eastern side of the geosynclinal belt. Contemporaneous with this deformation, deep-seated igneous activity was resumed, but instead of taking the form of extensive volcanic extrusions it was intrusive. The largest batholith in North America (the Sierra Nevada batholith, which makes up the core of the present-day Sierra Nevada) is one of these. The Sierra Nevada batholith was only one of a number of large intrusions of granodiorite. Some of the similar intrusions came in a little later in the early part of the Cretaceous. It is these intrusions that form the peninsula of Baja California.

Fig. 19-5. Paleogeography of the Jurassic. This generalized diagram shows the framework of the major Jurassic basins. It is drawn for a time before the Nevadan orogeny which elevated the geosynclinal belt in the west and strongly deformed the western United States. (Based on Paleotectonic Maps, Jurassic System, E. B. McKee, *et al.*)

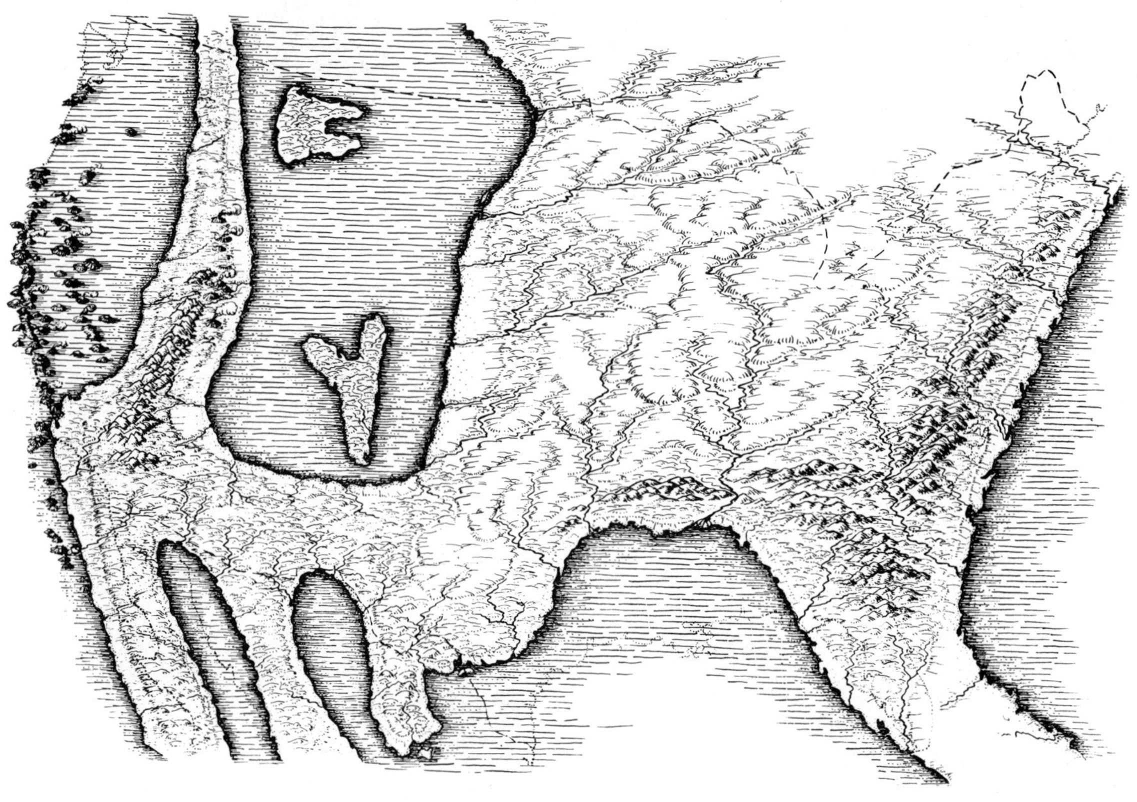

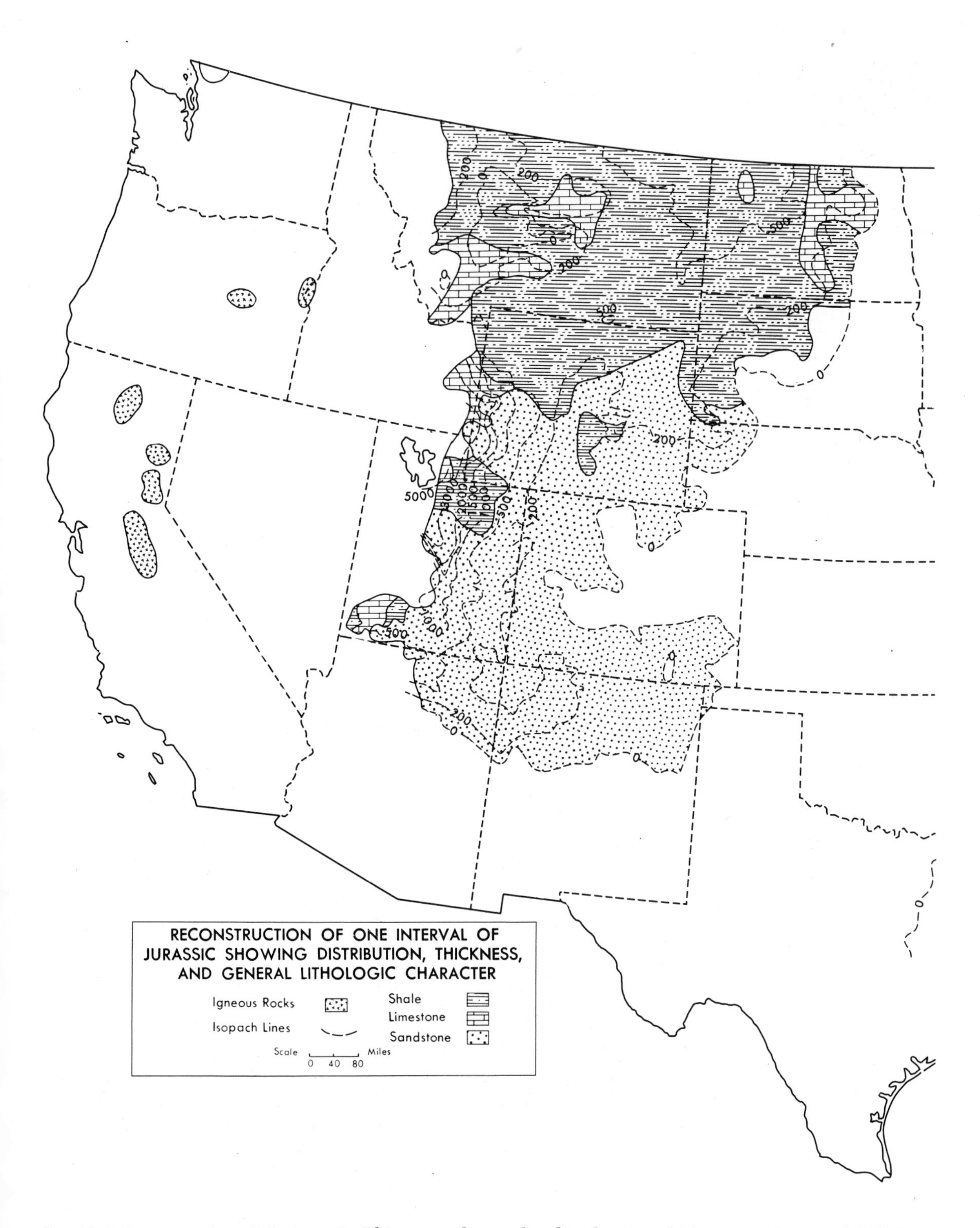

Fig. 19-6. Reconstruction of the Jurassic. This map shows the distribution, thickness, and general lithologic character of Jurassic strata for one interval of time. It is from maps such as this plus detailed descriptions of the character of the units that paleogeography is reconstructed. Examine carefully the relationships between the various types of data presented here. What questions about this interval of the Jurassic can be answered? (Modified after Paleotectonic maps, Jurassic system, E. D. McKee, *et al.*)

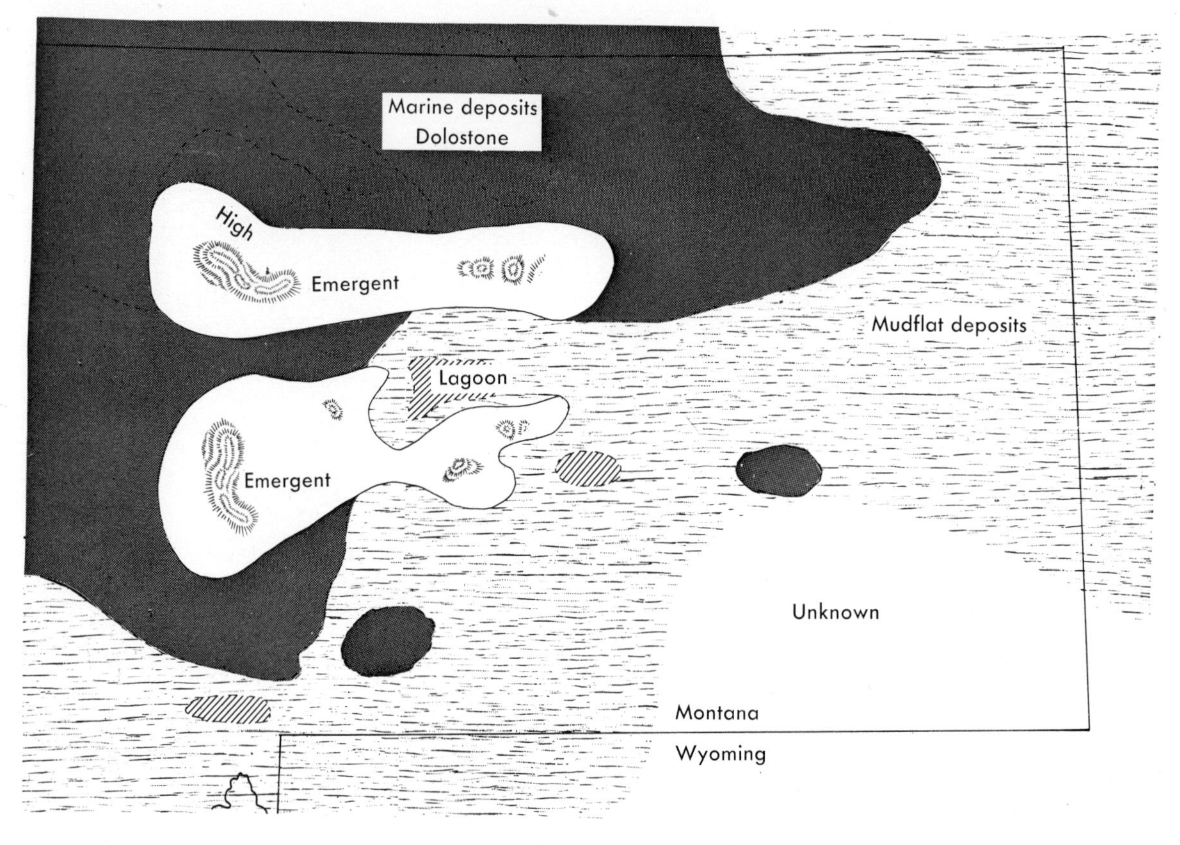

Fig. 19-7. The environments of deposition in Montana at the time during which the Piper and Sawtooth formations were deposited. (After E. D. McKee, *et al.*)

The major changes accompanying Nevadan orogeny along the west coast were·

1. Drastic deformation of the pre-Nevadan rock units, folding and thrusting of the older rocks from the west over younger units to the east.
2. Injection of the great Sierra Nevada batholith and other related batholiths and stocks.
3. Shifting of the geosyncline from eastern California to the western part of the state.

Following the orogeny, which so deformed and uplifted the eastern part of California that it has not since been the site of geosynclinal accumulations, a new geosyncline formed along the western coast about in the position of the Coast Ranges of today. Indeed, most of the sediments presently exposed in the Coast Ranges were those deposited within this geosyncline. The source of volcanic activity that had supplied tuffs and lava flows to the pre-Nevadan geosyncline continued to exist again west of the new geosyncline. These volcanoes provided a large part of the more than 20,000 feet of sediments that went into this geosyncline. Following this, another orogeny, the Diablan, affected this new geosyncline. Folding, faulting, and intrusion accompanied this orogeny as it had in the Nevadan.

Reconstruction of the Jurassic

It should be emphasized that the basis for the interpretation of the history of the geologic past is found in the distribution and character of contemporaneous sediments within an area, the variations within those sediments through

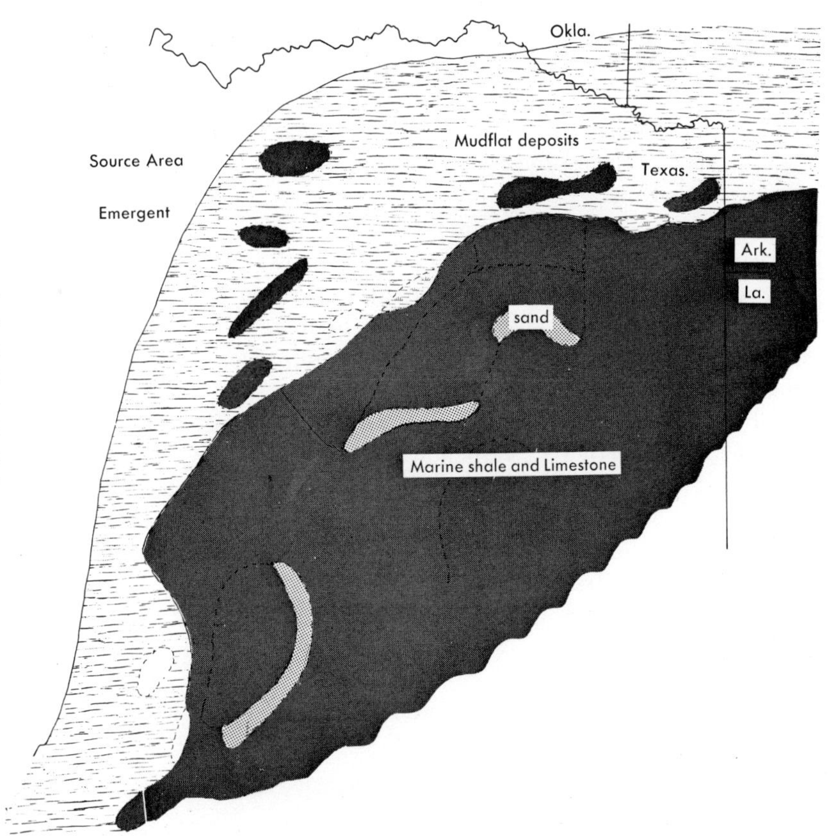

Fig. 19-8. Environments of sedimentation of Jurassic rocks during the deposition of the Schuler formation in eastern Texas. This map is based entirely on subsurface data since no Jurassic is exposed at the surface in the region. (After E. D. McKee, *et al.*)

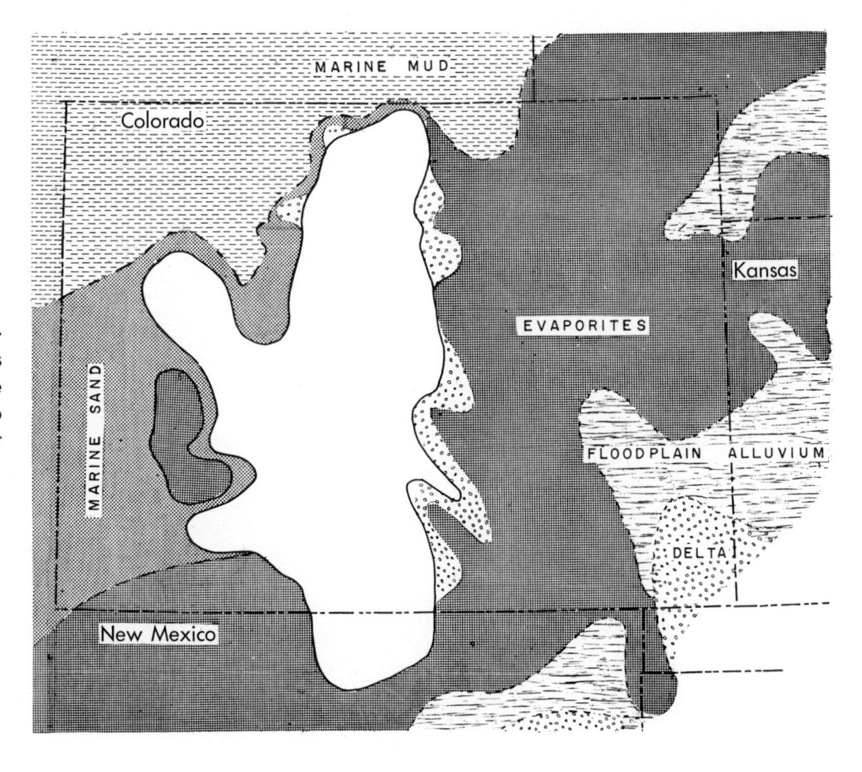

Fig. 19-9. Environments of sedimentation of Jurassic rocks during the deposition of the Middle Jurassic in Colorado and bordering states. (After E. D. McKee, *et al.*)

time, the internal structures of the sediments, and finally the results of diastrophism impressed upon these sediments. The availability of these data determines the extent to which we can accurately reproduce the history of a region. We are afforded an unusual opportunity to study the data upon which the Jurassic history of the United States is based through a compilation of many of these data by the United States Geological Survey. The figures are simplifications of maps from these compilations. From the study of these maps it is possible to reconstruct the following major features in the pattern of sedimentation for the Jurassic:

1. The distribution of Jurassic rocks known both from drilling and outcrop pattern, as well as the areas in which no exposures exist and in which no wells have been drilled.
2. The total thickness of the Jurassic rocks.
3. The lithofacies (the rock record of any sedimentary environment) for the entire country for one interval of time.

Ultimately we may hope to show the details of the environments of deposition for each time interval of a period. Such a task is difficult and in many cases impossible. In order to accomplish this there must be sufficient data:

1. Detailed correlations must be possible throughout the area of each rock unit.
2. The units must contain distinctive internal structures or compositions that indicate a particular environment.

Fig. 19-10. Cross-bedded Jurassic sandstones exposed in Zion National Park. These units were most probably part of a vast desert of drifting sand. (Photo by E. W. Spencer.)

Fig. 19-11. Jurassic sandstones exposed in the Arches National Monument of southeastern Utah. This famous locality is the Rainbow Bridge which crosses a tributary to the Colorado River. (Photo by courtesy of Santa Fe Railway.)

3. It must be possible to establish a time plane (that is, it must be possible to recognize the part of a rock unit that was deposited at the same time as the other units with which it is to be associated).

Environmental maps for three areas of the western interior are shown in Figs. 19-7, 19-8, and 19-9.

Jurassic of the Colorado Plateau

Many of the best-exposed formations in the Colorado Plateau are Jurassic in age. They were deposited in the southern end of the broad Rocky Mountain geosyncline. Maximum thickness of the Jurassic system occurs on the western side of the geosyncline, and it wedges out eastward to a very thin veneer before it passes under the Cretaceous system in the Great Plains. Most of the sediment is that characteristic of an inland sea, and largely made up of sandstone. The Jurassic began with deposition of thick sandstones which are probably continental in origin and possibly even of subaerial origin. They were most likely the windblown deposits of sand, weathered and eroded from the outcrops of older sandstones. The sands contain no marine fossils, and for this reason it is difficult to determine the exact age of some of the sands which may have been

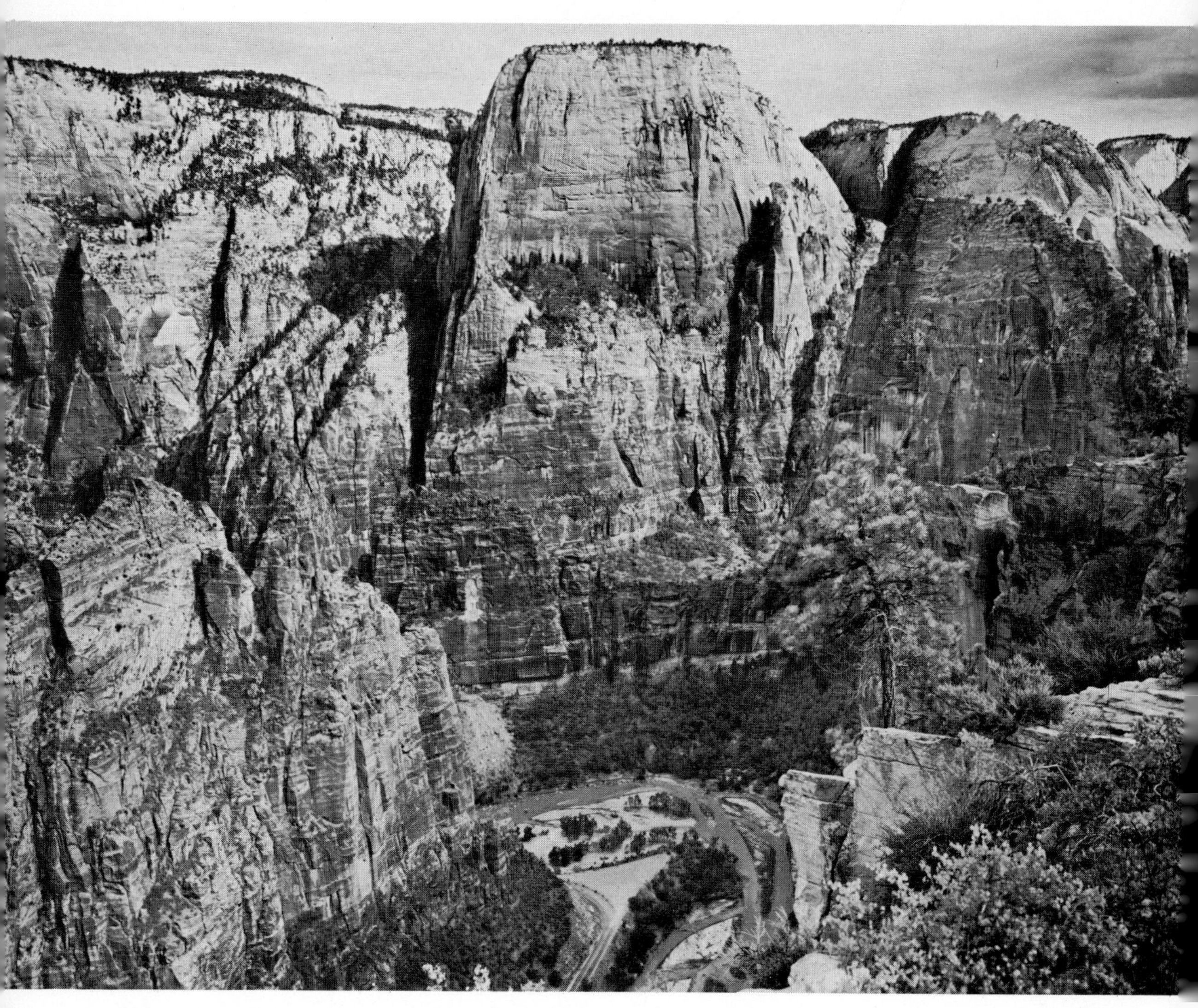

Fig. 19-12. The Great White Throne and the Virgin River of Zion National Park, Utah. Exposed in this cliff is cross-bedded Lower Jurassic Navajo sandstone, an ancient dune deposit. (Photo by courtesy of the Union Pacific Railroad.)

either Late Triassic or Early Jurassic age. These sandstones make up many of the spectacular features of the Colorado Plateau. Such features as the Vermilion Cliffs, the White Cliffs in the Glen Canyon area of Arizona and Zion National Park, Utah, and the arches in the Arches National Monument, Utah, are made up of the sand equivalents of this age, including such formations as the Wingate and the Navajo sandstones and its equivalent, the Nugget formation. In Nevada these sands reach thicknesses in excess of 3000 feet.

Following the deposition of these sands marine water came into the syncline from its northern connection with the Pacific Ocean. Three Jurassic inundations occurred and were accompanied by marine deposition of limestones, marls, and shales. Toward the southern and eastern margins of the seas, in shallow waters the marine deposits grade into red beds. In the southern part of the syncline the sea was often shallow and became restricted with the formation of gypsum and other salts over large areas at different times.

The last formation of the Jurassic is the Morrison, which is a nonmarine deposit very unlike the Lower Jurassic deposits. The Morrison consists of sandstones and greenish clays and shales. Some of the components are probably the alteration products of fine ash deposits carried from the sites of tremendous volcanic activity which were located along the western coast. It was at this time that the Nevadan orogeny was reaching its climax farther west. The Morrison overlies all the Jurassic and even covers parts of the Precambrian basement in Colorado. The Morrison is very colorful with white sands interbedded with purple sands and shales, conglomerates, red and green shales, and in places limestones. These deposits represent environments that were most likely fluviatile and lacustrine.

Paleogeography and lithogenesis of the Morrison formation

The exact configuration of land barriers and sea connections following the Triassic–Jurassic sandstone deposition is imperfectly known. Comparison of the faunas found in the Carmel formation of the Plateau region with those in the western geosyncline and those in the Gulf of Mexico area makes any marine connections between these areas seem unlikely. In the time of the Carmel formation the land surface was probably nearly flat and close to sea level so that slight changes in sea level inundated large areas. Under these restricted conditions large quantities of gypsum were precipitated in seas that bordered the desert. The Carmel beds show repeated alternation in

Fig. 19-13. Hypothetical paleogeography of Navajo County during deposition of the Morrison formation (late stage of deposition of the Salt Wash member). See the text for description of the events preceding and following these conditions. (After Harshbarger, Repenning, and Irwin.)

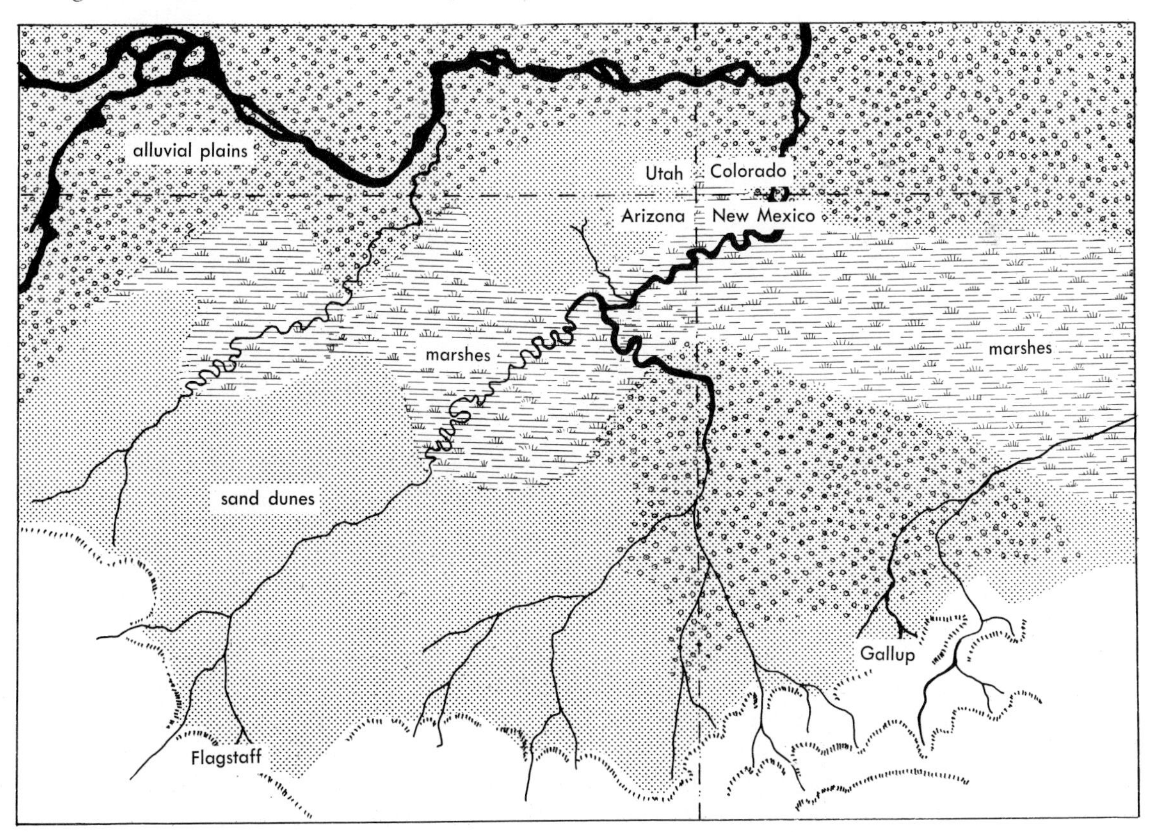

the environment. Shallow seas alternately covered the area, which was otherwise emergent, while emergent playa lakes and shallow embayments of the ocean permitted stratification of fine-grained material. At the margins of the seas wind-blown sand was deposited constantly. These sands are not thick, but they covered large areas and make up the Entrada group. During the formation of the Entrada units the margins of the basin continually received more wind-blown sand while the finer silts accumulated toward the center of the basin. These may be contemporaneous with the Sundance sands to the north in Wyoming.

When the sea finally entered the region, a slight erosional unconformity was formed. Above the Entrada sandstone lies a basal conglomerate which contains fragments of chert, shale, sandstone, and limestone. A few marine fossils appear in the overlying beds. Thin, evenly bedded sands and gypsum beds formed in the marine waters. These gradually gave way to more fresh-water marl deposits containing ostracods and algae. With these fresh-water deposits terrestrial sedimentation began, and it continued through the deposition of the Morrison formation. The first sandstone member (Salt Wash) was constantly reworked as old river channels were destroyed by new ones. Shale lenses were probably deposited on flood plains and in quiet waters or on an extensive plain just above sea level. Some carbonaceous beds containing petrified logs, dinosaur bones, and impressions of reedlike plants

Fig. 19-14. Restored belemnites of the Jurassic seas. These squid-like cephalopods flourished in the Jurassic but they became extinct before the end of the Mesozoic. Their cigar-shaped internal skeletons are all that remains. (Photo by courtesy of the Chicago Natural History Museum.)

Fig. 19-15. *Archaeopteryx*, the earliest known bird. This bird had feathers, but it resembled its reptilian ancestors in possessing teeth, claws on its wings, and a long, jointed tail. In this scene from the Late Jurassic 150 million years ago we see several small dinosaurs and the Archaeopteryx. (Painting by Charles Knight, Chicago Natural History Museum.)

are fairly common and indicate an environment favorable to terrestrial life for the first time in the Jurassic.

Toward the end of the formation of the Salt Wash the conditions were described as

> . . . a number of large streams issuing from a mountainous area and crossing a very broad, flat plain. Such streams would deposit much of their loads on their flood plains in the form of very flat alluvial fans. Deposition by distributaries, aided by tributaries and aeolian action, would tend to unite these fans into a broad alluvial plain. The main streams and tributaries consequent on the plain would gradually extend such alluvial deposits over a very broad area. In local basins between the principal streams and in abandoned stream valleys, lakes would probably form locally. In these lakes fine sediments would be deposited, with sandstones around the margins. Aeolian deposits would probably form to a certain extent between main stream areas. (Mook, 1916)

The Morrison is remarkably similar over an area of 360,000 square miles. Few other comparable units are known for the terrestrial environment.

After the deposition of the Morrison there was a cessation of active sedimentation. The top of the Morrison was eroded, and a widespread thin sheet of conglomerate was formed (the Buckhorn). This may represent a period in which the area was uplifted as a whole by epeirogenic diastrophism. The conglomerate has also been explained as a lag gravel left on this uplifted desert as winds blowing across the flat surface moved the finer sands and silts but left the thin veneer of gravels behind forming a "desert pavement." This explanation is favored for several reasons:

1. Gravels are common on the flanks of uplifted areas, but when they appear over such a broad area as that of the Colorado Plateau such uniformly thin beds can hardly be accounted for by uplift.
2. Such gravels are commonly associated with bentonite layers formed from wind-transported volcanic dust coming from the island-arc system of the western coasts of the continent.
3. The absence of an angular unconformity beneath the conglomerate makes high uplift even more unacceptable.
4. The similarity of overlying and underlying beds implies a slight interruption in the depositional environment rather than a complete break accompanied by great changes in the physiography of the region.

Fig. 19-16. *Rhamphorhynchus*, one of the Jurassic flying reptiles. These reptiles had teeth, claws on their wings, and a long, jointed tail. They are related to the first true birds, Fig. 19-15. (Painting by Charles Knight, Chicago Natural History Museum.)

These excellent studies of the Jurassic are particularly noteworthy because they demonstrate the techniques and logic used to analyze geologic history.

LIFE OF THE JURASSIC

I. NEW FORMS

1. *Mammals:* The first definite mammal remains are found in this period. The jaws of these small mammals, complete with teeth, have been found in many parts of the world. Teeth are one of the best-preserved and most useful structures for the classification of many groups of animals. These were the first multituberculate animals. Mammals' teeth are differentiated into molars, premolars, canines, and incisors only. These animals probably looked a great deal like small squirrels or other rodents.
2. *Birds:* The remains of the feathers of some of the earliest birds, called *Archaeopteryx,* have been found in the Solenhofen limestone of Bavaria. These birds, which were about the size of a crow, possessed sharp teeth and other

Fig. 19-17. *Brontosaurus*, a huge plant-eating dinosaur. The sauropod dinosaurs that lived at the end of the Jurassic Period, 145 million years ago, were the largest land animals of all time. *Brontosaurus* attained a length of 67 feet and an estimated weight of 30 tons. It probably spent most of its life in swamps, where there was plenty of vegetation for food. Supporting its great weight would have been less of a problem in the water than on land. (Painting by Charles Knight, Chicago Natural History Museum.)

Fig. 19-18. Reptiles that invaded the seas. The several groups of reptiles that became aquatic trace their ancestry back to land forms. In the seas of Early Jurassic times, 170 million years ago, two types of reptiles were abundant. The long-necked plesiosaurs were fish eaters that propelled themselves with their strong flippers. The fish-shaped ichthyosaurs fed mostly on squids and drove themselves through the water with their powerful tails. (Painting by Charles Knight, Chicago Natural History Museum.)

reptilian characteristics that establish the connection between these groups.

3. *Moths and flies:* These were among the insects that appeared for the first time. Insects were abundant and have been preserved in the remarkable deposits of the Solenhofen limestone and in the Purbeck beds of England where dragonflies, locusts, grasshoppers, butterflies, ants, and even beetles are beautifully fossilized. About 19 species of mammals are found in these same beds.

II. PEAKS AND ADVANCEMENT

1. Invertebrate faunas had by this time assumed very modern characteristics. With a few exceptions they resemble the life of the present seas. Those exceptions are in the ammonites and the belemnites. Ammonites flourished anew in the Jurassic after escaping extinction by a narrow margin at the end of the Triassic. Belemnites were cephalopods that probably resembled the modern squid. They had an internal calcareous skeleton that looks very much like a cigar. Some of these are as much as 5 feet long, so these animals must have been huge.
2. *Age of Reptiles:* See discussion below.

III. NOTABLE ASPECTS OF JURASSIC LIFE: THE REPTILES

Throughout the Mesozoic, reptiles dominated the world. The peak of their development was reached in the Jurassic, although they continued strong throughout the Cretaceous as well. Reptiles took to the air, to the water, and dominated the land environments. The number and variety are most impressive. (The evolutionary development of the reptiles is described later.) The flying reptiles, pterosaurs, were unlike *Archaeopteryx* because they lacked feathers, but the two were related in that both descended from reptiles. The pterosaurs probably could not fly like birds, but were reduced to gliding. They ranged in size from several inches to almost 4 feet in length. The marine reptiles, ichthyosaurs and plesiosaurs, attained the peak in their abundance. Dinosaurs roamed the land masses, inhabiting the swamps, river bottoms, and marshy alluvial plains. They ranged in size from one about the size of a rooster that has been found along with its young in the Solenhofen limestone up to the giants of them all, *Brachiosaurus*, *Brontosaurus*, and *Diplodocus*. These were as much as 90 feet long, and some weighed over 50 tons. These three spent most of their lives in swamps and fed on plants. One group of dinosaurs, camptosaurs, had bills shaped like ducks' bills, which they used to grovel in the sands and shallow-water sediments for food. The most ferocious of the dinosaurs of this time had jaws lined with sharp teeth. These huge beasts, allosaurs, lived outside the swamps and fed on their fat and less agile relatives. *Stegosaurus*, the dinosaur armed with bony plates that lined its back and tail, lived out of the swamps, but fed on plants.

Fig. 19-19. *Stegosaurus*. Of the many kinds of dinosaurs that lived during the Mesozoic Era, the majority were inoffensive plant-eaters. Some of them, such as the Late Jurassic *Stegosaurus* that lived 145 million years ago, evolved protective plates for defense against contemporary predaceous dinosaurs. (Painting by Charles Knight, Chicago Natural History Museum.)

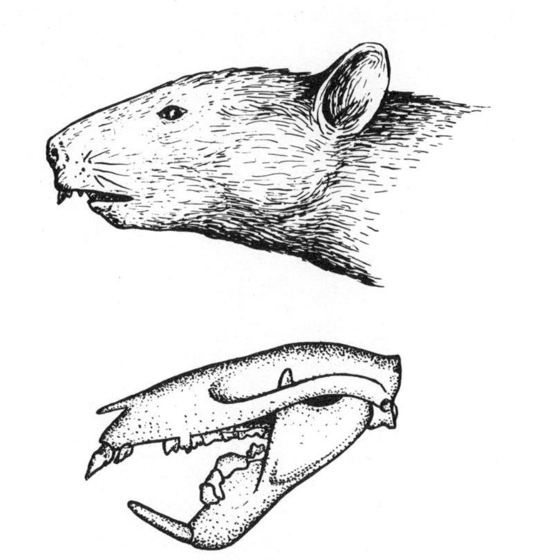

Fig. 19-20. Jurassic mammal, ctenacodon. (After G. G. Simpson, 1935, *Quarterly Review of Biology,* v. 10, p. 163.)

REFERENCES

BERRY, E. W., 1918, The Jurassic lagoons of Solenhofen: Sci. Monthly, October, p. 361-378

COLBERT, E. H., 1951, *The Dinosaur Book,* McGraw-Hill Book Company, New York, 156 p.

HARSHBARGER, J. W., REPENNING, C. A., and IRWIN, J. H., 1957, Stratigraphy of the uppermost Triassic and the Jurassic rocks of the Navajo Country: U. S. Geol. Survey Prof. Paper 291, 74 p.

IMLAY, R. W., 1957, Paleoecology of Jurassic seas in the western interior of the United States: Geol. Soc. America Mem. 67, v. 2, p. 469-504

MC KEE, E. D., *et al.,* 1956, Paleotectonic maps, Jurassic system: U. S. Geol. Survey Misc. Pub. map I-175, 6 p., 9 pls.

20 The Cretaceous Period

PHYSICAL HISTORY OF THE CRETACEOUS

Many notable events occurred during the Cretaceous in the United States. Seas returned to cover the Coastal Plain of the Gulf Coast and eastern seaboard states. These seas may have extended much farther inland than the presently exposed Cretaceous deposits. The Rocky Mountains were brought into existence from the western miogeosyncline; great fans of debris spread out from the uplifted highlands, and a thick geosynclinal accumulation began to form along the coast of the Gulf of Mexico.

Eastern United States

Cretaceous deposits are exposed from Cape Cod southward along the western edge of the Coastal Plain. In general, these little-deformed strata are gently inclined and thicken toward the ocean. They lie unconformably on Precambrian and Lower Paleozoic rocks along the eastern coasts and on later Paleozoic and Mesozoic formations in the Gulf Coast. The eastern coast deposits resemble deltaic deposits. They probably were deposited by the streams flowing from the Appalachian ranges raised at the end of the Paleozoic. In Florida the Lower Cretaceous is all limestones, but later in the period coarser detritus came into the region from the northwest from an uplifted part of the Appalachians. As this uplift was worn down the supply of debris was reduced and finally gave way to limestone deposition in an advancing sea. Westward the Gulf Coast Cretaceous reveals the gradual encroachment of the sea on the continent. The younger beds overlap the older units, and coarser deposits are overlain by those of a deeper-water environment. Unconformities developed within the section as the floor of the northern part of the Gulf subsided. The subsidence allowed the accumulation of thick sections of sediment eroded from the craton. This gives the Cretaceous sediments of the region a southward thickening. The rate of this thickening seems to have been progressively more rapid through the Cretaceous.

Western United States

In the Far West the Nevadan orogeny of the Jurassic had raised a high mountain range along the Nevada-California border and northward into Canada. The sediments from this range filled a deep geosyncline in California with 15,000 feet of sands and gravels. Later in the Cretaceous the direction from which the sediment came changed as an area west of the California geosyncline became uplifted and supplied debris.

In the Rocky Mountain region (western Montana, Idaho, Wyoming, eastern Utah, Colorado, and New Mexico) the early and middle part of the Cretaceous was characterized by irregular subsidence and uplift. Considerable thicknesses of terrigenous material were brought into the geosyncline from an elevated area in the west. At the same time the Rocky Mountain geosyncline, which occupied the area of the present-day Rocky Mountains, formed and collected Middle Cretaceous sediments before it was uplifted in the Late Cretaceous. Just before this uplift began, an extensive alluvial deposit of sandstone, the Dakota formation, was laid out into the plains states. At first, sediments came from west of the present Rockies, but the front of the uplifted area moved eastward until the present Rockies were elevated. The flood of debris from this uplift filled the seas, forced the mar-

Fig. 20-1. Big Horn Mountains. This view is of the western side of the Big Horn Mountains in Wyoming. This block of the crust was one of many uplifted along faults or folded upward during the Laramian orogeny toward the end of the Cretaceous Period. This was the time of the formation of the Rocky Mountains. Notice how the strata along the top of this mountain are flat-lying, while those on the sides are dissected to form flat-iron shaped masses. (Photo by E. W. Spencer.)

System	Series	Series	TEXAS	ALABAMA	COLORADO	MONTANA
CRETACEOUS SYSTEM	GULF SERIES	UPPER CRETACEOUS SERIES				Hell Creek fm.
			Navarro group	Prairie Bluff chalk	Mesaverde group	Bearpaw shale
				Ripley fm.		Judith River fm.
						Claggett shale
			Taylor marl	Selma chalk		Eagle sandstone
			Anacacho limestone		Mancos shale	
			Austin chalk	Eutaw fm.		Colorado shale
			Eagle Ford shale	Tuscaloosa fm.		
	COMANCHE SERIES	LOWER CRETACEOUS SERIES	Comanche series		Dakota sandstone	Kootenai fm.
	COAHUILA SERIES					

Fig. 20-2. Correlation chart for the Cretaceous.

Fig. 20-3. Guide fossils for the Cretaceous.

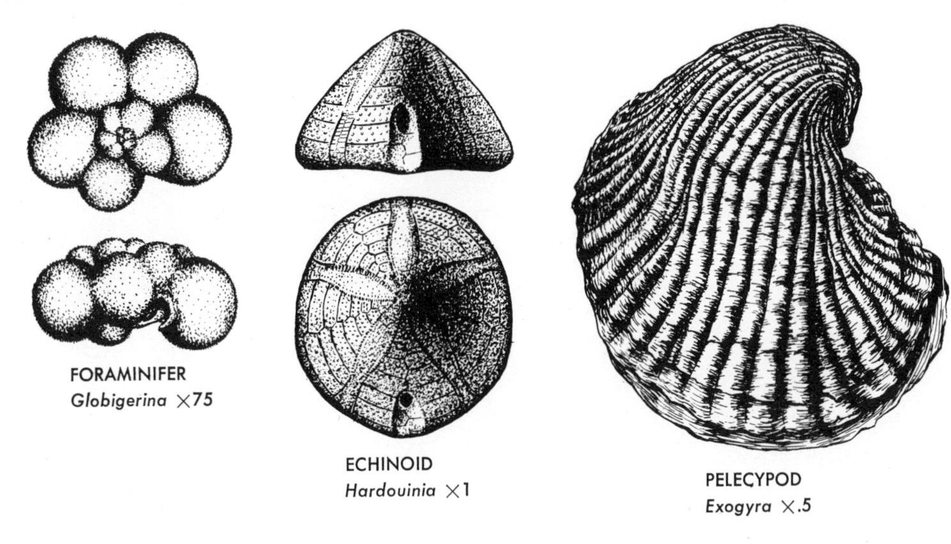

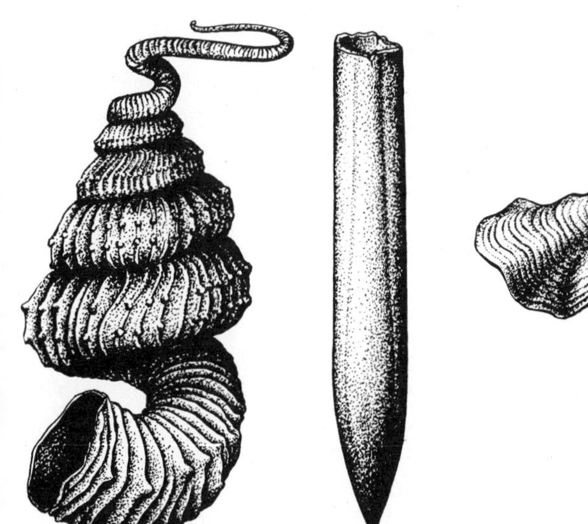

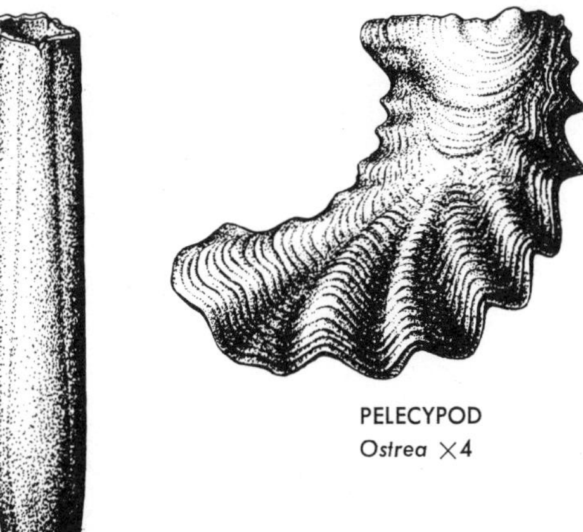

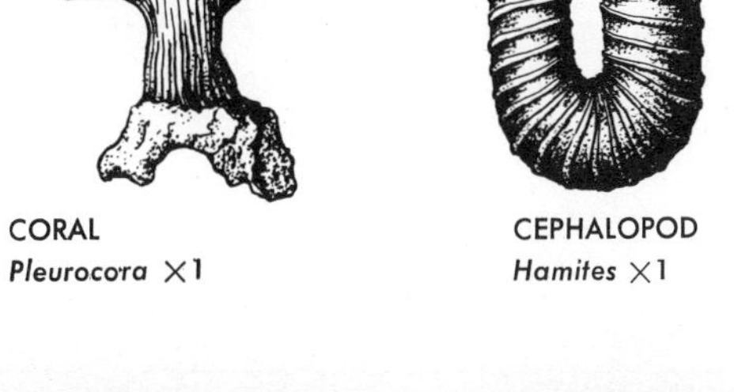

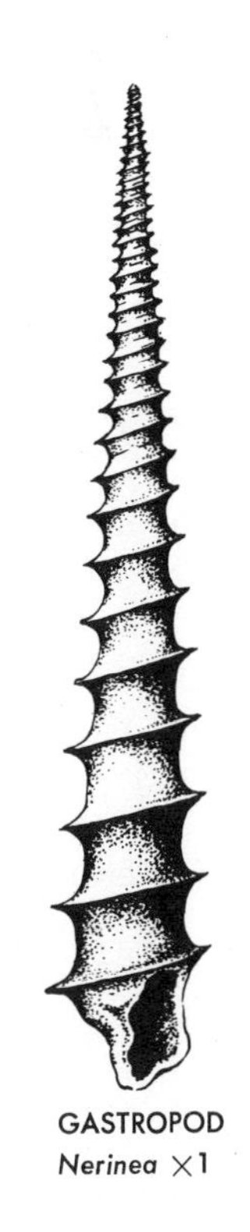

Fig. 20-4. The white cliffs of Dover. These English cliffs are one of the most spectacular exposures of Cretaceous strata. The name "Cretaceous" comes from a word meaning "chalk." These units are composed of chalk, the remains of microscopic-sized foraminifers. (Photo by courtesy of the British Information Services.)

gins inland, and finally filled them. This orogeny, which started in the Late Cretaceous and continued on into the Cenozoic, is called the Laramide (Laramian) orogeny.

LARAMIDE REVOLUTION

The deformation of the western interior of the United States in the Late Cretaceous, which is known as the Laramide orogeny, does not represent a single pulse of uplift or compression within the crust of the earth. Most orogenies seem to be similar in that they have long complex histories. There may be one phase of an orogeny which is the most intense part, but usually, where sufficient data are available, it is possible to demonstrate that orogeny began quietly with uplift of sediments within a geosyncline and through a long period of time marked by intermittent activity uplifted, fractured, folded, faulted, and severely distorted and altered the sedimentary sequences. Igneous bodies intruded the more deformed parts of the belts and entered along deep-seated faults and fracture zones. The deep parts of the belts are metamorphosed. The structures formed during the early phases of an orogeny are later distorted and altered by continued diastrophism, and, as the uplift proceeds, the higher portions are subjected to erosion and are beginning to be destroyed even as they form. The sediments from these uplifted areas seek a lower level where after deposition they may in turn be deformed by a later phase of the orogeny.

The Laramide orogeny started toward the end of the Cretaceous and continued in parts of the west well into the Paleogene. The area affected in North America may be divided into four major parts: the Northern Rockies, the Middle Rockies, the Southern Rockies, and the Central Rockies.

Northern Rockies

These include the eastern part of the Canadian Rocky Mountains and their southern continuation into northern Montana. The western part of these mountains was formed in the Nevadan orogeny of the Jurassic. The eastern part is Laramide. The rock units exposed in these rugged ranges include the Belt Series, Precambrian sedimentary rocks, and Paleozoic and Mesozoic sedimentary rocks. This part of the Rocky Mountains is bounded on the east by a zone of thrust faults that have carried

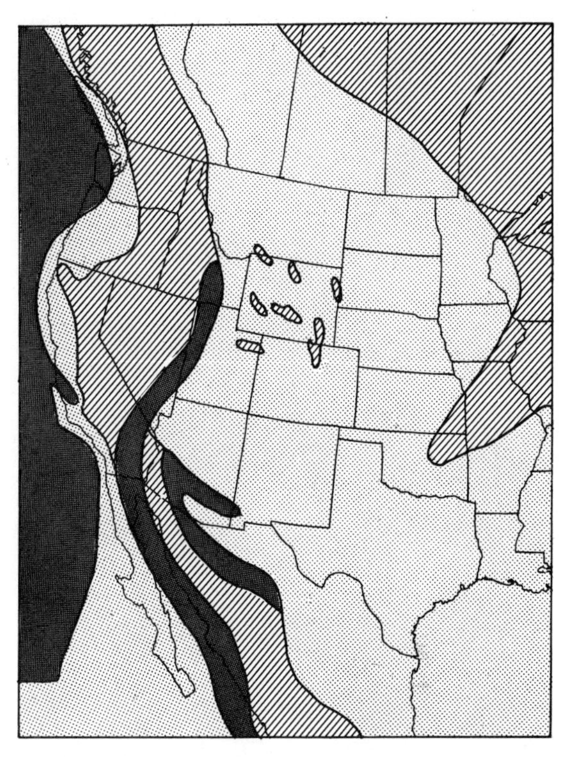

Fig. 20-6. Upper Cretaceous continental framework. The black belts were orogenic uplifts, the dot areas were shallow seas and the diagonals indicate epeirogenic uplifts. Notice that the position of the orogenic belts had shifted eastward from their Early Cretaceous locations. (After A. J. Eardley.)

Fig. 20-5. Lower Cretaceous continental framework. The black belts were orogenic belts, the dot filled areas were shallow seas, and the diagonals signify land areas uplifted by epeirogenic upwarping, not strong deformation. Compare this with Fig. 20-6. (After A. J. Eardley.)

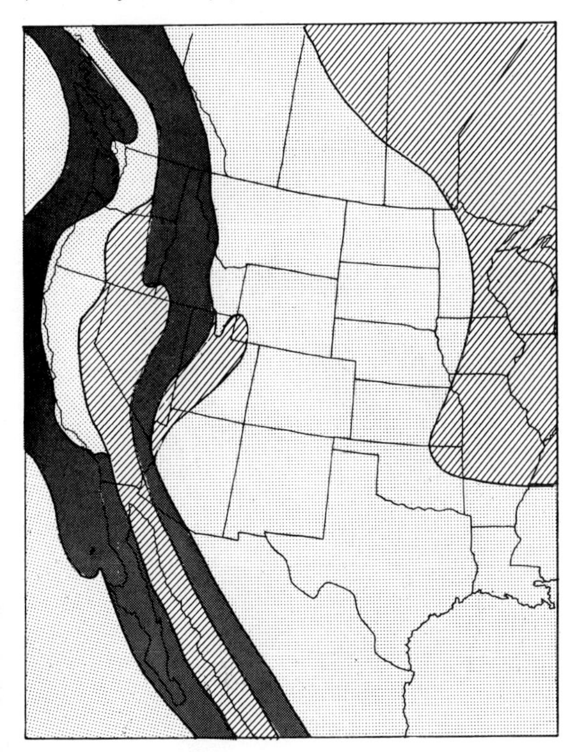

Paleozoic formations eastward out over the Lower and Middle Cretaceous formations. The Lewis overthrust in northern Montana is a notable example of these thrusts, which have as much as 10 to 20 miles of displacement. A number of masses of the overthrust sheets such as Chief Mountain still remain as klippes overlying the Cretaceous. Many of the thrust faults along the eastern margin exhibit what is known as imbricate structure. That is, a large number of thrust planes, all approximately parallel, have developed within the sediments. Many of these planes probably extend into a single plane of movement at depth. In addition to the thrust belt there is much folding, both in the high mountains and in the Cretaceous sections along the foothills to the east. These folds in the foothills developed under the weight and northeastward movement of the high mountains.

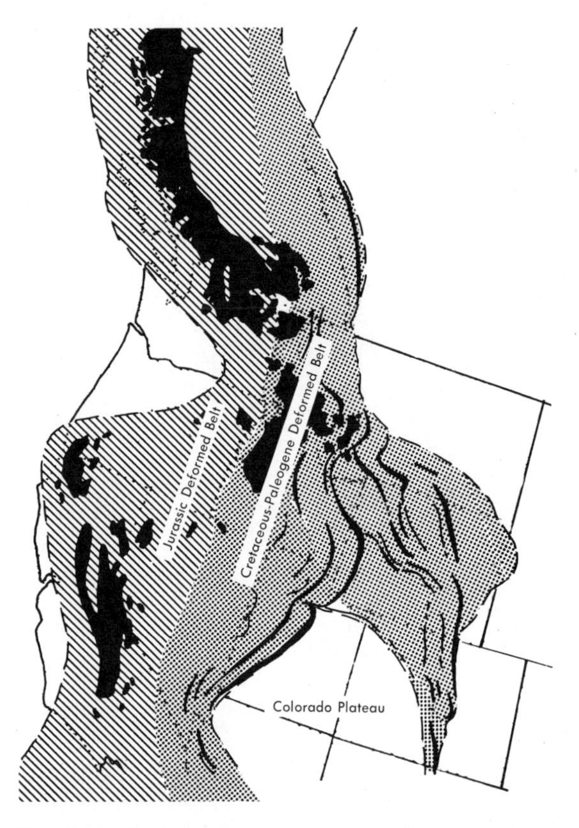

Fig. 20-7. Orogenic belts of the Jurassic and Cretaceous. The black areas are exposures of igneous intrusions, most of which are granitic batholiths of Jurassic age. The diagonal belt was deformed in the Nevadian orogeny while the region covered by dots was affected in the Laramide orogeny. The heavy black lines indicate the position of major folds. Note that the Laramide belt goes on either side of the Colorado Plateau. (After A. J. Eardley.)

Middle Rocky Mountains

Most of this part of the Rockies is located in south-central Montana and Wyoming. The behavior of this part of the Rocky Mountain system is strikingly different from that north, south, and west of it. It is characterized by large blocklike uplifts rather than long folded and faulted belts such as are found in the Northern and Central Rockies. Fig. 20-11 shows the positions of most of these big uplifts, which are separated by deep basins. Some of the blocks have not continued to rise since the Laramide, and they have been almost buried in their own debris and the alluvial deposits of other nearby ranges. Most of these blocks are bounded by high-angle faults. They have risen so high that post-Laramide erosion has bared Lower Precambrian rocks on most of their summits. Paleozoic and Mesozoic sections of sedimentary rocks are found on the flanks of these uplifts. Apparently uplift dominated the movement in the Middle Rockies while thrusting and folding controlled the formation of structures in the other parts of the Rockies. The explanation for this difference in behavior may lie in the fact that the Northern Rockies and Central Rockies had been occupied by deeply subsiding geosynclines through parts of

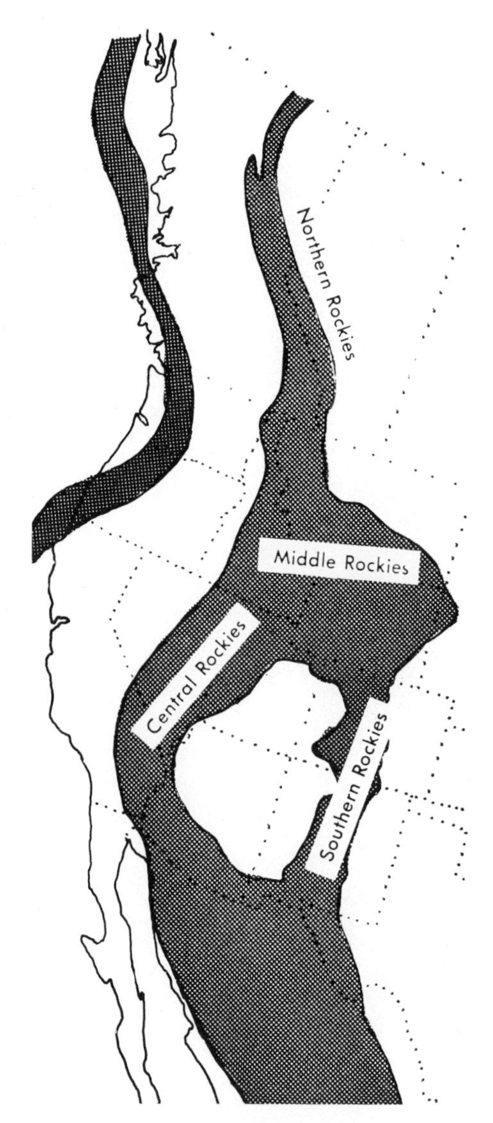

Fig. 20-8. Belts deformed in the Laramide orogeny. (After A. J. Eardley.)

the Paleozoic and Mesozoic. The Middle Rockies are located on the shelflike separation between these belts and the craton. Much thinner sections of sediment covered the shelf. Therefore, when diastrophism began to affect the Cordilleran geosyncline, the less competent sediments yielded by folding and faulting, but the shelf, which was underlain by extremely old crystalline metamorphic rocks and igneous rocks, was too strong to yield in that manner. Instead, it broke up along fracture and fault trends that had formed in the Precambrian, and the blocks that were outlined by these zones of weakness moved with respect to one another. Some moved up to form mountains, and others went down and formed basins.

Fig. 20-9. Chief Mountain, Montana. This large block of Precambrian units has been thrust out on Cretaceous shales. The block is now completely isolated, forming a klippe. (Photo by courtesy of the Montana Highway Department.)

Southern Rocky Mountains

This section includes the area in central Colorado and New Mexico. The uplift known as the Ancestral Rockies was covered by some Cretaceous sediments before it was uplifted as part of the Colorado Front Range. The Front Range is the largest single element of the Southern Rockies. It is over 200 miles long, extending almost north-south from Canyon City, Colorado, to the Laramie Range in Wyoming. Along the eastern margin this range rises abruptly from the plains. In places the sedimentary units are overturned, but along most of it monoclinal dips mark the eastern edge of this large elongate upwarp. The western edge of the Front Range is bounded by an eastward-dipping thrust fault. To the west of the Front Range three synclinal basins called parks separate the Front Range from a second elongate uplift with a Precambrian core, the Park Range. West of this second uplifted mass of Precambrian lies the central Colorado Basin. To the south, in southern Colorado and New Mexico, ranges with cores of Precambrian were uplifted along high-angle faults which are thrust eastward locally somewhat like those of the Middle Rockies. A belt of porphyry intrusions extends across the Colorado Rockies from the southwest to the northeast. These contain a great many of the most important ore bodies of this region.

Central Rockies

This part of the Laramide system includes the deformed areas in southern Idaho, western Utah, and eastern Nevada, and continues

Fig. 20-10. Cross section across the Canadian Rockies showing the effects of the Laramide orogeny. Note particularly the imbricate thrust faults and the one major low angle thrust at the left. (After Mackay.)

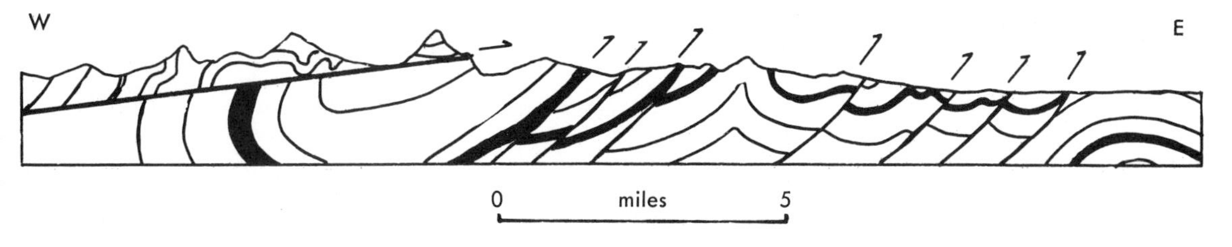

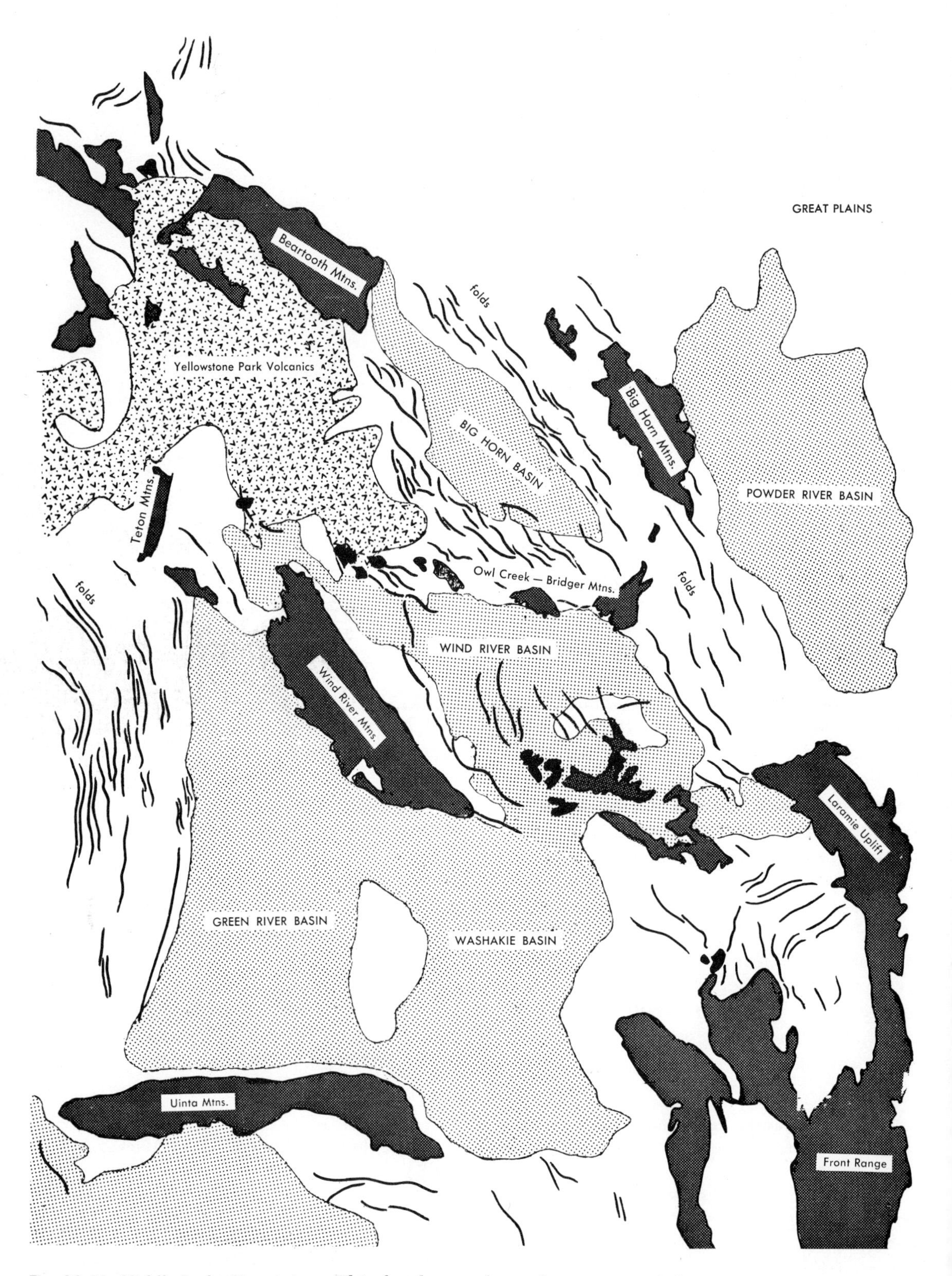

Fig. 20-11. Middle Rocky Mountains. This sketch map shows the positions of the principal ranges and basins of this part of the Rocky Mountain system. Most of these ranges are bounded on at least two sides by steep faults along which they have been uplifted. (After the Tectonic Map of the United States.)

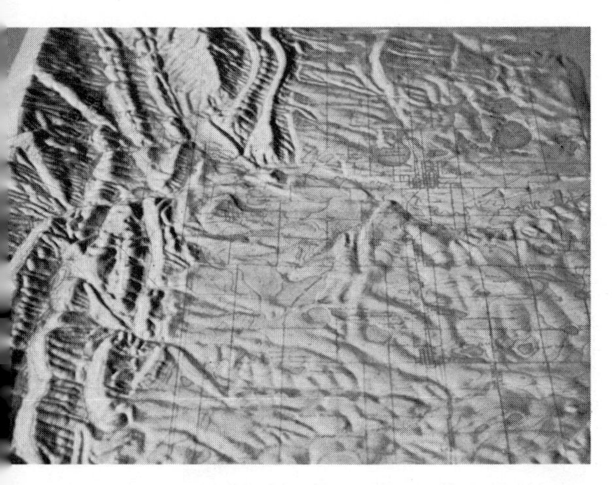

Fig. 20-12. Relief map of the Loveland, Colorado quadrangle. The structures of the Front Range of the Southern Rockies are reflected in the topography. Notice the large anticlinal uplift and the hog back ridges along the border of the range. (Map by Aero Service; photo by E. W. Spencer.)

southward into southwestern Arizona. It is the most complex of the four divisions of the Rockies, and its history is more difficult to decipher because much of it was broken up by block faults in the Cenozoic. The result of this later faulting was to shift some blocks up and drop others down, making an extensive pattern of grabens and horsts. The down-dropped blocks are filled by alluvial debris from the uplifted blocks. A second complicating factor is the absence of Cretaceous sediments in the western part of the Central Rockies. The structures in this area are complicated by the effects of the Jurassic Nevadan orogeny. The patterns of deformation resemble those of the Northern Rockies in that the thick accumulations of sediments were complexly folded and faulted throughout the area as they were forced toward the craton to the east.

Diastrophism and sedimentary facies: an example

One of the best examples of the nature of the deposition that was taking place simultaneously with the Late Cretaceous Laramide orogeny is found in central and eastern Utah. Here the Upper Cretaceous is almost completely exposed along the 200-mile stretch of the east-west trending "Book Cliffs." For almost 75 miles the units are exposed along the edge of the Wasatch Plateau of central Utah. The facies found in these exposures range from coarse conglomerates and associate heterogeneous sediments, which were laid down on the flanks of high mountains as alluvial fans, to the fine muds characteristic of the bottom sediments of an offshore sea. It is possible, through study of the facies changes between these two extremes, to reveal the effects of broad upward movements of the crust that accompanied the diastrophism that affected the Central Rocky Mountain system.

Lateral changes may be traced between the geosynclinal belt of western Utah and Nevada and the eastern part of Utah. The latter is a part of the Colorado Plateau, an area that was little deformed by the Laramide deformation. In the east the Upper Cretaceous consists of two major divisions, the Mancos shale and an overlying unit consisting of sandstones with a little shale and coal-bearing units. To the west, in central Utah, a much coarser and thicker section is found. Here the Indianola group, an equivalent of the lower Mancos shale, is 15,000 feet thick. The group consists of conglomerate with some sandstone, shale,

Fig. 20-13. The Book Cliffs of Utah. These cliffs are found trending east-west along the southern margin of the Uinta Mountains. Here we find exceptional exposures of Upper Cretaceous units in which sedimentary facies reflect the history of diastrophism which parts of the region were undergoing during the Cretaceous. (Photo by E. W. Spencer.)

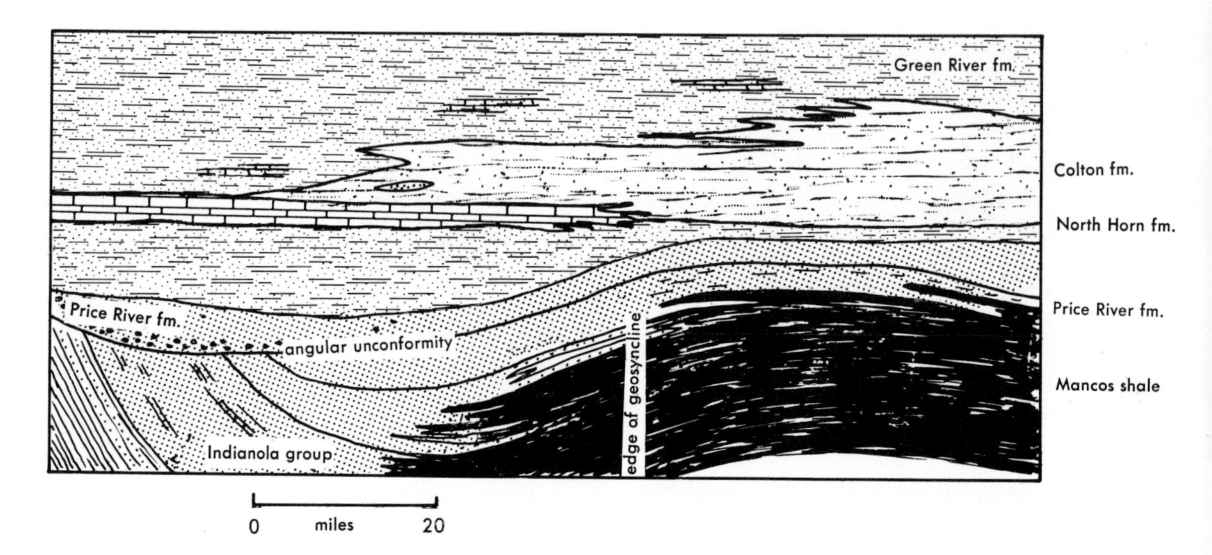

Fig. 20-14. Section showing Upper Cretaceous and Lower Paleogene strata along a line from the Colorado Plateau in Utah westward into the geosynclinal belt. See the text for a description of the variations in lithologies and the environmental conditions which they reflect. (After E. M. Spieker.)

Fig. 20-15. Cliff dwellings at Mesa Verde. These habitations are constructed under overhanging cliffs of the Mesaverde sandstone, a unit that was deposited in a continental environment. The sands are interbedded with coal seams in a few places in this part of the "four corners" region. (Photo by E. W. Spencer.)

Fig. 20-16. Mesaverde sandstone and underlying Mancos shale exposed in northwestern New Mexico, near Shiprock. (Photo courtesy of the New Mexico State Tourist Bureau.)

and limestone. Thus we see a striking difference in thickness and lithologic characteristics in the units of these two areas. In the east the entire Mancos shale formation is less than 4000 feet thick. In the central part of Utah the lower part alone of the time-equivalent units is 15,000 feet thick. The upper part of the units that would be equivalent to the Upper Mancos has been eroded away in central and western Utah.

Above the Mancos shale a formation known as the Price River appears. It is composed of sandstone and conglomerate in the west and sandstone, shale, and coal in the east. Over the Price River formation we find the North Horn formation. It consists of 2000 to 7000 feet of shale, sandstone, fresh-water limestone, and conglomerate in the west, but 100 to 500 feet of similar units is found in the east.

One of the most outstanding features of the westward progressive changes is the rapidity with which the sediments coarsen and change in character as the edge of the geosyncline is reached. The Mancos shale, for example, is a fine marine shale in the east; 20 miles west it is represented mostly by sandstone with some conglomerate, and only 5 miles farther west it is all conglomerate. The westward change from marine and lowland deposits to those on the flanks of high mountains is not a simple gradation. There is much interfingering of the units as conditions of deposition shifted irregularly through time. At least four types of deposits and environments may be recognized:

1. Conglomerate, red beds, with fresh-water limestone, typical of a piedmont or highland environment.
2. Conglomeratic sandstone, variegated beds, clay shale, fresh-water limestone, and sandstone formed as an inland flood plain, channel fillings, and lake deposits.
3. Coal-bearing successions of buff sandstone and shale deposited in the littoral zone of the ocean.
4. Gray shale and siltstone deposited offshore in the marine environment.

Fig. 20-17. Restoration of Cretaceous invertebrate life. Among the most important groups of animals in the Cretaceous seas were these ammonite cephalopods – some with straight shells (A) and others with planispirally coiled shells (B). Also shown are belemnoids (C), gastropods (D), and pelecypods (E). (Museum of Paleontology, University of Michigan.)

These four facies can be traced laterally and vertically in normal sequence. Laterally the continental deposits grade into the transition-environment deposits, which in turn grade into marine-environment deposits. Vertical sequences are also found, as in the case of a transgressing sea, in which continental deposits are overlain by those of a transition and then by those of a marine environment. There is much evidence of fluctuation in the shore line as the geosyncline was deformed. There was also cyclic deposition, suggesting periodic upward movements, but the overall trend through the Late Cretaceous was one of increasing uplift in the geosyncline with the gradual overlap of continental and littoral deposits on the marine shales of the Mancos formation.

LIFE OF THE CRETACEOUS

I. NEW FORMS

1. *Flowering Plants:* Modern types of trees with flowers and covered seeds evolved during this period, providing

birds and mammals with an abundant food supply. This gradually supplanted the older forest that had been dominated by conifers.

2. *New Mammals:* Two new groups of mammals appeared on the scene although neither was a challenge to the dominance of the reptiles. These new mammals were the marsupials and the insectivores. The marsupials are mammals that bear their young in a pouch, like the kangaroo. The first insectivores resembled shrews and moles, which are later descendants of this same stock.

II. PEAKS AND ADVANCEMENT

1. Dominance of reptiles continued through the Cretaceous. They had by this time become adapted to almost every mode of life and filled and dominated the air, seas, and land masses. Most terrible of these was the species *Tyrannosaurus rex;* they may well be the most voracious animals ever to roam the earth. They walked on their hind legs, like all the smaller dinosaurs, and their front legs were small, probably useless vestiges. The animal stood up to 20 feet tall and had a 4-foot head. Their long powerful jaws were lined with sharp teeth. Others of the dinosaur clan looked like large ostriches. They had no teeth at all and probably depended on the eggs of other dinosaurs for their food.

The first skulls of the large-horned dinosaurs, *Triceratops,* are found in the Cretaceous. They had two long horns that projected from their forehead and a shorter one over the nose. They were further protected by a massive bony shield that covered the neck. They probably needed such protection from the gigantic carniverous dinosaurs with which they lived. The duck-billed dinosaurs had been present in the Jurassic, and they were still abundant during the Cretaceous, as were the plesiosaurs. The most notable of the plesiosaurs has been found in Australia where the skull of one measures 9½ feet long. Similar giants flew over the Cre-

Fig. 20-18. Triceratops and Tyrannosaurus. Tyrannosaurus, one of the last of the dinosaurs, was the greatest land-living flesh-eater known. Standing 19 feet high, its jaws were armed with large saber-like teeth. The plant-eating Triceratops on the left was protected by its three horns and by the bony frill covering its neck. Both of these dinosaurs lived in North America at the end of the Cretaceous period, 78 million years ago. (Painting by Charles Knight, Chicago Natural History Museum.)

taceous seas. These were the pterosaurs, which first appeared in the Jurassic, but those of Cretaceous age were much larger. Some of them had a wing spread of more than 25 feet. The reptiles had by this time attained the culmination of their reign on earth, and before the end of the period all of the most important groups died out, leaving only a few rather inconspicuous members of their race behind. What caused this great "dying-off" is one of the most baffling problems in historical geology.

2. Mammals kept in the background during the period, but continued to become better adapted to the various environmental niches of the world in preparation for the coming age when they would succeed the reptiles as masters of the world. The multituberculates persist as the most important group. Their expansion was probably prompted by the new fruits, cereals, nuts, and grains that grew abundantly on the land areas.
3. Foraminifera: Several groups of forams became exceedingly abundant during the Cretaceous. In fact, the chalk deposits for which the period is named were formed of the minute remains of the globular forams. Such chalk deposits are common in many parts of the world. Notable among them are the cliffs of Dover.
4. Ammonites continued to be important among the invertebrate groups. They attained their maximum sizes at this time when some of the coiled ammonites were more than 7 feet in diameter. If that shell had been uncoiled, as some ammonites were, it would have been more than 35 feet long.
5. Development among the other invertebrate faunas had produced most of the modern types of marine invertebrates. Some of the more important of these are illustrated in Fig. 20-3.

III. EXTINCTION

Not a single dinosaur is known to have escaped the extinction which overtook the group at the end of the period. Many explanations have been offered for the disappearance of a group that had become so well adapted to life in all sorts of environ-

Fig. 20-19. Late Cretaceous dinosaurs. The peak of dinosaur evolution was reached shortly before the extinction of the group. Prominent in North America 90 million years ago were the duck-billed dinosaurs, such as Edmontosaurus on the right and the hooded Corythosaurus and crested Parasaurolophus in the swamp on the left. Other contemporary dinosaurs were the heavily armored Palaeoscincus in the center and the ostrich-like Struthiomimus in the background. (Painting by Charles Knight, Chicago Natural History Museum.)

Fig. 20-20. Protoceratops and its eggs. This small dinosaur belongs to the horned dinosaurs. Even though it lacks horn projections on its head, its neck is covered by a bony frill characteristic of all horned dinosaurs. Protoceratops lived in Mongolia about 90 million years ago during the Late Cretaceous Epoch. Many skeletons of young and adults have been found there. Unhatched eggs in the clutches of some of these dinosaurs have been found as fossils. (Painting by Charles Knight, Chicago Natural History Museum.)

Fig. 20-21. Tylosaurus, Protostega, Pteranodon. In the Late Cretaceous seas that covered parts of the present continent of North America 96 million years ago, the giant fish-eating sea-lizard Tylosaurus grew to a length of 30 feet. The sea-turtle Protostega had a shell as much as 6 feet in length. In the air, the flying reptile Pteranodon soared on wings that spread 25 feet in some cases. Painting by Charles Knight, Chicago Natural History Museum.)

ments. Why did they suddenly lose the ability to adapt to any further changes? The mountain building which occurred toward the close of the period has been cited by many as the most probable cause. Mountains interrupt and change the circulation of air and the climate in the regions near them. It could be that these climatic changes were too much for the dinosaurs and other reptiles. It has also been pointed out that many of the reptiles had evolved to extremes in size and structure, and that these forms were unsuited to adaptations. We cannot be sure what happened, but the close of this period saw the decline and extinction of:

a. All dinosaurs.
b. Pterosaurs (the flying reptiles).
c. Marine reptiles, the ichthyosaurs and plesiosaurs.
d. Ammonites.
e. Belemnites.

IV. NOTABLE ASPECTS OF CRETACEOUS LIFE

Were we able to visit the Cretaceous time undoubtedly the most impressive aspect of the life would have been the strange dinosaurs. The mammals would probably have been rather hard to find. Most of them were small and probably remained hidden from the larger reptiles as much as possible. Aside from the dinosaurs, however, we would probably be impressed by the forests, which were so changed from those of earlier geologic periods. The deciduous trees would be present for the first time. Deciduous trees are those that shed their leaves during part of the year. This characteristic almost certainly sprang up in response to climatic conditions, a seasonal variation in temperature and rainfall. The earliest of these trees are the magnolias, fig trees, and poplars. Of course, there were also flowering plants at this time. This too was something new on the earth, trees with flowers and seed protected by a covering. By the middle part of the period there were birches, maples, oaks, walnuts, tulip trees, sweet gums, laurel, ivy, and holly. These trees had come to replace the evergreen cone-bearing trees as the dominant land plants. However, conifers were still present and abundant. Among them sequoias, somewhat smaller than the giants of California, were widespread.

At the same time many other new plants appeared that belong to the angiosperms. These were the grasses, cereals, fruit-bearing trees, and vegetables. Try to imagine your diet without the products of the angiosperms, and you will see why it is thought that mammal evolution was tied in closely with the evolution of these plants. The birds for the first time found a food supply up off the ground where they could obtain it relatively free from harm. They no longer needed the teeth of the earlier birds to pick up small animals and fish, and thus many new varieties of birds began to evolve in the succeeding periods. Likewise, the mammals found a suitable food source for their needs, and they were able to sustain life through whatever the extremes were that killed the dinosaurs.

REFERENCES

EARDLEY, A. J., 1944, Geology of the north-central Wasatch Mountains, Utah: Geol. Soc. America Bull., v. 55, p. 819-894

PIKE, W. S., JR., 1947, Intertonguing marine and nonmarine Upper Cretaceous deposits of New Mexico, Arizona, and southwestern Colorado: Geol. Soc. America Mem. 41, 103 p.

SPIEKER, E. M., 1946, Late Mesozoic and Early Tertiary history of central Utah: U. S. Geol. Survey Prof. Paper 205-D, p. 117-161

STEPHENSON, L. W., 1939, Cretaceous system: *Geologie der Erde,* Geology of North America, Gebrüder Borntrager, Berlin, p. 519-549

21 The Paleogene Period

Subdivision of the Cenozoic

The Mesozoic Era closed with the Laramide deformation in the western United States, but without any event of comparable magnitude in the eastern and central parts of the continent. Many of the differences between forms of life, the fauna and flora, of more recent Cenozoic sedimentary rock units and those of older pre-Laramide sedimentary rocks have been attributed to changes in the physiography, climate, and environmental factors in different parts of the world. These changes are most often related primarily to late Cretaceous orogenies. The general change in the aspects of the fauna and flora is the basis for the designation Mesozoic (middle life), applied to the older assemblages, and Cenozoic (modern life), used for the younger groups. It now appears that these changes were not nearly so

Cenozoic. Geologic map showing distribution of Paleogene and Neogene strata and Cenozoic igneous rocks

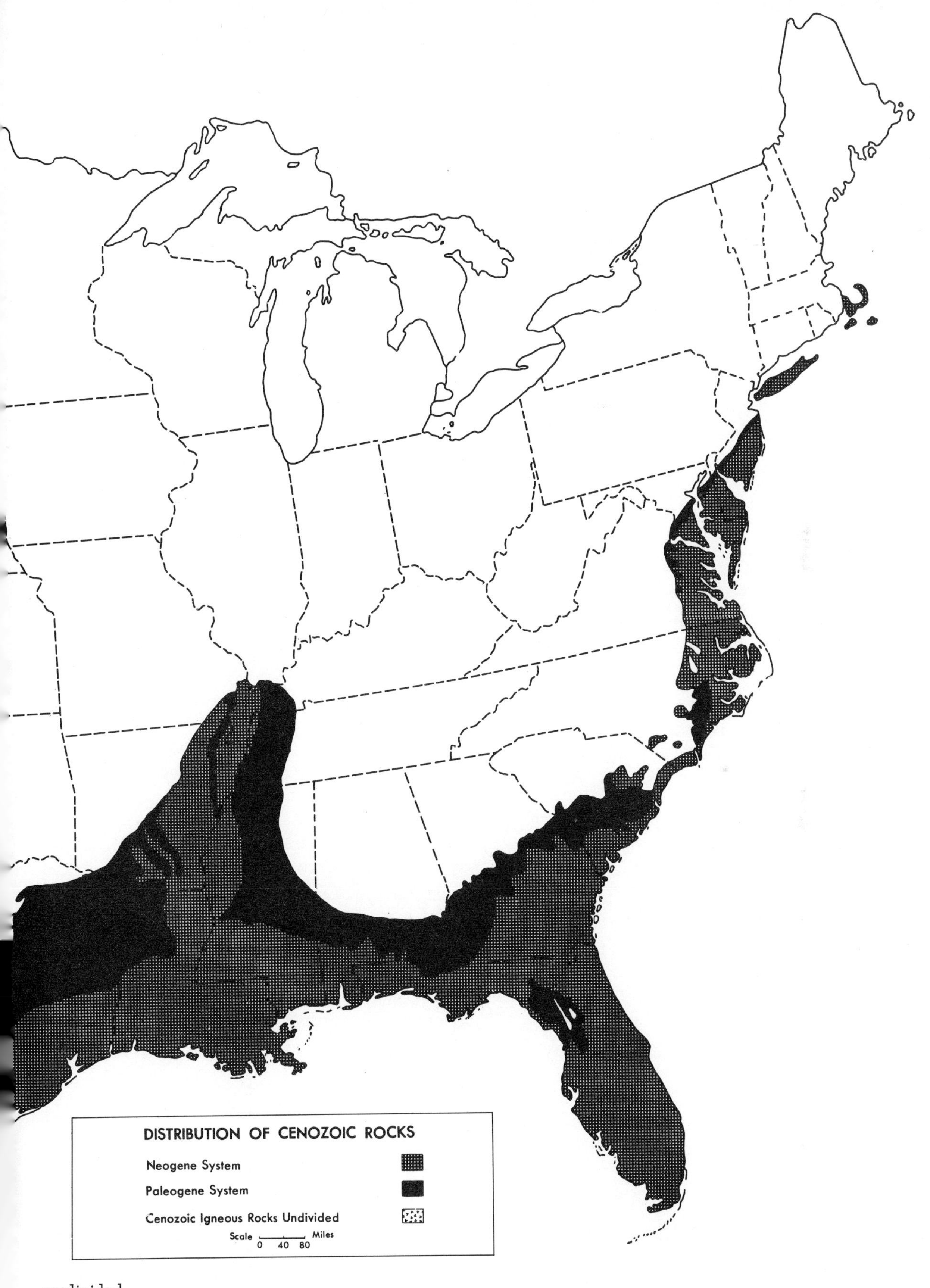
DISTRIBUTION OF CENOZOIC ROCKS
Neogene System
Paleogene System
Cenozoic Igneous Rocks Undivided
Scale
Miles
0 40 80

undivided.

System	Series	LOUISIANA	GEORGIA	VENTURA AREA, CALIF.	WESTERN WASHINGTON
NEOGENE SYSTEM	PLIOCENE	Citronelle fm.	Charlton fm. Duplin marl	Pico fm. Repetto fm.	Quinault fm. Montesano fm.
	MIOCENE SERIES	Pascagoula clay Hattiesburg clay Catahoula sandstone	Hawthorn fm. Tampa limestone	Santa Margarita shale Modelo shale Rincon shale	Astoria fm. Twin Rivers fm.
PALEOGENE SYSTEM	OLIGOCENE	Vicksburg limestone	Flint River fm. Suwannee limestone	Sespe fm.	Blakeley fm. Lincoln fm.
	EOCENE SERIES	Jackson fm. Yegua fm. Cook Mountain fm. Sparta sand Cane River fm. Wilcox fm.	Copper marl Barnwell fm. Twiggs clay member McBean fm. Wilcox fm.	Coldwater sandstone Cozy dell shale Matilija sandstone undifferentiated	Cowlitz fm.
	PALEOCENE	Midway fm.	Clayton fm.		Metchosin volcanics

sudden as was once thought, but the designation of Mesozoic and Cenozoic continues in usage.

Two systems of subdivision of the Cenozoic are currently in use. The later one will probably replace the older system, but so much literature has been written using the older terms that the students should be familiar with both sets of terms. The chart below gives the equivalents of the two systems:

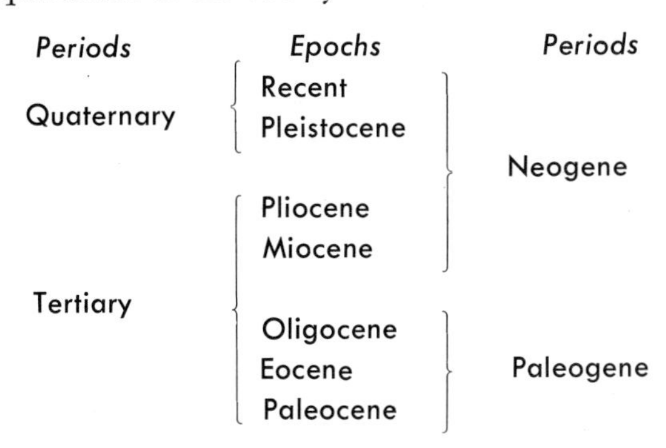

Fig. 21-1. Correlation chart for the Cenozoic.

The subdivision of the Cenozoic into Quaternary and Tertiary has been rejected for several reasons:

1. The terms first applied by Arduino in 1759 are no longer significant because the early systems of three- and fourfold subdivisions of time have been abandoned.
2. The Quaternary and Tertiary covered tremendously different amounts of time. The Quaternary lasted less than 2 million years, compared with about 60 million for the Tertiary.
3. The Cenozoic sedimentary sequences in their type localities in Europe are best explained in terms of the paleogeography if the division is put between the sedimentary units of the Oligocene and Miocene. The type locality for most of the epochs of the Cenozoic is the Paris Basin. The Cenozoic history of Europe is marked by two major marine invasions of different parts of the continent with the first withdrawal at the end of the Oligocene.

PHYSICAL HISTORY OF THE PALEOGENE

Atlantic Coast

After a short emergence following the Cretaceous, the seas advanced upon the Atlantic seaboard again and deposited thin sheets of marine sediments with an initial dip toward the ocean. Along the North Carolina and South Carolina border an anticlinal warp trending almost east-west interrupted sedimentation during the Late Eocene. The Paleogene outcrops become wider southward. Florida had been a subsiding platform in the Late Cretaceous and again in the Eocene. During most of the rest of the Cenozoic it has been a shoaling peninsula. Inland, the present-day topography of the Appalachian Highlands was beginning to become etched out of the Paleozoic and Triassic sedimentary units.

Gulf Coast

Paleogene sediments are thick in the Gulf Coast from Florida westward. A geosynclinal depression was beginning to form along the southern edge of the present-day coast. Most of the Cenozoic sedimentary units thicken toward the Gulf and for an undetermined distance out into the Gulf. Over the Gulf States the Paleogene thins northward. An embayment, known as the Mississippi embayment, developed in the Paleogene, and the seas occupied this area several times during the Cenozoic. The embayment extends along the Mississippi River and includes most of the Mississippi Valley from the Gulf northward to the southern tip of Illinois. Swamps formed within this embayment, leaving scattered beds of coal. A platform somewhat like the one Florida occupies stood about in the position of the present Mississippi delta during the Paleogene, and coral reefs grew around its margins in the Oligocene Epoch. Solid plugs of salt began to rise through the semiconsolidated sediments in the Gulf geosyncline, doming the sediments above them and pushing aside those on their flanks.

Western interior

The deformation that began in the Cretaceous in the Rocky Mountains continued into the Eocene Epoch, but by the Oligocene the uplifts, folding, and thrusting had stopped, and the Laramide orogeny came to an end. Long before the end of the deformation the tops of the uplifted areas had become the sites of erosion. The weathered debris and the material eroded off by running water and carried down slope by mass wasting spread huge fans of terrigenous sediments over the plains and filled the intermontane basins. The Wasatch formation, Eocene, is one of the most notable of these fillings. The only marine sedimentary formation in the interior of the United States is the Cannonball member of the Fort Union formation of the Paleogene Epoch. This unit appears in the basins of the Middle Rocky Mountains. How it was connected with the seas is unknown. In the high Rockies the dominant process was erosion. By the end of the Paleogene the mountains had been eroded down to a high base level. The erosion surface this produced is known as the Gangplank peneplane.

The Colorado Plateau had been affected by the deformation of the Cretaceous–Eocene orogeny, which intensely deformed units in the adjacent geosynclinal belts. The units in the plateau were arched slightly. These warped surfaces were eroded, and the Wasatch formations was deposited on this bevelled surface.

Volcanism continued in the Paleogene, but on a much smaller scale than prior to the

Fig. 21-2. Bryce Canyon, Utah. Unusual erosional forms were created in the Wasatch beds of Eocene age. These exposures are along the edge of a high plateau in southern Utah. The area is part of the Colorado Plateau. The Wasatch unit is composed of shales and calcareous sediment which contain snail shells. The beds were deposited in an inland sea or large lake. (Photo by courtesy of the Union Pacific Railroad.)

Fig. 21-3. Badlands of South Dakota. These deposits are typical of Paleogene units that cover large parts of South Dakota, North Dakota, Wyoming, and eastern Montana. They are continental deposits carried down into the plains from the Rocky Mountains which had just been elevated and were being further elevated during the early part of the Paleogene. These units are of the White River Group. (Photo by courtesy of the Publicity Division, So. Dakota Dept. of Highways.)

Fig. 21-4. Oligocene continental deposits southeast of Rapid City, South Dakota. These are part of the White River Group. (Official photograph of the U.S. Coast & Geodetic Survey.)

end of the Mesozoic. Basalt flows were extruded in the region of Yellowstone Park and in the Absaroka Range near the park. Basalts also flowed out on the surface in Washington and Oregon. In the Oligocene, explosive volcanic activity in this region spread a thick blanket of ash over large parts of the western plains.

Western coast

In California, orogenic deformation has been almost continuous throughout the Cenozoic. A number of deep subsiding basins formed during the Paleogene. Block faulting began toward the end of the Paleogene, and the large blocks have since been depressed and tilted. The tilting of one of these blocks along the fault bordering it on the eastern side has given rise to the structure of the present Sierra Nevada. Death Valley is on the down-dropped side of the same fault.

Fig. 21-5. Gulf Coast salt dome shown diagramatically in section. Consolidated and semiconsolidated sedimentary rocks through which the crystalline salt plug has penetrated are faulted and deformed. Faults form graben and horst structures in the domed strata over the salt plug. The top part of the salt is covered by a cap rock composed of dolostone, gypsum, anhydrite, and sulphur. Sulphur is produced commercially from a number of domes in the Gulf Coast, and many structures suitable for the accumulation of oil and gas are associated with the domes. These have been numbered in the diagram. What kind of trap is each?

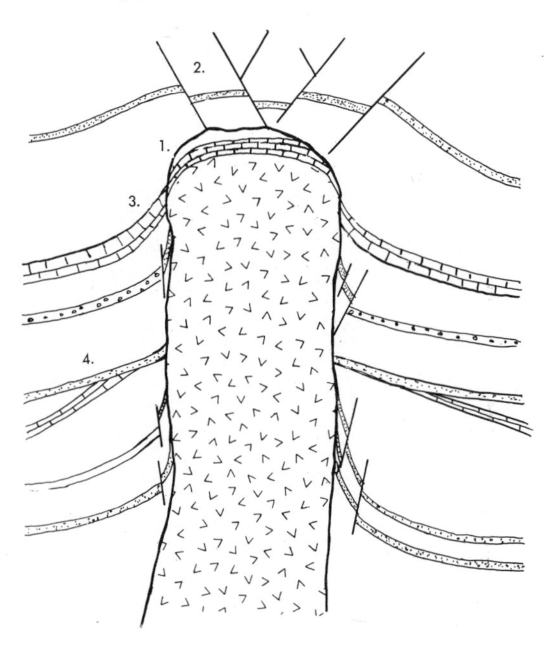

GULF COAST SALT DOMES

Two belts of salt domes can be recognized in the Gulf Coast region of the United States. The two belts are essentially parallel to the coast. One runs close to the coast, and the other is about 100 miles inland. Combined, they contain over 200 salt plugs, and there is every reason to expect that a good many more will be found in the sediments underlying the shallow waters of the Gulf of Mexico. Not all these domes originated in the Paleogene, but it seems likely that a good many of them did. Probably more of those in the belt near the coast began to rise in the Paleogene Period. Many of the domes continue to rise today.

A typical salt dome is a mile in diameter and of undetermined height. Many of them appear to have the shape of a carrot, with the top being broadened. Some taper off at depth, but others are nearly cylindrical all the way down to the source bed of salt, which is believed to be within the Jurassic or Cretaceous sedimentary sequences now very deeply buried under Paleogene and Neogene sediments. The Jurassic beds that have been reached by drilling in southern Arkansas contain salt, gypsum, and anhydrite, and appear to be a logical source for the salt. Because the source beds are so deep they have not been penetrated by wells drilled within the southern part of the Coastal Plain even though some of these have been drilled over 20,000 feet deep. The main body of the salt plug is coarsely crystalline salt, NaCl, which is usually pure. The top of the dome is covered by a cap, which contains gypsum, anhydrite, and brecciated sediments. The cap rock often contains sulfur, which is concentrated in sufficient quantities to make it commercially important.

The structures within the salt show that it has been strongly deformed. The crinkles and folds within the salt are nearly vertical and give the appearance of a mass squeezed upward through a constricted opening. These folds are the result of a process known as solid flowage. The salt recrystallized as it was forced upward, and flowed without ever becoming a liquid. A complex structural pattern surrounds the domes. Over the top of the typical salt plug the sediments are arched upward very broadly. Concentric outcrop patterns at the surface can be seen on air photographs of many salt domes even where the ground surface is almost flat. The strata over the dome are generally faulted as well as domed. The faults are normal and give rise to grabens and steplike blocks. The displacements along these faults are usually small, typically amounting to less than 100 feet. Many slight angular unconformities are found over some salt plugs. These resulted when the salt plug rose for a period, arching the strata, then ceased to move upward, allowing erosion to bevel the top of the dome. This was followed by deposition of sediments on the bevelled surface. This process may be repeated many times. On the flanks of the plugs, strata are pushed aside and faulted as the plug pierces them. Such structures provide many potential sites for the accumulation of oil and gas, and many of the outstanding fields in the Gulf Coast region produce from strata near salt domes.

The question of how these plugs start to rise is best explained in terms of the relative density of the salt and the sediments over the source bed of the salt. Salt has a lower density than the semiconsolidated and unconsolidated sediments which are covering the thick salt source bed. After the overlying sediments reach a certain thickness the weight on the salt bed becomes great enough to make it flow. An unstable condition already exists because the salt is lighter than the sediment and tends to rise. The weight of the sediments drives the salt upward. Once an upbulge in the source bed begins to move up the salt assumes a streamlined shape to make passage through the sediments easier. The upward movement of the plug may be stopped if the salt source bed becomes pinched off around the plug, or if the plug encounters a hard bed through which it cannot penetrate.

Fig. 21-6. Eocene Foraminifera. These are a few of the most important forams from the Paleogene. They inhabited marine, fresh, and brackish waters. It is often possible to recognize the type of water, temperature, and salinity in which certain sediments were deposited by the types of forams the sediments contain. (Photos of models by courtesy of the Chicago Natural History Museum.)

Fig. 21-7. Four-toed horses and Unitatherium. The horned Unitatherium, as large as a present-day rhinoceros, lived in North America in Middle Eocene times, 50 million years ago. It was one of the strangest of the archaic mammals that flourished while the evolution of modern groups, such as the horses, was just beginning. The four-toed horse Orohippus, on the left, was no larger than a collie dog. (Painting by Charles Knight, Chicago Natural History Museum.)

LIFE OF THE PALEOGENE

I. NEW FORMS

The Paleogene faunas and floras resembled the life of the present in most respects. All of the modern phyla and classes were represented. Even most of the modern genera either appeared in the Paleogene or were carried over from the Mesozoic. Thus the principal differences between modern plants and animals and those of the Paleogene are on the level of genera and species. The evolution of many of these groups will be treated later in the chapter on the evolution of the vertebrates. Practically all of the notable "firsts" in the Paleogene were mammals. Some of these familiar groups are listed below:

1. *Primates:* The first primates were lemurs and tarsiers, which appeared in the Paleocene Epoch of the Paleogene. Other primates that came later in the Cenozoic include monkeys, apes, and man.

2. *Modern Birds:* One of the most striking advances of the Cenozoic has been the explosive evolution of birds. They have become highly specialized and diversified. Their spread is undoubtedly tied to the appearance, in abundance, of flowering plants and trees.
3. *Rodents:* The first rodents were squirrel-like animals that appeared in the earliest epoch of the Paleogene.
4. *Horses:* These animals appeared for the first time in the Eocene Epoch. You would hardly recognize one of these animals as a horse if you saw it, however, for these were miniature animals, about the size of dogs. They roamed the plains of the northern Rocky Mountain states particularly.
5. *Whales:* These are one of the few groups of mammals that have become adapted to life in the seas. We saw the reptiles take over the marine environment in the Mesozoic Era. After the ichthyosaurs and plesiosaurs died out there was an important environmental niche left open, which mammals occupied. The first whales did not look very much like the modern whales, for they had not had time to become adapted to the environment.
6. *Sabertooth Tigers:* This famous animal is one of the most popular of the animals of the past. Along with several other lines of cats these tigers appeared for the first time during the Oligocene Epoch, but unlike other species of their family the sabertooth tigers became extinct before the end of the Pleistocene.

Fig. 21-8. Oligocene titanotheres. These were among the most spectacular large mammals of North America. The titanothere shown here lived at the climax of the evolution of this group in Oligocene times, 36 million years ago, was 8 feet high at the shoulders. Skeletons of these huge beasts are found in the badlands of South Dakota, together with those of the primitive flesh-eater Hyaenodon. (Painting by Charles Knight, Chicago Natural History Museum.)

7. *Apes and Monkeys:* They took advantage of a new environmental condition, the forests, with their abundance of food and safety from most other animals.

II. PEAKS AND ADVANCEMENT

1. Mammals came to dominate the earth in the Cenozoic just as reptiles did in the Mesozoic. The mammals tended to undergo evolutionary trends toward increase in size, and specialization of the teeth and limbs. At the same time they gradually expanded into all types of environments.
2. Toothless birds supplanted the older birds of the Mesozoic. These modern birds began to develop hollow bones or bones filled with air pockets, making them better adjusted to the environment in which they abound.
3. Foraminifera was an extremely important group throughout the Cenozoic Era. They have been especially useful in correlation and in helping to establish environmental conditions under which rocks were formed. Certain of them are known to inhabit fresh water, others live exclusively in marine waters of different temperature ranges. One of the most important of these in the Paleogene was the *Nummulites,* which were shaped like a small coin.
4. Expansion of pelecypods and gastropods started in the Paleogene and has continued to the present. They have been the most abundant groups of the larger marine invertebrates.
5. Of the fish, those known as the "bony fish" (teleosts) became the most abundant fish of the Paleogene. This group includes many of the most common modern fish such as the herring, sardine, shad, anchovies, salmons, trout, smelts, graylings, and catfish. At the present time this group makes up about half of all the living vertebrates. There are about 20,000 species of them.

Fig. 21-9. Whales of the Eocene seas. Whales certainly descended from land mammals although their early ancestry is unknown. When they first appeared in Eocene rocks, they were already well adapted to marine life. This one was a 55 foot giant of the seas of southeastern North America in Late Eocene times, 45 million years ago. (Painting by Charles Knight, Chicago Natural History Museum.)

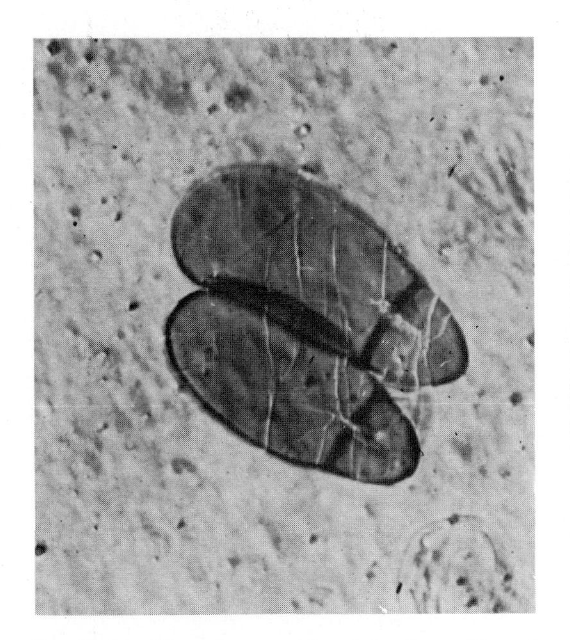

Fig. 21-10. Microphotographs of the Green River formations showing some of the micro-fossils. The remains of such animals account for the presence of hydrocarbons in these rocks. (Photos by U.S. Geological Survey.)

REFERENCES

BARTON, D. C., 1933, Mechanics of formation of salt domes, with special reference to Gulf Coast salt domes of Texas and Louisiana: Am. Assoc. Petroleum Geologists Bull., v. 17, p. 1025-1083

BARTON, D. C., RITZ, D. H., and HICKEY, MAUDE, 1933, Gulf Coast geosyncline: Am. Assoc. Petroleum Geologists Bull., v. 17, p. 1446-1558

CARSEY, J. B., 1950, Geology of Gulf coastal area and continental shelf: Am. Assoc. Petroleum Geologists Bull., v. 34, p. 361-384

KING, P. B., 1951, *The Tectonics of Middle North America,* Princeton University Press, Princeton, 203 p.

SPANGLER, W. B., and PETERSON, J. J., 1950, Geology of Atlantic Coastal Plain in New Jersey, Delaware, Maryland, and Virginia: Am. Assoc. Petroleum Geologists Bull., v. 34, p. 1-99

22 The Neogene Period

PHYSICAL HISTORY OF THE NEOGENE

The definition of the Neogene is based on the stratigraphic sections exposed in the Paris basin of France. A major unconformity is found there between the earlier Cenozoic sequence, including the Oligocene Series, and the overlying Miocene Series. The beginning of the Neogene in the type section is marked by the initiation of a widespread submergence of parts of Europe. With this transgressing sea we begin the last major period of earth history. This last period is 28 million years long up to the present time, and thus is much shorter than many of the preceding periods, some of which were three times as long. Nevertheless, Neogene strata are more widespread than are those of any other system within the United States. Since we are so close in time to the events of this period it is not surprising that we know the details of the events of this last period better than those of any of the preceding periods. More of the rock units formed during this time are still present, and many of the events are still in progress. You have become familiar with many parts of the history of the Neogene through your studies of physical geology, for most of the features you learned about were formed in the last 20 or 30 million years.

The Neogene marks the emergence of the modern world physiographically, structurally, and in terms of its animal and plant life. Every feature of the landscape you see about you and in fact every landscape in the world has been etched into its present form within the Neogene. There is not a river, plain, or mountain anywhere which is known definitely to be a hangover from the Paleogene. Certainly many of the structural features such as folds and faults in mountain systems were formed long ago, but they have only come to have surface expression during this last period. Some of the most notable features that have developed in this period are the Great Lakes, the Mississippi River, the Grand Canyon. The present continental borders, the mountains in the Appalachians, Rockies, Sierra Nevada, and those along the western coast have all been uplifted as have the Alps and the Himalayas, and masses of ice have accumulated in the high latitudes.

The Atlantic and Gulf Coastal Plains

The Appalachian Highlands. This area has been warped upward during the Neogene. These epeirogenic uplifts have been accompanied and followed by long periods of weathering and erosion during which the present topography of the region has been etched out. To the east and south of these highlands the Coastal Plain has been the site of deposition. The patterns of submergence and deposition that started earlier in the Cenozoic continue through the Neogene. Marine waters have occupied the Coastal Plain from Cape Cod almost continuously along the eastern coast to the tip end of Texas. No late Tertiary deposits, post-Eocene, occur north of Delaware. It may well be that this part of the coast started to become emergent shortly after the Miocene, while southward the coasts were covered by Pliocene seas. The Florida platform has been almost entirely beneath water a number of times during this period, but it has continued to be relatively near sea level as it is today.

Gulf. Along the Gulf Coast we find a continuation of the same patterns of deposition that started in the early Cenozoic. The Gulf Coast geosyncline, the axis of which runs about east-west near the present coast, has continued to become more depressed. A thick wedge of shallow-water marine sediments has been laid down in this trough. These wedges all thicken toward the south out under the continental shelf of the Gulf. Salt domes continue to rise through this mass of sediment.

Western United States

Great Plains and Rockies. The Laramide orogeny, during which the Rocky Mountains were uplifted, died out by the end of the Eocene. This was followed by a long period of erosion in the early Cenozoic. During the Neogene the Rockies have been warped upward again. This time the deformation has not been orogenic but consisted of renewed gentle uplift, warping, and displacement along old faults. As these uplifts have taken place, the mountains have continued to be eroded. Massive sheets of terrigenous debris eroded from the uplifted and upwarped blocks have filled the intermontane basins and spread as large sheets across the Great Plains. Uplift has continued into the Pleistocene, the last 2 million years. It is during this time that many of the highest peaks such as the Tetons and Cascades have been uplifted to such spectacular heights.

The Basin and Range Province. This is a physiographic province located west of the Rocky Mountains. This area occupies much of Nevada, Arizona, New Mexico, and southern California. Within it the topography consists essentially of large uplifted mountain blocks separated by down-dropped graben-like basins. Much of the faulting that has broken up this region and given it its present characteristics has taken place in the Neogene. The uplifted blocks become sources of sediment that is washed out into the adjacent basins where it is deposited as alluvial fans. Now we find that many of the basins contain saline sediments such as those deposited in the playa lakes.

Colorado Plateau. This large, almost square block of the earth's crust has been uplifted to its present elevation about a mile above sea level largely during the Neogene. During this same time the Colorado River has become entrenched in the nearly horizontal sedimentary sequences of the plateau and has cut down to form the Grand Canyon.

West Coast. The greatest tectonic activity of the Neogene has been concentrated along the western coast of the United States. About the middle of the Miocene Epoch orogenic deformation began in California. This strong folding and faulting created many local basins. Many of them have subsided very deeply, collecting many tens of thousands of feet of sediments. Later in the Pleistocene another strong pulse of this orogeny folded and faulted the ranges again. This deformation is known as the Cascadian revolution. During it the Cascade Mountains have been folded and upfaulted, and the Sierra Nevada has been tilted and uplifted again along older faults.

In the northwest the most spectacular event has been volcanic activity. The Columbia River basalt flows poured out on the surface inundating large parts of Washington, Oregon, and Idaho with several thousand feet of lava. These flows issued from long fissures that opened during the Miocene, and an estimated 35,000 cubic miles of basalt was erupted. Contemporaneously with the outpourings there was warping and faulting of the region.

Northern United States

Pleistocene glaciation has dominated the Neocene history of Canada and the northern United States. During the great ice ages of the past 2 million years, continental ice sheets have covered most of Canada and large parts of the northern United States at five different times. These ice sheets apparently were initiated in central eastern Canada. They grew to be several thousand feet thick and spread outward, pushing debris before them. The scouring and deposition by these ice sheets have given rise to the Great Lakes; the position of these sheets has determined the paths of the Missouri and Ohio Rivers, and in fact fashioned the entire drainage pattern of the northern United States. The deposits from these sheets cover large sections of the northern states. When the ice sheets melted the waters drained off, leaving large lakes near the ice margins and in the basins of the Northern Rockies and Central Rockies. Great Salt Lake is a remnant of one of these great lakes, called Lake Bonneville. Remnants of mountain glaciers still hang in the higher valleys of part of the Rockies. These are mere vestiges of the former masses of ice that carved out some of the most spectacular mountain scenery in the world. The Mississippi Valley is largely covered by deposits of loess dropped by winds that blew off the ice sheets and picked up small dust and silt-sized particles of finely ground rock produced by scouring action of glaciers. The Pleistocene glaciers have been so extensive and thick that they must have affected sea level throughout the world. Various estimates have been made of just how much sea level was lowered during the maximum periods of glaciation. It is entirely probable that the lowering amounted to as much as several hundred feet. There is still enough ice on the continents to raise sea level at least 70 feet if the ice should melt.

We live in the Pleistocene Period. To be sure, the ice sheets are greatly restricted at present compared with their maximum advances, but there have been a number of other warm interglacial periods as well. We very likely live in one such interglacial stage.

GULF OF MEXICO GEOSYNCLINE

The Cenozoic history of the Gulf of Mexico and the surrounding coastal plains is of particular interest for two reasons:

1. The deposits have become the sites for the accumulation of vast stores of petroleum. This is one of the most prolific oil-producing areas of North America.
2. The Gulf is the site of a modern-day geosynclinal accumulation of sediments.

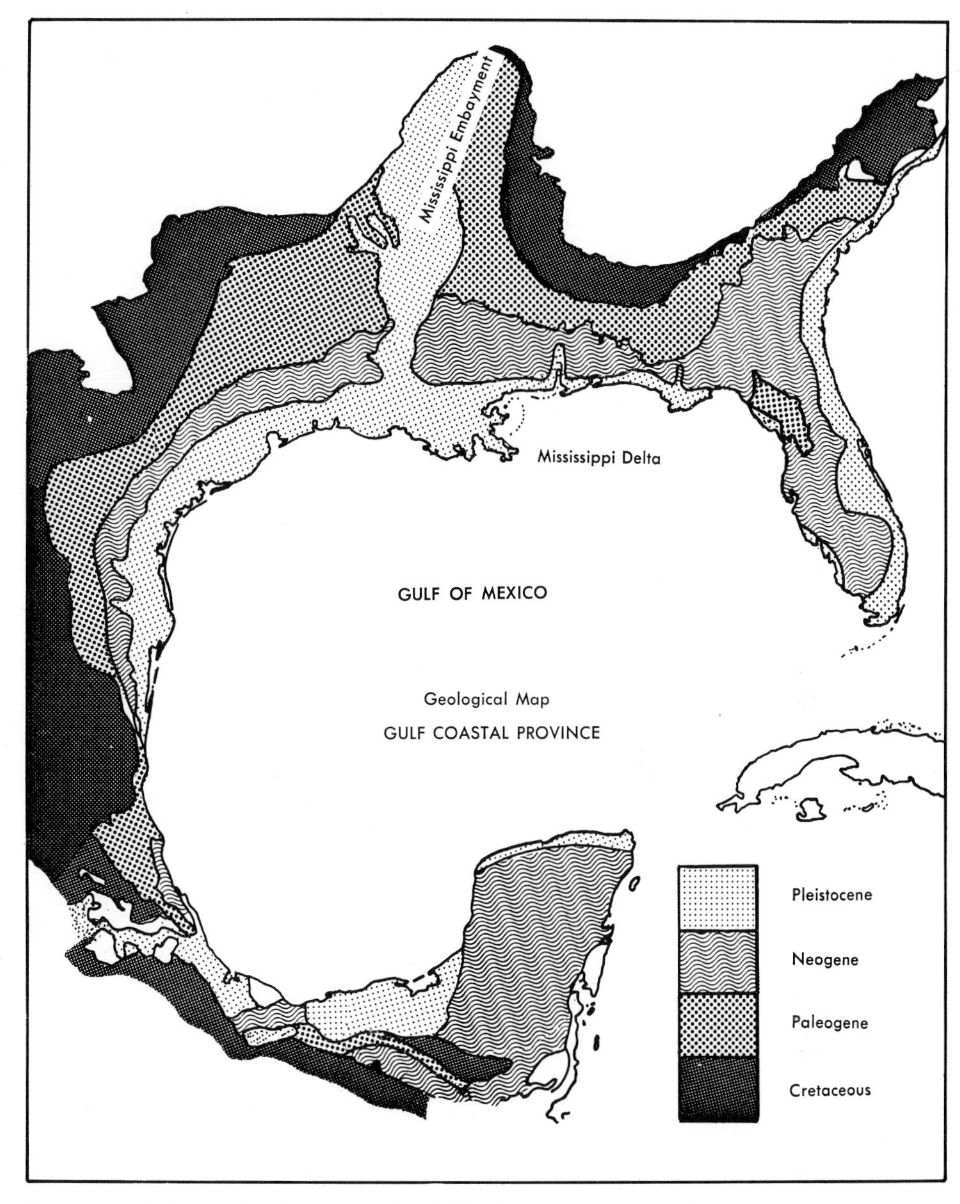

Fig. 22-1. Geologic sketch map of the Gulf of Mexico coastal plains in the United States, Mexico, and Latin America. (After the Geological Map of North America.)

The pattern of sediment distribution and the structures of the Gulf are relatively simple, Fig. 22-1. The outcrop pattern of the coastal province reveals a sequence of Mesozoic, Paleogene, and Neogene sediments exposed in successive belts. Progressively younger beds are exposed toward the coast. These sediments all dip toward the Gulf, and most of them are clastic wedges that thicken toward the Gulf. Seas transgressed the continental borders near the beginning of the Cenozoic, and since that time the broad pattern of deposition is that of a regressing sea.

The most important feature of the history of the Gulf is the development of the Gulf Coast geosyncline during the Cenozoic. The axis of this deeply subsiding belt trends almost east-west and extends parallel to the edge

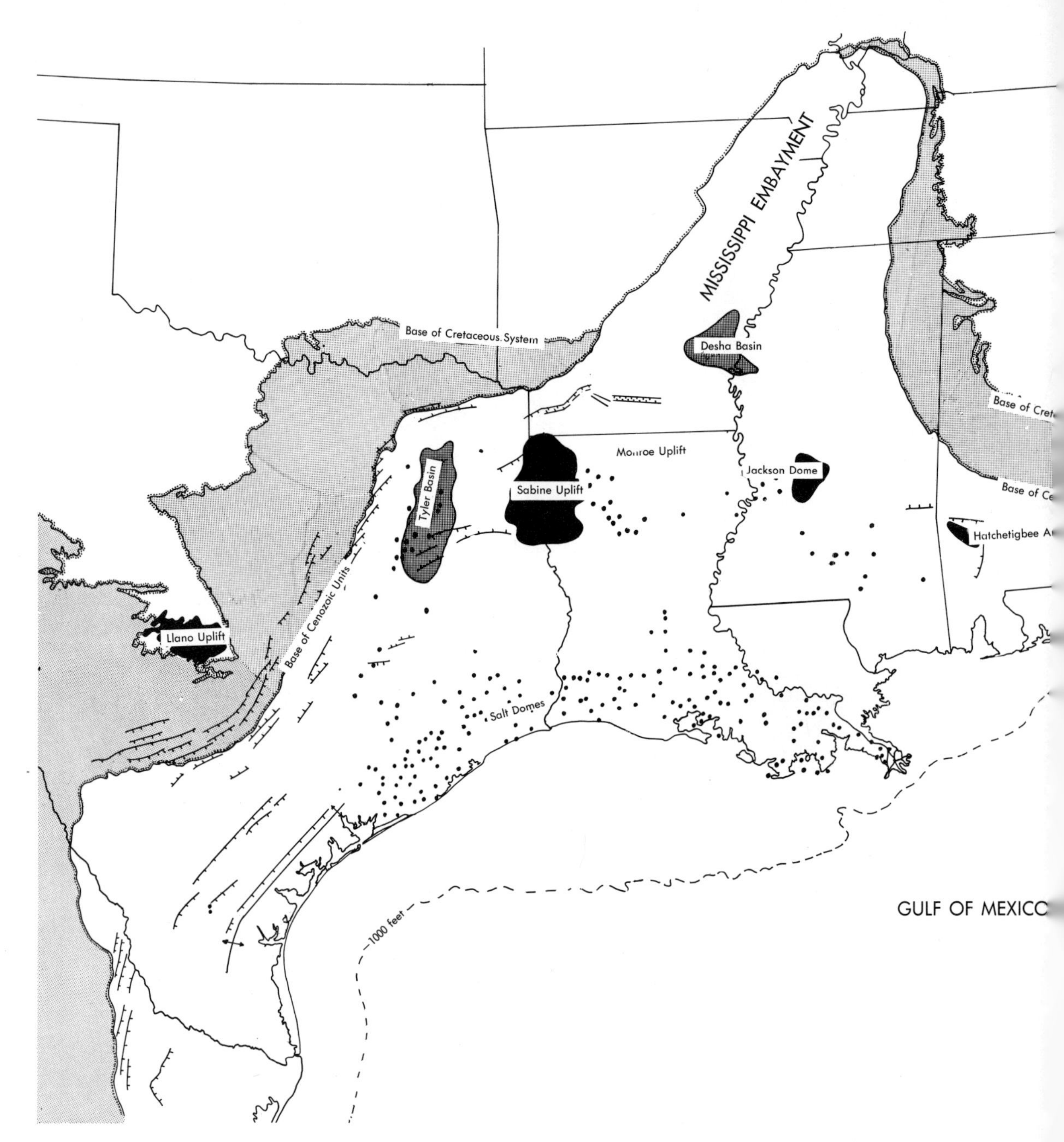

Fig. 22-2. Tectonic sketch map of the Gulf Coast. (From the Tectonic Map of North America.)

of the continental shelf along the northern side of the Gulf. Parts of the section in this geosyncline are well known from deep drilling in exploration for oil, and geophysical studies have provided information about the deeper portions within the crust. In general the Cenozoic sediments of this region change from dominantly nonmarine sands and shales to marine facies toward the axis of the geosyncline. Among the most prominent of these are the deltaic deposits of the Mississippi River. These and other older deltaic deposits are lens-shaped bodies that thin both toward the continent and toward the deeper parts of the Gulf. In cross section the entire sedimentary sequence in the Gulf geosyncline is lens-shaped. The units thin

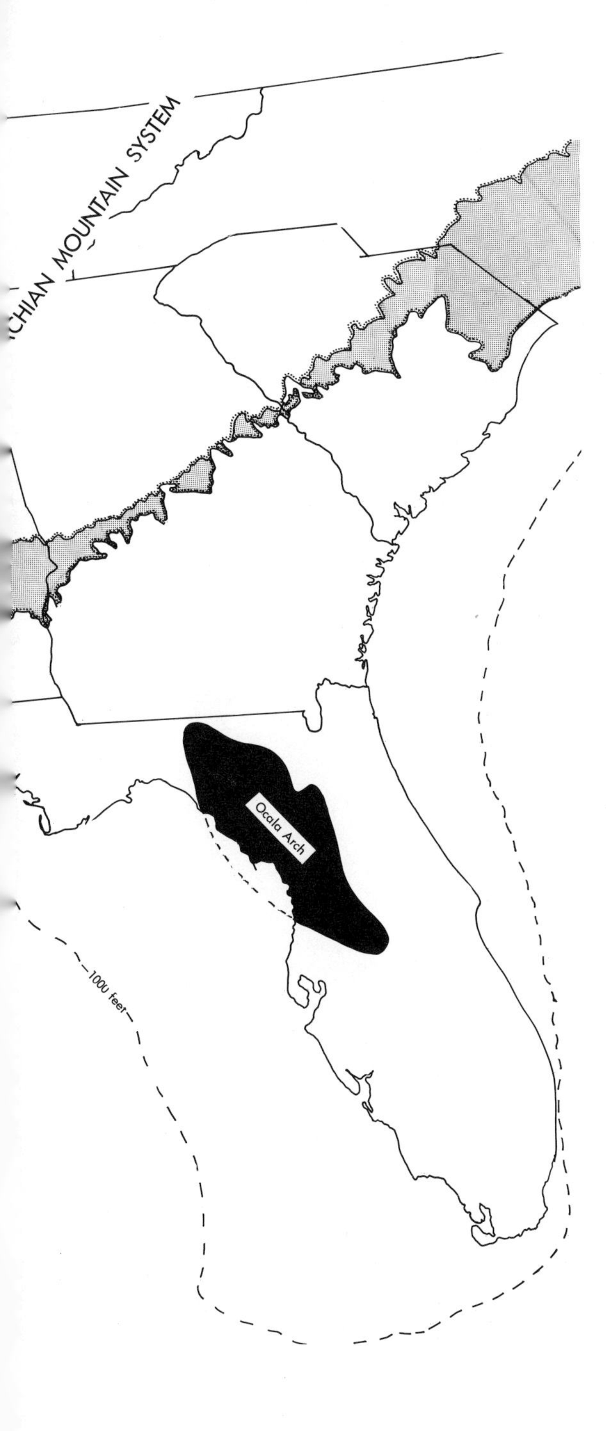

to the north and thicken southward to the edge of the shelf. Then they thin out again to the south. The deepest subsidence has taken place from the northern coast out to the edge of the continental shelf. The Neogene sediments alone in this region reach to a depth of about 35,000 feet. Paleogene sediments are an additional 10,000 feet or more thick, making the deepest subsidence during the Cenozoic equal to about 45,000 feet. One trend that is apparent from the history of the development of the geosyncline is that the position of greatest accumulation of sediments has tended to shift toward the Gulf.

Beyond the axis of this structure the units begin to thin out again toward the middle of the Gulf. The center of the Gulf is the deepest part, known as the Sigsbee Deep. It is an abyssal plain at approximately 12,000 feet depth. Below this plain the top of the Mesozoic section is buried about 10,000 feet, and the crystalline basement, which is presumably Paleozoic, is at a depth of nearly 32,000 feet.

Very little is known about the section on the southern side of the Gulf. We do know that the sea floor rises sharply from the Sigsbee Deep up to the continental shelf and that there is approximately 4500 feet of sediment between the surface and the top of the Cretaceous rocks. Another 3500 feet brings us to the top of the crystalline basement. Thus the southern side of the Gulf is nothing like the northern side. On the southern side there is apparently a large fault along which the Gulf has been dropped downward relative to the continent.

Oil in the Gulf Coast has been concentrated in a variety of structures. The salt domes are one of the most notable of these features. In addition there are major fault zones that parallel the outcrop patterns. Most of these zones are located inland 200 or even 300 miles from the coast. The faults in these zones are all normal faults in which the Gulf side has moved down relative to the continental masses around the Gulf. Other notable structures are nonorogenic folds, domes, and basins. Many of these trend almost perpendicular to the coast.

The lower part of the Mississippi River valley and the delta of the river have all undergone considerable change during the Neogene. When the Mississippi embayment was covered by the Neogene seas the Mississippi flowed into the Gulf not far south of the present position of St. Louis. At that time the Ohio River flowed in a distinctly different channel into the Gulf. As the seas retreated, drainage

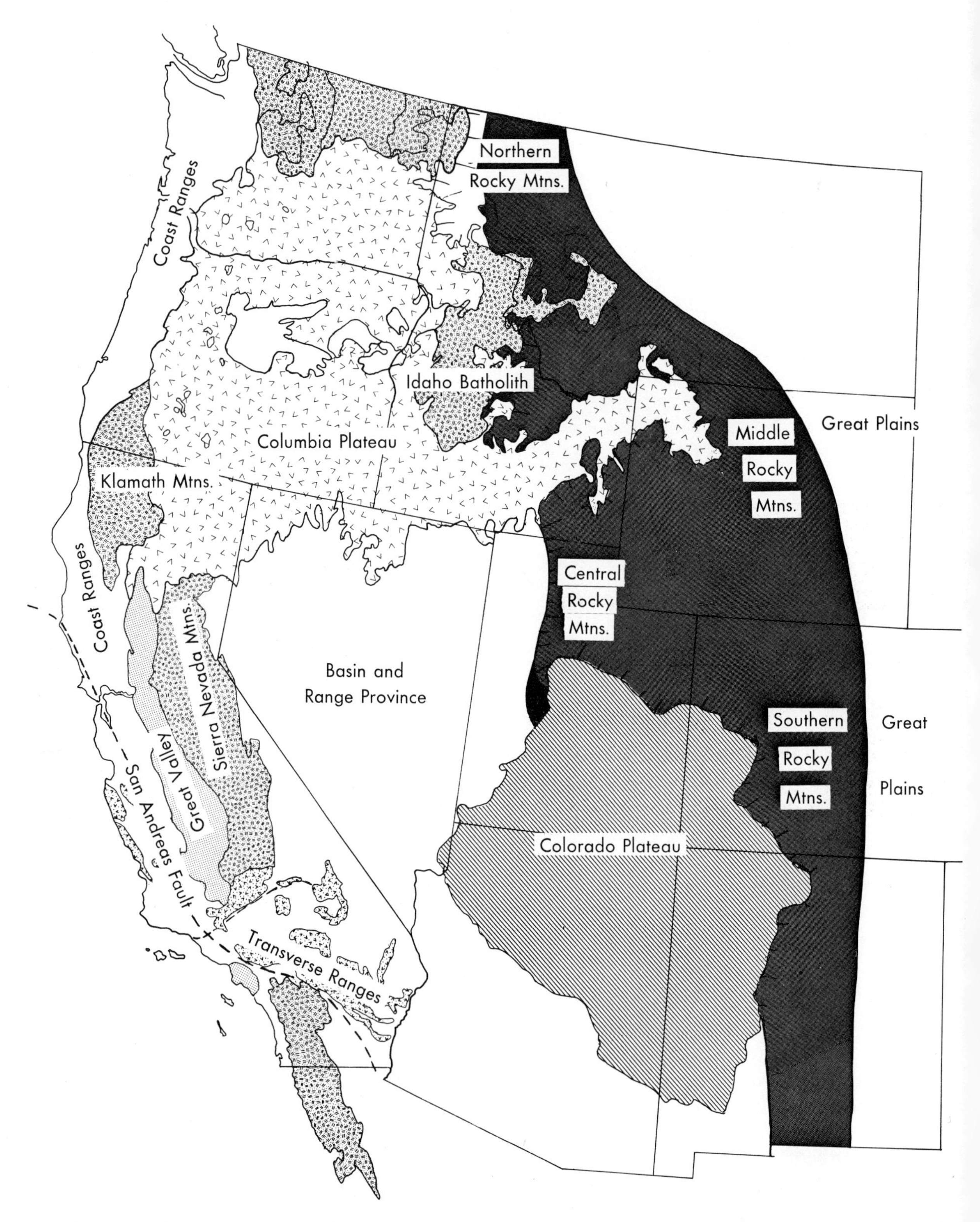

Fig. 22-3. Sketch map of the geologic provinces of the western United States. See the text for descriptions of the Cenozoic history of each.

shifts took place which brought the rivers into their present configuration. During the Pleistocene the changes in sea level that accompanied the development and wastage of continental glaciers affected coastal plains all over the world. When the sea level was lowered the Mississippi's gradient was steepened near the coast. This led to downcutting until a new gradient was established. Then a river terrace was cut by lateral planation. When the ice sheets began to melt and the sea level rose, these earlier valleys tended to become filled with sediment. Thus with each advance and retreat of the ice sheets the lower Mississippi Valley underwent periods of cutting and filling. Terraces which correspond to each of the stages of the Pleistocene glaciation can be recognized in the valley. The nature of the Mississippi delta has already been discussed (see "Environments of Deposition").

CENOZOIC HISTORY OF THE WESTERN UNITED STATES

The Cenozoic has been a time of great change and crustal activity in the western parts of the United States. As in all other parts of the country, the topography we see there now has been formed in this period, but the changes there have been even more dramatic and far reaching than those of other parts of the country. The Cenozoic has been a time of orogeny and volcanic activity in the west. The deformation is still in progress, and the freshness of the lava flows in many places makes it seem probable that volcanism stopped only recently.

For the student who is unfamiliar with the physical geography of this vast area it will be helpful to study the map in Fig. 22-3 carefully. The region can be subdivided into a number of large provinces each of which we will consider as a unit. These are:

1. The Coast Ranges.
2. The valleys and basins: San Joaquin, Ventura, Los Angeles, and Sacramento.
3. Cascade Mountains.
4. Columbia Plateau.
5. Klamath Mountains.
6. Sierra Nevada.
7. Basin and Range province.

East of these units we find the Colorado Plateau in the south and the folded belts of the Laramide orogeny in the north.

Coast ranges

This group of mountains bounds the western coast of the United States. They contain thick sections of deformed Cenozoic sediments. These sediments rest on several types of basement rocks. In places we find the highly altered intruded and metamorphosed rocks of the eugeosynclinal belt of the Nevadan orogeny. These are now solid crystalline rocks. They date back to the Jurassic Period. Where younger sediments lie on them the younger rocks have been relatively undeformed. These crystalline rocks compose the Sierra Nevada and Klamath Mountains, and make up the Transverse and Peninsular Ranges south of Los Angeles.

In other places the basement rocks are

Fig. 22-4. Relief map of the Coast Ranges north and south of San Francisco. (Maps by the U.S. Army Map Service. Photo by E. W. Spencer.)

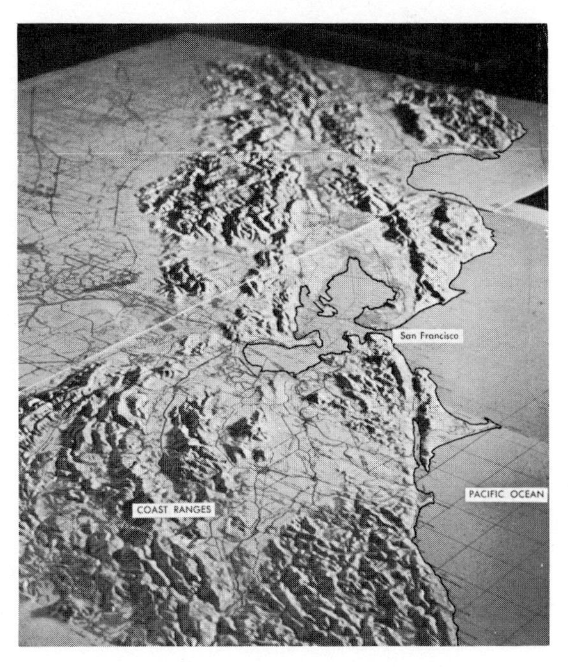

parts of a group of formations known as the Franciscan group. The units of this group are highly deformed. They include graywackes, shales, cherts and limestone lenses, and interbedded basaltic lava flows. This eugeosynclinal accumulation has been cut by serpentine intrusions and partially metamorphosed to a schist. Such a sequence is unfossiliferous in many places, and this has been one of the major problems in determining the age of the Franciscan group; however, it is certainly pre-Cenozoic.

During the Cenozoic thick sedimentary sections have been deposited over at least parts of these basements, and these have been deformed almost continuously. The sections contain many angular unconformities, particularly near the margins of the subsiding basins. There appear to be two major periods during which deformation has been stronger than at other times. These were during the middle of the Miocene and about the middle of the Pleistocene. During the first of these many of the major folds were formed, and during the latter most of the region was brought above sea level.

California basins

A number of basins in California are closely associated with the Coast Range deformation. These include the Great Valley of

Fig. 22-5. Relief map of the southern California region with the major physiographic and structural features outlined. (Maps by the U.S. Army Map Service. Photo by E. W. Spencer.)

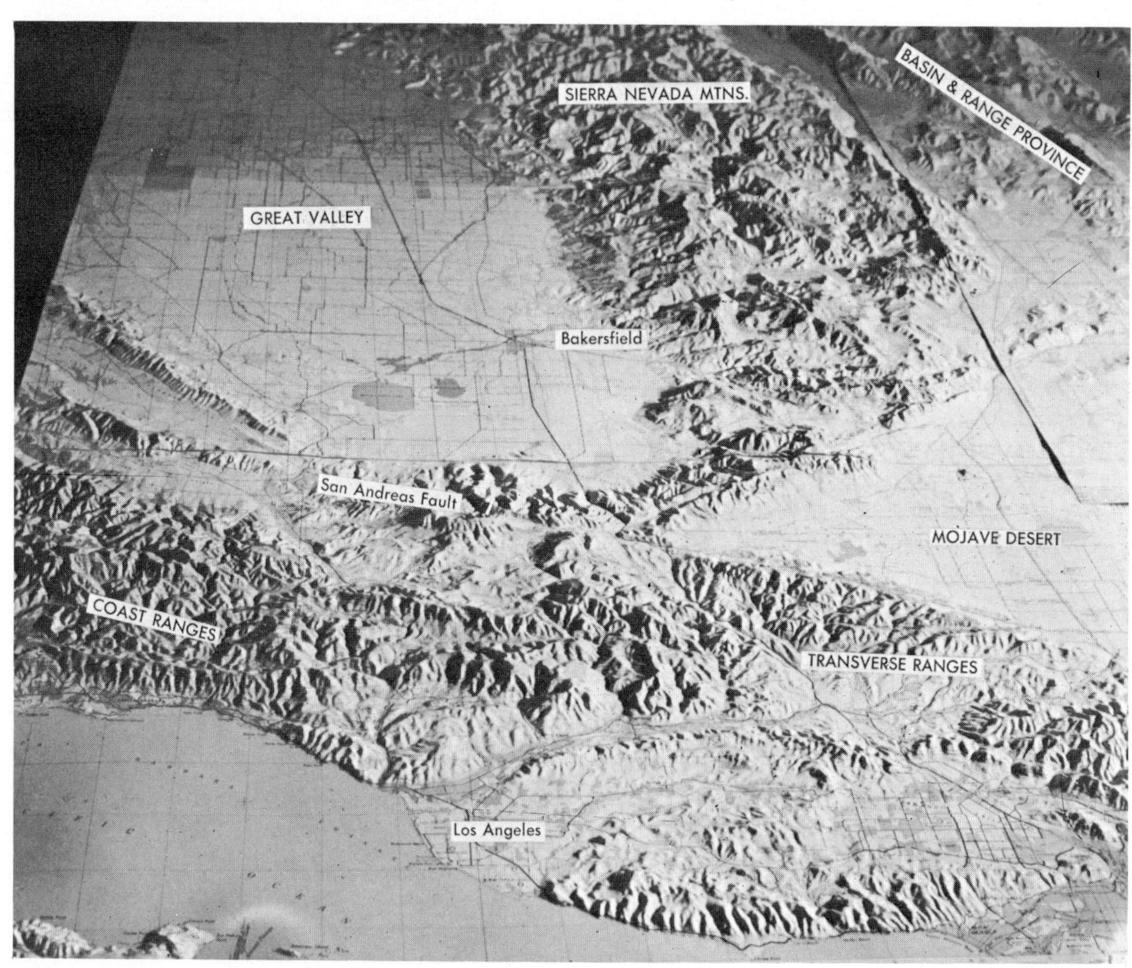

Fig. 22-6. Mt. Hood. This mountain is one of the Neogene volcanos which stand upon the axis of the Cascade Range. (Photo by E. W. Spencer.)

California and the Los Angeles and Ventura basins. The history of these basins is not identical in detail, but there are certain similarities in all of them. They have been rapidly deepened during the Neogene and filled with vast quantities of sediment in the Pliocene and Pleistocene epochs. In the Los Angeles basin these amount to about 40,000 feet of marine deposits, in the Ventura there is nearly 35,000 feet, and in the San Joaquin there is about 20,000 feet of marine clays, shales, and sand in the Miocene and Pliocene series, and an additional 9,000 feet of nonmarine deposits of Pleistocene age. The trend in the sedimentation within these basins has been toward deposition in progressively shallower water. As already mentioned, these sequences contain many unconformities, particularly near the margins of the basins. In the mid-Pleistocene, however, they were steeply folded, and upper Pleistocene units are nearly flat across the upturned edges of the older units.

Faulting. Every student of geology is familiar with the San Andreas rift fault by the time he studies historical geology. This fault is one of a system that strikes northwestward along the coast. The movement along it is strike-slip, with the oceanward side moving northward relative to the continental mass. This and the system of faults that cuts across southern California have made possible the shifting of blocks of the crystalline basement, such as those in the Transverse and Peninsular Ranges and the Sierra Nevada, northward along the faults. It is possible to estimate the position of the two sides of this fault system at various times in the past by reconstructing the strand lines of the period, shifting the blocks back to a position at which the strand may be traced continuously across the fault. A 65-mile shift is necessary to re-establish the position of the two sides near the end of the Miocene Epoch. The total displacement may amount to something over 300 miles.

Fig. 22-7. Air view of basaltic lavas and intrusions in the Dalles along the Washington-Oregon state line. (U.S. Air Force photo.)

Cascade range

The Cascade Mountains start near the northern border of California between the Klamath Mountains and the Sierra Nevada. They extend northward as a narrow belt through Oregon and Washington into Canada. The range is separated from the Coast Ranges by a large synclinal valley. This range, which is famous for its beautiful high and rugged mountain peaks, is composed almost entirely of volcanic rocks. An estimated volume of 25,000 cubic miles is postulated for the range. In the northern part of the belt the Neogene volcanic rocks are situated on a basement that is composed of the crystalline rocks of the Nevadan orogenic belt, but southward we find only a thick sequence of Paleogene and Neogene igneous intrusives and extrusives. These include breccias, tuffs, mudflows, and andesite lavas. The age of these extends over a large part of Cenozoic history, and most seem to be contemporaneous with the Columbia River basalts that lie east of this belt, Eocene to Pliocene in age. The main differences in the two provinces are found in the quantity of volcanic rocks, their composition, and the amounts of intruded material. The Cascades are an unlifted belt that has been the site of excessive volcanic activity. The lavas of the Columbia Plateau are very uniform. They are basalts that contain no olivine. The intrusions and extrusions of the Cascade Range are highly varied in composition. They include andesites and granodiorite intrusives. These might be formed by partial melting of the lower part of the continental crust. They contain sialic material, in contrast to the Columbia Plateau basalts.

During the last stages of the Pleistocene, the activity in the Cascades has been the extrusion of great quantities of lava flows and ash and the construction of a series of large composite cones along the range. These cones include such peaks as Mt. Baker, Mt. Hood, Mt. Lassen, Mt. Shasta, Mt. Washington, Mt. Jefferson, and Mt. Mazama. The last of these, Mt. Mazama, exploded, blowing the top of the mountain off. Other parts of it subsided to form a caldera in which Crater Lake is found.

Columbia Plateau

Directly east of the Cascade Mountains we pass into the Columbia Plateau. This province includes most of southeast Washington, eastern Oregon, and parts of northern California and Idaho. The region has been the site of volcanic activity during most of the Cenozoic. The first outpourings of lava began in the Paleogene in the westernmost parts of the region. These older lavas are largely covered by later flows and deposits. The main flood of basalt came in the Miocene Epoch. These flows cover about 100,000 square miles with an estimated 35,000 cubic miles of basalt. There are many flows, one on the other, aggregating thicknesses of as much as 5,000 feet in places where the entire sequence is exposed. Some of the individual flows are several hundred feet thick. All of the flows are of nearly the same composition. They contain no olivine.

Fig. 22-8. Deformation within the Columbia River basalts along the Dalles. Notice the folding and faulting. This is related to the deformations which affected the Basin and Range Province. (Photo by E. W. Spencer.)

Fig. 22-9. Volcanic agglomerates exposed east of Yellowstone Park. These are part of the Cenozoic volcanics which make up the Absaroka Mountains of Montana. (Photo by E. W. Spencer.)

The Miocene eruptions came from a number of large fissures located in southeastern Washington and northeastern Oregon from which the lavas poured out. The lava must have been very fluid, for the individual flows can be traced over great distances, and tops of individual flows are nearly flat over large areas. As this tremendous quantity of lava poured out on the surface, the surface became warped downward into the vacated space below. This has created a basin-shaped regional structure.

Activity continued into the Pliocene and Pleistocene. During these epochs, flows poured forth in the eastern part of the province, covering the Snake River plain and the region in and around Yellowstone Park. In general we may say that the province is a plateau; however, parts of it are folded and faulted. In the southeastern edge there are broad warps and folds that parallel the direction of Jurassic deformation. Along the southern edge the margins are involved in the faulting of the Basin and Range province.

Basin and Range province

This physiographic province is characterized by large, high mountain ranges that are separated by broad, nearly flat basins. Such topography is found in a wide belt from southern Oregon, covering all of Nevada and parts of Utah, Arizona, New Mexico, southern California, and Mexico. Almost all of this region is arid or semiarid. Included in the province is the Great Basin. This is a large area of internal drainage — that is, there are no rivers flowing out of it into the ocean. Rainfall is sparse since most of it falls in the ranges along the western coast before it reaches this region.

Before the Neogene Period, this region had been eroded down to a broad low surface. This erosion followed the Nevadan orogeny, which had so strongly deformed the geosynclinal accumulations of the Paleozoic and Mesozoic eras. Similar erosion surfaces were produced farther east over the region that had been uplifted in the Laramide orogeny to form the Rocky Mountains. We get some idea of the elevation of the region from the fossil flora. Fossils of deciduous trees have been found in Miocene sediments at an elevation of 9000 feet on the sides of the Sierra Nevada. These plants would not grow at elevations above 2500 feet, so this represents a maximum elevation for the highest of the ranges of this province at the beginning of the Neogene.

Early in the Neogene Period lavas and tuffs were erupted and flowed out across the western and northern parts of the province. This was the period in which so much volcanic activity took place in the Cascades and the Columbia Plateau. Following this volcanism, faulting and tilting of some of the blocks began. The Sierra Nevada began to be tilted up and may have risen several thousand feet at this time. One reason for believing this is the presence in the region of a Pliocene flora that now characterizes savannas and grasslands. These assemblages grow where the rainfall is on the order of 15 inches per year. Thus, by Pliocene time, the ranges had risen high enough to intercept a large part of the moisture that comes inland from the ocean.

Fig. 22-10. A mountain range of the Basin and Range province. The mountain peaks rise sharply above the gently sloping alluvial fans at the base. Many such ranges have bordering high angle faults along which they have been uplifted. The flat surfaces extending out into the basins are pediments close to the mountains. Internal drainage characterized this region; playa lakes are often found in the center of the basins. This view is in southern Nevada. (Photo by E. W. Spencer.)

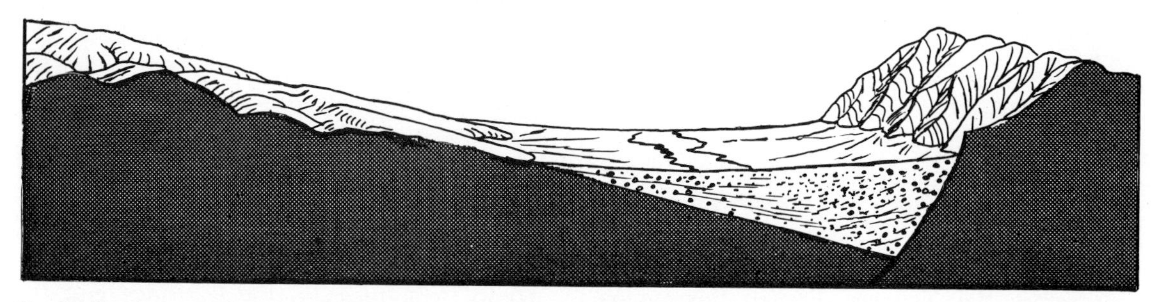

Fig. 22-11. Cross section of a typical basin and range within the Basin and Range province. Not all of the ranges are faulted. Some are folded or the result of differential erosion. (After P. B. King.)

During the Pliocene and Pleistocene, block faulting continued and accentuated the topographic relief as block mountains were uplifted relative to the adjacent basins. Some of these basins moved downward. Death Valley is one such example. Here we find sediments that were of marine origin depressed over 200 feet below sea level. The faulting of these later Neogene epochs has been normal, creating graben and horst structures. Although the topographic expression is the same throughout the province, the topography does not reflect similarity of structures that existed before the faulting occurred. At least three very different

Fig. 22-12. Model of part of the Basin and Range province. This view is looking southward from over the Sierra Nevada Mountains. The large scarp along the eastern margin of the Sierras is a fault along which the range has been tilted upward. Notice how flat the valley floors are. Death Valley is at the left. (U.S. Army Map Service. Photo by E. W. Spencer.)

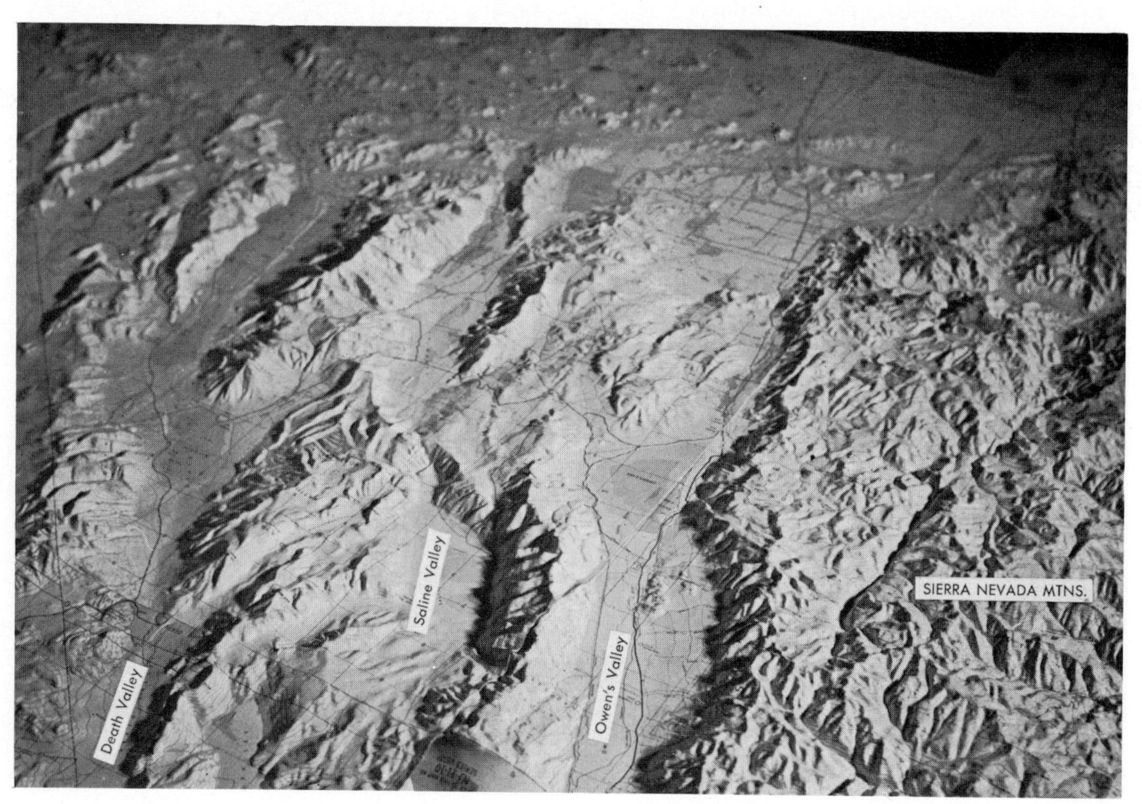

types of older structures are found in the block mountains:

a. Those that were part of the geosynclinal accumulation that was deformed in the Nevadan orogeny.
b. Those deposits that were laid down on the continental shelf and were only slightly deformed. These are found in New Mexico.
c. Those that are part of the Columbia Plateau province.

The margins of many of the ranges in the Basin and Range province are faults. In some places recent faulting has produced very fresh scarps. Along a few ranges the old structures parallel the mountain sides, and may have simply become etched out by erosion following the general unwarping of the region that had occurred during the Neogene. Still other ranges are bounded by scarps that most likely have been produced by retreat of the original fault scarp, as is typical of erosion in arid and semi-arid climates.

Fig. 22-13. The Grand Tetons of northwestern Wyoming. These mountains are one of the ranges of the Middle Rocky Mountains which have been uplifted along high angle faults. This side of the range rises very abruptly from Jackson Hole. The western slope of the range is gentle. Faulting movements during the Neogene have raised the block to its present height. It has been dissected in the Pleistocene. Note the river terrace in the alluvial fill of the basin. (Photo by E. W. Spencer.)

NEOGENE EROSION OF THE ROCKIES AND THE APPALACHIANS

The topography of these two mountain systems has evolved in Neogene time. Geomorphologists now tell us that from 20 to 25 million years would be sufficient for the processes of gradation to reduce the continents of the world to an almost featureless plain close to sea level. Obviously then the 28 million years of the Neogene would have been sufficient time if there had been no uplift within this time. The structural features we find exposed in the Appalachian Mountains date back at least to the Appalachian revolution at the end of the Paleozoic. Those in the Rockies date back to near the close of the Mesozoic. However, within the Neogene, both of these mountain systems have been warped upward by epeirogenic deformation of the crust. It has been after these last uplifts that the present physiographic features came into existence. It has been during and after these last broad upwarps that the Colorado River has cut the Grand Canyon to its present depth and the Arkansas and Gunnison Rivers have cut their spectacular canyons at the Royal Gorge and at the Black Canyon. Both of these are almost 1500 feet deep in places. In the Appalachians the Delaware, James, Susquehanna, and other rivers have cut water gaps through the folded belts of the Valley and Ridge province in this time.

As you will remember from your study of physical geology, there are conflicting opinions about the evolution of land forms where running water and mass movement are the dominant processes, as is the case in these two regions. One of these conflicts concerns the relative importance of peneplanation and pediplanation. According to the adherents of the peneplane hypothesis the land can eventually be worn to an almost flat surface as a result of running water. The supporters of pediplanation maintain that the landscape is reduced by

Fig. 22-14. Model of the Appalachians. This view is looking eastward across Pennsylvania from a position above the Delaware River. From this view the folds are apparent as is the fact that the ridges are at approximately the same elevations as are the valley floors. Water gaps are seen where the Delaware River crosses the resistant Paleozoic units which make up the ridges. (U.S. Army Map Service. Photo by E. W. Spencer.)

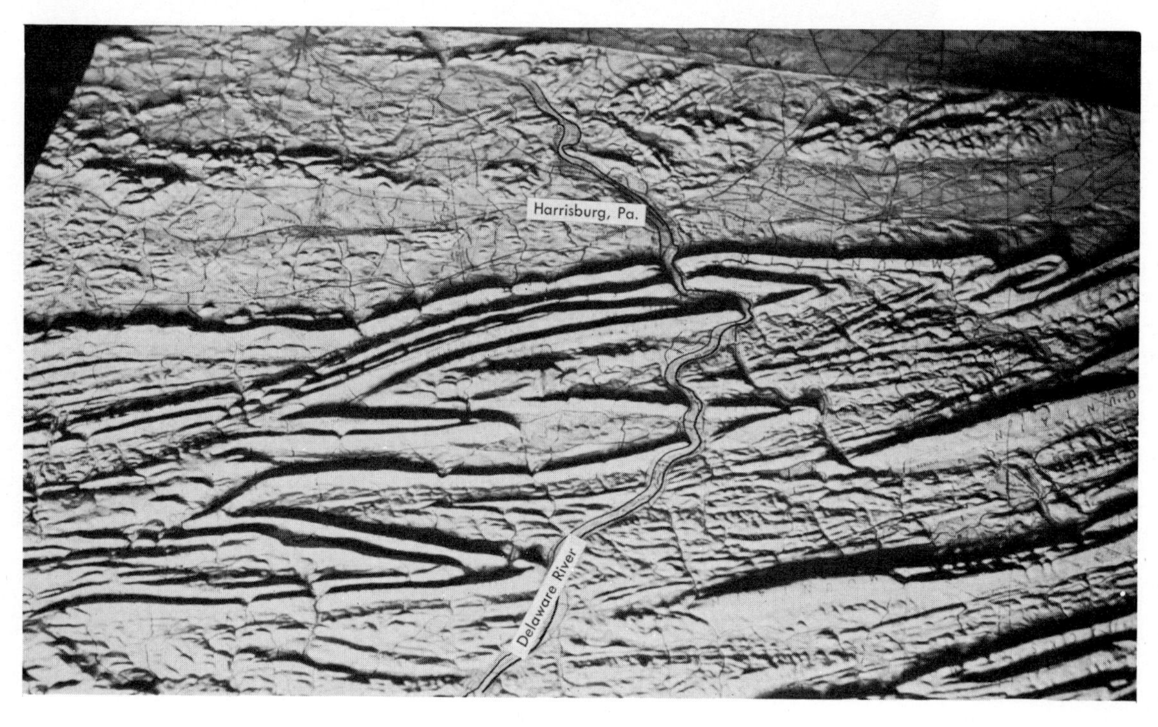

Fig. 22-15. Miocene plains mammals. This scene depicts some of the richly varied mammalian life of 25 million years ago on the Early Miocene plains of Nebraska. In the foreground is a group of piglike mammals. On the right are two Moropus, curious plant-eaters that had claws instead of hoofs. (Painting by Charles Knight, Chicago Natural History Museum.)

slope retreat and that the end form of this is a pediplane that has a slope adjusted to permit the transport of debris across it by sheet wash and streams. Most of the adherents of both of these points of view agree that there were broad, nearly featureless, erosion surfaces over both the Rockies and the Appalachians before the start of the Neogene Period. During the Neogene these erosion surfaces have been uplifted and dissected.

Appalachians

During the Neogene the greatest amount of uplift in the Appalachians has amounted to about 4000 feet. Early students of the Appalachian region were struck by the near coincidence in elevation of the tops of the resistant ridges that are so prominent in the Appalachians. This coincidence may well be because the ridges are remnants of an old erosion surface that predates the Neogene. It is generally known as the Schooley surface or peneplain. At lower levels through the region we find other striking coincidences of the tops of hills within the valleys. These have been called the Harrisburg erosion surface or Harrisburg peneplain. According to the theory of William Morris Davis this second erosion surface formed after the older erosion surface was warped upward and streams cut down and finally reduced the topography of the less resistant units to a second level. At least one other erosion surface is widely recognized in the region. Opponents to the peneplane concept point out that many of the hills that correspond to the theoretical Harrisburg surface are composed of chert and more resistant units than the lower land around them. This suggests that these may simply be erosion remnants, a product of differential erosion rather than remnants of a peneplane. In either case it is generally believed that the present topography has been developed during the Neogene and that present drainage patterns have been established either by superposition of streams on an older erosion surface that was uplifted or by headward erosion and stream piracy by streams that developed on the upwarped Appalachians.

Fig. 22-16. **Miocene plains mammals.** In the left background is a herd of long-necked camels. In front of them are some three-toed horses (Parahippus) and two-horned rhinos. (Painting by Charles Knight, Chicago Natural History Museum.)

Rocky Mountains

As in the Appalachians, we find several erosion surfaces in the Rocky Mountains. These surfaces have been only partially dissected, indicating that they must be relatively young. One of the most prominent of these is known as the Flattop erosion surface, which occurs at approximately 11,000 feet. Another even more striking surface is that which corresponds to the summits of the highest mountains in many areas of the Front Range of the Rockies. This highest surface is known as the Rocky Mountains peneplane. It is dated as Pliocene by projecting it onto the plains where it coincides with the contact between the Miocene and Pliocene series. Other surfaces have been described in the region, although none is as prominent as these two. Since these surfaces were warped upward erosion has etched out the present topography.

LIFE OF THE NEOGENE

The Neogene began about 28 million years ago. While this seems like a long time in terms of human history you should have come to

Fig. 22-17. **Pliocene rhinos and mastodonts.** Nine million years ago, in the Early Pliocene times, the mastodonts, relatives of the elephants, were recent immigrants to North America. In the center is one type characterized by tusks in both upper and lower jaws. The short-legged animal on the left was a swamp-dwelling rhino that lived on this continent. (Painting by Charles Knight, Chicago Natural History Museum.)

appreciate it as a relatively short amount of geological history. The last part of the Neogene is the present time. We live in this part of the Neogene, and the description of its fauna and flora is the rightful realm of the botanists and zoologists. We cannot attempt to describe the rich variety of living plants and organisms of the present. Very few of us will ever see more than a fraction of these forms although we spend most of our life among them. This last period of geologic time has been a time of modernization of life. At the start of it most of the modern genera were present, and the evolutionary changes have been on the species and subspecies levels. Nevertheless, some of the most important forms appeared for the first time. Of course, none of these is as important to us as the appearance of the first man. We now have reason to believe that manlike animals were present as long as 11 million years ago. These will be described later, however. Other notable new appearances were made:

1. Apelike animals first appeared in the Miocene Epoch.
2. Manlike apes appeared in the Pliocene Epoch.
3. Camels, giraffes, hyenas, mastodons, and many other modern mammals appeared for the first time during this period.

PEAKS AND ADVANCEMENT

1. Mammals dominate the animal life of the earth. During the early parts of the period, grazing animals advanced rapidly; the evolution of horses and other hoofed animals is among the best-documented part of the record. The abundance of grasses and cereals made these advances possible.
2. The plant life of the earth has been dominated by the angiosperms throughout the period.
3. Of the invertebrates the protozoans and mollusks have been most important.

Fig. 22-18. Fossil ant preserved since the Miocene near Florissant, Colorado. (By courtesy of the U.S. National Museum.)

REFERENCES

FENNEMAN, N. M., 1931, *Physiography of Western United States:* McGraw-Hill Book Company, Inc., New York, 534 p.

FISK, H. N., 1943, Summary of the geology of the lower alluvial valley of the Mississippi River: Mississippi River Commission, Vicksburg, 49 p.

GILLULY, JAMES, 1949, Distribution of mountain building in geologic time: Geol. Soc. America Bull., v. 60, p. 561-590

KING, P. B., 1959, *The Evolution of North America:* Princeton University Press, Princeton, 190 p.

MURRAY, G. E., 1947, Cenozoic deposits of central Gulf Coastal Plain: Am. Assoc. Petroleum Geologists Bull., v. 31, p. 657-672

23 The Pleistocene Epoch

At the mention of the ice ages most of us think of a period of time long removed in the past when cave men roamed the earth and large masses of ice covered most of the northern hemisphere. Actually we are now living in the ice ages, or Pleistocene Epoch. Certainly we are not now experiencing a period of maximum glacial advance, but even so about 10 per cent of the land area of the world is covered by ice. This ice is concentrated largely in the Antarctic Ice Sheet and in the Greenland Ice Sheet, with minor amounts in mountain glaciers distributed on every continent on earth. By comparison, the maximum land area covered by ice during any one advance of continental glaciers amounted to about 30 per cent of the land area of the world. The Pleistocene Epoch began with the formation of large ice sheets on the continents. This cooling caused changes to take place in the faunas and floras of the world. These faunal differences serve as a guide to the boundary between the Pleistocene and the Pliocene epochs. Thus, cooling climates and glaciation have been the diagnostic feature of this last period of time. The best indications available to us of the date of the start of the Pleistocene put it between 1 and 2 million years ago.

PHYSICAL HISTORY OF THE PLEISTOCENE

This epoch has been the time of the evolution of modern topography. As was pointed out earlier, every feature of the world's physiography is thought to be Neogene in age. Most of it formed during the latest epoch of the Neogene, the Pleistocene. We think of the Pleistocene as being a time dominated by ice sheets; however, two-thirds of the land area of the world was not covered by ice during this period. Volcanic activity and diastrophism as well as erosion and glaciation are important features of the history of the last 2 million years.

Volcanic activity

The present is a period of active volcanism. You will remember the distribution of volcanoes around the Pacific Ocean in what is known as a "ring of fire," and the activity within recorded time in the Mediterranean region and in the Caribbean Sea. Apparently there is less volcanic activity now in this most recent part of the Pleistocene than there was earlier. Within the last million years the belt from Alaska to northern California has been very active. Recent cones and flow are common in New Mexico, Arizona, Idaho, and over large parts of Mexico. Many of these could not have been exposed to erosion very long. They are composed of cinders and easily eroded materials that would not stand up many thousands of years without considerable alteration. Volcanoes have been active throughout the length of the Andes. Pleistocene volcanism has been prolific in the Mediterranean region, in East Africa and in Asia. And in Iceland and Spitsbergen we find lavas interbedded with the glacial drift.

Diastrophism

Attention has already been given to the diastrophic history of North America in the

Fig. 23-1. The origin of a mountain glacier as seen in this view of part of the White Mantle Range, Knight Inlet, British Columbia. (Photo by courtesy of the Royal Canadian Air Force.)

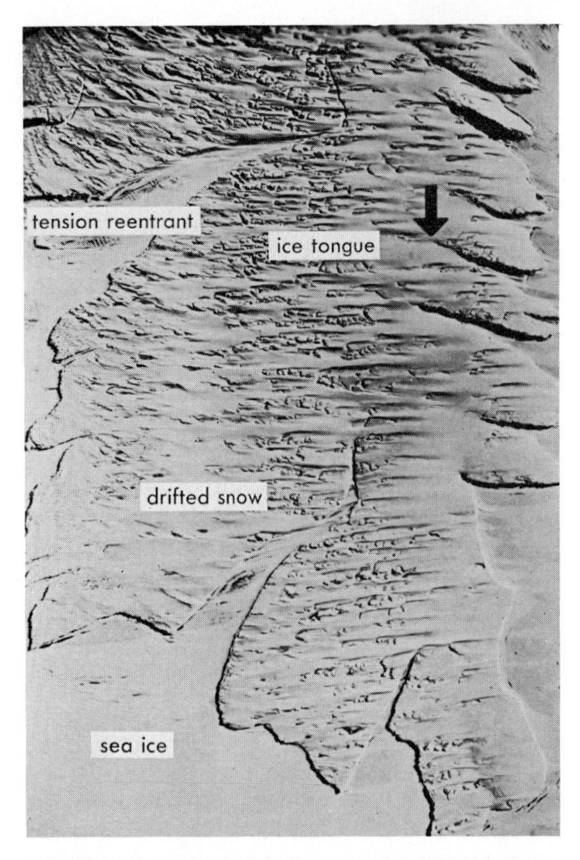

Fig. 23-2. A floating ice tongue extending for more than four miles to sea in the Antarctic. Some ice tongues are so long that they have been explored and named independently of their glacial roots. The apparently strong and constant local winds from the left have blown the snow into dunes. (Photo by courtesy of the U.S. Navy Dept.)

Neogene. However, it should be emphasized that upwarping and block faulting has occurred in the Pleistocene. It is for this reason that we find so many mountains still as high as they are today. The Tetons, Sierra Nevada, Central Rockies, and Northern Rockies have all been uplifted in the Pleistocene. In fact, almost the entire region of the Great Plains and the Appalachians has been warped upward during this time.

Glaciation

Huge ice sheets formed in both the Northern and Southern hemispheres and advanced across extensive areas of the world. The continental ice sheets formed in Canada and moved down over the northern border of the United States. There were several advances. At least four main stages can be recognized from the drift deposits left by them. Each is separated by an interglacial stage during which the ice sheets retreated, warmer conditions prevailed, old glacial deposits were eroded, and new soils developed before the next advance. Even the glacial advances can be subdivided into substages during which there were relatively minor changes in the positions of the sheets and deposits left by them. Among the most outstanding effects of these glacial advances have been:

1. Lowering of the level of the oceans, with each advance of the ice sheet, by as much as 400 feet. As a result of the fluctuations of sea level, terraces have been formed along continental borders, canyons have been cut across parts of the emergent continental shelves, and the gradients of streams flowing into the oceans have been shifted with the consequent development of stream terraces.
2. Derangement of drainage occurred with each advance and retreat. The drainage patterns of most of the major streams in the central part of the United States have been brought into their present positions since the last glacial advance.
3. Formation of the Great Lakes. These lakes are remnants of much more extensive and even larger lakes that were formed by glacial scouring and deposition of moraines.
4. Formation of periglacial lakes: Beyond the margins of the ice sheets, water that had drained off into low areas formed large and extensive lakes. Many of these developed in the Great Basin of the west where interior drainage held and prevented escape of the waters. As we have seen, Great Salt Lake is the remnant of one of these lakes. Many hundreds of others dotted the Basin and Range province during the Pleistocene.
5. Wind-blown deposits and loess, derived from the glacial deposits of the outwash

Fig. 23-3. Mt. Fuji, Japan. This is one of the physiographic features which has risen during the Pleistocene. It is typical of composite cones that have grown in many parts of the world in this last epoch of geologic time. Volcanic activity is one of the most important aspects of the Pleistocene history. Mt. Fuji is 12,400 feet high. (Photo by courtesy of the Japan Tourist Association.)

Fig. 23-4. The Tetons, one of many ranges in the United States which have been uplifted during the Pleistocene. No completely new mountain ranges have formed in this short epoch, but many of the older ones have been warped upward or uplifted along ancient faults. (Photo by courtesy of the Union Pacific Railroad.)

plains, cover most of the Mississippi Valley.

6. The development of some of our most beautiful scenery, for which glacial erosion by mountain glaciers has been responsible. The arêtes, horns, cols, and U-shaped valleys that now characterize most high mountain ranges formed during the Pleistocene. Topography over which the ice sheets moved tended to become suppressed and smoothed out.
7. Deposits from the ice sheets, from lakes formed near their margins and from the wind-blown deposits, lie on the surface over more than half of the area of the United States. Modern soils are developed in these materials.

Fig. 23-5. Cirques, U-shaped valleys, hanging valleys, and glacial lakes, all present in this view of the Beartooth Mountains, Montana. Remnants of the glaciers which carved these land forms are still found in the high cirques. (Photo by E. W. Spencer.)

In the following discussions we will be concerned with the history of the Pleistocene. You should review the processes of glacial erosion, transportation, deposition, and the cause of glaciation in your physical geology textbook.

UNRAVELING PLEISTOCENE GLACIAL HISTORY

In many ways our approach to unraveling the history of the Pleistocene is different from those techniques used for other periods and epochs. Pleistocene deposits are different in several important respects. First, they are generally well exposed, so that detailed analysis and mapping of Pleistocene units can be much more comprehensive than we can ordinarily hope for in dealing with older formations. The glacial deposits are fresh. They are not metamorphosed, and most of them have not even been consolidated into sedimentary rocks. They have been weathered and slightly eroded, but far less so than those of any other epoch. Among them are lake, stream, and all types of continental deposits that are only rarely found in the older systems.

As in all our studies, the law of superposition is of fundamental importance, but for so recent a time as the Pleistocene we find other relatively unused techniques available to us. Among these are the use of carbon-14 dating, which gives reliable results for the last 30,000 years at least. Pollen analysis, spore analysis, and varved clays have also played an important role in studies of the Pleistocene deposits.

Although there are more methods available for us to use in deciphering Pleistocene history, in many ways the problems we have to solve are more complex. Continental deposits are always more difficult to interpret than marine sediments because there is great variability within them, and they contain fewer fossils. The character of the sediment in a single exposure of drift often changes so abruptly that correlation over any distance by means of the lithology is virtually impossible. This problem is accentuated by the uneven and scattered distribution of glacial deposits. It is even difficult to apply the laws of superposition effec-

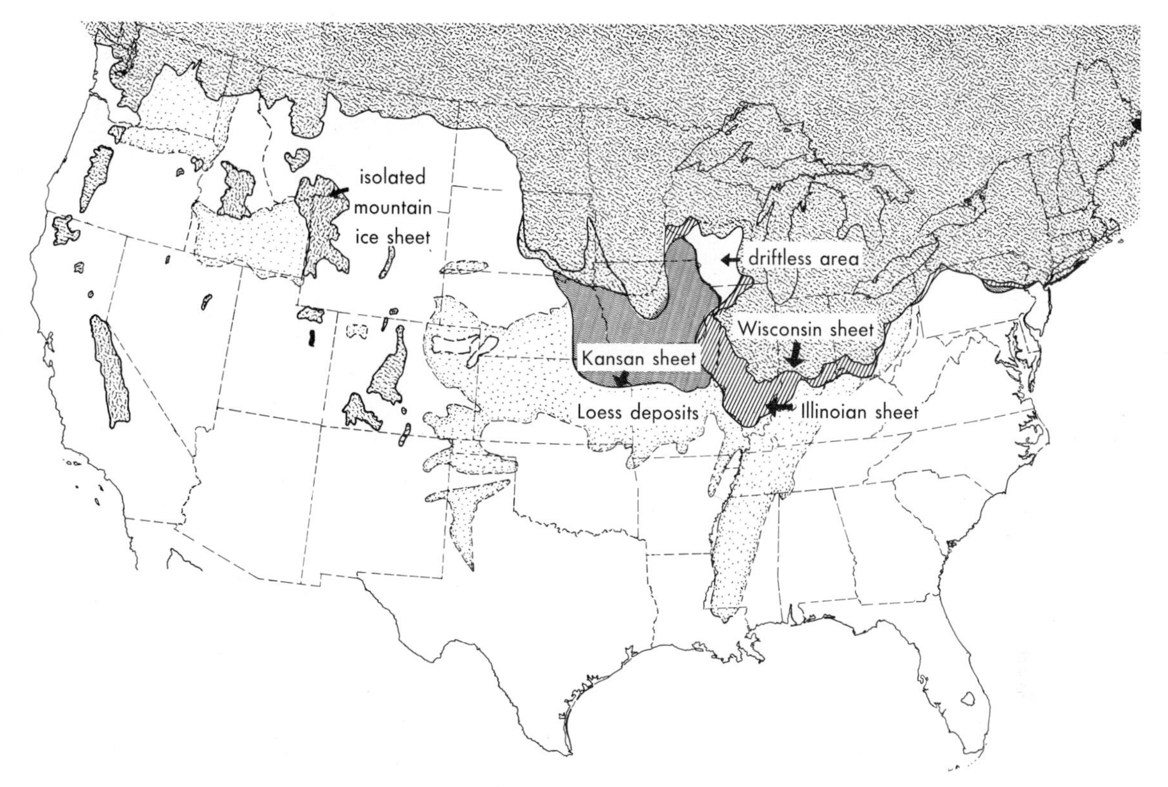

Fig. 23-6. Distribution of glacial deposits in the United States. The areas covered by ice sheets and the regions which are overlain by loess deposits are indicated. Most of the loess deposits are thought to be windblown deposits, but some are most likely stream deposits.

tively in the case of many of the Pleistocene deposits. They tend to fill stream valleys, lying on either side as terraces. Thus, even in a short distance laterally, the age of units may change or be obscured. In addition, over most of the central United States loess deposits have been dropped over the drift.

Subdivisions of the Pleistocene

For many years the glacial erratics, moraines, till, and stratified drift deposits and most other Pleistocene continental deposits were ascribed to the flood during the time of Noah. It was assumed that the large erratics were blocks that had floated into their present position while frozen into icebergs. It was not until 1840 that Louis Agassiz pointed out that the glacial deposits in the valleys and plains below the alpine glaciers were deposited there when the glaciers were expanded. He postulated a huge ice sheet covering all of northern Europe to explain the glacial deposits that cover that region. This became one of the most controversial questions of the time. The validity of his work has now been so well documented that no doubt about the origin of these and similar deposits in other parts of the world remains.

Soon after Agassiz made his first studies of glaciers it was recognized that there are two or more superposed sheets of glacial drift. Thus glaciation was early known to be multiple. Although we rarely find evidence of more than two sheets superimposed on one another in a single locality, there were at least four periods or stages of glacier advance during the Pleistocene in North America. The sequence of these stages has been determined by means of correlation and dating. Sinçe most glacial tills look very much alike, regardless of age, it is obvious that we are limited in the use of the deposits formed under and at the sides of the ice sheets. Instead, use is made of the deposits laid down in front of the ice sheets, and particularly the sediments that were deposited during the interglacial periods when the ice sheets were retreating or nonexistent. Most common of these deposits are the varved lake clays formed in marginal lakes, loess, glacier outwash, and peat. Within these units we can establish time equivalence by means of correlation of the varves, by use of fossil fauna and flora, or by use of carbon-14.

One of the effects of the interglacial periods is that the deposits formed during the previous glacier advance are weathered. Thus the soil profiles have been used as the best means of identifying tills. The depth of oxidation, the amount and kind of chemical weathering, or the extent of decay may be used as a means of estimating the relative ages of different tills. The most recent sheet of glacial till is very fresh by comparison with the older sheets, making it relatively easy to identify the last continental ice sheet that covered North America, called the Wisconsin sheet.

Fig. 23-8. The great Irish deer. This extinct species of western Europe had the most ponderous antlers of any known deer, some showing a spread of nearly 10 feet. It lived during the Middle Pleistocene times, about 100,000 years ago. (Painting by Charles Knight, Chicago Natural History Museum.)

Fig. 23-7. Extinct giant Moas. In the absence of mammals to prey upon them, many flightless birds evolved in New Zealand. This scene on South Island in postglacial times, 5000 years ago, shows giant moas standing 10 to 11 feet high. They are now extinct, though there is evidence that some were still alive when man came to New Zealand. (Painting by Charles Knight, Chicago Natural History Museum.)

Studies of these till sheets and the interglacial deposits have led to the following subdivision of the Pleistocene: Each is known as a stage.

Wisconsin Glaciation: defined on basis of till in Wisconsin.
Sangamon Interglacial: for deposits in Sangamon County, Illinois.
Illinoian Glaciation: for deposits in Illinois.
Yarmouth Interglacial: for deposits in Yarmouth, Iowa.
Kansas Glaciation: for sections in northeastern Kansas.
Aftonian Interglacial: for deposits in Afton Junction, Iowa.
Nebraskan Glaciation: for deposits in the State of Nebraska.

Various substages are known for some of the above stages. This is particularly true of the most recent of the stages, the Wisconsin. One of these substages, the Iowan, may actually represent a separate period of glacier advance comparable to the Nebraskan, Kansas, and Illinoian.

In the type locality for each of the stages, lithologic characteristics may be used to help identify the stages, but variability makes this of relatively little use. Criteria for identification of the stages are:

1. *Topography.* The Wisconsin till sheet may be distinguished from older sheets by the development of the drainage pattern on it. The older sheets tend to be more dissected by stream erosion. Some of the sub-stages of the Wisconsin, and to a lesser extent the older stages, may be distinguished in this way.
2. *Weathering.* The use of the degree of weathering has already been mentioned. All of the till sheets with the exception of the Wisconsin have reached advanced stages of weathering. In the lower or B horizon of these soils there is a layer of material which is called gumbotil, or silttil, depending on the texture. The thicknesses of these zones are sometimes used as an indication of the relative age of a till.
3. *Carbon-14.* Radiocarbon dating is the most exact means of dating and correlating deposits of the Pleistocene. It may be used on any pieces of wood, bones, peat, and other organic materials. However, it is applicable only to the Wisconsin Stage because the half life of carbon-14 is not long enough to make it useful in dating objects more than about 30,000 years old.
4. *Pollen Analysis.* When the angiosperms flower, the trees and other plants shed grains of pollen in great abundance. These and spores of the plants are widely distributed by winds. Through careful study of the various types of spores and pollen grains it is possible to identify the genus and even the species of the plant from which the pollen came. Thus the pollen grains found in a lake or bog deposit will re-

Fig. 23-10. Giant kangaroos and wombats. Marsupials predominated in isolated Australia throughout the Cenozoic Era as they do today. 100,000 years ago there lived some giant relatives of the modern Australian marsupials. The kangaroo seen here could easily stand 10 feet high, while the wombat was as large as a living rhino. (Painting by Charles Knight, Chicago Natural History Museum.)

Fig. 23-9. The American mastodon. In postglacial times, 5000 years ago, mastodons roamed the North American continent south of the retreating glaciers. Skeletons have been found in the Chicago area where these great animals were buried in ancient swamps. (Painting by Charles Knight, Chicago Natural History Museum.)

flect the types of plants that were living near it at the time the sediment was laid down. By taking a section through a sequence of pollen- and spore-bearing sediments, we can determine the assemblage of plants that was nearby at successive times. Thus the pollen reflects the changes in relative abundance of different plants as the ice sheets advanced and retreated. The presence of certain types of plants serves as a climatic indicator.

5. *Varves.* Correlation by means of varves has already been discussed. These have been used in relating the lake deposits of the glacier marginal lakes to one another.
6. *Deep-Sea Sediments.* The sediments deposited in the ocean during the Pleistocene are very simple compared with the terrestrial deposits. These can be recovered by means of the piston-coring device, which has yielded many cores that are 40 to 50 feet long. Layers in the topmost parts of these cores may be dated by means of carbon-14, but fossil content has been most useful in the lower parts of the sections thus obtained. A great deal of work is being done on the interpretation of these cores as a means of reconstructing paleoclimates during the Pleistocene. Among the interesting results that have been obtained is the discovery that the rate of deep-sea sedimentation is related to the temperature of the surface water and thus to the climatic conditions of the region. Many Foraminifera are guides to water temperature, so the variation in the geographic distribution of these also serves as a climatic indicator.

Fig. 23-11. Scattered lakes and connecting drainage in Alaska. Glaciers have scoured this region as well as the Canadian Shield several times during the Pleistocene. These advances have tended to suppress the relief and have left morains which cover vast areas with lakes, marshes, and poor drainage. (Photo by courtesy of the U.S. Air Force.)

Fig. 23-12. Glaciated mountains in Yellowstone Park. These peaks named Pilot and Index are the results of glacial erosion in the Absaroka volcanic rocks. (Photo by E. W. Spencer.)

Fig. 23-13. The Sierra Nevada Mountains, California. The large valley in the center is a glaciated valley. (Photo by U.S. Geological Survey.)

Fig. 23-14. Ground sloths and glyptodonts. Many strange mammals evolved in South America during the Cenozoic Era. This scene in Argentina during Middle Pleistocene times shows three clumsy ground sloths, nearly the size of living elephants, and two armadillo-like glyptodonts, covered with great bony shields to protect them from attacks of predators. (Painting by Charles Knight, Chicago Natural History Museum.)

History of the Mississippi drainage system

The Mississippi River now drains a basin that extends from the Rocky Mountains in the west to the Appalachian Highlands in the east and northward to the edge of the Great Lakes and almost into Canada. Virtually the entire southern perimeter of the continental ice sheets drained into the Mississippi River during and following their greatest advances, bringing about repeated shifts in the northern part of the Mississippi River and its two main tributaries, the Ohio and Missouri Rivers.

Before the advances of these ice sheets, the drainage pattern was strikingly different

Fig. 23-15. Mammoth and woolly rhinoceros. In Late Pleistocene times, perhaps 25,000 years ago, the mammoth and woolly rhinoceros lived close to the edge of the ice sheet. Carcasses that have been found frozen in the tundras of northern Siberia show that both had a heavy coat of hair, in contrast to the nearly naked skins of living elephants and rhinos. Cave paintings indicate that Late Paleolithic men were familiar with the mammoth and woolly rhinoceros. (Painting by Charles Knight, Chicago Natural History Museum.)

from that which we now find. The northern part of the Missouri River drained northward into Hudson Bay. That segment from Kansas City eastward has maintained its course. The source of the Mississippi was probably someplace near its present head in Minnesota, but the northern part of the stream channel north of St. Louis was shifted a number of times during the ice ages. The northern and eastern parts of the Ohio River from central Ohio to West Virginia drained northward into the Gulf of St. Lawrence. The lower part of the Ohio drainage went into a preglacial stream known as the Teays River, which flowed across central Ohio and Indiana.

When the great ice sheets moved southward they blocked and filled the valleys of many parts of the preglacial streams. The Teays River valley was filled with glacial till. Its position can now be traced by the unusual thicknesses of glacial drift in it. The waters of the rivers in places became ponded or blocked by the edges of the ice sheet, and the waters established new lines of drainage around the edges of the sheets. The greatest advances of the ice sheets coincide approximately with the present positions of the Missouri and Ohio Rivers. Thus the present drainage pattern was established by these ice-marginal channels. Before this pattern became established there were many shifts in channel positions along the front of the ice.

Gradient of the Mississippi

The advances and retreats of the ice sheets have left other impressions upon the Mississippi Valley. During each of the glacial advances water was removed from the oceans, lowering sea level and increasing the gradient of the lower parts of the Mississippi Valley. At the same time, with the advance of the ice, the upper parts of the valleys became clogged with a load the streams could not possibly carry. Each time the glaciers began to retreat, the reverse situation occurred. The upper parts of the river received great quantities of water from the melting ice, whereas the sea level rose, and the gradient along the lower reaches was decreased.

Thus, during the periods of glacial advance, the upper parts of the Mississippi Valley became filled with sediment, while the lower parts of the valley were cut more deeply as a result of steepened stream gradients. During glacial retreats, the upper valley was washed clear of debris by the increased flow of meltwater, and the lower parts of the valley became filled with debris because the sea level was rising and thus lowering the gradient of the stream. The evidence of the effects of the fluctuations of sea level in the lower parts of the valley are found in four river terraces, which correspond to the four periods of glacial advance.

Development of the Great Lakes

Before the Pleistocene there were no lakes in the region of the present-day Great Lakes comparable to them in size. Instead, the Pliocene streams of that area drained northward. Lake Superior is located in a structural basin of Precambrian rocks, and most of the other lakes are situated on the sedimentary sequences that probably were low in the Pliocene topography. As Pleistocene ice sheets moved into the region, these earlier valleys were enlarged by scouring and were depressed under the weight of the ice mass. The lakes began to form in the last stages of the Wisconsin glaciation as the ice sheet began to melt and retreat. Melt-waters became trapped between the margins of the ice sheet and the high ground along the drainage divide of the Mississippi basin.

During the first part of the history of the lakes they actually drained into the Mississippi, but later, as the ice retreated farther, a new outlet was opened so that waters from the southern margin of the ice front drained westward across Michigan. A sequence of positions of the lakes at different times is illustrated in Fig. 23-16. Note the changing shapes and shifting in the position of the outlets through the passage of time.

The sequence of events known to have taken place in the development of the Great Lakes is extremely complex. The following are among the most important factors that have

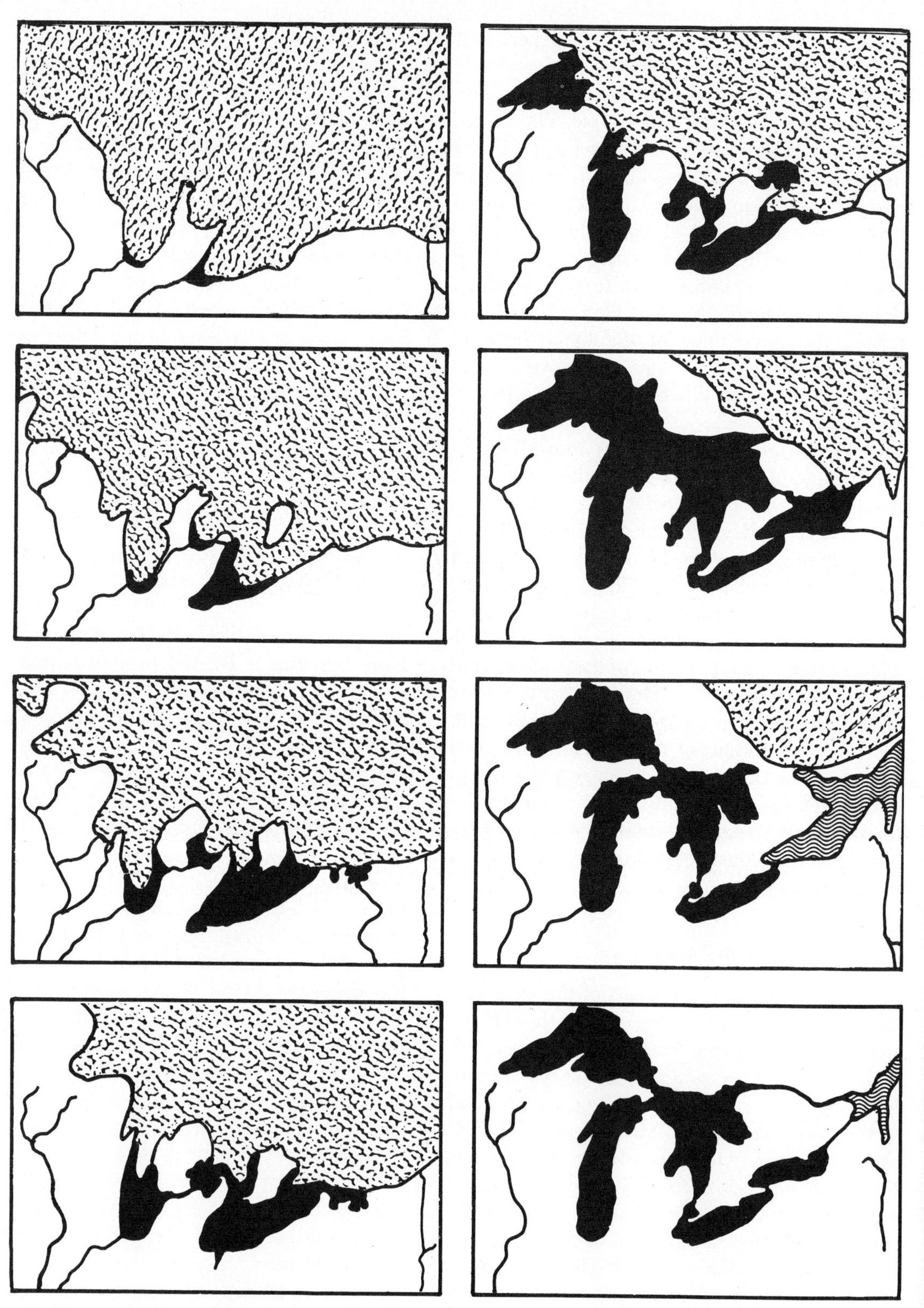

Fig. 23-16. Evolution of the Great Lakes during the Pleistocene. These lakes are a direct result of the glacial advances. Lake Superior occupies a synclinal structure, but the others have been shaped by scouring and deposition of moraines. Read left column, to bottom; then right.

Fig. 23-17. Lower Falls, Yellowstone River. Waterfalls occur along many rivers which have not yet become adjusted to recent changes in their courses. The drainage patterns in many parts of the world have assumed their present configuration during the Pleistocene either as a result of glaciation, diastrophism, or volcanism within the Pleistocene. (Photo by courtesy of the Union Pacific Railroad.)

contributed to the course of events in this region:

1. During glaciation the weight of the ice sheet caused the continent to be depressed. As the ice wasted away the land rose. Thus the old shore lines have become tilted by this upward rise of the central part of the Canadian Shield.
2. The ice front did not remain steady during the evolution of the lakes. It oscillated back and forth, advancing and retreating in different places at different times.
3. The shape of the lakes has naturally been partially determined by the configuration of the land surface that has become exposed as the ice sheet wasted.
4. With each advance of the ice sheet, morainal debris was pushed into new positions and partially removed from older ones, thus changing the outlets and barriers to the lake waters.

In spite of these complicating factors, the history of the lakes has been largely worked out. It is possible to trace the position of the lakes by means of mapping the beaches, wave-cut cliffs, sand dunes, bars, and other shore-line features formed at each stage in the lakes' history. Along these old shore lines it is possible to find outlets that were used at the time the lake occupied each position. It is not possible to outline exactly the position of each lake at every time during the evolution of the lakes, because the story has not been one of a gradually receding body of water. Some of the more recent lake shore lines cross and obliterate earlier shore-line features. In addition, most of the earlier lakes were marginal to the ice so no shore-line features are found where the beaches ran into the ice sheet.

Lake Agassiz. The largest of the former lakes was glacial Lake Agassiz. The remnants of this lake are Lake Winnipeg, Rainy Lake, and several other smaller bodies of water. We can now determine the position of Lake Agassiz by mapping the lake deposits that appear in a thin cover that is almost continuous over this large portion of southern Canada. This magnificent lake disappeared when the retreating ice sheet had moved far enough north to permit the waters to escape into Hudson Bay.

REFERENCES

DEMOREST, MAX, 1943, Ice sheets: Geol. Soc. America Bull., v. 54, p. 364-400

FLINT, R. F., 1957, *Glacial and Pleistocene Geology:* John Wiley & Sons, Inc., New York, 553 p.

HEUSSER, C., 1954, Palynology of Taku glacier: Am. Jour. Sci., v. 252, p. 308

LEIGHTON, M. M., and WILLMAN, H. B., 1950, Loess formations of the Mississippi Valley: Jour. Geology, v. 58, p. 599-623.

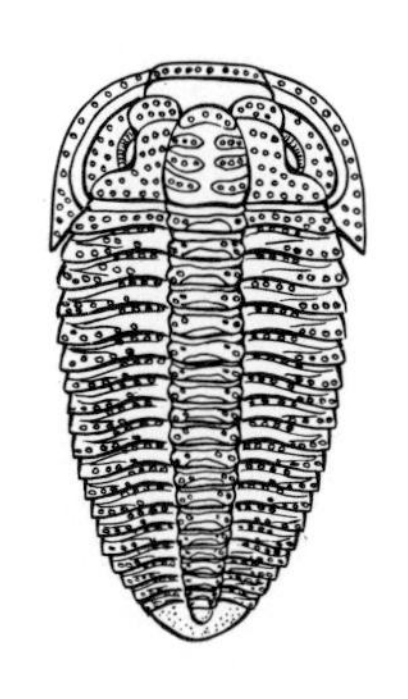

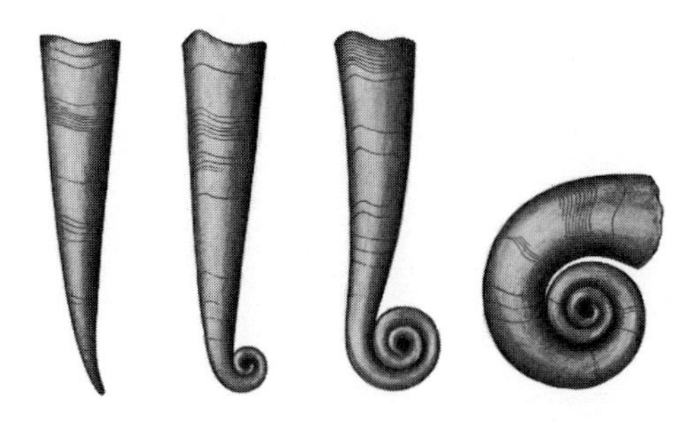

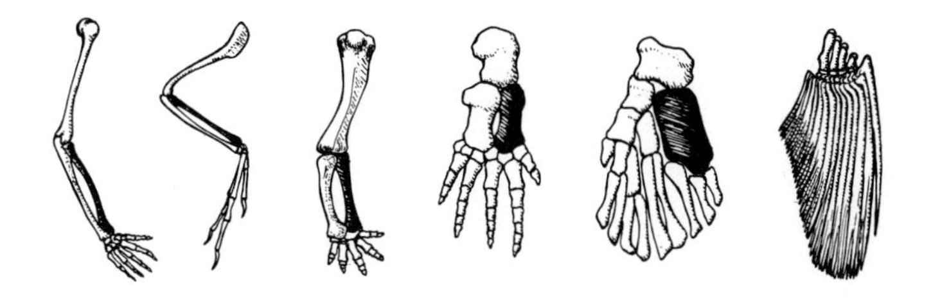

VI EVOLUTION

24 The Theory of Evolution

Introduction

Few scientific theories have had an impact on scientists and nonscientists alike comparable to that of the theory of evolution as stated by Darwin in *On The Origin of Species.* The theory precipitated a controversy between science and religion that has not yet completely subsided. The idea that man, as well as all other animals and plants, has evolved through an almost unimaginable period of time from lower forms of life and perhaps ultimately from inorganic materials through inorganic processes was totally contrary to the religious dogma of the 1800's. This initiated an open "conflict between science and religion." As a result, many religious faiths have readjusted their ideas in such a manner as to resolve the conflict. Others hold tenaciously to their original dogma on the grounds that, no matter how conclusive the scientific facts may seem, there is always ample margin for error and misinterpretation. The theory of evolution did far more than affect the relationship between science and religion. Darwin's mechanism for the evolutionary process is *natural selection,* a process that has often been misconstrued as meaning "the survival of the fittest," in a very strict sense of the phrase. This concept has even become an underlying principle in some political and economic philosophies. We will turn in this chapter to the meaning of natural selection as a process for determination of which forms survive and evolve.

Basis for theory of evolution

Evidence of the validity of the idea of evolution of life now abounds on every side. Various lines of evidence of the proof of the theory may be found in the fields of embryology, genetics, and anthropology, but we will confine our attention to the evidence obtained primarily from the field of paleontology. The body of geologic data revealing the fossil content of the successively younger rock strata is the most dramatic and conclusive proof of the changing character of the life through time. This record formed the basis for many of the basic ideas expressed by Darwin.

Because geologists use the fossil content of a rock unit as a basis for the recognition of the age of the unit and its place in the stratigraphic column, it is commonly assumed that the theory of evolution is the basis for the geologic time scale and that all of our historical geology is based on the assumption of systematic evolution of life through time. This is most emphatically not true. If it were, the science of geology would indeed be on uncertain ground. Geologic time cannot be based directly on evolution of life for two reasons. First, the question of the rate of evolution is largely unanswered. Furthermore, there is no way to predict exactly in which direction evolution is likely to turn the development of a particular organism.

Instead, evolution is based on the rock record. One of William Smith's major contributions to geology was the recognition that each stratum of rocks contained a definite assemblage of fossils, and that it is possible to predict what part of a sequence you are in by its fossil content. It is not possible to predict on the basis of evolution alone what fossil forms will be in the next higher or lower strata in a sequence. It took many years of detailed description and field investigation to establish a stratigraphic column that is applicable over large parts of the world. At first, the normal (right side up) sequence had to be established, and intervals of erosion and nondeposition accounted for. This had to be accomplished through correlations based on physical criteria such as continuity of outcrop, lithology, and position in a sequence. Once these correlations were complete, it became possible to compare and correlate the faunas and floras of one unit of rocks with those of the same age in other places. It became obvious that the assemblages of fossils were characteristic of certain of the units, and that, for purposes of correlation, they were as reliable as physical properties.

After the stratigraphic column had been established, it was apparent that the fossil faunas and floras within the successively younger units showed remarkable progressive changes. Many types of changes could be noted. Instead of finding that man, horses, sharks, crinoids, and algae all appeared at one time in geologic history we discovered that the simplest forms of life are found in the oldest rocks and progressively more advanced animals and plants came in later periods. In addition to these, we note that certain groups underwent changes in shape, and that there were shifts in the size of populations of animals and plants as well as in individuals. The study of these changes through time leads to the idea of evolutionary changes. We have already reviewed the life of each of the periods of the geologic past. This is the main evidence of evolution. Now we may turn to the mechanisms by which these changes took place.

The individual and his heredity

Until Gregor Mendel performed his now-famous series of experiments in cross breeding different varieties of peas, our present understanding of the mechanism of inheritance of traits was impossible. Even Darwin apparently believed that we inherit our characteristics through the blood of our parents, and they in turn from their parents. Mendel's work led to the recognition that traits are carried by certain nucleic acids called genes, which are transmitted as discrete units from the parents through the egg and sperm to the new individual. Some traits, such as dark-skin pigmentation and height, tend to be dominant, while others are recessive. These genes do not fuse in the new individual. They remain discrete, and half of them are passed on to the next generation. Some of these will determine the physical traits of the individual, and others may remain recessive within the first generation. However, some of these recessive genes may be passed along to the second generation, in which they may become active determinants of the traits of the individuals. The laws derived from Mendel's work are considered by many to be the most fundamental biological laws. These laws make it possible to predict the traits that will appear in successive generations of offspring descended from a given group of individuals.

Reaction range

Although the genes an individual receives from his parents determine in a general way the developmental pattern for his traits, the individual's actual development is not completely independent of his environment. The individual possesses a certain "reaction range" within which these traits may vary as a result of the environment. For example, an individual's skin color may be white as a result of the combination of genes received from his parents, yet, on exposure to sunlight, the skin colors may vary within rather wide limits. The reaction ranges of different traits are highly variable and little known.

One of the most important aspects of genetic inheritance is that the genes that are passed on from one generation to the next are the same regardless of the extent to which the individuals of one generation are able to adapt to a specific environment. In other words, acquired characteristics are not passed on from generation to generation through the genes. What is passed on is the developmental pattern, which can function within a certain reaction range. What happens if the new generation does not have a wide enough reaction range to enable it to adapt to certain environmental conditions? It either moves into an environment to which it can adapt, or it dies out.

Mutation changes may occur in the genes. Alterations of those genes that are copied when reproduction occurs are called gene mutations. These show up in the physical traits of the individuals produced and in their norms or reaction ranges. In some cases the mutants are better adjusted to the environments in which they find themselves and are likely to flourish and pass on their genes to the next generation.

It should now be clear that what an individual inherits comes through the genes. Three main factors will introduce variation among the population of any species. They are mutation in the genes of parents, the combination of genes from two parents some of which are dominant and others recessive, and finally the range of reaction within which development may occur.

Populations

Although the individual is the basic unit of life, evolutionary processes must be understood in terms of populations. We are, after all, talking about changes in vast populations over long periods of time. While a mutation within one individual may suit that individual to live a more effective existence within its enviornment, this is of little significance for a population as a whole unless the mutation becomes widespread.

One fundamental characteristic of populations is that variations are represented within them. The individuals of a population of any given animal or plant are not identical. They vary in size, shape, and to some extent in structure. If, for example, we collect a large sample of leaves, or sea shells, all of which belong to a certain species of plants or animal, and measure the ratio between the length and width of the shells or leaves, we can immediately obtain an idea of the magnitude of the variation. If the number of individuals having a certain length/width ratio are plotted as a histogram we will ordinarily get a bell-shaped (normal) distribution, Fig. 24-1.

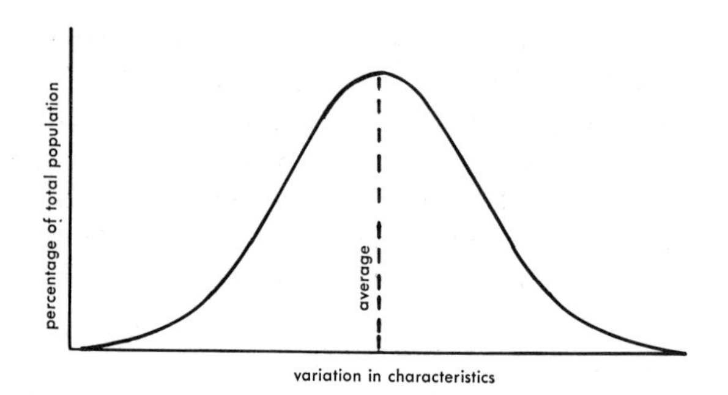

Fig. 24-1. A normal distribution. This bell-shaped curve shows the theoretical distribution of some variables within a large population if the distribution is normal. The variable might be the height of individuals.

It is also helpful to think of this population as having a certain pool of genes upon which to draw for the next generation. If no mutations are introduced within this gene pool, if the environmental conditions remain fairly constant or at least within the reaction range of the organisms, and if all of the individuals of mating age breed, then we may predict that no change in the overall gene pool or in the pattern of variation within the population would occur from one generation to the next. Nevertheless, we may be sure that in a biparental population the processes of mutation and recombination will maintain an enormous variation within the population as a whole. It is this variation within the population that makes evolution possible. This variation is passed on from generation to generation and is maintained even when no evolutionary change is occurring. Changes in the species may arise from differences in the inherited reaction ranges if the environmental conditions for the entire population of a species are the same. Changes may also arise from differences in environmental conditions even if the reaction range of all members of the population is the same, or it may come from a combination of the two. Within the population there is always some variation in the genes resulting from mutations. Both the environmental variations and the inherited genetic variations may cause the population to have a bell-shaped curve of population variation.

Natural selection

In the broadest terms, the effect of the evolutionary process is to bring the great diversity of animal and plant life into a better adjustment with its environment. It is not a mere coincidence that some fish are able to withstand the cold water and great pressures found at the bottom of the ocean, while others flourish in shallow sun-lit waters. Nor is it chance that a woodpecker has a long pointed beak and is able to chip pieces of wood from a tree, while a humming bird has a long delicate beak and the ability to hold its body almost motionless in air while it sips the nectar from a flower. The variety of adaptation is evident in the adaptation of the mammals of today. The whale is more closely related to an ape than it is to a fish. Both are mammals; yet one adapted to life in the sea, and the other to life in the trees. Sometimes the progressive

Fig. 24-2. Homology of forelimbs. Homology is correspondence between structures of different organisms due to their inheritance of these structures from the same ancestry. Compare here the forelimbs of man, an early bird, a dinosaur, whale, lobe-finned fish, and a modern fish.

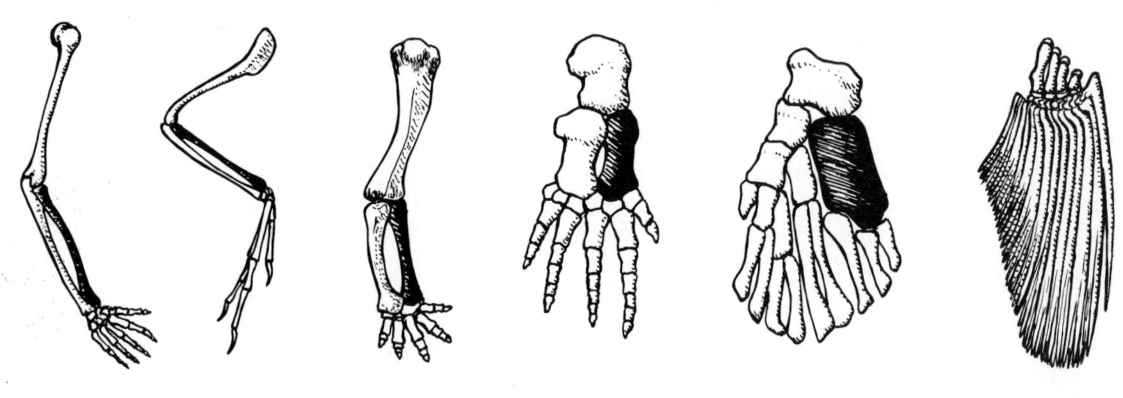

evolution of particular groups brings about the adaptation of two or more unrelated forms to the same environment. In such a case, the two may have very similar outward appearance, as in the case of the fish and the whale.

How does the mechanism of natural selection work? In general, it is a simple process of nonrandom reproduction resulting in changes that tend to improve the ability of the population as a whole to survive and reproduce in the environment they inhabit. If the organisms exercise no choice in selecting partners for reproduction, then we would say that the reproduction is random. The population from generation to generation would maintain variants through mutation and recombinations of genes, but no evolutionary changes would be introduced such as those that take place when the selection of mates is nonrandom. Individual mate selection is of little significance in this connection. What does matter are group tendencies. If individuals possessed of certain characteristics are more desirable to the group as a whole, then in a sense a premium is placed on the genes of that group, and they are likely to become more abundant in the population.

Perhaps more important is the fact that certain of the variants within a population may possess certain physical traits which make it easier for them to get along in their environment or adapt to changes within the environment. When changes do occur these groups are more likely to survive than those variants which are not fortunate enough to have received a sufficiently wide reaction range. Thus through a long period of time we may find that a certain segment of the total population is able to produce more offspring carrying their genes than the original norm of the population. This brings about a shift in the norm, and the population as a whole has evolved slightly. A most important point in evolution is the fact that the individuals that survive long enough to reproduce are the only ones that make a contribution toward the continued existence of the group, and it is only their genetic heredity plus any introduced mutations that will be passed along to the next generation of the population.

The factors that determine natural selection, adaptation, and therefore evolution include:

1. Nonrandom mating.
2. An adjustment of the number of offspring to increase survival.
3. Ability to survive within the physical environment.
4. Ability to survive in competition with other organisms.
5. Ability to reproduce.

A good example of the idea of natural selection and adaptation is seen in the adaptive skin coloration of certain organisms. Some insects have become so perfectly adapted to their habitat that they closely resemble the plant stems and leaves on which they feed. This, of course, gives them the great advantage of being hard to see and, thereby, reduces the chances that they will fall prey to their natural enemies. This increases their ability to live and reproduce. Those variants that most closely resemble a plant stem or leaf have a better chance for survival and therefore reproduction. Thus their genes are the ones which are most likely to be passed along to the next generation. After this process continues for 1000 years the cumulative effect is a considerable shift in the physical appearance of the populations as a whole.

As we study the history of some of the major groups from the geological past it becomes apparent that some force seems to drive particular forms into environments which they had not previously occupied. In short, there appears to be a certain pressure to diversify in such a way as to enable the organisms to survive under new conditions. This may be explained in terms of natural selection. Any given environment may become crowded with organisms, cutting down on the food supply and on room to such an extent that some of the forms are forced to move into a new environment, either to escape consumption or to find food. Those groups of variants that are particularly suited to make use of the new environment are the most likely to reproduce and survive within it. There are, however, a number of conditions that must be met before such a move can be made.

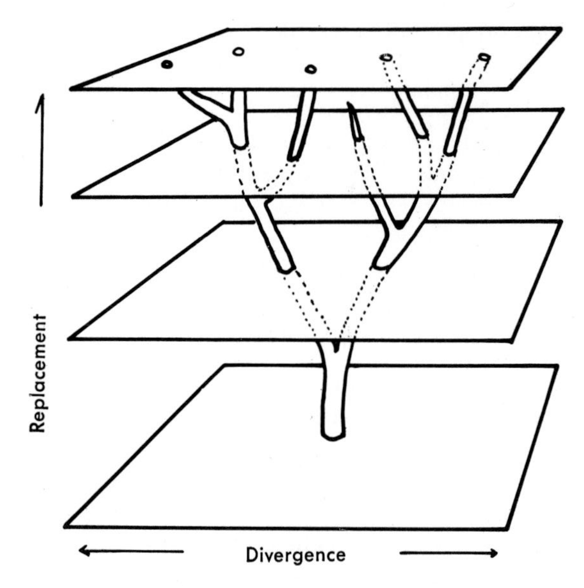

Fig. 24-3. A simplified phylogenetic tree showing divergence of a population through time. The horizontal planes represent four times. Within each plane divergence of characteristics of the population is shown. Through time each generation is replaced by the next. The characteristics of each new generation are determined by the gene pool from which it was produced. Between the first and second time planes the initial population is split and after that divergence continues until by the time of the fourth plane there are five species, one having become extinct. (After N. D. Newell.)

1. There must be an opportunity to have access to such a new environment.
2. The organism must have the necessary physical constitution to live in the new environment.
3. Finally, the new habitat must be such that the newly introduced organism can survive in it at least until a better adaptation can be effected.

Species

The question of exactly what "species" means is one that has long been debated by biologists and paleontologists. The concept of the species most often used by paleontologists defines it as a group of individuals essentially indistinguishable from some specimen selected as a standard of reference. The biologist's concept of species, on the other hand, considers a species to be made up of one or more usually highly variable populations which are capable of interbreeding and producing fertile offspring. Unfortunately the fossil record fails to supply the necessary information to satisfy fully the requirements of the biologist's definitions. The paleontologist is usually forced to rely on:

1. Similarity of morphology (shape of the fossil parts).
2. Association (relating variants within a population) on the basis of proximity within a stratum.
3. Biogeography.
4. Paleoecology.
5. Biostratigraphy.

On the basis of the biologist's definition there are over a million different species living today. Each represents a population capable of interbreeding and producing fertile offspring. Each is unlikely to combine with any other species. If over a million species exist today one can understand the magnitude of the problem confronting the paleontologist who is trying to describe and relate the hundreds of millions of species which have lived on the earth since the beginning of Cambrian time over 520 million years ago.

The time factor

It is considerably more complex to apply the concept of species to the fossil record than to living groups, because changes of great magnitude have occurred through time. In our consideration of a population we have described the nature and cause of the variations that exist within it, and some of the processes which give the population a tendency to evolve. Now we must consider the effect of another dimension, that of time. Consider a species that starts initially as a simple highly variable population capable of adaptation. If the species is now separated in such a way as to isolate certain parts of it in different environments, then through the combined processes of natural selection and mutation the two groups may begin to undergo morphological and genetic divergence (the gene pool as a whole changes). That is, the two populations change in general physical traits and appearance.

If the two groups continue to be isolated long enough, changes within the two groups may become so great that they no longer resemble one another superficially. It is possible, even probable, that they would no longer be capable of interbreeding if they should be given the opportunity of freely mixing. Fig. 24-3 shows a theoretical simplified phylogenetic tree (a diagram that traces the race history). The horizontal planes in the diagram indicate stratigraphic horizons and also time lines. The segments of the limbs of the tree correspond to the populations of this race that were present at one time. Each segment consists of a species population of almost identical individuals. But, as we have already seen, such species are transient in nature. They may undergo change through time. A number of these cross sections of the tree limbs combine to represent a succession of species. Any two adjacent sections would contain populations that would be almost identical, but the farther apart the segments are, the more diverse they would appear.

Now we may ask how truly the above picture portrays the record we find in the stratigraphic sequences. Some of the main problems should be readily apparent. There are few instances in which we can trace the history of the successive changes in species very far through their race history. The reasons for this are:

1. The data are inadequate. First of all, only the hard parts of the organisms are preserved. This makes direct comparisons of groups of almost identical animals somewhat difficult.
2. Studies of whole populations of fossil species have not been made because the required number of specimens have not been found, and because the task is very time-consuming.
3. The record is incomplete. As we have seen, there are many gaps in the rock record. Some of these were caused by periods of nondeposition; others result from periods of erosion during which previously formed units are destroyed.

In spite of these shortcomings, which prevent the complete piecing together of the phylogenetic trees for each and every group of animals and plants, our record is adequate to point out the general direction of most major evolutionary changes. It also allows us to make convincing connections between many of the groups. There are, as we shall see in the following chapters, well-documented cases of successive changes in species.

MODES OF EVOLUTION

Professor George Simpson has described three major styles or modes of evolution: speciational, phyletic, and quantum. All three are brought about by the action of the same general processes of natural selection and mutation.

Fig. 24-4. Speciation. Each bell-shaped curve represents a population within which there is variation of traits. The population splits, and after a number of generations the two segments are so different that they are no longer considered members of the same species. (After G. G. Simpson, *Tempo and Mode in Evolution*, Columbia University Press.)

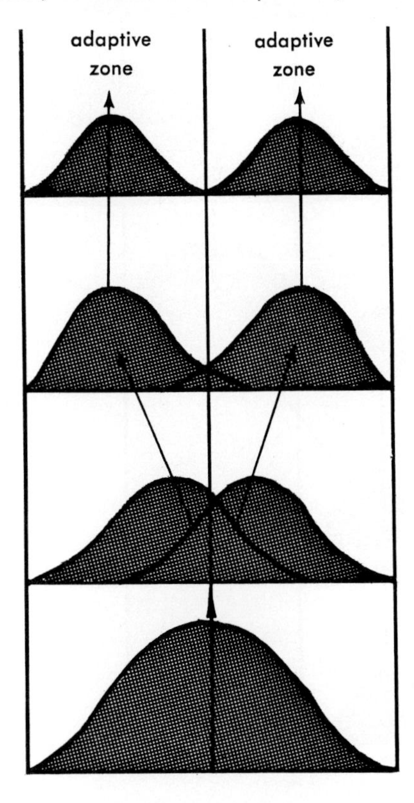

Speciation

Speciation is the splitting of one species into two or more groups through isolation of groups of a widespread population followed by the local differentiation of the groups. For example, two groups of a population may separate so that one occupies slightly deeper water. The differences which are likely to arise at first may be so slight as to be unnoticed, but this may be the first step toward complete isolation and eventual complete differentiation of the two groups.

Fig. 24-5. A local population, shown spreading into several adjacent subzones or environmental niches. Within each of these the descendants of the group in it become specially adapted and eventually diverge significantly from those in the adjacent subzones, giving rise to new species. (After G. G. Simpson, *Tempo and Mode in Evolution.*)

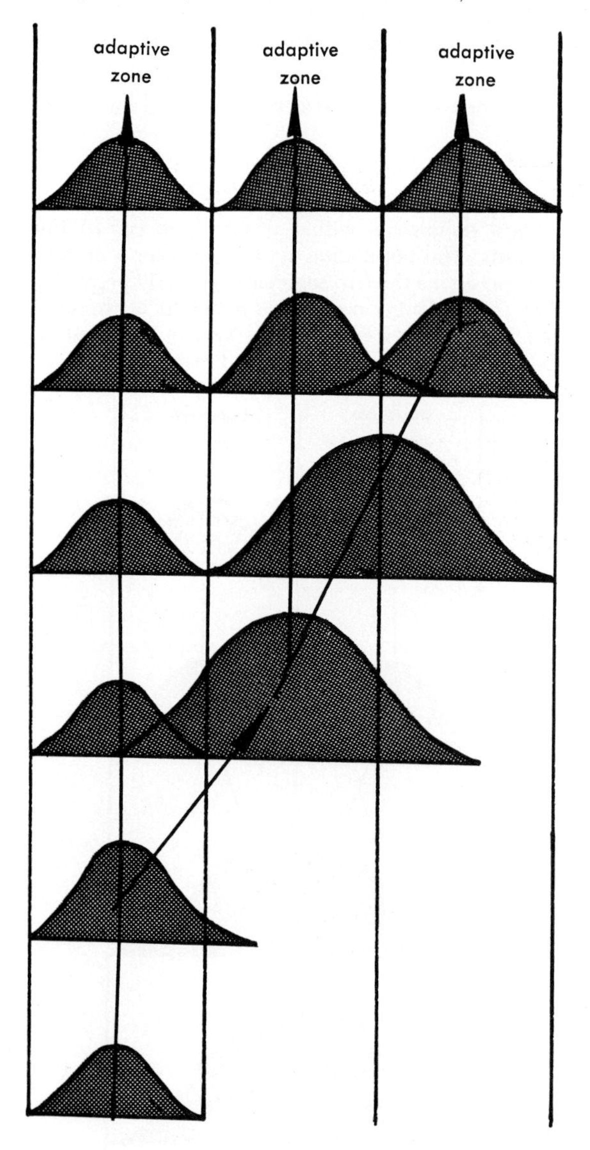

Earlier we discussed the nature of rock units and the various types of subdivisions of rock units. One of these was the zone, which has been defined as "a definite paleontological horizon characterized by the constant occurrence in it of certain species which do not occur in the preceding or succeeding neighbor zones." A zone may be divided into subzones, which show minor lateral and vertical changes. As a result of the evolution through speciation, a certain species population may become differentiated either by fanning out across adjacent subzones or by becoming widely spread into different zones. Both are adjustments of the organisms to slight differences in the ecological conditions under which they live. As a result of scattering of a population, there may not be an even distribution of the variants within that population. This may give rise to minor differences within the species after a few generations. Of course, there may be mutations during the process of fanning out and adaptation to the new conditions each segment of the population encounters. If the population is able to accumulate characteristics that are favorable to existence under the new conditions, evolution proceeds, but if nonadaptive characteristics are accumulated the group is headed for possible extinction.

Phyletic evolution

A second mode of evolution is that which involves a sustained directional shift of the average characters of the populations. It is not so much a splitting up of the species as a general overall change in the population's mean characteristics. Phyletic evolution leads to "successional species," whereas speciation leads to evolution of several contemporaneous species. A very large majority of the paleontological data falls into the patterns of phyletic evolution.

Within phyletic evolution three patterns

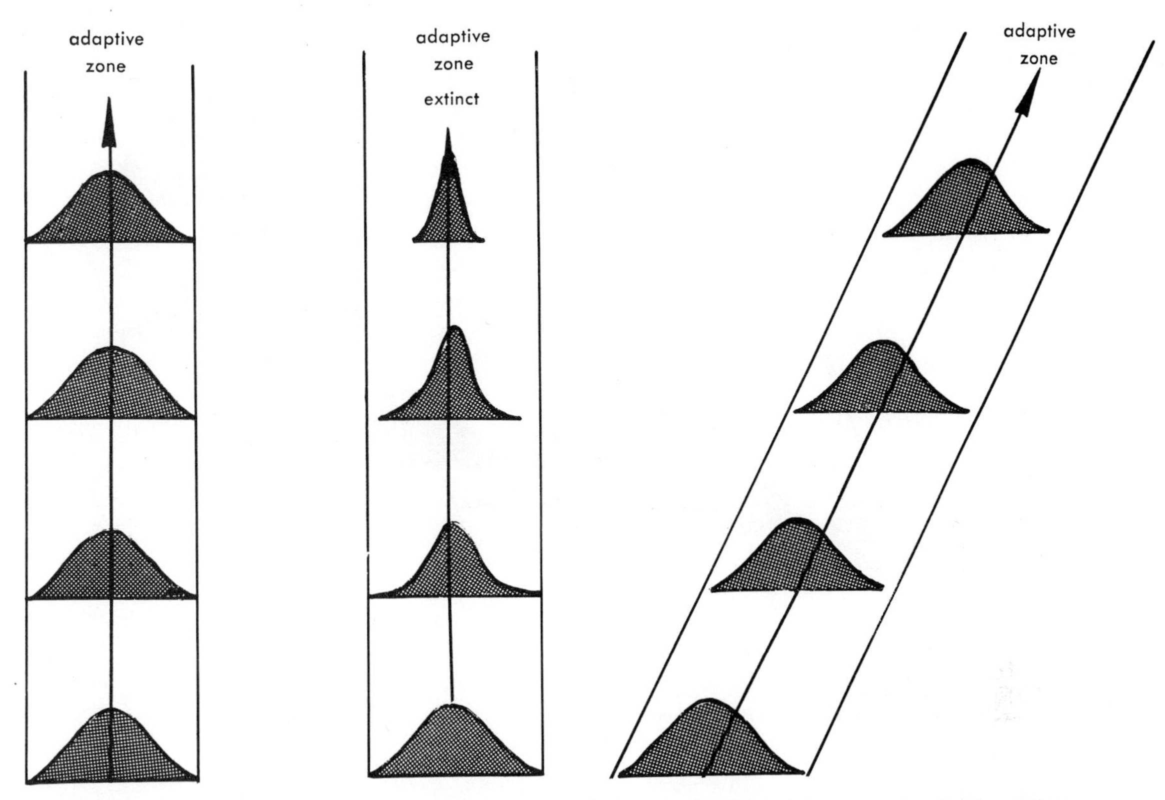

Fig. 24-6. Phyletic evolution. At the left is a species which is well adapted to a zone in which no changes are taking place. Successive generations show little change in characteristics. In the middle the population becomes more specialized with each new generation until the adaptation is so narrow that survival is threatened. As the tendency continues the species becomes extinct. At the right the successive generations show a slowly changing norm in the population characteristics. This is in response to a gradual shift in the environmental conditions (adaptive zone). (After G. G. Simpson, *Tempo and Mode in Evolution.*)

are found (Fig. 24-6). In the first of these the population is more or less in a state of equilibrium. The norm for the group is such that the organism is well adapted to the environment. There are some variants that are less well adapted, but these make up a small part of the group. Through time, there is an adequate response within the group to any slight changes in the environment. The responses are such that the group as a whole is maintained in a state of equilibrium.

A second pattern is that of a population that is becoming more narrowly adapted to its environment. The organisms, through a long series of changes, become more and more specialized to carry on their life functions within special restricted conditions. As a result, the group is headed for extinction because environmental conditions are certain to change eventually, and the species will have so limited its adaptability that it can no longer accommodate itself to these changes.

The third pattern is that of a slow change in response to a shifting ecological condition. Here the environment is undergoing a more or less steady progressive change. Progressively warmer climates or continually increasing salinity of sea water are examples. As these changes continue, the group as a whole adjusts to them by the natural selection for survival of those members of the population that have the necessary genetic makeup and reaction range to survive and reproduce.

Quantum evolution

The same processes of selection and adaptation that promote speciation and phyletic

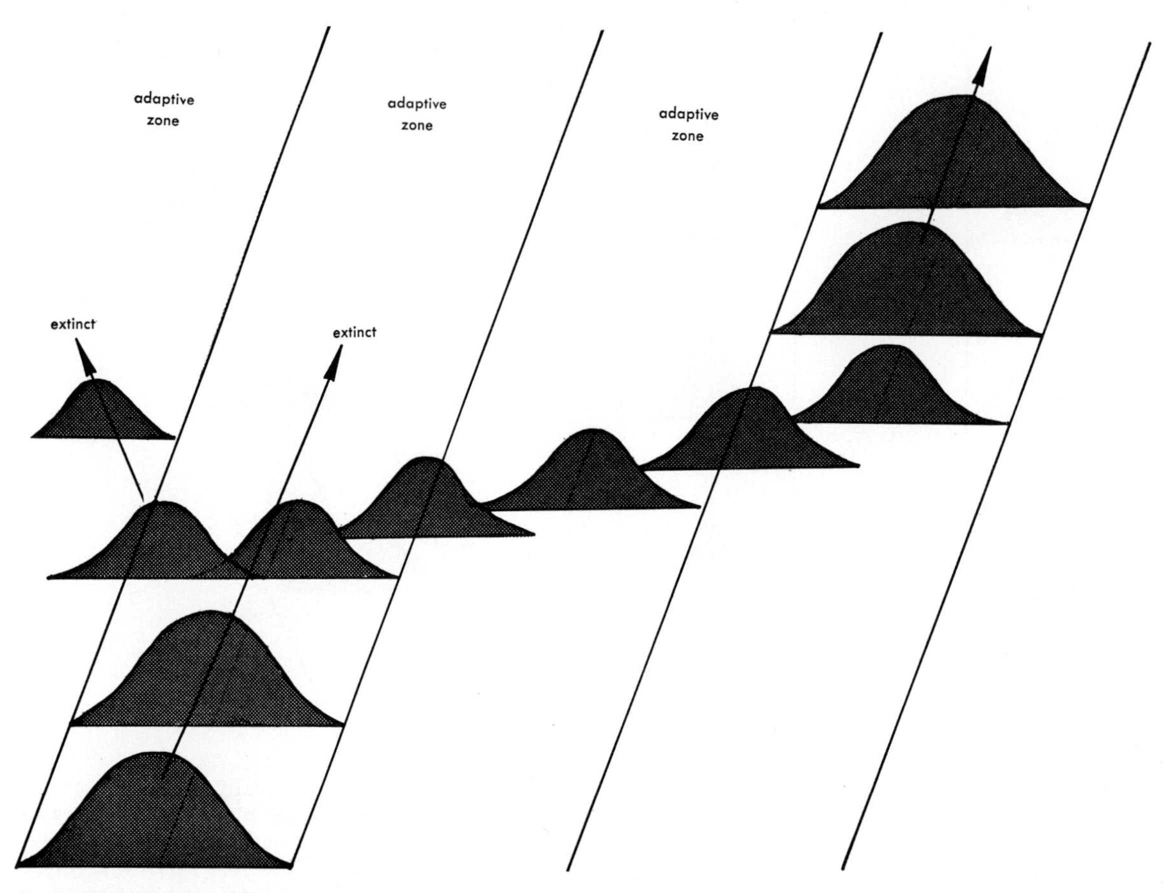

Fig. 24-7. Quantum evolution. The diagonal lines mark boundaries between adjacent adaptive zones within which conditions vary. The population evolves by phyletic evolution up to a certain time when the species ceases to be adapted to that zone, and that segment of the population which remains in it becomes extinct as does that segment which spreads to the next zone, left. By a series of very rapid changes, perhaps aided by selection of mutants, the successive generations shift to the right across one or more zones into one in which they become well adapted. (After G. G. Simpson, *Tempo and Mode in Evolution.*)

evolution are responsible for quantum evolution, which differs from the first two modes in the rapidity of the change and the apparent temporary failure of the state of equilibrium to continue through the process. By quantum evolution we mean that there is a sudden change in the adaptive zone such as might give rise to new families, orders, and classes. By comparison, speciation gave rise to subspecies and new species, and phyletic evolution to species and perhaps families. Quantum evolution is discontinuous; there is a change by a certain quantity or amount. There is an absence of the progressive shift which characterizes the other modes of evolution.

The evidence that quantum evolution does occur is found in the paleontological sequences. It is not uncommon to find examples that seem to indicate sudden small changes in group characteristics. Further, much indirect paleontological evidence indicates that major transitions take place at great rates over short periods of time. There is also some experimental and observational evidence from the field of population genetics. For example, some organisms have left scanty remains in the fossil record for long periods of time, during which they were relatively simple and restricted forms. Suddenly, for some reason, these quiescent organisms seem to diversify and multiply at such a great rate that the term "explosive evolution" is used to describe the changes.

The initial stage in the quantum evolutionary process is thought to be the development of a condition to which the population cannot readily adapt itself. For a period the species is inadaptive, and the population loses equilibrium. The usual thing at this point is for the population to move into a new environment or suffer extinction, but in a few rare cases apparently a great pressure is built up to select the extreme variants (such as the mutants), and these multiply rapidly. Then, through successive generations of sustained highly selective pressures, the population begins to move toward a new equilibrium stage. The final step is the realization of equilibrium again, but when this is reached the changes that have taken place may be of such great magnitude that the structure, size, and organization of the organisms have virtually completely changed from their former state, and we recognize the new form as a member of a new order or class.

REFERENCES

BOUCOT, A. J., 1953, Life and death assemblages among fossils: Am. Jour. Sci., v. 251, p. 25-40

CLOUD, P. E., JR., 1948, Some problems and patterns of evolution exemplified by fossil invertebrates: Evolution, v. 2, p. 334-341

IMBRIE, JOHN, 1957, *The Species Problem with Fossil Animals:* Am. Assoc. Adv. Sci., Washington, D. C., Pub. 50, p. 125-153

JEPSEN, G. L., MAYR, E., and SIMPSON, G. C., 1949, *Genetics, Paleontology, and Evolution:* Princeton University Press, Princeton, 474 p.

SIMPSON, G. G., 1943, Criteria for genera, species, and subspecies in zoology and paleozoology: New York Acad. Sci. Ann., v. 44, p. 145-178

———, 1944, *Tempo and Mode in Evolution:* Columbia University Press, New York, 237 p.

———, 1951, The species concept: Evolution, v. 5, p. 285-289

———, 1953, *Life of the Past, an Introduction to Paleontology:* Yale University Press, New Haven, 198 p.

SIMPSON, G. G., PITTENDRIGH, C. S., and TIFFANY, L. H., 1957, *Life, an Introduction to Biology:* Harcourt, Brace and Company, New York, 845 p.

25 Trends of Evolution

Does man represent the culmination to date of the trends of evolution throughout all of geological time? Is he, in fact, the last and most advanced form that will ever inhabit the earth? Much of our philosophy of life is based on this fundamental assumption, although the question is rarely given serious consideration. Some biologists agree with this assumption. They think that a final state of completion of evolution has now been reached. However, change has been the dominant theme of evolution in the past. It has been slower at some times than at others, and it has been slower among some groups of organisms than it has among others, but there is no evidence that evolution tends to approach a state of equilibrium. There is no evidence that it has, as a whole, slowed down, nor is there any evidence to support the contention that it will reach a final completion. There is hardly any basis for the assumption that evolution has stopped. Many biologists contend, moreover, that there has been an acceleration in the rate of evolutionary change. They hold that this has been a tendency since the first life appeared on earth and that the rate of change at the present time is the greatest in the history of the world. Only time will answer these questions.

We will confine our attention to the evolution of life in the past and up to the present. Nothing characterizes life in the past billion years more than the single word "change." This has been the essence of evolution. What we know of the past comes mainly from the fossil record, and an abundant record it is. The fossil species of plants and animals that have inhabited the earth in the past number in the millions. Even so, they represent only a part of all the forms that have lived on the earth. Others without hard parts to be preserved must also have lived in the past. The fossil record is sufficiently complete to give us a very accurate picture of the relative abundance and the principal types of organisms that lived in the marginal seas and in and around swamps during each of the major divisions of geologic time since the beginning of the Cambrian Period. However, some important parts of the record have been lost during periods of emergence when the older fossil-bearing sequences were eroded and gradually worn away. Thus the record is replete with gaps of time that are forever lost. These gaps are extremely important because they make it impossible to achieve a complete reconstruction of the evolution of life in detail. That is, we cannot expect to obtain a perfect picture of each step in the evolution of the various living organisms. A second important handicap in attempting such a reconstruction is the fact that life had become quite advanced, and many steps in the evolution of higher forms had already taken place before the first fossils were preserved. For all practical purposes the fossil record begins with the Cambrian Period. The rock units of that age confront us with a rather advanced and complex group of organisms such as the trilobites. Until fossils are found in abundance in the Precambrian rocks we cannot hope to reconstruct accurately the earliest stages of evolution. It is possible that we will some day find fossils in rocks of the Precambrian. The most likely sites for them are the slates in which we may find the Precambrian counterpart of the Burgess shale.

Although the two limitations described above—lack of a fossil record for the Precambrian and lost intervals in the rock record—form important obstacles in solving the detailed steps in the evolutionary sequences, they have by no means prevented the detection of the major trends or tendencies of the evolutionary process. These major trends are closely tied in with what you have read of the mechanisms of evolution, and they provide a background against which the description of more detailed evolutionary trends among the invertebrates and vertebrates may be viewed.

GENERAL TRENDS—VERTEBRATES AND INVERTEBRATES

Changes in structure

The most positive and direct evidence of evolution comes from the observable changes in form or structure of the hard parts of the fossils. One or more of the following trends have characterized the evolution of most organisms at one time or another:

1. Increased divergence of forms—the emergence from the population of a single species of two or more groups that initially are similar in form and structure but become more differentiated with time. Eventually the structure of the two groups becomes so divergent that the groups cannot be considered as the same species.
2. Complexity of structure. These trends may be illustrated by such tendencies as those of certain invertebrates to:
   a. Coil their shells.
   b. Increase the complexity of partitions within the shells.
   c. Accentuate any special structures—such as spines or shell.
3. Trends toward extremes. Some trends have been toward the development of extreme sizes or structures. These have included such trends as increase in size, decrease in size, elaboration of ornaments on the shell or body. In some cases these changes have enabled the organism to achieve a better adaptation to its environment, but others have resulted in the extinction of the species.
4. Changes in structure or function. Such changes have in some instances opened up for the organisms new ways of life previously blocked to them. One of the best and most important examples is the development of the enclosed egg in reptiles. This made possible new modes of life on land and in turn provided the opportunity for a great variety of new divergences and changes of structure that led to the explosive evolution and expansion of the reptiles.

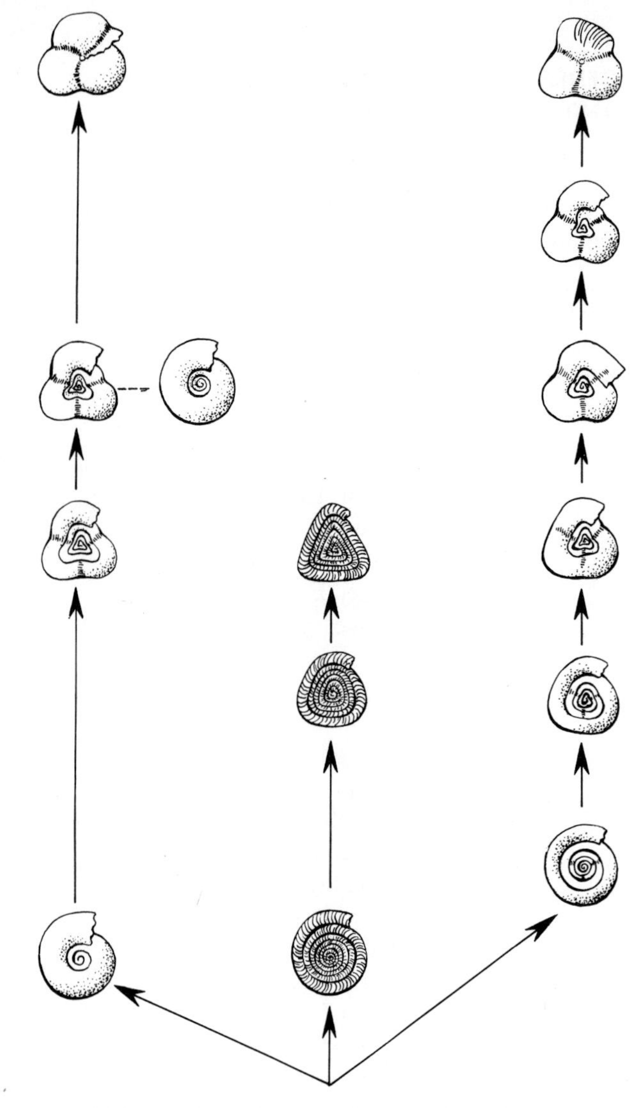

Fig. 25-1. The nature of evolutionary trends is a slow shift in physical traits. (After Schindewolf.)

Changes in level of organization

If the world did not possess such a myriad of organisms representing all levels of organization from that of the amoeba to that of man, it would be an extremely complex problem to ascribe certain levels of organization and function to the hard parts of fossils. Because such a distinction is possible we can detect that one of the major trends of the evolutionary process has been toward the development of higher levels of organization. The single cell accomplishes all the life functions of the protozoans. These cells are organized as tissues among the coelenterates and sponges. Specialized organs appear in the brachiopods and echinoderms. These organs become increasingly complex and more specialized among the higher animals. The fossil record dramatically documents these trends for us. The oldest fossil plants are among the simplest in structure. The most advanced, the angiosperms, appeared very late in our time scale. Likewise, the progression of important animal groups may be traced.

Lower Paleozoic—Invertebrates.
Mid-Paleozoic—Fishes.
Late Paleozoic—Amphibians.
Mesozoic—Reptiles.
Cenozoic—Mammals and Man.

Changes in level of organization and structure have in general made possible a better and more precise adaptation of the organisms to their environments. The mechanism responsible for the development of many of the changes has been natural selection. The effects of natural selection have usually led to improvement of the organism in the sense that it has become better adapted to a particular environmental niche. While this has been a common tendency through the past, we have but to consider the great number of extinct forms to see that it has not been universal. The long-range effects of this generalized improvement through structural modifications and changes in levels of organization have been:

1. More intensive and extensive occupation of environments and even the creation of new environments.
2. Overall expansion of life. This has consisted of general increases in number of organisms, increased diversity, and increased number of types of organisms.
3. Replacement of the older orders by newer and usually better-adapted organisms.

Overall tendencies

Environments. If we could have an opportunity to go back in time to the Cambrian Period to follow the gradual development of life, we would find ourselves in an amazing world indeed. There would be no trees, shrubs, or grasses anywhere. We would also be impressed by the absence of birds and reptiles, and there would not even be any of our familiar pests such as ants or rats. We would find the only signs of life in the seas, and even that would be unfamiliar to us. As millions of years passed we would witness a gradual change in the distribution and types of life. At first the marine organisms would expand in numbers and diversity. The first fishlike organism would appear. Until the Silurian Period there would be no life on the lands of the world. At about that time a general movement toward a new environment, the land, started. This required certain special new modes of life, and we would have to wait for the trial and error of evolutionary development to provide satisfactory adaptations to this new realm. In the succeeding hundreds of millions of years the adjustment to the land and its great variety of environmental niches becomes a reality. Plants and animals now inhabit almost every environment you can think of, and in great numbers. These include conditions ranging from those at the margins of glaciers to caves, deserts, plains, swamps, and even sand dunes, which appear at first glance to be devoid of life.

Expansion. Expansion of life has taken place in several ways. The overall number of organisms has become greater. The total number of different species has tended to increase. There has been increased diversity of form and structure, and even more phyla have appeared through time. We cannot say much about the rate of expansion during the initial stages of the development of life. The first signs of life may have appeared far back in the Precambrian, and early diversification may have required more time than all of that which has passed since the start of the Cambrian. However, there was rapid, almost "explosive" diversification early in the Paleozoic Era. Throughout the record some groups were on the decline, while others began to expand, but on the whole life expanded until the Silurian when the rate of increase stabilized somewhat. Only once toward the end of the Paleozoic did it appear that the overall expansion of life was stopped and even reversed, but following that period there has been another great expansion, which has continued up to the present.

Fig. 25-2. Abundance of life. One of the major trends in the history of life on earth has been an expansion of the number of groups represented. This chart shows in a general way the relative changes in the abundance of life at various times in the geologic past. The single restriction occurs at the end of the Paleozoic Era.

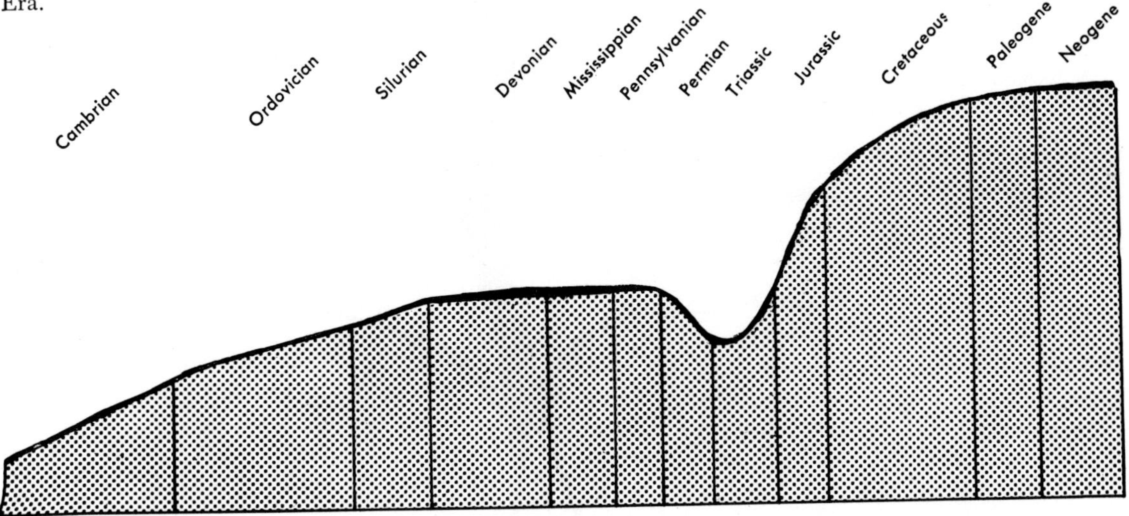

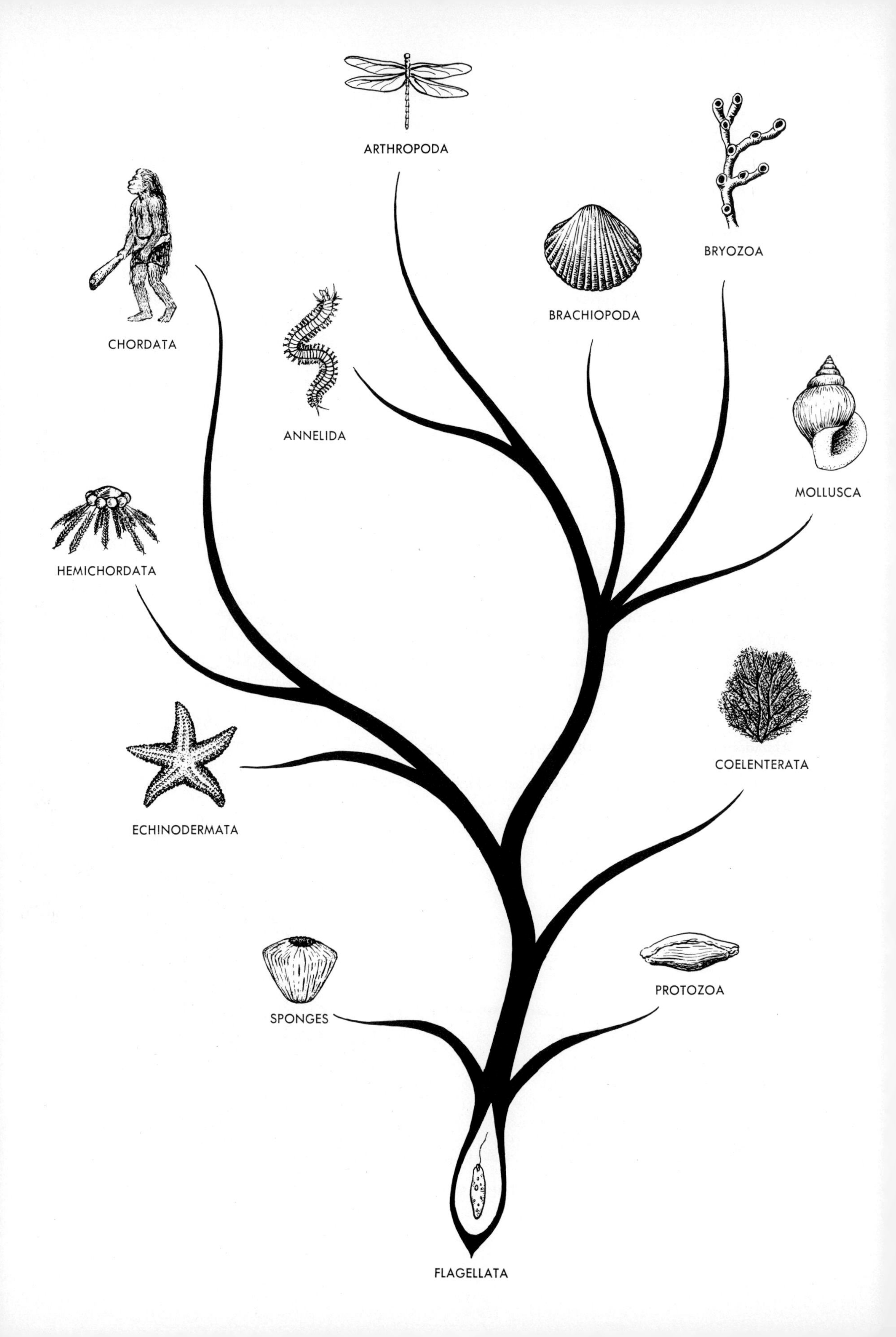
ARTHROPODA
BRYOZOA
CHORDATA
BRACHIOPODA
ANNELIDA
MOLLUSCA
HEMICHORDATA
COELENTERATA
ECHINODERMATA
PROTOZOA
SPONGES
FLAGELLATA

Fig. 25-3. One of the major trends in the evolution of life through the geologic past has been toward the evolution of higher forms representing a more complex level of organization. A schematic pattern of the evolution of the major groups is shown. (Modified after Hyman.)

Replacement. There are some rather remarkable instances in which species that developed in the early part of the Paleozoic have persisted and may even be found in modern-day seas. Such an example is *Lingula*, a brachiopod. If you were given shells of a fossil of the animal and a recently dredged *Lingula* you would find almost no difference in the form of the two. Many of the organisms that have had such a history are simple in structure and apparently well adjusted to their environments and capable of maintaining that adjustment even as the environment undergoes slow changes. Such instances are rather rare. While it is true that many of the same groups that lived in the Cambrian Period are represented today, the modern forms are replacements of older forms of the same group. Replacement is prompted by the development of a new form that is better adapted to a given environment.

EXAMPLES OF EVOLUTIONARY TRENDS AMONG THE INVERTEBRATES

Some of the evolutionary trends described in the preceding section are apparent from what you have learned about the faunal succession recorded in the stratigraphic sequences formed since Cambrian time. The expansion, divergence, and diversity of life have been implicit in our discussions of the appearance and spread of new groups in almost every period of geologic time. That they have occupied new environments is also obvious from our everyday knowledge of the habits and nature of fishes, birds, reptiles, and mammals. What is not so obvious from the common experience of man is the exact nature of the small-scale changes that bring about the gradual development of new forms and new ways of life. Only rarely are such changes of a dramatic nature. Instead, where we find complete unbroken sequences of fossiliferous rocks, the fossils show very small changes through time, and these are restricted to a few of the features of the animal. Furthermore, these changes do not necessarily apply to each and every member of the fossil population. When changes are indicated they are changes in the average characteristics of a fossil population, not of every individual or even every group within the population. If the entire population changed uniformly then there would be no divergence of forms, and there would be no survival of older species after new ones had developed. This is contrary to all our knowledge. A few illustrations

Fig. 25-4. *Lingula*, one of the most primitive brachiopods. *Lingula* appeared first in the early Paleozoic, but it has persisted to this day without notable change.

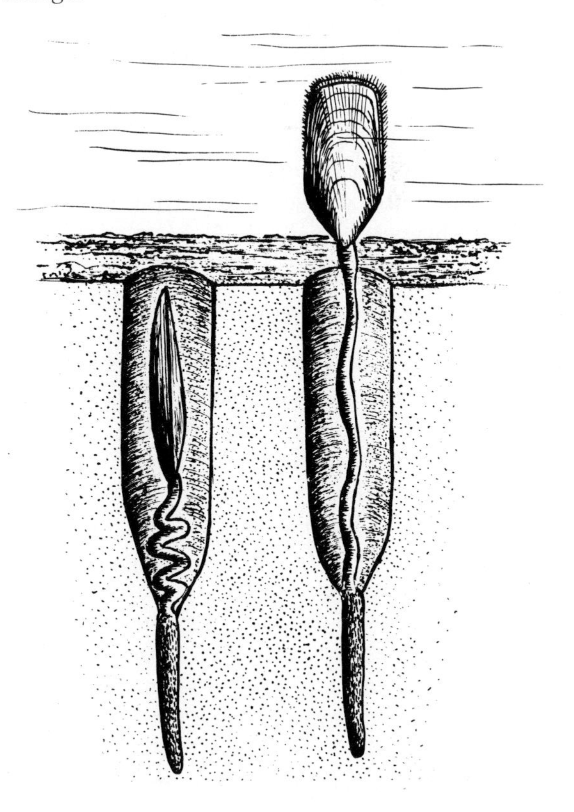

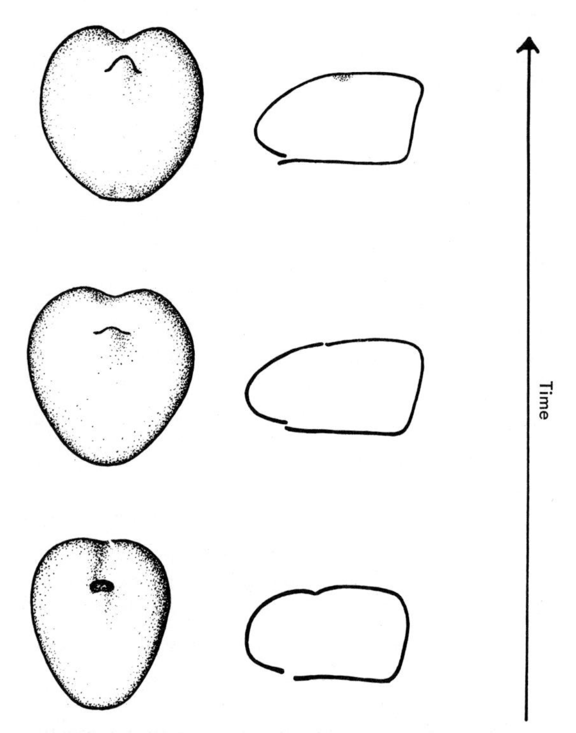

Fig. 25-5. The evolution of *Micraster*. The record of the small evolutionary changes which took place in these echinoderms during the Cretaceous is one of the most complete we have. It is possible in this case to see an unbroken series of changes in morphological features which lead to the evolution of several species. (After Neaverson.)

of the evolutionary changes in certain groups of invertebrates will serve to portray the nature of the changes we actually find.

Evolution of Micraster

Micraster is a sea urchin, an echinoderm of the class Echinoidea. They lived most abundantly in the seas off the western coast of Europe some 70 million years ago. Like other echinoids before and since, they lived on the sea bottom in marine waters. They were gregarious animals, and great numbers lived together, scavenging the sea floor for bits of food. When food is abundant they consume that which is found on the sea floor, but when it becomes more scarce the echinoderms will eat some sea-bottom sediments for their organic content.

Many other forms of life existed at the same time and in the same region with *Micraster*. In fact, the numbers of protozoans were so great that when the echinoids died their remains were buried in the tests or shells of the protozoans. Thus, over a long period of time in the late part of the Cretaceous Period, the unbroken "Chalk" formations of England were deposited. Parts of this sequence are exposed in the famous chalk cliffs of Dover. Within these units large numbers of *Micraster* have been found. Because the chalk is soft, it is a simple matter to remove the skeleton or test of *Micraster* without seriously damaging it. The echinoid tests possess many structural features that are readily identified, and the functioning of these may be interpreted by analogy with living echinoids. Thus these fossils make ideal material for the study of evolutionary changes.

Large numbers of the fossils have been collected, and their structural features have been carefully analyzed. A number of changes in form can be noticed. So reliable is the sequence of these changes that six zones in the Cretaceous are identified by this means. It is possible for a student of these units to take a collection of fossils from any one zone and predict the form of the fossil echinoids that will be found above and below it. This is somewhat surprising when we consider the nature of the changes that have taken place. They are (from the lowest to the highest zone):

1. Change from a small test to a larger test.
2. Shift of the widest portion of the test from a position ahead of midlength to the middle of the test.
3. The gradual development of a plate to cover the mouth, and a shift in the position of the mouth toward the anterior notch in the test.
4. A gradual increase in the ornamentation of the test.
5. Development of a larger "subanal fasciole," a hole in the top of the test connected with the water circulatory system.
6. Development of a deeper anterior notch.
7. Development of more complex plates in the test.

These evolutionary changes represent the main line of development, but within the zones there are several divergent lines. One of these leads to the development of an echinoid that is taller on the whole than the main line and in which the "subanal fasciole" tends to become smaller and almost to disappear, rather than to become larger.

Now we must ask the inevitable question "What caused these changes?" The interpretation is made in terms of environmental adaptations. The main stock underwent a series of changes leading to a progressively better adaptation to a life of burrowing in the bottom sediments. Many echinoids live this sort of life today. They burrow through the loosely consolidated sediments, obtaining food from the organic debris in it. It is obvious from modern echinoids that the plate over the mouth greatly increases the efficiency of the mouth as an organ of ingestion. It may well have been that the large populations of echinoids on the sea bottom in the Late Cretaceous made for short supply of food at the surface of the bottom. Thus those members of the population that could burrow effectively were better able to prosper and reproduce. In living echinoids the subanal fasciole is surrounded by a dense mass of cilia, which produce strong water currents directed toward the back of the animal. These would be most effective in discharging water from the burrow, and probably explains the large size of the hole in the more advanced forms.

The offshoot from this main stock appears to have become adapted for living on the surface of the bottom rather than in the bottom sediments. For this mode of life the subanal fasciole is unnecessary and thus decreased in size.

Gryphaea

Gryphaea is the name of an extinct genus of pelecypods, in a sense ancestors of the present-day oysters. They were most abundant during the Mesozoic Era when they lived a life very similar to that of the oyster. The shell was attached to the bottom of the sea, to a stone, or to some other shell. Like other pelecypods *Gryphaea* had two shells, but unlike most other pelecypods the two shells are not symmetrical nor even nearly alike. There is no plane of symmetry either within or between the shells. The attached shell is typically much larger and heavier than those of other pelecypods, and it grew in a tight coil at one end. The other shell was small, light, and flat. Like the *Micraster* echinoids, *Gryphaea* thrived in the Cretaceous in southern England, and from studies of these sequences some of the evolutionary trends of the animals have been traced.

The *Gryphaea* at that time thrived on the surface of the muddy sea bottoms. This is a very difficult environment for an animal that is attached to the sea floor so that it cannot move about and stay out of the dirty water. The problem is accentuated by the fact that as the animal grew larger the shell became heavy enough to break loose from its attachment and fall to the bottom, lying flat there. In response to this sort of environment several changes in structure occurred:

1. There was a general decrease in the size of the area of attachment between the shell and the bottom.
2. The size of the shell tended to increase.
3. The rate of coiling increased with the development of tighter and heavier coils.

Fig. 25-6. *Gryphaea*. This extinct group of pelecypods underwent evolutionary changes which lead to a tighter coiling of the shell and concentrated the weight of the shell at one end. The young animals attached their shells to rocks, but when they grew larger the shells broke loose and fell in the sediment. The weighted end tended to go down first allowing the animal to receive food from the unburied portion of the shell.

These trends in development may be simply explained in terms of the special habits of the animal and its need to stay out of the mud. The increased size and odd shape of the shell evolved in such a way as to keep the opening into the shell pointed upward so the animal could receive food and clean water. The end of the shell that developed into a tight heavy coil would tend to become oriented downward when the shell broke loose from its attachment. This left the aperture or opening to the shell upward above the bottom.

Another interesting development took place among the *Gryphaea.* Coiling continued throughout the life of the animal. This, combined with an evolutionary trend toward increased coiling, eventually led to the development of coils that were so large and tight that the small top shell became wedged into a closed position, in the later stages of life. This, of course, brought on death by starvation. This condition affected mainly the oversized adults but was not responsible for the eventual extinction of the group.

Fig. 25-7. Evolutionary changes in the suture patterns of the ammonoids.

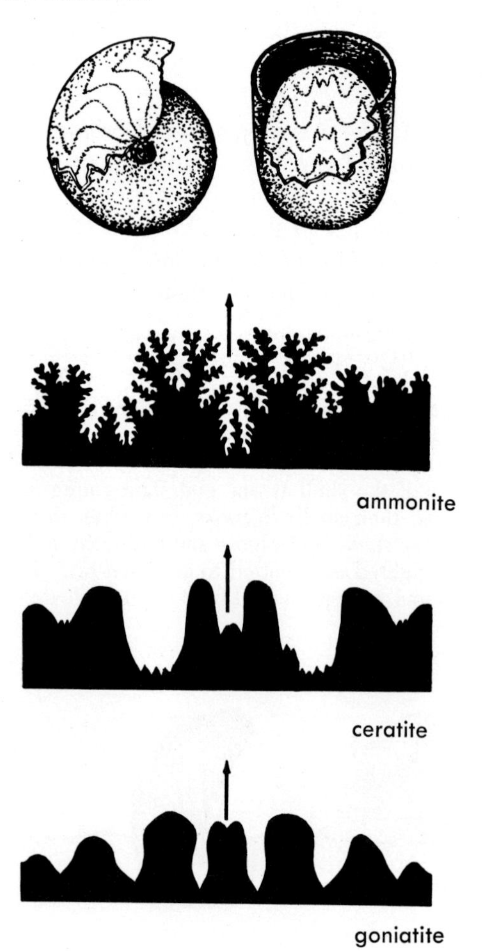

Evolution of the graptolites

Not all evolutionary changes can be directly related to the environment or habits of the animals. This is especially true of the extinct forms that have no closely related modern counterparts. Such is the case with the graptolites. Fossil remains are abundant in black shales and slates from lower Paleozoic rocks of many parts of the world. The abundance of the record allows the delineation of several distinct trends in the pattern of their development through time, but the nature of the remains leaves us without a good explanation of the function of some parts or the reason for the changes. Unfortunate as this is, it does not necessarily detract from the value of the graptolites for the purposes of stratigraphic correlation. In fact, they have certainly proven to be one of the most important groups for world-wide correlation of the lower Paleozoic shales and slates.

Studies of graptolite zones of the Ordovician and Silurian by Dr. Gertrude Elles have revealed these trends:

1. Progressive simplification of the branching of the stipes. In the Early Ordovician some of the graptolites had between 32 and 80 stipes, but by the end of the period the number had been reduced to a single stipe.
2. Change in the direction of growth of the stipes. In the early forms the stipes hung down, but they progressively shifted from this position toward a horizontal orientation and finally in the later forms extended straight up. Both of these trends seem to have developed together in the successful forms. Those forms in which the trend toward reduction in numbers of stipes proceeded

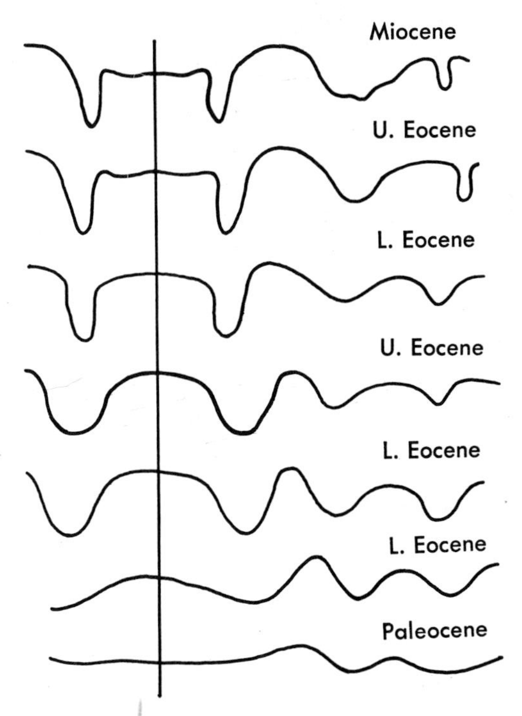

Fig. 25-8. Progressive series of nautiloid sutures. (Miller and Furnish.)

more rapidly than the change in growth direction tended to die out for some unexplained reason.

3. Elaboration of the thecae. This new trend began about the middle of the Ordovician Period. Up to that time the thecae (cups in which the individuals lived) had been simple and cylindrical in shape. Then a trend toward elaboration of the thecae began, and the walls of the thecae began to become twisted.

Ammonoid suture patterns

The ammonoids are an extinct group of the cephalopods. They evolved from nautiloids in the Early Devonian and inhabited the seas of the world in large numbers until they died out about the end of the Mesozoic. Ammonoids are easily identified by the suture patterns formed where the septa, or partitions, they built behind the living chamber intersect the outside walls of the shells. Most, but not all, ammonoids were coiled. Toward the end of the Paleozoic and in the Mesozoic they became highly diversified in structure. The most remarkable diversification occurred in the shapes of the suture pattern. This underwent progressive evolutionary change from a relatively simple pattern toward increasingly complex and intricate designs, as illustrated in Fig. 25-7. In the early forms the pattern makes a smooth-flowing curve that is not very different from the pattern of many nautiloids. But later the smooth curve becomes crumpled, and a large number of folds are formed. By the end of the Paleozoic many forms began to show even more intricate patterns. The sutures became folded until the patterns became dendritic (treelike), and finally after millions of years the ammonoids disappeared from the earth.

As mentioned above, the nautiloids also have suture patterns which are somewhat simpler than most ammonoids. These suture patterns also underwent progressive modification through time as illustrated in Fig. 25-8.

Fusulinids

The family Fusulinidae has proven to be one of the most useful groups of index fossils.

Fig. 25-9. Parallelism in the development of the hingement of two groups of brachiopods. Evolutionary changes in members of different species or even higher orders is sometimes found to follow very similar lines. Such a case is illustrated here. At the bottom the profile of the two shells is shown. Notice that they are very different in curvature, but the hingement areas are almost identical.

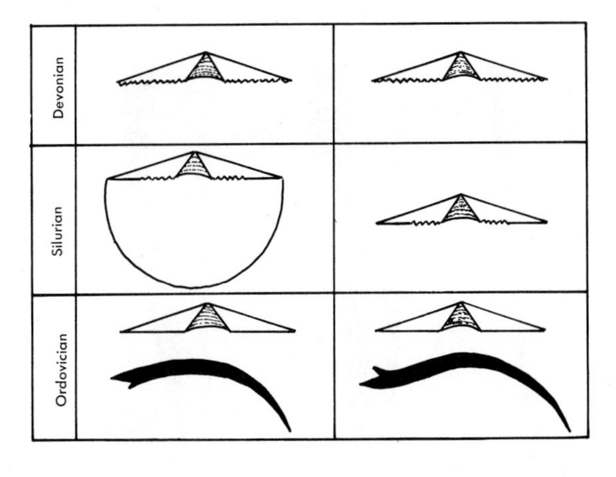

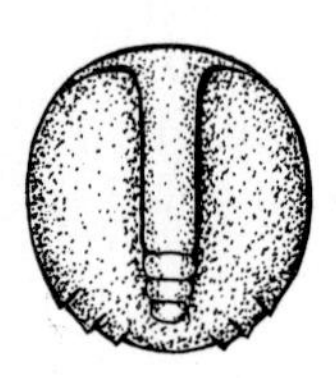
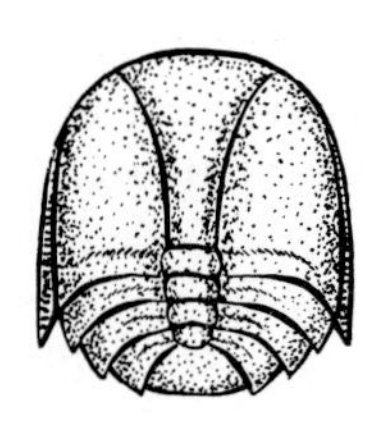
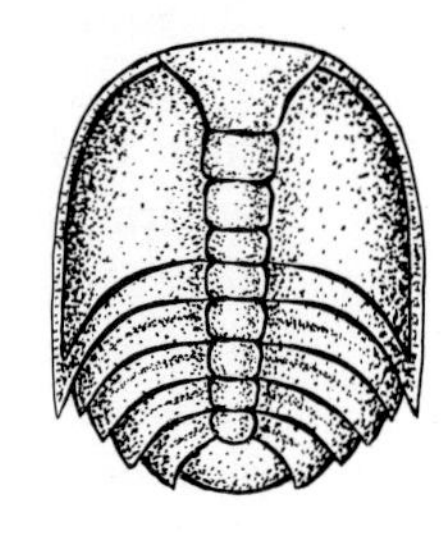
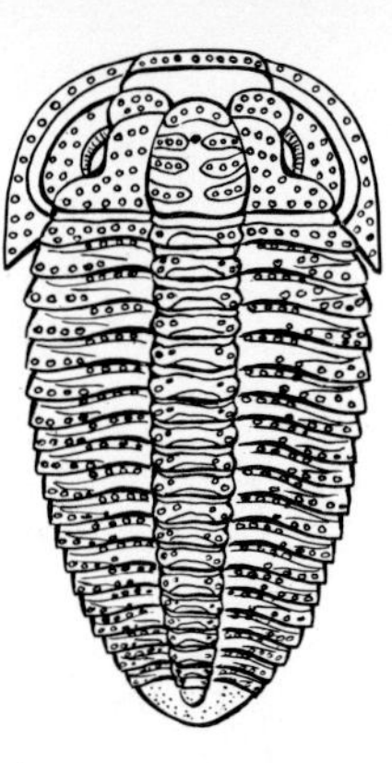

Fig. 25-10. Development of a trilobite. The recapitulation theory states that "ontogeny recapitulates phylogeny." Phylogeny is the history of a race, while ontogeny refers to the sequence of stages through which each individual goes in development. Thus the theory states in effect that each individual retraces the steps of its ancestry in the stages of its development. This diagram sketches four stages in the development of a particular species of trilobites. It is through studies based on this theory that we come closest to establishing the ties among the various phylae and classes, and in determining the most probable Precambrian ancestors of the groups found in the Cambrian System.

They are members of the phylum Protozoa, the single-celled animals, and are sometimes known as the larger Foraminifera. Of course, one of the main reasons they are useful for correlation is that they have tended to undergo changes, to become diversified structurally, so they may be easily differentiated. They first appeared in rocks of Late Mississippian age and became numerous before becoming extinct at the end of the Permian. We tend to lose sense of the time involved in a span like this one, 60 million years. By contrast the presence of man on earth is well documented for the past 2 million years, and some of the earliest forms may date back as much as 11 million years, but even this will be only a fraction of the time the fusulinids flourished before they became extinct.

Judging from the nature of the sediments in which fusulinids are found, it appears that they lived primarily in shallow waters on the continental shelves, but far enough out to be in clear water. The shells are most commonly shaped like grains of wheat. They are coiled around an axis which in most forms is the same axis as the greatest diameter. The interior of the shell is divided by a number of septa. In the later parts of the Paleozoic they underwent very rapid evolutionary changes throughout the world. Some of the trends were:

1. Change in shape. They tended to change from rounded spherical shapes to the slightly elongate "wheat-grain" form. Finally they became very elongate and almost cylindrical in shape.

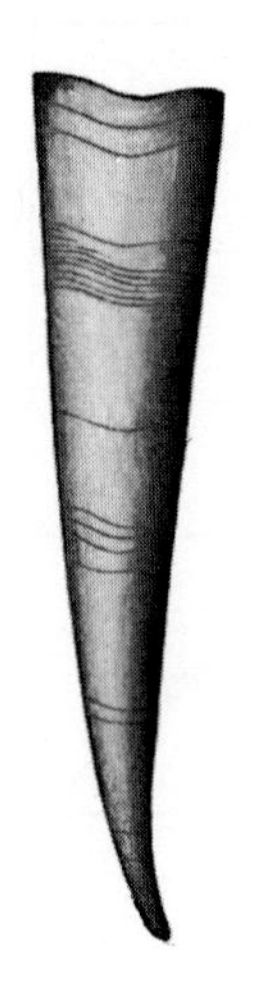
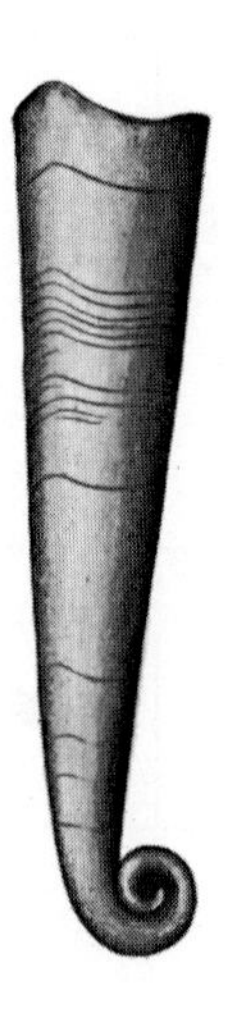
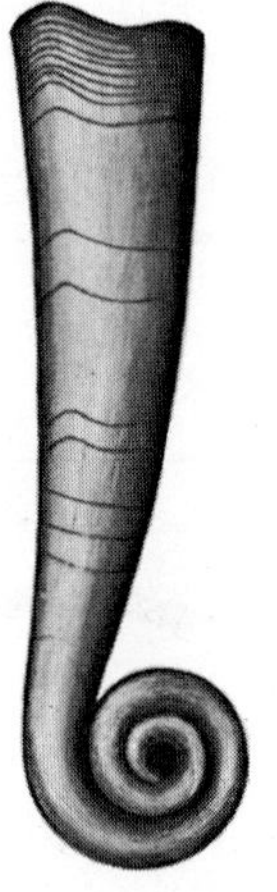
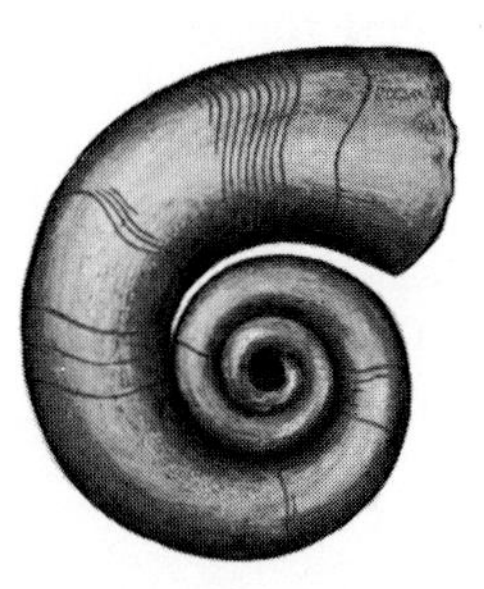

Fig. 25-11. Evolution of coiling in cephalopods.

2. Increase of size. The magnitude of this change was from less than 1 mm in diameter to more than 60 mm. Imagine some of the animals you are familiar with undergoing such a change.
3. Fluting of the septa.
4. Complication of the wall structure. These changes are worthy of special note. The walls are made of very small calcite crystals that are firmly cemented together. The trend was toward an increase in the number of layers in the wall structure and its general complication.

REFERENCES

CLOUD, P. E., JR., 1948, Some problems and patterns of evolution exemplified by fossil invertebrates: Evolution, v. 2, p. 334-341

SCHINDEWOLF, O. H., 1950, *Grundfragen der Palaontologie:* Schweizerbart, Stuttgart, 506 p.

SCOTT, W. B., 1917, *The Theory of Evolution:* 3d ed., Macmillan Company, New York, 183 p.

SIMPSON, G. G., 1944, *Tempo and Mode in Evolution:* Columbia University Press, New York, 237 p.

SIMPSON, G. G., PITTENDRIGH, C. S., and TIFFANY, L. H., 1957, *Life, an Introduction to Biology:* Harcourt, Brace and Company, New York, 845 p.

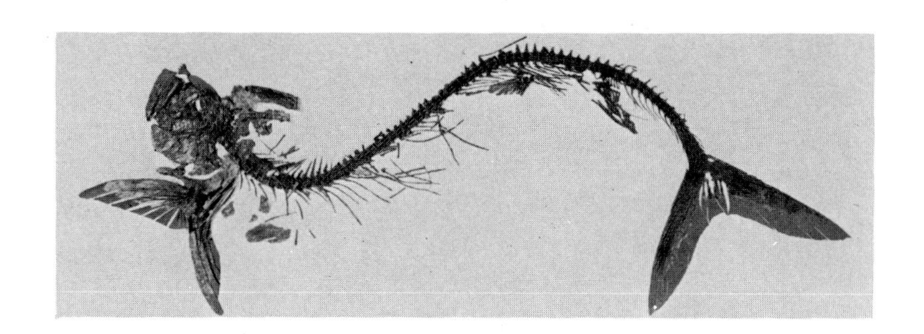

VII EVOLUTION OF THE ANIMALS WITH BACKBONES

26 Evolution of Fishes and Amphibians

THE EARLIEST VERTEBRATES: THE FISHES

So little evidence remains of the first animals with backbones that it is almost impossible to tell accurately what they were like. The only indication of these early fishes is a few scales of bony structure, which have been found in fresh-water sediments of Ordovician age in Colorado. But this is enough to establish their presence and to give rise to the hope that better-preserved specimens will be found in time. A recently described fossil from the Silurian rocks of England supports the idea that these early fishes bore a strong resemblance to the modern lamprey. The lamprey is a representative of the class Agnatha, the jawless vertebrates. It has a round, cup-shaped mouth, which enables this eel-like vertebrate to attach itself to the side of another fish. Its tongue has a rasplike surface, which is used to scrape the side of the victim fish, thus allowing the lamprey to lead the life of a parasite, feeding off its prey. It is quite probable that the first fish had a somewhat similar mouth, which was used to suck up food from the sea and lake bottoms. The lamprey is also a soft-bodied fish. It has no bones and its body is supported by cartilage. It has neither scales nor paired fins. Although certainly not identical to these relatively simple, present-day vertebrates, the first fishes are thought to have been quite similar.

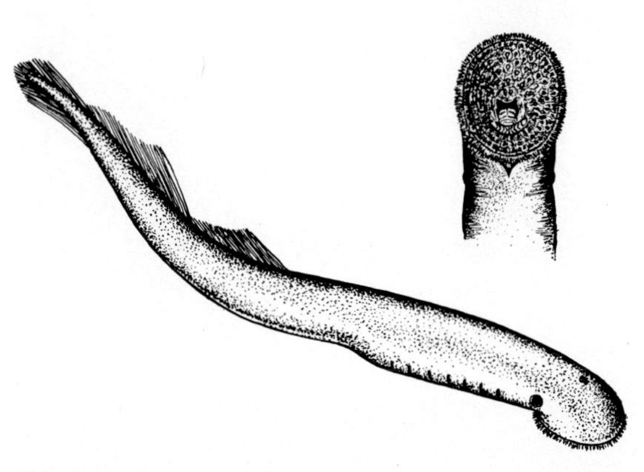

Fig. 26-1. Lamprey. The lampreys probably resemble the early fishes. Note the rasplike projection in the mouth. These are used by the lampreys to attach themselves to their prey.

Ostracoderms

The first group of fishes to be well documented in the fossil record is the ostracoderms. Like the lampreys they belong to the class Agnatha, or jawless vertebrates. They also resembled the lampreys in their lack of paired fins and a bony skeleton, but, unlike the latter fish, the ostracoderms did have bony plates or scales as an outside covering. The earliest trace of the ostracoderms to be found so far is from upper Silurian deposits. It is probable though that they were in existence long before that time. In the Devonian an explosive radiation occurred in the evolutionary history of the fishes. Many new forms appeared, and they became much better adapted to life in the oceans. From the Devonian to the present the fossil records abound with the great variety of fishes which has led up to the present-day forms.

The name ostracoderm is broadly applied to a great variety of the primitive fishes that are characterized by the absence of a lower jaw. There had already been a considerable amount of divergence among the ostracoderms before their first appearance in the fossil records.

One of the best-known genera of the ostracoderms was *Cephalaspis,* a heavily armored, foot-long fish. Its head was covered by a single, solid, rather flat shield, and its elongate body was similarly protected by heavy scales. As in many of the primitive fishes, the body tapers back to the base of the tail where it bends upward, forming strong dorsal support for the tail. Movements necessary for swimming were accomplished by flexing the body from side to side, setting up waves which traveled down the body length to the tail. The scales were arranged in vertical rows, making this flexibility possible.

Placoderms: fish with jaws

An extremely important evolutionary development took place when the first jaws were formed. The first fossil fishes known to have jaws have been found in Upper Silurian and Devonian sediments. Although it might seem probable that these evolved from the ostracoderms, there is no evidence to suggest such a connection. The two forms lived side by side for many millions of years in the Silurian and Devonian seas, but during the Devonian Period the placoderms, far better prepared to dominate life in the seas, apparently killed off the ostracoderms, since their extinction as written in the fossil record occurred at that time.

The importance of the development of jaws and the great advantage held by those animals possessing them is immediately apparent. The mode of their development can be seen in the structure of the gill arches. These structures, bony or cartilaginous supports for the gills, are roughly V-shaped with the V pointing toward the tail and opening toward the mouth. The transformations that took place

Fig. 26-2. Ostracoderms. These fish were abundant in the Late Silurian and early Devonian, but disappeared before the end of the Devonian. *Pteraspis,* below is one of the best known members of these jawless vertebrates. It was only about 2 1/4 inches long. (After A. S. Romer.)

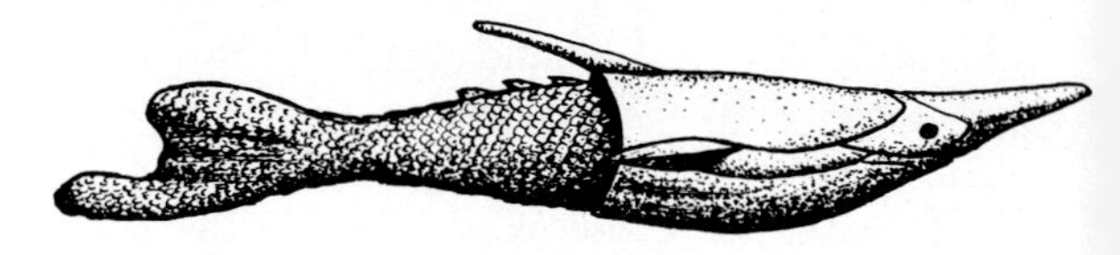

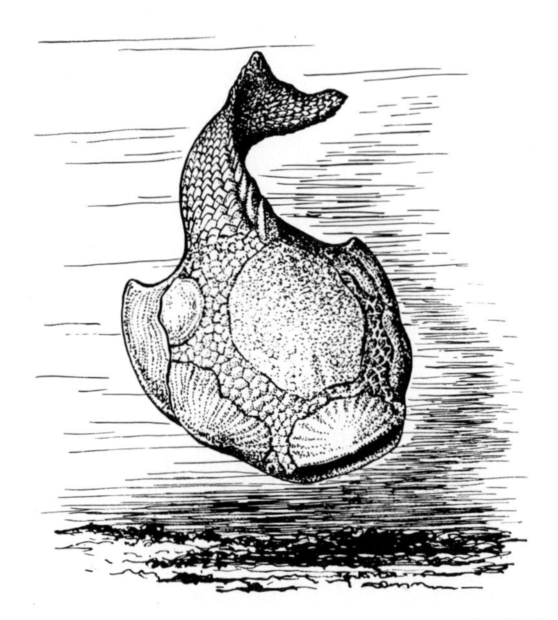

Fig. 26-3. Ostracoderms. This is one of the flat-bodied members of the group, *Psammolepis.* This one grew to be about a foot long. Note the bony plates arranged in the skin. (After Mark and Bystrow.)

in the evolution of these gill arches were essentially the enlargement of the lower side of the forward arch, the development of teeth, and a hinge at the pointed end of the V.

A great variety of placoderms inhabited the Middle Paleozoic seas; they were most abundant during the Devonian. Although one order survived into the Permian, the majority became extinct as the Devonian Period drew to a close. As in other instances, it was the most primitive form that survived the longest. Only a few inches long, this early fish, except for its blunt head and tail supported by the upward-bent body, had the appearance of many of the common, modern fishes.

Other varieties of the placoderms bore no resemblance at all to living vertebrates of today. In this group is the huge, Late Devonian fish, *Dinichthys.* The head and shield of some of these fishes were as long as 10 feet. Sharp, bony plates functioned as teeth, and the structure of the head-shield attachment allowed the *Dinichthys* to open its mouth not only by dropping its lower jaw, but by raising the upper one as well—a distinct advantage for a carnivorous fish. These fish were the giants of the Devonian seas, and it is likely that they dominated the waters of that time.

Still another of the placoderms resembled the Devonian sharks. They were small fish and had broad, flat heads, a tapering body, and a mouth lined with pointed teeth. The fins were greatly enlarged, as are those of the modern rays.

The cartilaginous fishes (sharks)

A third major group of fishes that evolved in the Devonian seas were those whose bodies are supported by cartilage, as are the sharks and their close relatives. The most unfortunate aspect of this structure is the absence of many hard parts that are likely to be preserved. The sharks did have hard teeth and, in some cases, hard spines, and these make up a large part of the available record. One of the best-preserved sharks to be discovered comes from the Upper Devonian shales south of Lake Erie. This nearly perfect preservation has made it possible for us to form a reasonably accurate picture of the appearance of these early sharks. They bear a remarkable similarity to the small modern shark. The differences become apparent in details such as the structure of the jaw hingement and the structure of the teeth. All of the sharklike fishes, such as the rays, the modern sharks, and the skates, evolved along two major lines from the primitive forms. One line, similar to many modern sharks, became extremely well adapted for the predaceous life they lived. They were streamlined and torpedo-shaped for fast motion; their

Fig. 26-4. Placoderms. This group was the first to have well defined jaws. Think of what an advantage this gave the group over the jawless vertebrates! Shown here is a mid-Devonian placoderm, *Pterichthyodes,* which was about six inches long. (After Traquair.)

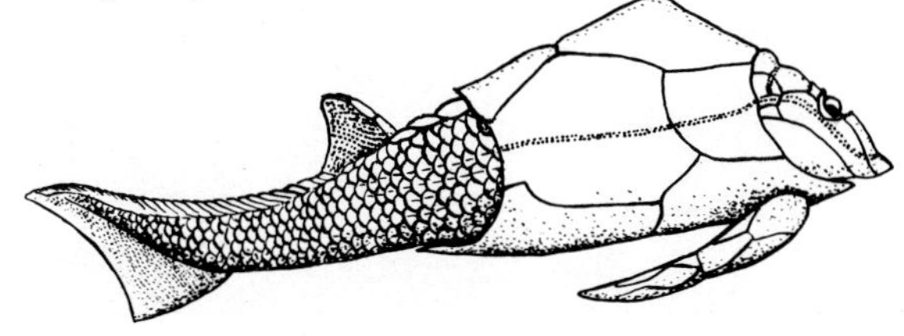

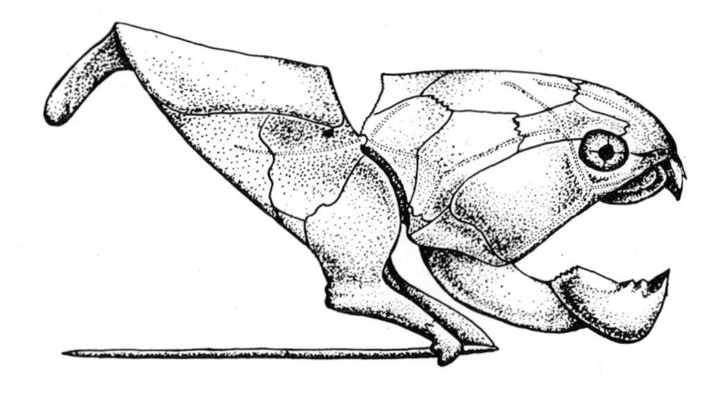

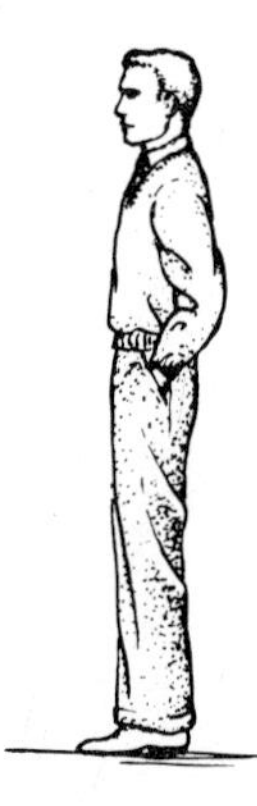

Fig. 26-5. Placoderms. This specimen of *Dinichthys*, an Upper Devonian placoderm, has a head which was over 10 feet long. It could open its mouth both by raising the upper jaw and lowering the lower jaw. (After Heintz.)

tail and fins allowed great freedom of movement. Their mouth and head structure became adapted in such a way as to permit the sharp teeth-like jaws to open widely. The other evolutional line led to the rays and skates, which are peculiarly suited for life on the bottom of the seas. Some of the modern rays are 6 feet across, and a few measure as wide as 20 feet. The pectoral fins are greatly enlarged, and their motion is controlled through the movement of these fins. The mouth, which opens on the under side, has very stout, platelike teeth suited for crushing and grinding, a feature essential for an animal living primarily on shellfish.

A remarkable thing about the sharks and their evolution is the similarity between the Devonian and modern sharks. Rarely does an animal become so particularly well adapted to a mode of life and fit so well into its ecological niche that it is able to maintain its position through so many millions of years, as the sharks have done. The modern mackerel sharks, including the most aggressive and fastest, such as the white shark, are the largest predatory animals in the present-day seas, but their 20- to 30-foot lengths seem small compared with some of the large Paleogene sharks. These grew to lengths of 50 feet or more, and their jaws gaped open widely enough to allow

Fig. 26-6. Lungfish. These fish are found in South America and in Africa. They have the ability to burrow into the bottom sediments and spend the dry seasons in the mud breathing through lungs during these periods when they are not surrounded by water. (Photo by courtesy of General Biological Supply House.)

Fig. 26-7. A group of fishes from a Tertiary lake. A school of bony fish (teleosts) is seen swimming over a pair of rays. (Chicago Natural History Museum.)

a man to walk through them erect. In the course of the evolutionary process not all sharks have been predators. This is especially true of the largest sharks. One of these less dangerous groups is the whale shark, which reaches lengths of 50 feet and lives on the small floating and swimming organisms in the upper reaches of the sea.

The bony fishes

This is by far the largest and most varied group of the fishes. They represent the culmination of this phase of evolution and make up the largest part of the fish population found in the lakes, streams, and seas of the modern world. The first representatives of this group made their appearance in the Devonian Period also. The distinguishing characteristics were the bony structures, highly developed both internally and externally. The body is completely covered by scales, and there is a covering over the gills with only one opening, whereas the sharks have an opening for each gill. The vertebrae are harder than the body supports found in the other fishes. The primitive bony fishes had lungs that functioned to enable them to breathe air, but through time this feature has evolved to become an air bladder that helps control the buoyancy of the animal.

Air-breathing fishes

Two primitive groups of the bony fishes were able to breathe air and thus survive periods out of the water. These were the lungfishes and the lobe-fin or crossopterygian fishes.

Fig. 26-8. The fossil remains of a large upper Cretaceous bony fish, *Ichthyodectes*. From the Pierre Formation of Niobrara County, Wyoming. Photo by courtesy of the U.S. National Museum.

The lungfishes are represented by three living genera, which inhabit fresh waters in Africa, Australia, and South America. Two varieties each have two lungs and are able to live for several months in the stream beds and pond bottoms after the water is completely evaporated. The Australian lungfishes are even able to walk a little, using their fins for locomotion. This certainly suggests the method by which the first amphibians must have evolved, but the early lungfishes do not represent the most probable forerunners of the amphibians.

The lungfishes and crossopterygian fishes have never been extremely abundant since they first appeared in the Devonian. Until the late 1930's it had been thought that the crossopterygians had been extinct since the end of the Cretaceous, but in 1938 one was brought up alive off the coast of Madagascar, and since then a number of others have been caught. The excitement that surrounded these discoveries was great because it was from this line that the amphibians almost certainly evolved. One very important fact about the fossil record was pointed out by this discovery of a fish thought to be extinct for more than 70 million years. This fact is the uncertainty of negative data or lack of data.

Even though the fossil remains of the primitive crossopterygians became quite scarce in deposits of later periods, they were relatively abundant in those of Devonian age. It was from this latter group that the connection between the lobe-fin fishes and the amphibians became apparent. Among the features of the crossopterygians that indicated this connection were their internal nostrils and their lungs. Their fins were exactly the kind from which the amphibians' legs might evolve. Not only was their skull pattern like that found in the first amphibians, but there was also a striking similarity in the structure of the backbone of the two.

Evolution of the bony fishes

Dr. E. N. Colbert, in his text on evolution of the vertebrates, traces the evolution of the bony fishes through the characteristics of three superorders of bony fishes: the Chondrostei (most primitive), the Holostei (intermediate), and the Teleostei (advanced). All three of these orders are represented by living forms, but the Teleostei are by far the most abundant. They include such familiar fishes as the perch, pike, eel, salmon, catfish, and bass. The intermediate form is represented by the alligator gar of the Mississippi Valley rivers, and the most primitive, by the sturgeon.

The first bony fishes appearing in freshwater deposits of Middle Devonian time were small. Their scales were diamond- or rhombic-shaped. They had large eyes and long mouths extending the length of the skull. There were paired fins in front and back, and the vertebrae were not hardened.

Among the general trends that are typical of the successive stages in the evolution of these bony fishes was a change in the shape and thickness of the scales from the early, heavy, rhombic scales to thin, rounded ones. The internal skeleton, which was initially all cartilaginous, became increasingly harder. In the most primitive group (Chondrostei) the lungs were not transformed into an air bladder, but in the later groups where this did occur they became effective means of balancing the animal. Other changes that took place involved the jaw hingement, the tail structure, and the position of the fins.

THE AMPHIBIANS

The first group of animals to encroach upon the land areas of the world and become adapted to a terrestrial life were the amphibians. This major step forward in the evolutionary story was to lead to the eventual conquest of the land by the reptiles and finally by the mammals. The first amphibians are now known to have appeared in the Devonian, and until the close of the Carboniferous they represented the most advanced form of life on earth. But their greatness was soon overshadowed by the better adaptation of the reptiles to life on land. By the end of the Triassic the amphibians had dwindled to a relatively small and unimportant class represented then, as now, by three groups—the frogs, salamanders, and several wormlike forms.

Most of us are familiar with the life of a typical amphibian, the frog. The small eggs covered by a jellylike mass are laid in the water. When they hatch, the embryo is a tadpole which must swim around to find its own food, the vegetation in the water. For this life in the water the tadpole is equipped with a flexible tail, and it uses special gills for breathing. As maturity is approached, metamorphosis occurs, and the life of the tadpole changes remarkably. Lungs develop, the gills disappear, limbs grow rapidly, and the young frog is soon adapted to a life on the land. It must return to the water only for the purpose of breeding.

The amphibians that have survived are a highly specialized and rather degenerate group. The remarkable thing about the class as a

Fig. 26-9. ***Latimeria.*** The only lobefin which still survives, *Latimeria,* was long thought to be extinct until one was caught near Madagascar. It was from a fish very similar to this one that the first amphibians are thought to have evolved. (Photo by courtesy of the American Museum of Natural History.)

Fig. 26-10. A restored *Eusthenopteron*, one of the lobe-finned crossopterygians. This fish is known from Devonian strata in the United States. The fins are stout enough to support the animal out of water; however, it probably could not move far away from water. (Modified after W. K. Gregory.)

Fig. 26-11. One of the most primitive amphibians from the Upper Devonian of Greenland. The limbs are no longer finlike in appearance, but the tail still resembles the fish tail fin. Compare this earliest amphibian with the lobe-finned fish (Fig. 26-10.)

Fig. 26-12. *Eryops*, one of the early labyrinthodont amphibians. This genera was one of the most abundant late Paleozoic amphibians.

whole is its early development from the fishes and its adaptation to the problems of living on the land. The first amphibian was beset by all sorts of problems which no previous animal had been forced to face. These included dependence upon lungs and respiration for oxygen, the necessity of strong limbs to support the body when its weight was not buoyed up by water, the need for a way of preventing the desiccation or drying out of the body, and finally a new means of locomotion. The amphibians evolved in such a way as to solve all of these problems. They are most closely related to the bony lobe-finned forms of the crossopterygian fishes. Among the most important characteristics of the crossopterygian fishes was their development of lungs suitable for breathing on land. The main difference between these and the first amphibians was the way in which the two made use of their lungs. The lung fish depend almost solely upon gills for oxygen and use lungs relatively little, while the amphibians depend almost exclusively upon their lungs. A second important difference is the development of strong legs in the amphibians. The legs of the early amphibians have structural patterns very similar to those that were characteristic of the majority of later land forms. These had evolved from the paired fins of the fish. Another important structural change took place in the backbone. The vertebrae of the amphibians became altered to form much stronger structures, which are better suited to support the weight of the animal out of water. Another necessary structural adaptation was concerned with sound. The fishes had no specialized mechanism for the transmission of sounds to the inner ear. An effective amplifying system evolved in the amphibians, making it possible for them to hear sounds propagated through air, an important feature for any land dweller.

The ancient amphibians

Labyrinthodonts. The amphibians that lived in the Paleozoic and early part of the Triassic were characterized in general by a skull that was completely covered by an armorlike mass of bone. On this account they are known as

Fig. 26-13. Whale shark. (Courtesy of the American Museum of National History.)

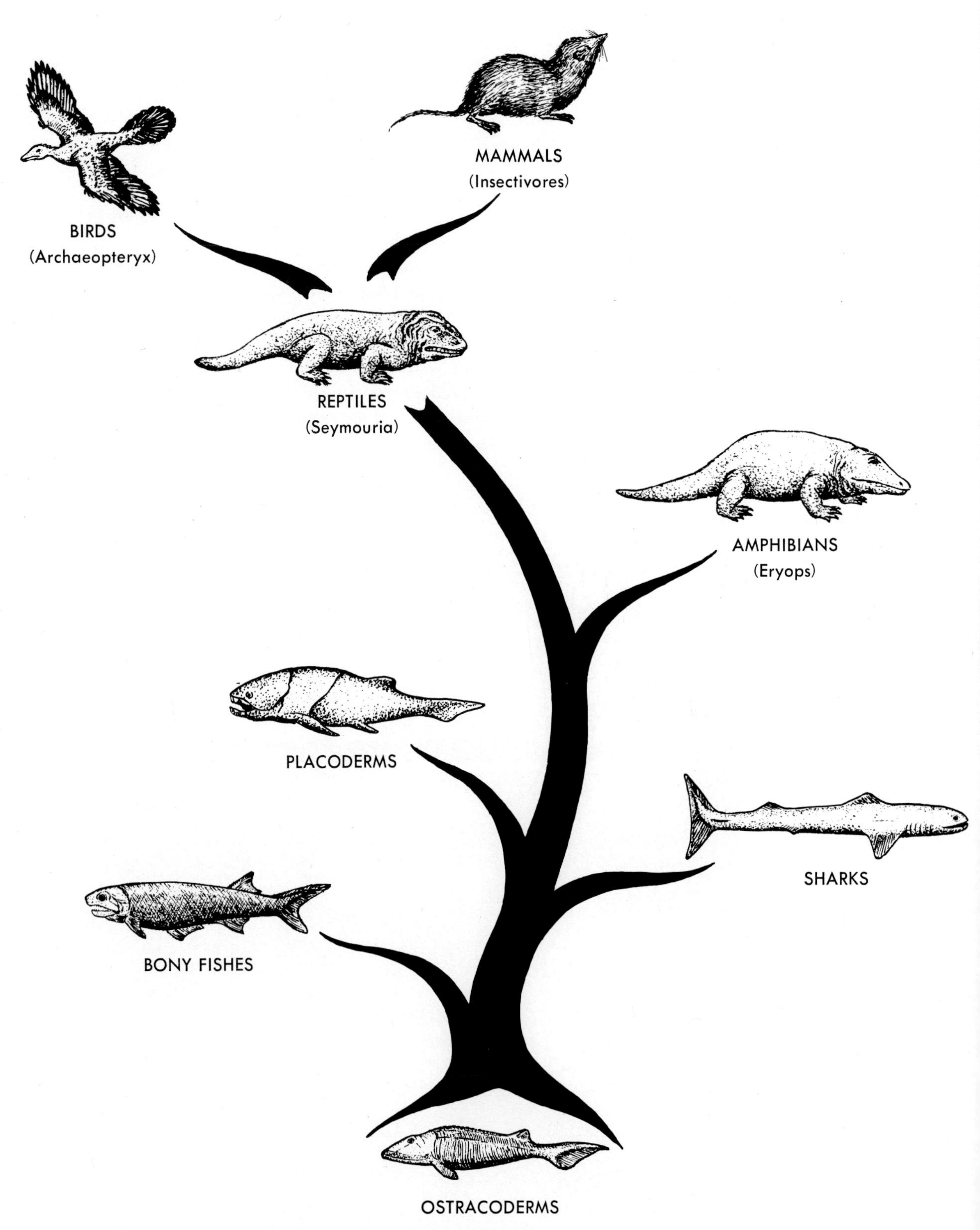

Fig. 26-14. Generalized evolutionary connections among the various major groups of fishes and the amphibians, reptiles, birds, and mammals.

the stegocephalians (roof-headed amphibians). The largest group of ancient amphibians were the labyrinthodonts, a name derived from the structure of their teeth, which were grooved and infolded in a complex pattern.

Until recently the oldest amphibians had been found in the swamp deposits (Coal Measures) of the Carboniferous Period. Many diversified forms were present in these deposits, indicating a long period of development before the Carboniferous. The gap in our knowledge has now been closed by the discovery of amphibian remains in the Devonian beds of Greenland. These earliest remains reveal an amphibian with a head and tail fin much like those of the crossopterygian fishes, but they also possessed short stubby limbs. In general aspect the early amphibians resembled the present-day salamander, although some varieties grew to be 8 feet long. One of these, *Eryops*, is a fairly typical late Paleozoic amphibian. *Eryops* was a heavily built animal with a broad, flat skull of irregularly thick bone. This amphibian was well adapted to life on land because of its unusually strong and large bone structure. It probably lived an alligatorlike existence along the streams and lakes of the Carboniferous coal swamps. Its sharp teeth serve as a good indication that *Eryops* may have lived on fish and smaller land-dwelling forms.

In addition to the labyrinthodont amphibians and their relatives (frogs are a modern descendant), there is one other important group of primitive amphibians, the lepospondyles. Among the differences in these groups is the structure of the vertebrae, which in the lepospondyles consists essentially of a thin sheath or cylinder of bone surrounding the notochord. A modern descendant is the salamander. The lepospondyles have been less progressive than the labyrinthodonts, and most of them have continued to live the largest part of their lives in water. The majority have been small with weak limbs and an eel-like shape. They were best suited for life in the shallow water and among the underbrush of the Carboniferous swamps. One very interesting representative of this group is the *Diplocaulus*, known from the Permian sediments of Texas. Its peculiar characteristic represents the culmination of a trend toward flattening of the skull. The skull bones and roof grew laterally, eventually giving the animal hornlike projections. The width increased to the point that the head was far wider than it was long. It is difficult to imagine what possible reason there could have been for the development of this strangely shaped head.

The appearance and development of the amphibians is an extremely important step in the evolution of the vertebrate animals. What conditions prompted their evolution? One widely accepted idea is that the lobe-finned crossopterygians such as the one shown in Fig. 26-10 inhabited streams and ponds over an area subjected to occasional dry spells. During these periods many of the streams and pools dried up, leaving the fish stranded, frequently to die. The unique structural advantages of the lobe fins enabled the crossopterygians to move for short distances across dry stream beds into other bodies of water. Thus selective pressures were built up favoring those crossopterygians which were best adapted for movement on land. This selective pressure led in time to the first amphibians, similar to those in Fig. 26-11. Confronted with no opponents on the land, these early amphibians could make full use of their newly developed ability.

REFERENCES

COLBERT, E. H., 1951, *The Dinosaur Book:* McGraw-Hill Book Company, New York, 156 p.

———, 1955, *Evolution of the Vertebrates:* John Wiley and Sons, New York, 479 p.

FENTON, C. L., and FENTON, M. A., 1958, *The Fossil Book:* Doubleday and Company, Garden City, 482 p.

ROMER, A. S., 1945, *Vertebrate Paleontology:* The University of Chicago Press, Chicago, 687 p.

———, 1959, *The Vertebrate Story:* The University of Chicago Press, Chicago, 437 p.

STIRTON, R. A., 1959, *Time, Life, and Man, the Fossil Record:* John Wiley and Sons, New York, 558 p.

YOUNG, J. Z., 1954, The evolution of vertebrate organization: Quart. Jour. Geol. Soc. of London, v. CVI, no. 437, p. 1-9

27 Rule of the Reptiles

There is no more fascinating story in the history of the earth than that of the rise, spread, and eventual fall of the reptiles as the dominant form of life on earth. They ruled for a period of more than 130 million years during which they adapted themselves to and dominated life on land, in the deep seas, in the marshes, and in the air. The most prominent members of the reptile family during the Mesozoic Era were the dinosaurs, which eventually vanished from the face of the earth, leaving only their scattered remains preserved for later discovery in the sediments of the era. The dinosaurs, like other reptiles, were of various sizes ranging from 1 up to 90 or more feet in length.

The first evidence of the existence of reptiles has been found in the fossil record of the Carboniferous Period. The correct classification of these first reptilian remains has been much debated, for they closely resemble those of the Permian amphibians, the labyrinthodonts. Since the reptiles are now known to have evolved from the labyrinthodonts, it is not surprising that the initial branchings from the amphibian patterns are only slightly different.

An almost perfectly intermediate fossil form between reptiles and amphibians has been discovered. Known as *Seymouria* (see-moor-e-ya), it has anatomical features partially characteristic of amphibians and partially of reptiles.

The amphibians had made a tremendous step forward in developing a means of living effectively on land. However, one weak link continued to exist in their pattern of life, and this probably caused them to be overcome eventually by the reptiles. That weak link was the necessity of the amphibian to lay its eggs in or near water. Evolution of a hard egg covering, the shell, made it possible for the reptiles to overcome this problem and allowed their young to hatch out on the land surface far from water.

The first reptiles appeared shortly after the first labyrinthodonts. For a time they coexisted on the land, competing with one another, but eventually the reptiles won the struggle. As the history of the labyrinthodonts drew to a close they retreated back into the sea and after a short time became extinct.

Characteristics of the reptiles

The development of the shell covering over the reptile egg should be emphasized as one of the most important differences between two otherwise similar classes (reptiles and amphibians), and furthermore as a significant step in the evolutionary history of organisms toward higher degrees of development. The shell protects the egg from physical harm, provides it with oxygen, and contains the necessary food for the development of the embryo. At the same time it frees the reptile from an early youth in water.

The reptiles, like the amphibians, contain no system for the regulation of body heat. This is important in that it confines such cold-blooded animals to warm, temperate, or tropical climates.

In all respects the reptiles developed to a higher degree than the amphibians. They are superior in the manner of organization of their skeletons, muscles, and circulatory system. Although the reptile brain is small compared with that of the mammals, its capacity still exceeds that of its ancestors, the amphibians. Reptiles were the first animals to have even the most elemental forms of higher brain centers. One of the basic structural characteristics of the reptiles is the skull design. On this basis the reptiles may be roughly classified into five types:

Anapsida (an-aps-i-da). The top of the skull is solid.

Synapsida (sin-aps-i-da). An opening is found directly behind the eye.

Parapsida (par-aps-i-da). The opening is behind the eye and high.

Euryapsida (your-e-aps-i-da). The opening is back, high, and underlain by a bone structure different from that of the Parapsida.

Diapsida (dye-aps-i-da). There are two openings behind the eye.

These openings have been compared with similar ones on living animals, and it is found that the muscles that close the jaws have their attachment under the bones covering this area. When contracted, the muscle bulges. These openings facilitated this muscle action.

Forerunners of the dinosaurs

Cotylosaurs. The reptiles branched from the Paleozoic amphibians, the Labyrinthodontia, and for a time coexisted with them.

Fig. 27-1. Reptile leaving the egg. The hard egg covering was first evolved among the reptiles. It is one of the most important steps in the spread of life onto the land areas of the world. For the first time animals were free to roam far from water.

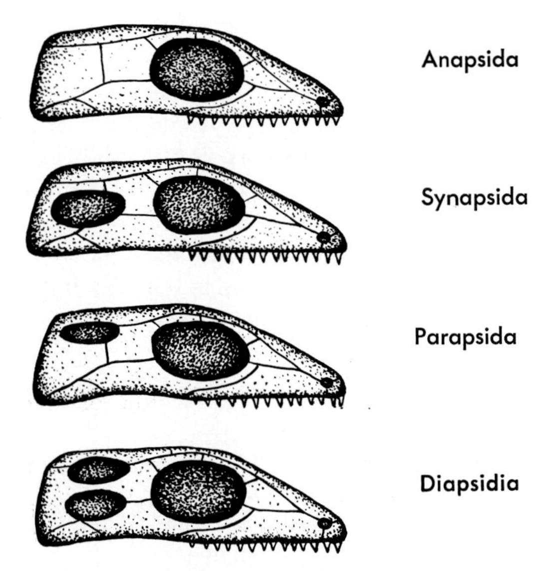

Fig. 27-2. Generalized skull structure of various classes of reptiles. Omitted is the class Euryapsid in which the structure is almost identical with that of the Parapsida except for the bone structure under the opening behind the eye.

These early forms of reptiles are called the cotylosauria (Ko-tile-o-sawr-e-ya). Mammal-like reptiles, fishlike mammals, dinosaurs, and turtles all radiated from the cotylosaurs. The cotylosauria evolved into several groups along slightly different lines during the Permian and Triassic periods before they died out in the Triassic. One line became smaller. They had a long low body and awkward sprawling limbs like those of the primitive reptile, *Seymouria.*

Thecodontia. One of the branches that evolved from the cotylosaurs was a very small, lizardlike reptile with a pointed head, sharp teeth, and two openings in the back of the skull. This was the first diapsid reptile and a member of the order Thecodontia (theek-o-dont-e-ya). The thecodonts were the first dinosaurs, and all of the others radiated from them. Unlike many of the dinosaurs that were to follow, the thecodonts were only about 4 feet long. They became adapted to bipedal locomotion, an important advance over the first land-living vertebrates, which walked on all fours. Bipedal locomotion was made possible by the hinged pelvis and the development of a long tail behind the pelvis which functioned as a counterbalance for the weight of the front of the body. Thus the pelvis acted somewhat like a fulcrum. With the two front feet off the ground, they soon became adapted in such a way that they could use them to grasp objects. The hind legs, which had to support the body weight and enable them to run, became stronger and longer, while the front feet diminished in size.

The phytosaurs (parallelism in evolution)

One group of Triassic thecodonts, the phytosaurs (fite-o-sawrs), became specialized in such a way as to suit them for a particular type of life in swamps. They do not look anything like most of the thecodonts, but their relationship to them is shown by the similarity of the structure of their skull and skeleton. They were large, some more than 20 feet long, four-footed reptiles that became adapted to live a life almost identical to that of the present-day crocodiles. They lived in swamps and along streams and lakes, where they preyed upon any animals that came within their reach. The average person would recognize only one difference in the phytosaurs and the crocodiles. That is the location of the nostrils directly in front of the eyes on the phytosaurs. It might appear that the simplest explanation of this is that the phytosaurs were primitive crocodiles and that the nostril has simply moved forward through time, but such is not the case. The phytosaurs became extinct at the end of the Triassic and are only distantly related to crocodiles. The evolution, even at different times, of similarity in outward appearance is known as parallelism. This is commonly found when related animals develop similar features as they become adapted to similar types of environments and similar types of lives. Can you think of any mammals that outwardly resemble fish or birds?

THE DINOSAURS

Dinosaurs were only one of the important forms to radiate from the early reptiles. When the first dinosaurs were discovered, an argu-

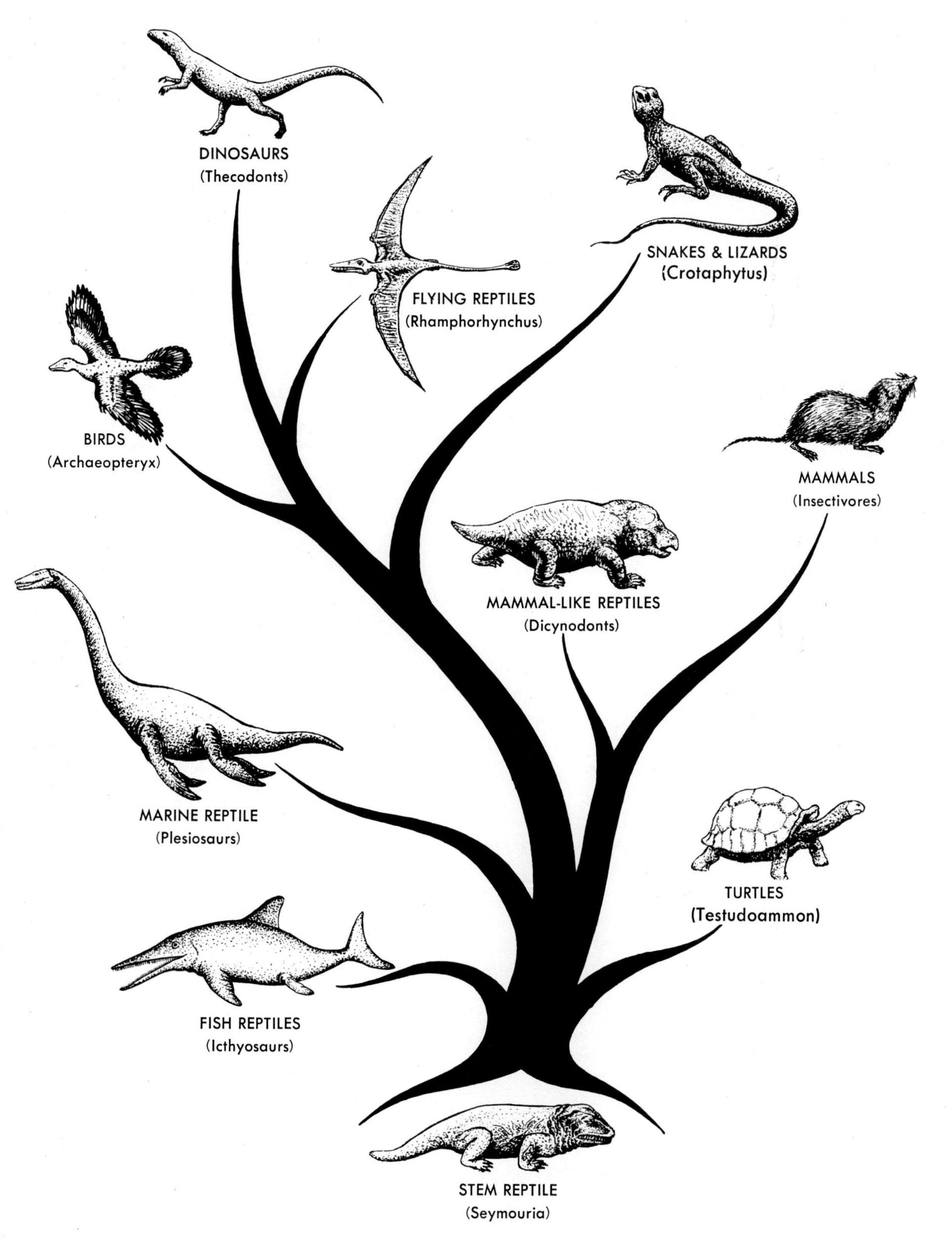

Fig. 27-3. Family tree of the reptiles showing their relationship to the amphibianlike reptile Seymouria, the birds, and mammals.

ment arose as to what they were. This might be expected since no such creatures had ever been seen before. The name "dinosaur," meaning "terrible lizard," was applied to the first fossil remains of these reptiles. Unfortunately it was not until many years later that it was realized that two distinctly different groups of fossil remains had been classed together under this name. As a result, the term dinosaur is now applied in somewhat the same context as the name "ungulate," which refers to animals with hoofs, although they may be as different as horses and cows.

The basic distinction between the two groups of dinosaurs is the structure of the pelvis. The immediate forerunner of the dinosaurs were the Thecondontia.

Classification of dinosaurs

ORDER SAURISCHIA. These were characterized by reptilelike pelvis structure. Some of them were herbivorous, others carnivorous. They had teeth along the sides and in front of the jaws.

Suborder Theropoda. A very active group that walked on two feet and were carnivorous. They lived during the Mesozoic Era.

Included are: *Ornitholestes.*
Allosaurus.
Tyrannosaurus.
Struthiomimus (the ostrich dinosaur).

Suborder Sauropoda. These dinosaurs had a tendency toward giantism. They were herbivorous, walked on all fours, and lived in swamps. They had long necks and tails, small heads, and few if any teeth. They lived during the Jurassic and Cretaceous periods.

Included are: *Plateosaurus.*
Brontosaurus.
Diplodocus.

ORDER ORNITHISCHIA. These dinosaurs had a birdlike pelvis. They lived during the Jurassic and Cretaceous periods and ate plants.

Suborder Ornithopoda. These are known as the duck-billed dinosaurs. Some were bipedal, others were quadrupedal. They lived in marshes and swamps.

Included are: *Ornithischians.*
Trachodonts.

Suborder Stegosauria. These were the large, plated dinosaurs that probably lived in uplands out of the swamps. They possessed dermal armor, were spiked, and very heavy-limbed.

Suborder Ankylosauria. These were heavily armored with bony plates. They were large dinosaurs that walked on all fours.

Suborder Ceratopsia. These heavy quadrupedal dinosaurs possessed a shieldlike extension of the skull. It covered the back and neck. They had a pointed beak and horns.

Included are: *Protoceratops.*
Triceratops.

Fig. 27-4. Pelvis structure of the two major orders of dinosaurs, the Saurischia and Ornithischia.

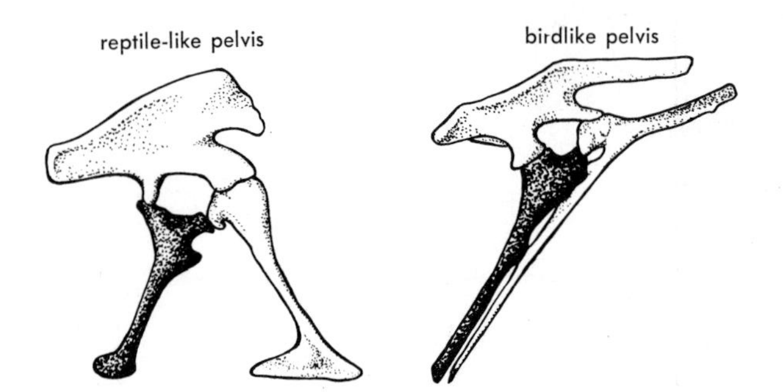

SAURISCHIAN DINOSAURS (REPTILELIKE PELVIS)

Theropoda (carnivores)

Ornitholestes. The theropods (ther-o-pods) continued to resemble their forerunners, the thecodonts, much more closely than any of the other dinosaurs, although for the most part they were much larger. One exception to this was the *Ornitholestes* (orn-i-tho-les-teez). These were no more than 6 feet long, and they continued to retain the general thecodont posture and shape. They were small, light, and strong reptiles that were efficiently built to enable them to prey on the small animals of the

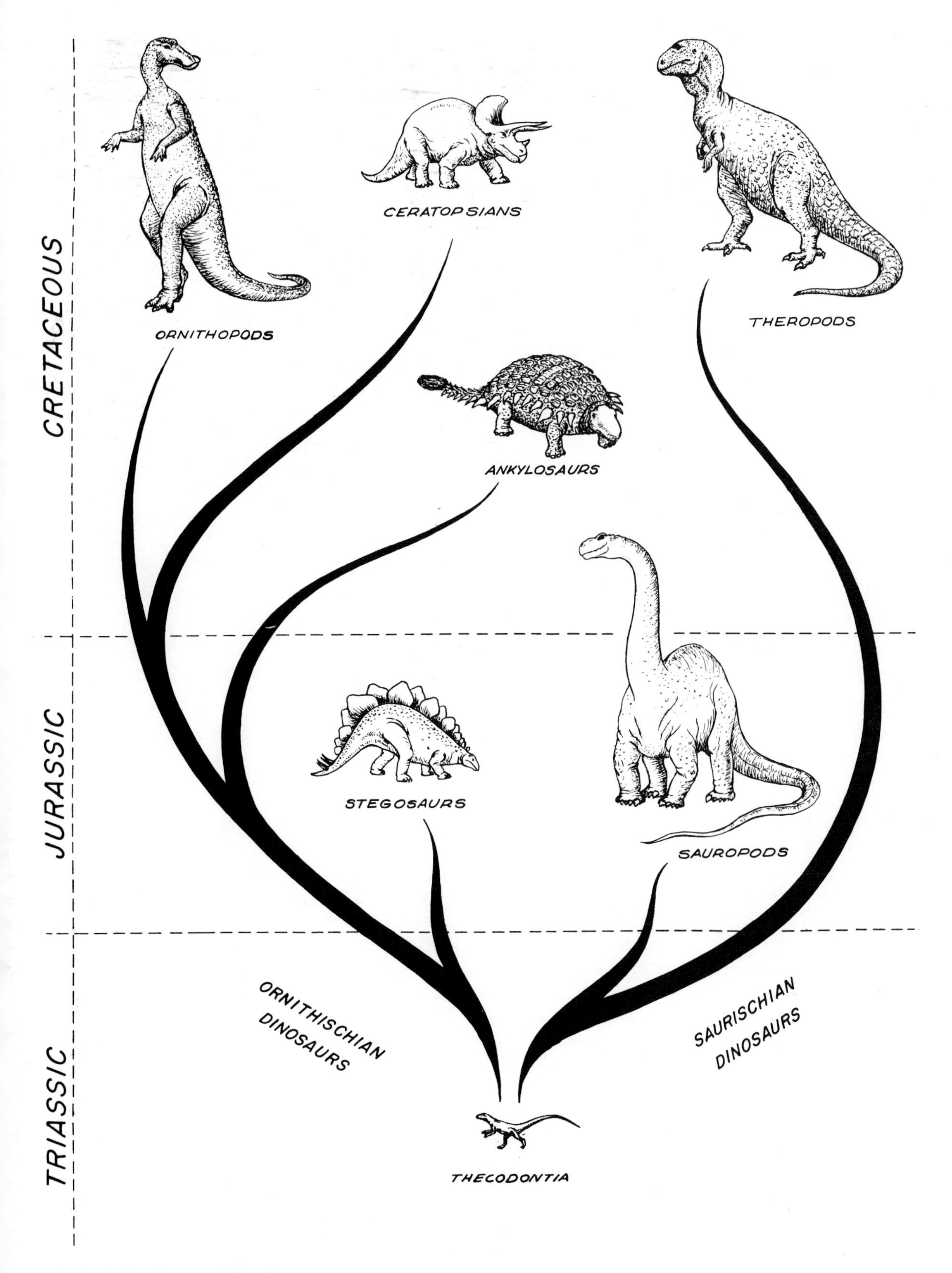

Fig. 27-5. Family tree of the dinosaurs.

Fig. 27-6. Giant sauropod dinosaur, *Diplodocus longus* Marsh. From the upper Jurassic Morrison formation in the Dinosaur National Monument, Uintah County, Utah. These dinosaurs are close relatives of the *Brontosaurus*. (Photo by courtesy of the U.S. National Museum.)

Jurassic Period. This meant that they had to be able to run fast and to possess a certain amount of agility.

The Allosaurs and Tyrannosaurus (a tendency to giantism). These theropods were small in the early stages of their evolution. *Allosaurus* appeared for the first time in the Jurassic Period. They grew to be 35 feet in length. This tendency toward giantism necessitated an adjustment in the structure of the animal. Bone sizes and structures suitable to hold up a 6-foot animal are not comparable to those that must be developed to hold up a 35-foot-long hulking mass. One result was the development of strong, thick hind legs, and the birdlike feet became much enlarged. Hooklike claws of the front feet and a large mouth with daggerlike teeth suited it well for its role of big-game hunter. The trend, which started with the growth of the allosaurs, culminated when the largest carnivorous dinosaur, *Tyrannosaurus* (tye-ran-o-sawr-us), appeared in the Cretaceous. The tyrannosaurs were probably the most ferocious beasts ever to walk the face of the earth. They grew to some 50 feet in length and stood as much as 20 feet off the ground. Their forearms diminished in size from those of the allosaurus, and the head and mouth became even larger. Apparently the animal depended on its large mouth, powerful legs, and sharp teeth for its power.

Sauropoda (herbivorous)

The sauropods are the second suborder of the saurischian dinosaurs. They too had the reptilelike pelvis and a strong tendency to giantism, but unlike the theropods they lived on plant matter and became adapted to life in swamps and low land areas where plants were in abundance. They reverted to walking on all fours, and developed long necks. The early sauropods lived in the Triassic. They were intermediate in size between the thecodonts and the later Mesozoic forms, which were to become the largest land animals in the history of the world. As they were relatively light they could walk around on their strong hind legs, but they must have assumed a four-footed stance for the purpose of grazing on the plants. Their teeth were blunt on the ends, a feature which was useful for cutting and chewing plant matter.

In the Jurassic the giants of the dinosaur dynasty appeared. One of these, *Brontosaurus*, was as long as 80 feet. They walked on all fours, probably as a result of their great size and weight. The problem of developing bones strong enough to support the weight of such a monster on its hind legs was never solved in the evolutionary scheme. The head was extremely small compared with the rest of the body, and its brain could have weighed no more than a few ounces. Probably these large defenseless animals escaped from their enemies by getting out into the water, for which they seem well adapted. The *Diplodocus* was particularly adapted for life in the water. It even evolved nostrils located on the top of its head. Thus it could be totally under water except for the top of the head and still get the necessary air

ORNITHISCHIAN DINOSAURS (BIRDLIKE PELVIS)

These were in general a more highly developed group of dinosaurs than the saurischian dinosaurs. Among the special develop-

Fig. 27-7. Plant-eating ornithopodous dinosaur, *Camptosaurus brownii* Gilmore. From the upper Jurassic Morrison formation of Albany County, Wyoming. (Photo by courtesy of the U.S. National Museum.)

Fig. 27-8. Duck-billed dinosaur, *Anatosaurus annectena* Marsh. From the upper Cretaceous Lance formation of Niobrara County, Wyoming. (Photo by courtesy of the U.S. National Museum.)

ments characteristic of this group are the specialization of the head and the teeth. Saurischians evolved mainly in the Jurassic, while the innovations in the ornithischians came later in the Cretaceous.

Ornithopods (orn-i-tho-pods)

These are the least highly specialized of the ornithischians. One of the first of them was *Camptosaurus,* a rather small (only 8 feet tall) herbivorous duck-billed dinosaur. They had a mouth particularly suited for groveling in the sands and muds of shallow-water bodies. Another rather strange member of the order was the *Troodon* (tro-o-dahn). The peculiar thing about these was that their brain cavities were covered by an extremely thick bone, giving them the name bone-headed dinosaurs. The ultimate in boneheadedness was reached in the late Cretaceous when one form evolved a skull bone about 9 inches thick and ornamented with various knobs and bumps, Fig. 27-9.

Stegosaurus

These herbivorous dinosaurs were contemporaries of the allosaurs and tyrannosaurs. They were able to survive because of a heavy armor. They were equipped with large finlike plates of bone armor down the back bone and with spikes on the end of their tail. Like many other ornithischians their fore legs were much smaller than the more powerful hind legs, but the animals walked on all fours. The small head of the *Stegosaurus* contained an unusually small brain, about the size of a peanut, but the spinal cord was enlarged at the hip. This enlargement, which functioned to control the movement of the rear end, was about 20 times larger than the total brain capacity of the head.

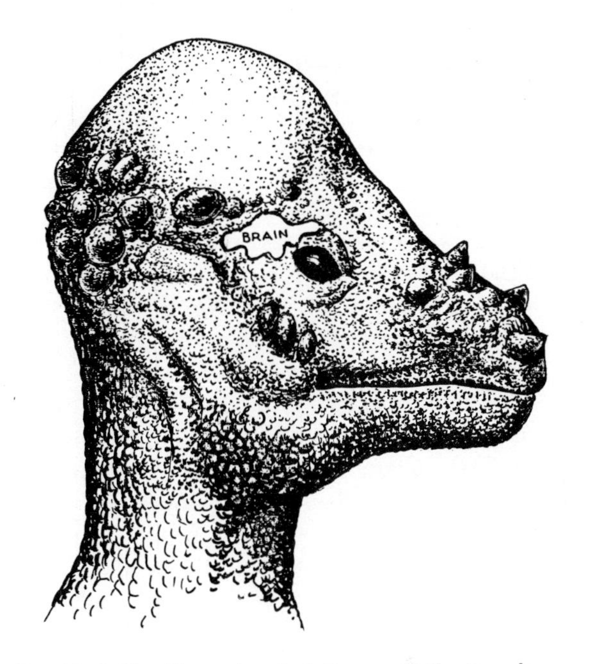

Fig. 27-9. The "bone-headed dinosaur," the *Troodon*. This dinosaur lived in the late Cretaceous. It was kin to the *Camptosaurus* and other ornithopods.

Ankylosaurus (an-kyle-o-sawr-us)

These armored dinosaurs evolved in the Cretaceous following the same pattern for survival set by *Stegosaurus* in the Jurassic. They probably come closer to being comparable to a tank than any other animal. They were low on the ground, of medium size, heavily armored with plates that fit together, and they were hinged in such a way as to articulate. The skull was broad and flat with a thick bone covering, and the tail was heavy, stiff, and contained a large mass of bone.

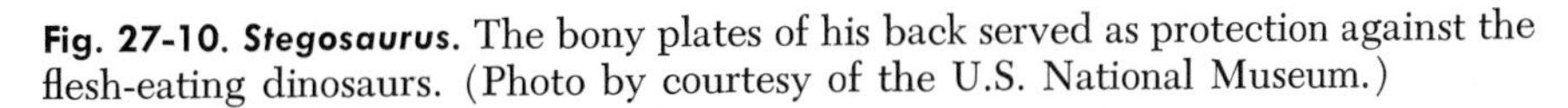

Fig. 27-10. *Stegosaurus*. The bony plates of his back served as protection against the flesh-eating dinosaurs. (Photo by courtesy of the U.S. National Museum.)

Ceratopsia (ser-a-tops-e-ya)
(adaptation of a shield covering)

These are commonly known as the horned dinosaurs. They did not appear until the Cretaceous and they were the last major group of dinosaurs to evolve. They provide us with one of the most extensive records of a progressively better adaptation of the morphology. They evolved a head shield that, combined with sharp horns, provided one of the most effective defenses against the tyrannosaurs. Their forerunners were small bipedal dinosaurs of the Early Cretaceous, which were characterized by a very deep and narrow skull. The front of the skull formed a beak. The first true ceratopsian was a small dinosaur with the beak and an extension of the skull backward over the neck. The shield of this 6-foot-long quadrupedal dinosaur was frilled to allow strong muscle attachments. In the development that was to follow, the cerotopsians became larger, reaching a length of 30 feet and standing 8 feet high. The shield developed to become a good 8 to 10 feet long. Thus about one-third of the animal was head and shield. In order to support this huge mass, the neck muscles were greatly enlarged. One of the best known of the ceratopsians was *Triceratops*, which was also one of the largest. They had a pointed beak, a large frilled shield, and two long pointed horns, a formidable enemy for the tyrannosaurs, but since the ceratopsians were herbivorous the armor was strictly a defensive mechanism.

THE AQUATIC REPTILES

The reptiles invaded and adapted to life in almost every type of environment. Some of them evolved in such a way as to become adapted to water, like amphibians, spending part of their life history in water and part on land. Others developed in such a way as to spend their entire lives in the water. We have seen that the cotylosaurs were the stem reptiles, from which all the other forms evolved.

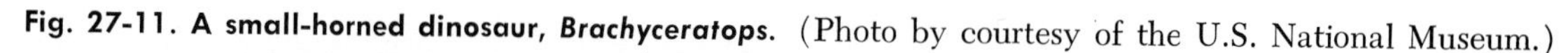

Fig. 27-11. A small-horned dinosaur, *Brachyceratops*. (Photo by courtesy of the U.S. National Museum.)

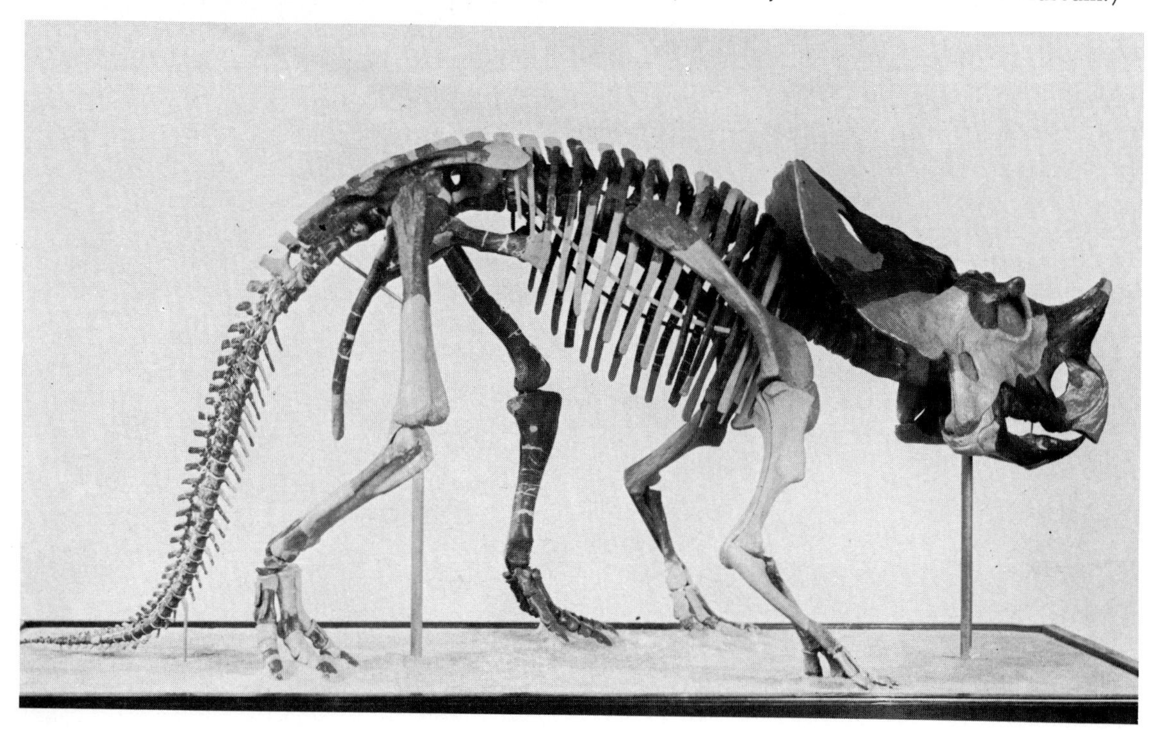

Fig. 27-12. Horned dinosaur, *Triceratops prorsus* Marsh. From the upper Cretaceous Lance formation of Converse County, Wyoming. (Photo by courtesy of the U.S. National Museum.)

Several of the lines that evolved from them were adapted to life in the water. The ichthyosaurs and the plesiosaurs are two of the best known of these. It should be emphasized that these reptiles were not true dinosaurs. Some dinosaurs did live in the water at least part of the time, and a number of the largest of them such as *Brontosaurus* sought refuge in the water from their adversaries.

Ichthyosaurs (convergence in evolutionary patterns)

The ichthyosaurs (ik-thee-o-sawrs) were parapsids, having the roof of the skull perforated by one opening behind the eye. They first appeared in the Triassic seas, at which time they were fully adapted to life in the water. These fishlike reptiles were shaped much like a modern porpoise. Their bodies were perfectly streamlined for fast swimming. The four limbs were altered to form fins (a reversion to the original use of limbs). The jaws grew out to form a tapering pointed beak. The jaws were armed with a large number of sharp teeth, which were used to catch and chew fish. They propelled themselves as fish do by a side-to-side movement of the body. They had no neck, and the head simply made up a part of the front of the streamlined body. The ichthyosaurs reached the height of their development in the Jurassic and Cretaceous. One interesting change occurred in the tails of the ichthyosaurs as they became more perfectly

Fig. 27-13. Convergence, an evolutionary trend toward similarity of outward appearance in unrelated groups. Compare the shark, a fish, the porpoise, a mammal, and the ichthyosaur, a reptile.

suited to life in the water. The end of their tails evolved into a fishlike tail, which served to stabilize the animal in swimming. The early ones were not so well adapted for this purpose as were those that lived toward the end of the Mesozoic. The development of the tail, head, feet, and other morphological features into fishlike organs makes the ichthyosaurs an excellent example of the pattern of convergence in evolution. Convergence in evolution is the assumption of very close resemblance of two or more unrelated forms. Compare the ichthyosaur (a reptile), the shark (a fish), and the porpoise (a mammal). All adapted to the same environment, and each evolved to forms particularly suited to a successful life in that environment.

Plesiosaurs (plees-i-o-sawrs)

Another pattern of adaptation to the marine environment began to develop during the Triassic. These early forms were small to medium-sized reptiles with long flexible necks, and limbs which took on the form of paddles. These limbs were very strong and probably enabled the animal to crawl out of the the water up on land in much the same fashion as a present-day seal or sea lion does. The heads were small, but the jaws were equipped with very sharp teeth suitable for catching and holding fish. The plesiosaurs evolved from this earlier stock in Jurassic time, and they survived until the end of the Cretaceous. The main change through this time was an increase in size. Some of the Cretaceous plesiosaurs were 40 feet long. The paddlelike limbs became strongly attached in such a way as to allow the paddles to be used very effectively. Studies of the muscle attachments and bone structure suggest that the plesiosaurs were able to operate these paddles like oars, rowing forward or backward or working them in opposite directions to make a fast turn. Since the animal had to rely on its ability to catch fish for food, it evolved in such a way as to do this effectively. One group evolved longer necks – so long, in fact, that they were over twice as long as the rest of the body. These long flexible necks could move from side to side as the animal caught fish with its sharp teeth. Another line evolved to form large heads. The extreme in this line was reached when some possessed heads over 12 feet in length.

HISTORY OF THE BIRDS

The fossil record contains the remains of birdlike reptiles which developed toward the middle of the Mesozoic Era. Indeed some of them became so large as to make the largest of today's birds seem small. The birdlike life of these creatures required adaptations and specializations that represent a more sensitively balanced system than any other trend in reptilian evolution. The requirements for flight are rigorous. The organism must overcome the gravitative pull on it, and this requires a special lightness in structure and strength of muscles which are usually effected by hollow bones and a light skeleton. In addition, the structure and amount of wing area must be adjusted to compensate for and balance the

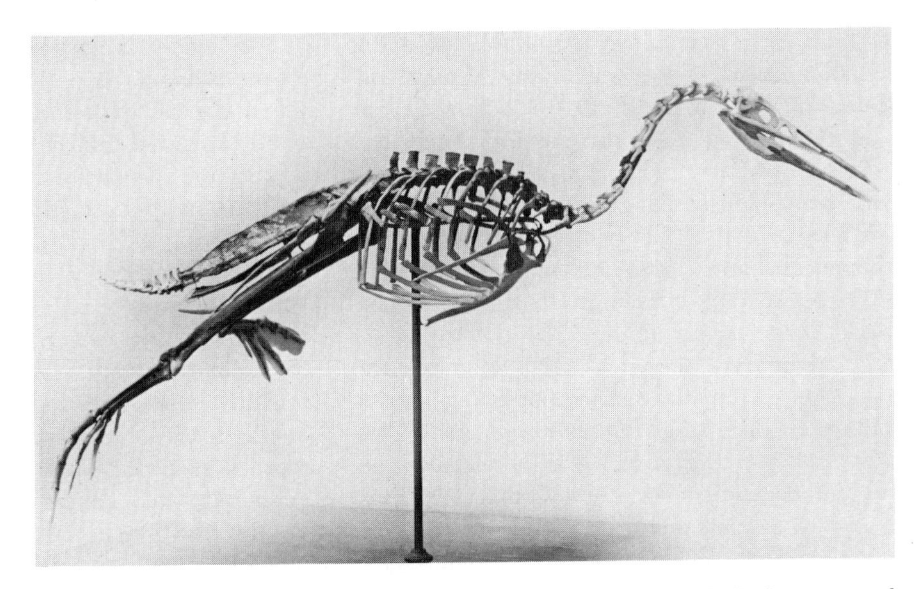

Fig. 27-14. Extinct toothed bird. From the upper Cretaceous Chalk formation of Logan County, Kansas. (Photo by courtesy of the U.S. National Museum.)

weight of the bird, even for soaring. For true flight even greater specialization is required. Flying animals also need some very effective guidance system, either good eyes or a mechanism such as the radar of the bats.

Unfortunately the record of fossil birds is very incomplete. This might be expected since most birds live on land and their remains are apt to be devoured by scavengers, and their small delicate bones are not so well suited for preservation as are those of larger animals. We are very fortunate, however, in having almost perfectly preserved fossil remains of two bird skeletons from the Jurassic Solenhofen limestone in Bavaria.

Birdlike reptiles (pterosaurs)

One of the Jurassic reptiles that became adapted to flight is *Rhamphorhynchus.* This reptile was about 2 feet long. The jaws and skull became elongated and contained sharp

Fig. 27-15. Restored skeleton of the flying reptile *Pteranodon ingens.* From the upper Cretaceous Chalk deposits of western Kansas. (Photo by courtesy of the U.S. National Museum.)

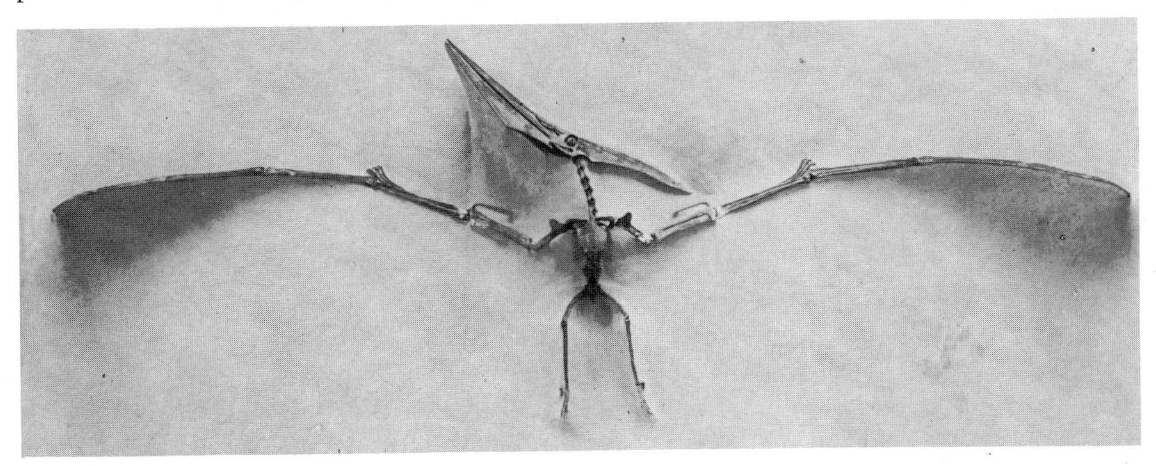

pointed teeth, which were probably used for catching fish. The tail was relatively long and flared out into a rudderlike structure at the end. Of particular interest are the shape and structure of the forelimbs. The fourth finger was tremendously elongated to form a support for a large wing. The first three fingers were shaped like small hooks with which the pterosaurs could hang to trees or rock ledges. The back limbs appear to have been very weak and might have served as wing attachments.

Late in the Jurassic another flying reptile branched from the *Rhamphorhynchus*. This was the pterodactyloid, which reached the peak of its development in the Cretaceous. This awkward-looking reptile had a wing spread of more than 25 feet, but the body was not substantially larger than a modern turkey or goose. Pterosaurs became extinct at the close of the Cretaceous. One important factor in their extinction must have been the evolution of true birds, which were better adapted for flight.

The first birds (*Archaeopteryx*)

The oldest fossil birds are found in the Solenhofen limestone. They are beautifully preserved, and were this not the case their remains probably would have been classified as those of another flying reptile, for the structure of the skeleton is extremely reptilelike. But in the calm scavenger-free waters of the Solenhofen Sea even the feathers of this bird were preserved. The *Archaeopteryx* was a little over a foot long. It had a long neck and a long tail, and its hind legs appear well adapted to walking or running. It probably walked somewhat like a chicken. The front of the skull and jaws were elongated and contained teeth, but they lacked the backward extension of the skull found in the pterosaurs. The long tail was characteristic of the reptiles. Three digits of the feet were greatly elongated to support the wing. Feathers extended out from the hand and lower arm bones, and some apparently were on the body. Other feathers were arranged along either side of the tail. Besides having feathers, the first bird differed from the reptiles in having an expanded brain capacity denoting a complex central nervous system.

By the Cretaceous time the birds were rapidly becoming more modern in aspect. Some of the steps in the modernization of the birds included the fusing of the bones of the hand and the development of a lighter body and a beak suited for picking berries and fruit. Birds of the Paleogene Period were probably very similar to some of the present-day forms. Among the evolutionary trends of the birds has been return to the ground, which characterizes such birds as the ostrich, but this has in general proved unsatisfactory since the mammals have controlled the lands of the Cenozoic. The most notable characteristics of the evolution of the birds in modern times is their adaptation to life in so many different ecological niches. A moment's thought on the different characteristics of the owl, the snipe, the hummingbird, the sea gull, and the hawk should be enough to remind you of the extreme variety of these adaptations.

28 The Rise of the Mammals

The mammals are now rulers of the earth in much the same fashion that the reptiles were in the Mesozoic Era. Like the Mesozoic reptiles, mammals live in the seas, they dominate the land areas, and they have become adapted to a great variety of modes of life. Their origin and development are of peculiar interest to us because man is a mammal. Although the mammals hold an exalted position now, they evolved from the lowly reptiles in the Jurassic and didn't come to be important for many millions of years.

MAMMAL CHARACTERISTICS

The most notable distinguishing characteristics of the mammals are:

1. THE SIZE OF THE BRAIN. This is the most outstanding mammalian attribute. Even the most stupid mammals possess much larger brains than the reptiles, especially if considered in relation to the total size of the animal. This enlargement in the brain size has been largely confined to one particular area of the brain, a part known as the cerebral hemispheres. This part, which is often called the "gray matter," governs the thought processes. This is the area in which sensory impressions are received and stored as memories that may later be used in the thought processes. The brains of all mammals are not alike, nor is the size a direct measure of the intelligence of the animal. The more progressive mammals have brains in which the cerebrum is folded in a complex manner.

Intelligence seems somewhat related to the surface area of this part of the brain.

2. A HIGH BODY TEMPERATURE. We say that mammals, like birds, are warm-blooded. This enables them to have a high rate of metabolism which in turn makes possible some of the complexities of the organization of the body. Associated with the warm blood is a system of cooling and maintaining the body temperature, such as sweat glands and hair covering the body. Other highly specialized systems include the circulatory system and the mammal's mechanisms for respiration.

3. REPRODUCTION. The mammals bear their young and give live birth to them. The young are nourished within the body of the mother, and then taken care of after birth until they have developed enough to take care of themselves.

4. STRUCTURE OF THE SKULL. One of the main bases for the classification of the reptiles is the structure of the skull, particularly with reference to the temporal openings. The skull of a mammal is very different. The penial eye is gone from the mammal skull. The jaw is changed considerably with the seven bones of the reptiles being represented in mammals by a single bone. The reptiles have a single bone connecting the head to the backbone, while mammals have two. The mammal brain case is much enlarged to hold the large brains, and the structure of the temporal region includes an arch at the edge of the cheek.

5. TEETH. The teeth provide one of the more important means of differentiating the various mammals. The teeth of the reptiles were comparatively simple, they were replaced many times during the life of the animal, and they were generally about the same shape throughout the jaw. In very general terms mammal teeth include four sharp teeth suited for nipping, at the front of the jaw; two large piercing teeth, the canines, located on either side; six premolar teeth; and finally four molars which are used for grinding.

REPTILELIKE MAMMALS

The earliest and most primitive reptiles were members of the order of which *Seymouria* was one of the best known members (Cotylosauria). It is strange that the first mammal-like reptiles should have come from this most primitive reptile stock, and not from one of the more advanced reptiles. One radiation from the cotylosaurs led to the dominant forms of life for the Mesozoic, the dinosaurs; another line of radiation led to the mammal-like reptiles, the pelycosaurs; and a third led to the therapsids. This last group and their survivors lived more or less as onlookers throughout the 150 million year reign of the reptiles. But at the end of that reign in the early Cenozoic, these forms, which had evolved as mammals, took over and have ruled the animal kingdom ever since.

The pelycosaurs (mammal-like reptiles)

Pelycosaurs branched from animals like *Seymouria* and were the first to have a skull structure known as synapsid, characterized by a temporal opening behind the eye. The first of this group were so much like reptiles that they almost certainly would be classified as reptiles, but as they evolved they came to resemble true mammals more and more closely until the two cannot be distinguished. A well-known genus of the pelycosaurs is *Dimetrodon.* They walked on all fours in a rather clumsy fashion, with legs protruding out to the side, and with an outward resemblance to lizards. Their mammal-like features included differentiation of the teeth into incisors, canines, and molars, and the structure of the bones of the cheek region were distinctly mammal-like with an arch structure in the cheek. One of the more peculiar features of the *Dimetrodon* was a row of spines which grew on its back and supported a sail-like skin covering. This sail-like feature has been the object of much speculation, very little of which can be supported by factual evidence. One explanation is that it was a primitive type of mechanism for the regulation of body heat. The blood vessels flowing through the skin covering the spines could absorb heat from the sun or lose it, like a radiator, when extended. The heat flow would be reduced by lowering the spines along the back.

The therapsids

Dimetrodon and other pelycosaurs were the dominant carnivors of the Permian, but another form branched off from them in the middle of the Permian, and these, the therapsids, lived on into the Triassic. The therapsids are best known from the beds of the Karroo in South Africa. They were about the size of a large dog, and among the more important changes from the reptiles represented in them is a bone structure in the legs, which indicated that they were adapted to a fast four-footed gait. Another important feature is the shape of the skull, which is intermediate between reptile and mammal. Some of the bone structures that are absent in mammals were much

Fig. 28-1. *Dimetrodon*, one of the mammal-like reptiles. This pelycosaur is characterized by a lizardlike appearance and the sail. The purpose of this sail has been a subject of much debate. One of the most reasonable explanations is that it was a crude mechanism for the regulation of body temperatures, a need of warm-blooded animals such as the mammals. (Photo by courtesy of the U.S. National Museum.)

reduced in size in the therapsids. Two bones connected the head with the backbone, the teeth were much like those of the mammals, and the penial opening had just about disappeared. Therapsids were meat-eaters, and their bone structure must have given them a considerable advantage over some of their prey, the more awkward of the reptiles. This advantage was soon lost to the larger dinosaurs, which the mammal-like reptiles were unable to kill. By the early Jurassic they were gone.

THE FIRST MAMMALS OF THE JURASSIC

The remains of the Mesozoic mammals are rare. Most of the known remains are little more than fragments of teeth, jaws, and other skull pieces. From such a sparse record it is hard to get a very good picture of what the mammals of the Jurassic and Cretaceous were like, but we know from the size of the teeth and jaws that they must have been very small animals, probably about the size of rats, and they may have resembled the modern rat or squirrel rather closely. It is not hard to understand why so little remains. As the dinosaurs radiated very rapidly in the Mesozoic, the mammal-like reptiles were destroyed, and when the mammals finally reached the scene they too were under the constant threat of destruction, for the various reptiles inhabited almost every environment in the world. During this period of trial the mammals apparently developed their brains rather than their bodies, and when the dinosaurs became extinct at the end of the Mesozoic, the mammals were ready to assume leadership and to radiate into the space left vacant by their adversaries.

Despite the scarcity of remains, four orders of mammals have been described from the Jurassic sedimentary rocks. One of these is the triconodonts. They possessed a long jaw with many teeth, differentiated as in modern mammals and showing a much greater specialization in this respect than the mammal-like reptiles. Three cusps in the molar teeth gave these animals their names. Another group that evolved at this time, the multituberculates, was the most probable forerunner of the herbivorous mammals. Their front teeth were a pair of large, elongated incisors specialized to assist them in clipping. The other teeth were arranged in two parallel rows. The last premolar was enlarged into an effective shearing blade.

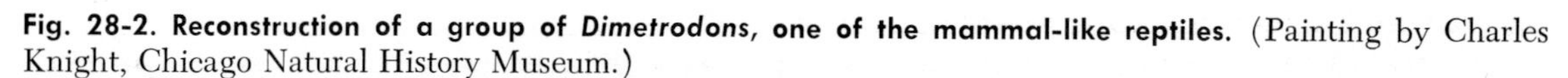

Fig. 28-2. Reconstruction of a group of *Dimetrodons*, one of the mammal-like reptiles. (Painting by Charles Knight, Chicago Natural History Museum.)

Fig. 28-3. Two mammal-like reptiles *(Cynognathus)* which were close to the actual ancestors of the mammals. These were flesh-eaters. (Painting by Charles Knight, Chicago Natural History Museum.)

They may have lived a life somewhat like that of modern rodents.

A third group of the Jurassic mammals, the pantotheres, is thought to be the forerunner of most of the higher mammals of the Cenozoic because the arrangement of the molars is exactly like that of the later mammals. A fourth group, the monotremes, has survived to be represented among the most primitive living mammals today by the duckbilled platypus and the spiny anteaters. The duckbill is adapted to burrowing in mud in search of soft animals for food. Because it lives on such soft material, the teeth are lost, and two hard pads replace them in the adult. The feet are also adapted to this environment as webbed paddles. Another unusual feature of these animals is that they, like the most primitive mammals, lay eggs, and their general structure bears a strong resemblance to that of the reptiles.

CRETACEOUS MAMMALS

The remains of Cretaceous mammals are also hard to find, but it has been established that the first of two of the largest groups of mammals made their first appearance in the Cretaceous. These were the marsupials and the placentals.

Marsupials

Most prominent of the marsupial characteristics are the short gestation period and the pouch in which the newly born animal is

Fig. 28-4. A therapsid from the Permian of South Africa restored under the direction of E. H. Colbert by J. C. Germann. Notice how the skull has many mammal-like characteristics and the legs are adapted to enable the animal to run rapidly. The typical reptiles had sprawling legs which made them awkward. (After J. C. Germann.)

Fig. 28-5. Duckbilled platypus. (American Museum of Natural History.)

placed, where it develops further. The opossum and the kangaroo are members of this group. The marsupials are more primitive than the placentals. They have smaller brains, more teeth, and other more subtle differences in bone structure, particularly in the skull, pelvis, and feet. Although marsupials may be thought of as second-class mammals they have undergone an adaptive radiation that enables them to live many different modes of life. Evidence of this is found among the living forms in Australia today, where various marsupials closely resemble mice, moles, wolves, kangaroos, woodchucks, squirrels, rabbits, and many others.

Placentals

This group, which evolved in the Cretaceous, includes most of the modern mammals of the world. Radiation of the placentals has been so extensive that they are classified in 28 different orders, which compose over 2500 genera and make up about 95 per cent of the mammals. Placentals are those mammals in which the young go through a long period of gestation before they are born at a rather advanced stage in their development. In some cases the young are quite active soon after birth. Their most important feature is the enlarged brain case of the skull, which is cov-

Fig. 28-6. A shrew. This animal is thought to be very similar to the first placentals which evolved in the Cretaceous. (American Museum of Natural History.)

ered by a solid bony plate. The most important feature, however, for the purposes of classification is their teeth. The teeth are so specialized in each group that almost the same classification of placentals would exist if nothing but the teeth remained as fossil evidence.

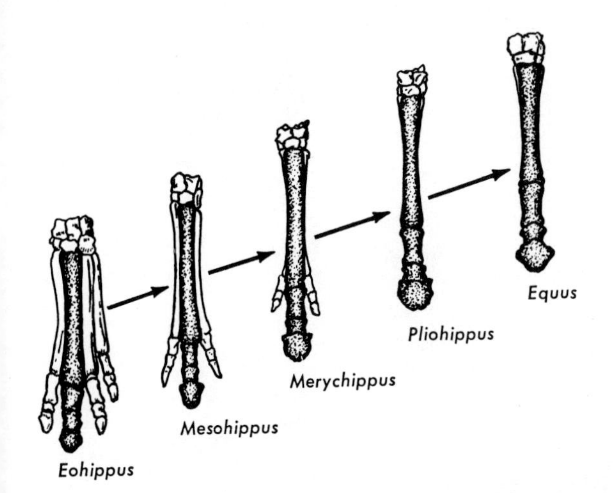

Fig. 28-7. Evolution of the foot of the horse. From left to right are the forelimbs of *Eohippus* from the Eocene Epoch, *Mesohippus* from the Oligocene Epoch, *Merychippus* from the Miocene Epoch, *Pliohippus* from the Pliocene Epoch, and *Equus*, the modern horse. (After G. G. Simpson, *Horses*, Oxford University Press.)

Origin of the placentals

The first placentals from which the more advanced mammals have evolved appeared in the Cretaceous. Reconstruction of skulls that have been found in the Cretaceous of Mongolia indicates that these first placentals were insectivores. Some placentals living today have a similar existence as, for example, shrews, moles, and hedgehogs. Of these, the shrews come closest to approximating the size and form of the first placentals.

Fig. 28-8. Evolution of the horse.

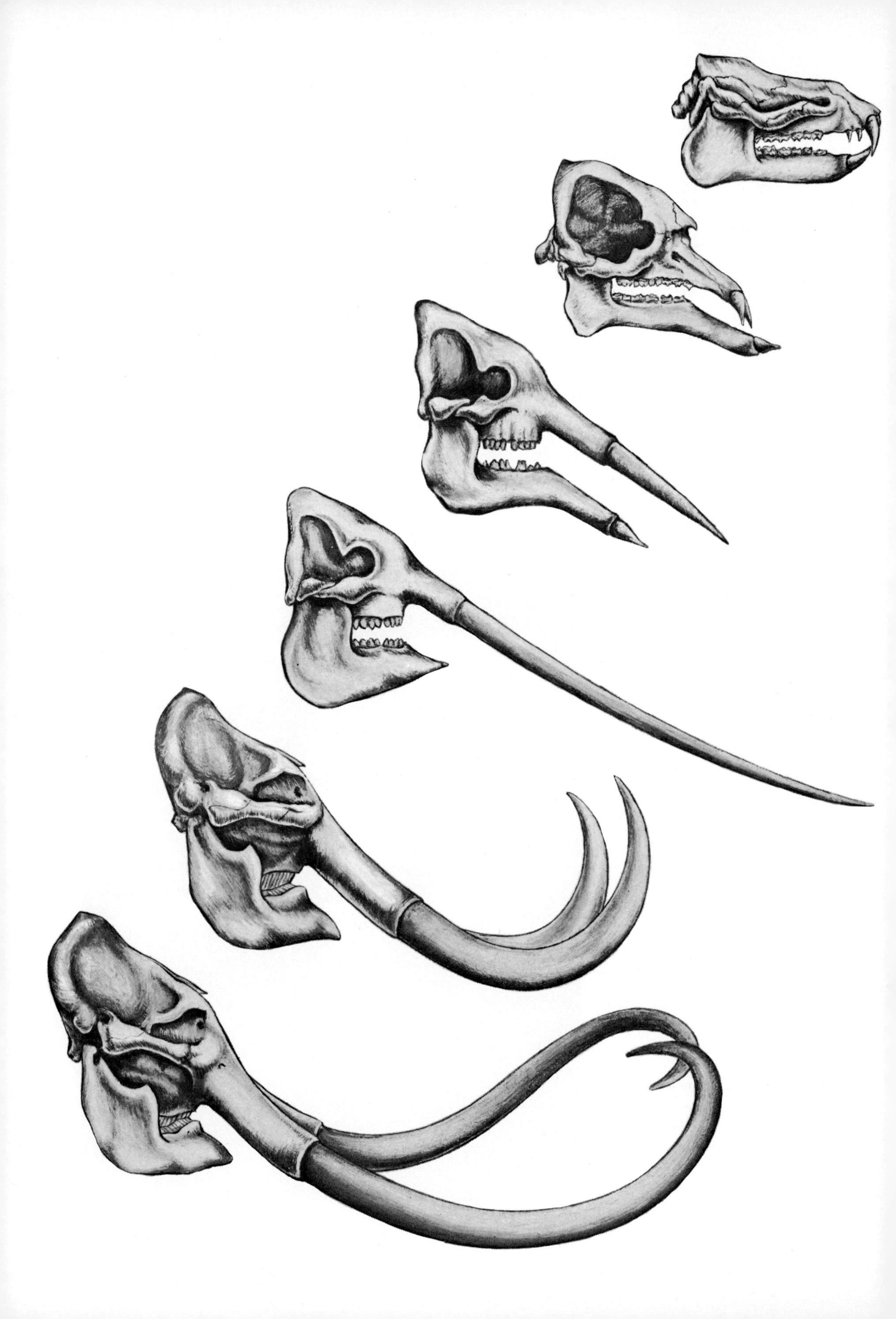

Variety in the placentals

Space does not permit coverage of the evolution and nature of all 28 of the orders of placentals. Much of this story is covered in works on vertebrate paleontology, and the great variety of living forms makes up the subject matter of parts of zoology. Of the 28 orders, 12 are extinct, and 16 are living. These include the following:

Shrews, moles, and hedgehogs.
Bats.
Flying lemurs.
Anteaters, tree sloths, ground sloths, and armadillos.
Pangolins.
Primates: lemurs, tarsiers, monkeys, apes, and men.
Rodents: squirrels, beavers, mice, rats, porcupines, and chinchillas.
Rabbits.
Porpoises and whales.
Carnivores: dogs, wolves, bears, raccoons, minks, otters, badgers, skunks, hyaenas, cats, sea lions, and seals.
Aardvarks.
Conies.
Elephants, mastodons, and mammoths.
Sea cows.
Horses, titanotheres, and rhinoceroses (odd-toed hoofed mammals).
Pigs, hippopotamuses, and camels, deer, giraffes, antelopes, goats, sheep, and cattle (even-toed hoofed mammals).

Some of the above animals are extinct forms of groups which are still represented.

THE PRIMATES

Of the 28 orders of placental mammals the primates are of greatest interest to man since he belongs to this group along with the lemurs, tarsiers, monkeys, and apes. It is the part of the story of evolution that deals with this order that has caused the greatest amount of controversy over the theory of evolution. If man had a unique body structure completely unlike that of any other animal, it is likely that the theory of evolution would have received little attention from others than scientists. However, the fact remains that the bone structure of man

Fig. 28-10. Evolution of elephants during the Pleistocene. (After Schindewolf).

Fig. 28-9. Evolution of the elephants (Proboscideans). From the top to bottom, *Moeritherium* from the Upper Eocene, *Phiomia* from the Lower Oligocene, *Cetrabelodon* from the Miocene, *Anancus* from the Pliocene, *Mammonteus*, the woolly mammoth, from the Pleistocene, and *Elephas*, the modern elephant. (After Abel, Andrews, and Romer.)

Fig. 28-11. The lemur. Lemurs probably evolved from a primitive insectivor like the modern tree shrew. The lemur, like man and the ape, is a primate. The anthropods evolved from lemuroid ancestors in the Eocene Epoch.

strikingly resembles that of other members of the primate group. Furthermore, there is enough evidence available now to demonstrate many stages in the gradual evolution of man from more primitive forms.

The fossil record of man is far more extensive than that of many other vertebrates, but it will probably never be as complete as we might wish. This is especially true of the early origin of the primates. Almost all of these primates lived in trees. This means that they lived in forested areas of the world, which are usually in temperate or tropical climates. The tropical terrestrial environment is one least favorable for the preservation of fossils because there is a rapid rate of decay of dead organisms. Burial by natural causes is too slow, and there are many scavengers present to destroy the animal's remains. The first primate probably appeared in the Cretaceous. These were much like the modern tree shrew. From this primitive insectivore there were two periods of radiation – one in the early part of the Paleocene Epoch when the lemurs and tarsiers branched off, and a second in the Eocene Epoch when the anthropoids, man, apes, and monkeys evolved from lemuroid ancestors.

Characteristics of primates

Many of the characteristics that distinguish the primates are thought to be associated with their life in the trees. Of the primates, only two, man and the baboons, have abandoned the trees to live on the ground. Five features are of particular importance among the primates:

1. A prehensile hand with an opposable thumb developed. This mechanism enables the primates to grasp tree limbs and branches, making it much easier for them to move about in the trees. The ability to grasp soon became important in their feeding habits and opened the way for many other advances, including the close inspection of objects and the ability to manipulate those objects with precision.
2. Primates developed the ability to move with agility and rapidity. This flexibility in body movements gives them another great advantage over other animals. This flexibility was necessary for climbing about in trees.
3. Sight is greatly improved in the primates. They have large eyes which at first were needed to detect food, and to assist movement in the trees. One of the unusual adaptations of the visual apparatus is stereoscopic vision, whereby the primates can see in three dimensions. To make this possible an advance in the structure of the nerves governing sight had to be effected. This structure has to be sensitive enough to bring about, within the brain, a superposition of the images seen in each eye. Another development is the highly developed area in the center of the retina, which makes it possible to see small details. Most of the eye is incapable of such great resolution.
4. Teeth in the primates are not very specialized. They are suited for the om-

nivorous diet. Their structure and arrangement is such that the group has a short jaw and consequently a short face.

5. Their brains are the largest developed among the mammals. This brain power probably evolved in part because of the natural selection of those forms that were best suited for life in the trees. Such a life requires agility, muscular co-ordination, good eyesight, and other characters that depend in part on the capabilities of the brain. Such great advantages came to those groups with superior brain power that much pressure was exerted toward their continued evolution to superior forms.

Lemurs

The higher primates, the anthropoids, evolved from an earlier primate, which closely resembled the modern lemurs. These are small arboreal animals with a bushy hair covering, a long tail, moderately long limbs, and a shortened face with a muzzle somewhat resembling that of a fox. The name "lemur" was applied by the Romans to the souls of the dead which haunted the night. Similarly, lemurs have nocturnal habits.

These seem to represent a form intermediate between lemurs and the monkeys. The *tarsius* is definitely more advanced than the lemur in that its vision is stereoscopic, its eyes are rotated forward rather than to the sides, the foxlike muzzle is gone, and the brain is larger. There is not enough fossil evidence to establish clearly the relationship between the lemurs, tarsiers, and monkeys. It is most probable that the Anthropoidea evolved from the lemurs to an ancestral form of tarsiers and then branched into manlike creatures.

ANTHROPOIDEA

The more advanced primates include monkeys, apes, and man. These three belong to a single suborder because they are structurally similar. That man evolved from apes or monkeys is a common misconception. The similarities between the members of this group do not mean that one evolved from the other, but simply that they had a common ancestry if traced far enough back. We may be sure that man did not evolve from any living types of apes or monkeys, for each represents a separate branch from a common stock.

Monkeys

The first monkeys appeared in the Oligocene Epoch. It is most probable that they evolved from a lemurlike animal. Two distinctly different groups of monkeys are found in South America and in Africa, Asia, and Europe. They are known respectively as the New World and Old World monkeys. Both developed about the same time and have had about the same geographic distribution since the Oligocene. Among the features that distinguish them as members of the anthropoids are their brains, eyes, hands, and of course the general framework of the skeleton. The face of the monkey is short and flattened. Both eyes are directed forward, and the fields of vision overlap considerably, giving them good stereo vision. Both their hands and feet are prehensile; that is, they can be used for grasping and facilitate swinging from tree branches. The monkey brain is larger than that of the lemur. This is particularly true of the upper part of the cortex. Thus the monkey has more brains than its ancestors and undoubtedly can use them more effectively.

Apes

Modern apes include the orangutan of Sumatra and Borneo, the gorilla and chimpanzee of central Africa, and the gibbon of southeastern Asia. Judging from the distribution of known fossil remains, apes have always inhabited the warmer parts of Africa and Asia since the first of them appeared in the Oligocene Epoch. Either they evolved from some line of the Old World monkeys, or there was a common ancestor. Apes have never been particularly abundant, and relatively few fossil remains of them are found. They must have been much more highly varied and probably more numerous during the Miocene Epoch than during any other time. It was at that time that the immediate ancestors of the modern apes arose.

One of the most interesting of the early Miocene apes is Proconsul, one of the less specialized apes of that time. These early forms probably were the forerunners of all the modern apes, with the exception of the gibbons. Unlike the modern apes, these were comparatively lightweight, agile, and not nearly so specialized as the orangutan, chimpanzee, or gorilla.

Several of the trends that have characterized evolution of the apes are increase in size, development of the brain, change in structure of the teeth, and brachiating. Brachiating is the feat of swinging from branch to branch. This became necessary for an animal that was evolving to larger sizes. With increased size the apes found it increasingly difficult to walk along tree limbs and thus developed the ability to swing from one part of the tree to another. The gibbons are the most skilled brachiators of all the primates. They are relatively small and have long arms that facilitate their acrobatic jumps and swings through the tree tops. Orangutans and chimpanzees are somewhat less talented along this line, and the gorillas have given it up altogether. Undoubtedly the size of the gorillas has been an important reason for their abandonment of the trees as a way of life. Some of them climb trees, but none live there. They are the largest of the apes, and some are the largest of the primates. They are larger than man and much stronger than the strongest men. Even so, the modern gorillas were surpassed in size by a giant gorilla that lived in the early Pleistocene.

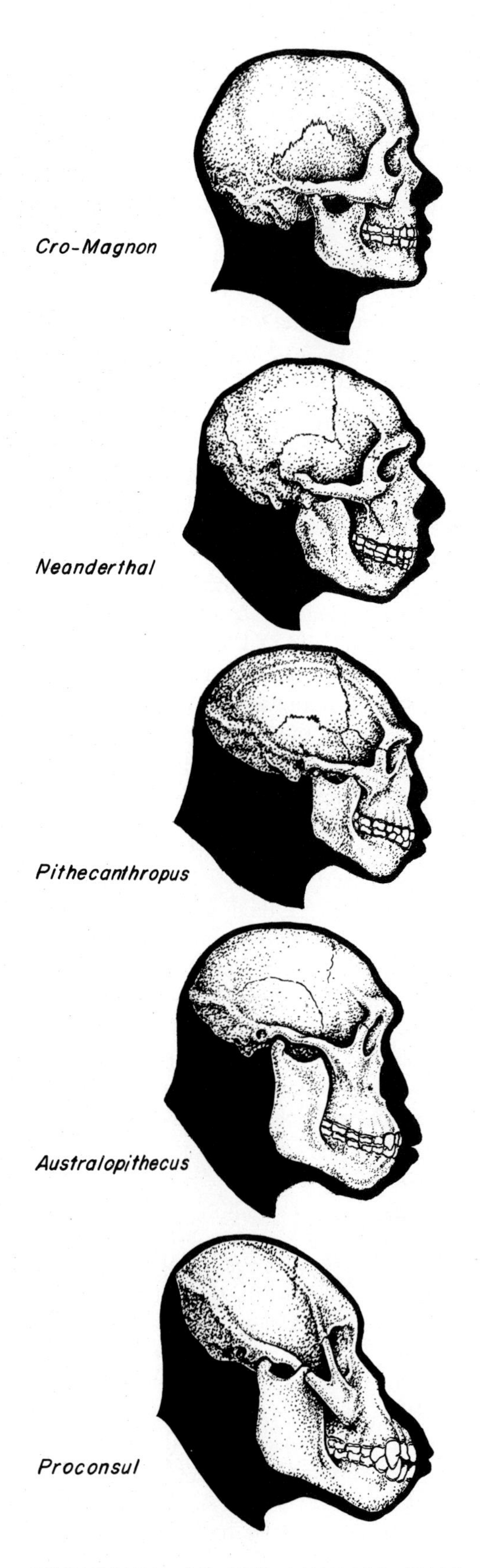

Fig. 28-12. Apes, manlike apes, and man. *Proconsul* was one of the less specialized apes of the Miocene Epoch. *Australopithecus,* a man-like ape, has been found in Pleistocene cave deposits of South Africa. *Pithecanthropus* is most frequently accepted as the first fossil man. Neanderthal man is the most primitive member of the genus, *Homo*. Cro-Magnon man was so similar to modern man that he would easily be mistaken for modern man.

Man-apes: *Australopithecus*

Fragments of the skulls, teeth, and skeletons of a peculiar manlike ape have been found in Pleistocene cave deposits of South Africa. The remains are those of an animal that falls in an intermediate position between the structures typical of men and those associated with apes. The skull is comparable to that of modern apes. The animals had a brain case that is much smaller than that of men and about the same size as that of an ape, but the teeth are much more like those of men than apes. The head was set up on the shoulders instead of thrust forward as in apes, and the structure of the pelvis indicates that these creatures were able to walk in an upright position. Gibbons walk on their hind legs, holding their arms up for balance, but all other modern apes normally walk on all fours. Thus this primate possessed a peculiar mixture of manlike and apelike characteristics.

We might immediately conclude that this is a definite intermediate form showing the connection between man and apes, but this appears improbable on account of the age of the remains. They are much too recent to represent an early man or an early ape. Instead they must be a separate line that evolved independently of apes or men. However, it is probable that their forerunners were ancestors of both apes and men.

Ape-men: *Pithecanthropus*

Search for the oldest men, the "connecting links," continues and undoubtedly will continue as long as our civilization lasts. Each new discovery tends to clarify certain anatomical relations among the fossil men already known to us. There are already so many of these fossil remains of animals that possessed varying degrees of manlike characteristics that the question of which we shall call true men is strictly a matter of definition. Generally the australopithecines are excluded as men although it is likely that their ancestors back in the Miocene or Pliocene were the stock from which *Homo sapiens* evolved.

Fragments of skulls, teeth, jaws, and other bones found in Java and near Peking, China, are most commonly accepted as remains of the first fossil men. Java men are known as *Pithecanthropus,* and, although those found near

Fig. 28-13. Reconstructions of prehistoric man. From left to right, *Pithecanthropus,* Neanderthal, and Cro-Magnon man. (Photo by courtesy of the American Museum of Natural History).

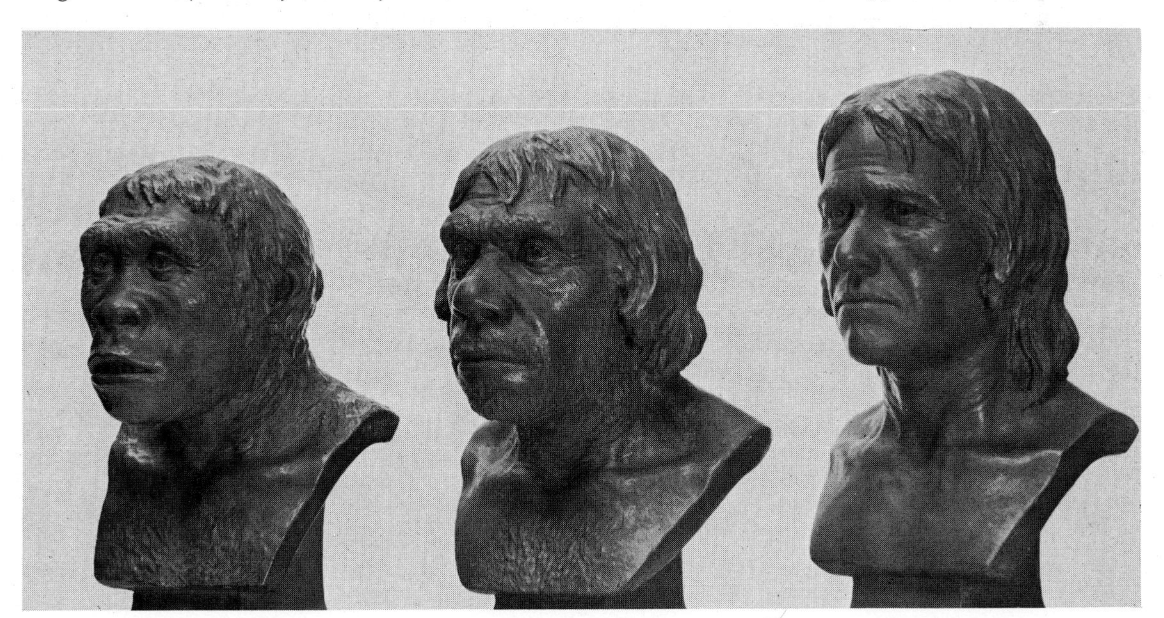

Peking are given another name, *Sinanthropus,* they were probably no more different from one another than the modern races are from one another. Other fossils of these men have been found in Africa and in other parts of Asia, although none have been turned up in the New World. These men resembled apes in some features but were much more manlike than *Australopithecus.* Their brain case was large enough to hold a brain of 800 to 1300 cubic centimeters. In contrast, modern men have brains on the order of 1200 to 2000 cubic centimeters in size. Like modern man, they walked upright, and their teeth were very similar, although they protruded in front. The protruding teeth, retreating chins, and heavy ridges above the eyes gave them a distinct apelike appearance.

Neanderthal men

The most primitive member of the genus *Homo* is the Neanderthal man. Neanderthal remains are quite abundant in Europe, Asia, and Africa. There are variations in the various skeletal remains, but none that cannot be attributed to individual and racial differences. These men lived during the third of the four periods of glacier advance. They were sufficiently developed to make tools, draw, and bury their dead. We even find offerings or sacrifices in the graves of some of these people, suggesting that they had a religion.

They were short, stocky, and powerful people. They undoubtedly depended on their strength and superior mental abilities to trap and kill their prey. They differed in appearance from modern man primarily in that they had a heavy brow ridge and a large head. The forehead retreated more than that of most modern men, but the capacity of the brain case was about equal to that of modern man.

Cro-Magnon men

The Neanderthal man was of the Old Stone Age. One of the last of the groups whose culture was based on chipping of flint for weapons and tools was Cro-Magnon men. These were truly modern men and belong to the species, *Homo sapiens,* of which we are members. They resemble modern man in all respects. The forehead was high and wide, and the backbone formed an elongate S, giving the man an upright posture; he was tall and had a large brain.

These men lived in caves during the last stages of the Pleistocene glaciation. Their

Fig. 28-14. Cave men of the Neanderthal race. (Photo by courtesy of the American Museum of Natural History).

Fig. 28-15. Cro-Magnon artist painting in the cave of Font de Gaume. (Photo by courtesy of the American Museum of Natural History).

drawings of the animals around them in the last ice age are now famous for their accuracy and beauty. They were skillful tool makers and highly intelligent in other ways as well.

We cannot be sure yet if the various Pleistocene men were of different species or if they all belonged to the same species. It seems very likely that they were all of a single species that split up into a number of widely separated populations. Within each of these populations there may have been some variants that retained more of the archaic characteristics than others. In addition, the norms of different populations evolved in slightly different ways through the Pleistocene. But during this time natural selection within the groups tended to eliminate the archaic variants and produce types more nearly characteristic of modern man.

The alternative hypothesis is that Neanderthal man was a different species from that of early *Homo sapiens*. When the two came into direct competition the modern man won out and eliminated his adversary.

INDEX

Index

B

C

D

E

F

G

H

I

J

K

L

M

N

O

P

S

T

U

V

STUDY SET OF GEOLOGIC MAPS

STUDY SET OF GEOLOGIC MAPS

This set of maps includes portions of the following maps, listed in the order of their appearance:

- Geologic map of the Middletown Quadrangle, Connecticut
- Geologic map of the Candelaria Mining District, Nevada
- Geologic map of the Lexington Quadrangle, Virginia
- Geologic map and structure sections of the Lynchburg Quadrangle, Virginia
- Geologic map of the White Pine District, Nevada

These maps are included as a supplement to the text material and as examples of geologic maps showing a wide variety of geologic structures and rock types. These maps will prove useful both in laboratory study of geologic maps, and as a basis for independent study of map interpretation. Refer to the map symbols on the back inside cover.

Eight pages of additional geologic and topographic maps will be found in *Basic Concepts of Physical Geology*.

Geologic Map of the Middletown Quadrangle, Connecticut

Geology by Elroy P. Lehmann
Courtesy of the Geological and Natural History Survey of Connecticut
John B. Lucke, Director

scale 1 / 24,000
contour interval 10 feet
abbreviations: (note that the youngest unit is at the top of this stratigraphic column)

TRp	Triassic	arkose	(yellow)
TRha	Triassic	basalt	(pink)
TRb	Triassic	shale and mudstone	(blue)
TRho	Triassic	basalt	(green)
TRS	Triassic	shale and mudstone	(purple)
TRt	Triassic	basalt	(orange)
TRn	Triassic	arkose	(brown)

Geologic Map of the Candelaria Mining District, Nevada

Geology by Stanford Geological Survey
Nevada Bureau of Mines Bulletin 56, plate 1
Courtesy of Vernon E. Scheid, Director

scale 400 feet to the inch
contour interval 20 feet
abbreviations:

Qt	Quaternary	talus material
Qal	Quaternary	alluvium
Qb	Quaternary	olivine basalt
Qmb	Quaternary	andesitic mudflow breccia
Tv 20	Tertiary	basalt, with underlying gravel
Tv 19-Tv 11		Tertiary dacitic tuffs and welded tuffs
Tv 10	Tertiary	olivine basalt
Tv 9	Tertiary	rhyolitic tuff
Tv 8	Tertiary	basalt
Tv 7	Tertiary	dacitic and rhyolitic tuffs
Tv 6	Tertiary	rhyolite flow
Tv 5	Tertiary	welded tuff
Tv 4-Tv 1		Tertiary tuffs
Red lines		Upper Jurassic veins of quartz
dol & alt	Jurassic	altered rocks, dolomite
alt-sp	Jurassic	altered serpentine
ai	Jurassic	dike rocks and quartz monzonite porphyry
bi	Jurassic	basic dike rocks, diabase
sp, ms	Jurassic	serpentine (sp) with metasedimentary inclusions (ms)
Trc	Triassic	Candelaria formation (chiefly shale)
Trg	Triassic	thin grit bed
Pd	Permian	Diablo formation (chiefly sandstone)
Op	Ordovician	Palmetto formation (phyllite and shale)

Geologic Map of the Lexington Quadrangle, Virginia

Geology by Kenneth F. Bick and R. O. Bloomer
Courtesy of Virginia Division of Mineral Resources
James L. Calver, Commissioner

scale 1 / 62,500
contour interval 20 feet
abbreviations:

Omb	Ordovician	Martinsburg shale
Oe	Ordovician	Edinburg formation
Ol	Ordovician	Lincolnshire limestone
On	Ordovician	New Market limestone
Ob	Ordovician	Beekmantown dolomite
Och	Ordovician	Chepultepec limestone
Єco	Cambrian	Conococheague limestone
Єe	Cambrian	Elbrook formation
Єr	Cambrian	Rome formation
Єs	Cambrian	Shady dolomite
Єer	Cambrian	Erwin quartzite
Єh	Cambrian	Hampton formation
ЄpЄu	Cambrian	Unicoi formation
ЄpЄs	Cambrian	Swift Run formation
pЄp	Precambrian	Pedlar formation

Geologic Map and Structure Sections of the Lynchburg Quadrangle, Virginia

Geology by William R. Brown
Courtesy of the Virginia Division of Mineral Resources, James L. Calver, Commissioner

scale 1/62,500
contour interval 20 feet
abbreviations:

Qal	Quaternary	alluvium
Td	Triassic	diabase (basalt)
sg	Lower Paleozoic	Slippery Creek greenstone
mm	Lower Paleozoic	Mount Athos formation (quartzite, mica schist)
ps	Lower Paleozoic	Pelier schist
am	Lower Paleozoic	Arch marble
Js	Lower Paleozoic	Joshua schist
cq, cm, cp	Lower Paleozoic	Candler formation (phyllite, schist, and quartzite)
g	Lower Paleozoic	greenstone
cg	Precambrian	Catoctin greenstone
ub	Precambrian	ultrabasics
lyg, hg	Precambrian	Lynchburg formation (gneiss, schist, and amphibolite)
p	Precambrian	Pedlar formation (granodiorite)
mg	Precambrian	Marshall gneiss
rm	Precambrian	Reusens migmatite

Geologic Map of the White Pine District, White Pine County, Nevada

Geology by F. L. Humphrey
Nevada Bureau of Mines Bulletin 57, plate 1
Courtesy of Vernon E. Scheid, Director

scale 4000 feet to the inch
contour interval 40 feet
abbreviations:

Qal	Quaternary	alluvium
Tpbf	Tertiary	Belmont fanglomerate
Pe	Pennsylvanian	Ely limestone
Mj	Mississippian	Joana limestone
Mp	Mississippian	Pilot shale
Dn	Devonian	Nevada limestone
Sim	Silurian	Lone Mountain dolomite
Ohc	Ordovician	Hanson Creek dolomite
Oe	Ordovician	Eureka quartzite
Opl	Ordovician	
Opdl	Ordovician	
Opcl	Ordovician	Pogonip formation (limestone)
Opsl	Ordovician	
Cgd	Cambrian	Goodwin formation (limestone)
Єgl	Cambrian	
Єd	Cambrian	Dunderburg shale
Єslu	Cambrian	
Єssu	Cambrian	Secret Canyon shale
Єsll	Cambrian	
Єssl	Cambrian	
Єg	Cambrian	Geddes limestone
Tg	Tertiary	granodiorite intrusive
Tqm	Tertiary	quartz monzonite intrusive

Savage Hill
HARTFORD
MIDDLESEX
NEW HAVEN AND HARTFORD
Northwest Cem
West Cromwell Sch
MATTABESSET
Little River
Brook
Westfield Falls
Westfield
Old East Cem
Miner Cem
Old Westfield Cem
Fall Hill
Sawmill
West Swamp
Highland Pond
Old South Hill Cem
M I D D L E

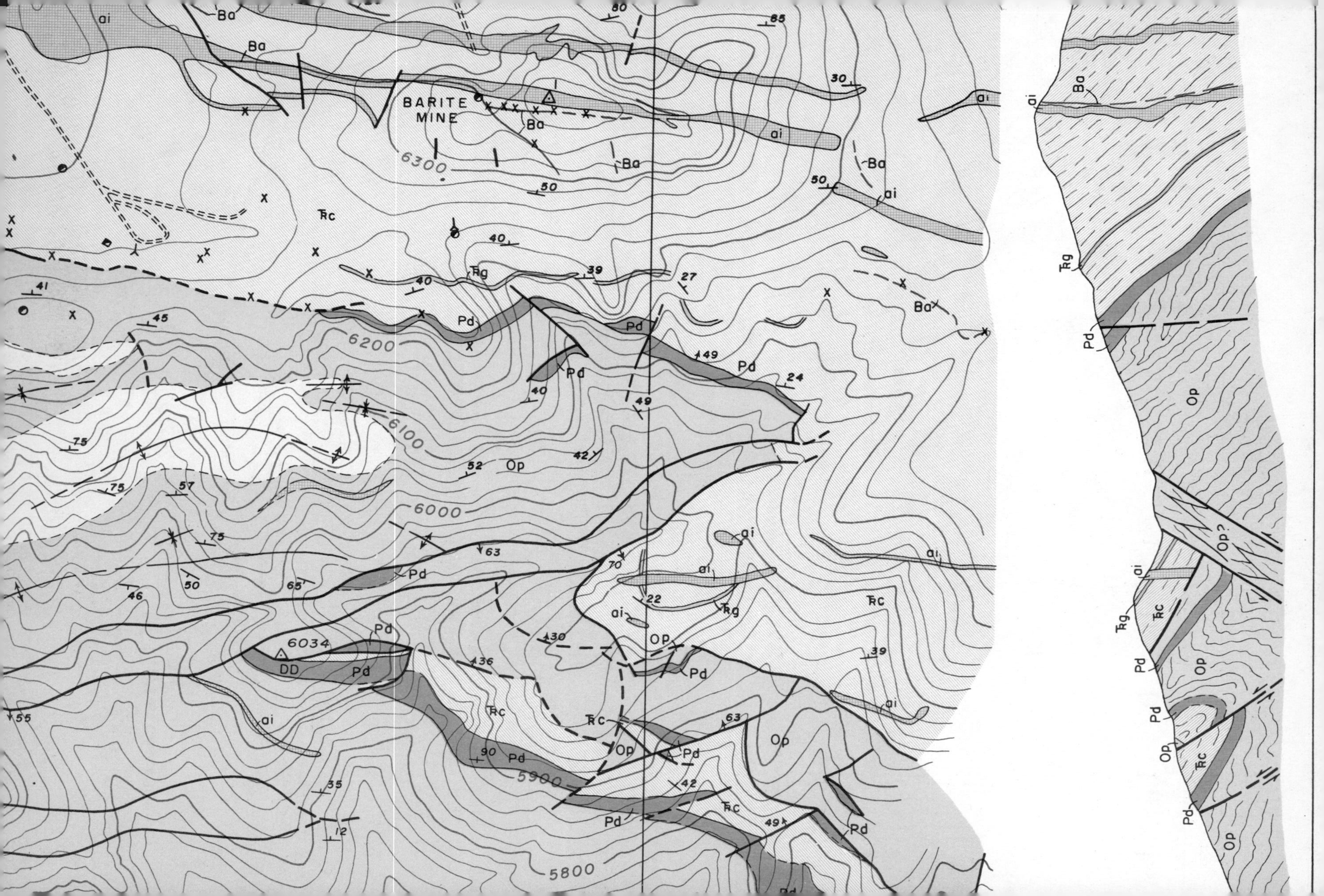

BARITE MINE
DD
6034
5800
5900
6000
6100
6200
6300
Pd
Op
TRc
TRg
ai
Ba
Op?

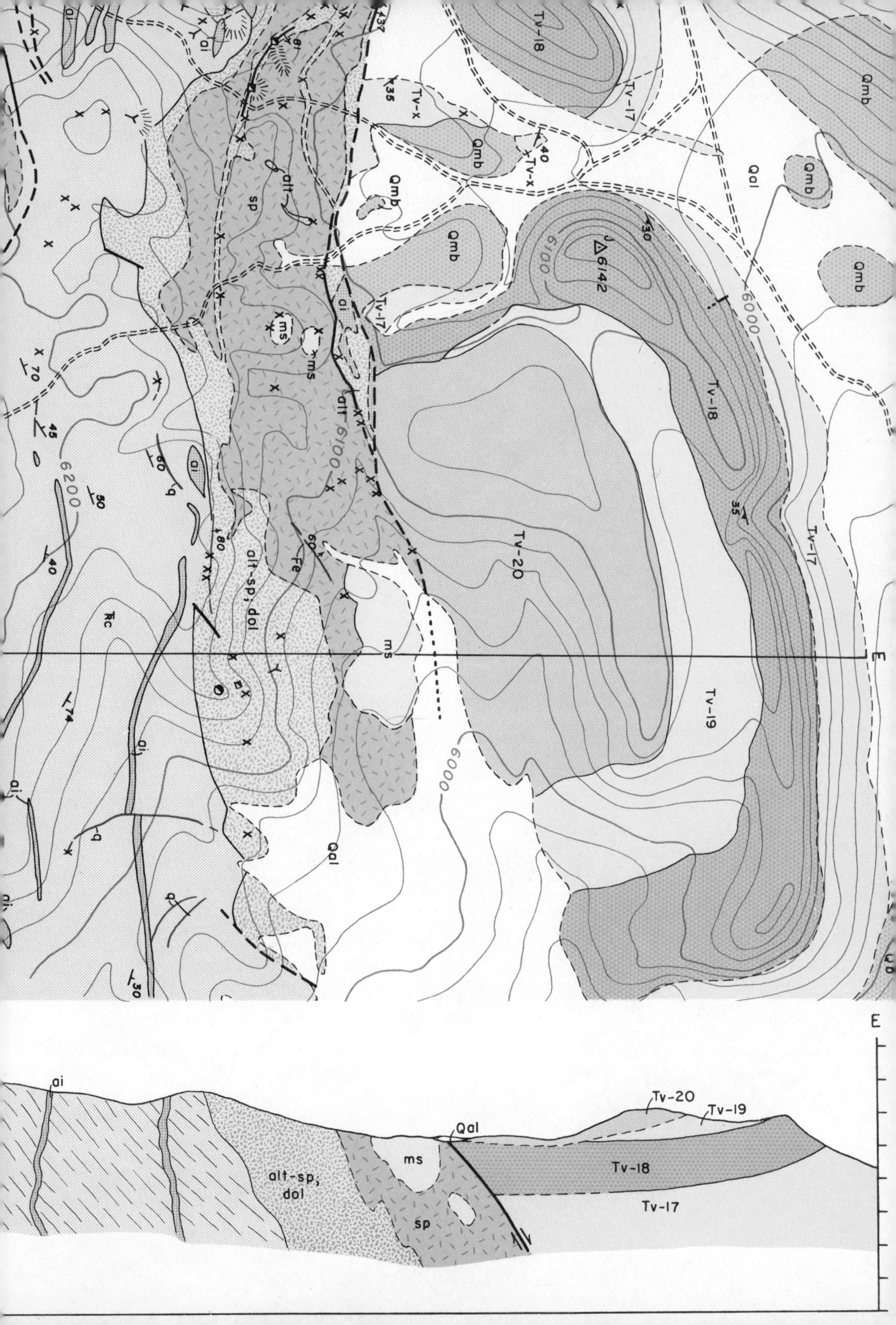

Tv-18
Tv-17
Tv-x
Qmb
Qal
6142
6100
6000
6200
sp
alt
ms
ai
Fe
alt-sp, dol
Tv-20
Tv-19
E
ai
alt-sp;
dol
ms
sp
Qal
Tv-20
Tv-19
Tv-18
Tv-17
E

PULASKI FAULT
SOUTH RIVER FAULT
MIDVALE FAULT
East Lexington
Polecat Hollow
Grassy Ridge
Lee Creek
Mill Run
Dry Branch
Poorhouse Mtn
TIMBER RIDGE
Timber Ridge Ch
Paxton Hill
Marl Creek
Riverside
Cypress Falls
Deckers Hill
Cornwall
Sheep Creek
Crossroads Store
Henry Hill
Prospect Hills
Greens Store
Round Hill
Chalk Mine Run
McClure Peak
Whites Peak
Chestnut Sag
Coates Mtn
Whites Gap
ROCKBRIDGE CO
AMHERST CO
BLUE RIDGE
SOUTH MOUNTAIN
NORFOLK AND WESTERN
South River
Ob
Och
Oe
Omb
Ol
Oeb
On
Ꞓe
Ꞓco
Ꞓr
Ꞓs
Ꞓer
Ꞓh
Ꞓhs
ꞒpꞒu
pꞒp
D/U

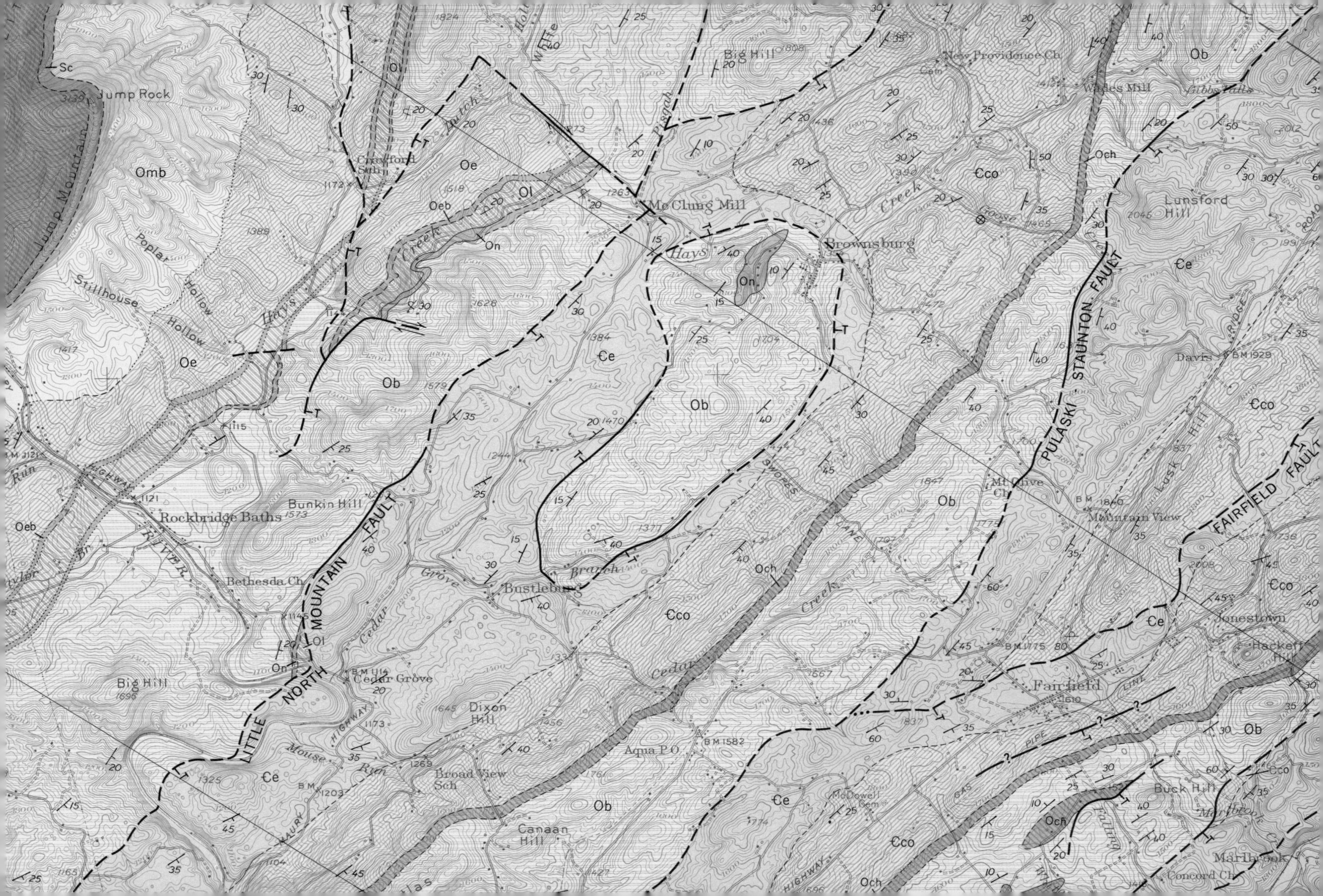

LITTLE NORTH MOUNTAIN FAULT
PULASKI - STAUNTON FAULT
FAIRFIELD FAULT
Jump Mountain
Jump Rock
Stillhouse Hollow
Poplar Hollow
Crawford Sch
McClung Mill
Brownsburg
Big Hill
New Providence Ch
Wades Mill
Gibbs Falls
Lunsford Hill
Davis
Rockbridge Baths
Bunkin Hill
Bethesda Ch
Bustleburg
Cedar Grove
Dixon Hill
Broad View Sch
Canaan Hill
Aqua P O
Mt Olive Ch
Mountain View
Jonestown
Hackett Hill
Fairfield
McDowell Cem
Buck Hill
Marlbrook
Concord Ch
Hays Creek
Cedar Creek
Mouse Run
Pisgah
Goose Creek
Grove Branch
Falling
RIVER
HIGHWAY
Lusk Hill
Sc
Omb
Oe
Oeb
On
Ol
Ob
Ce
Cco
Och

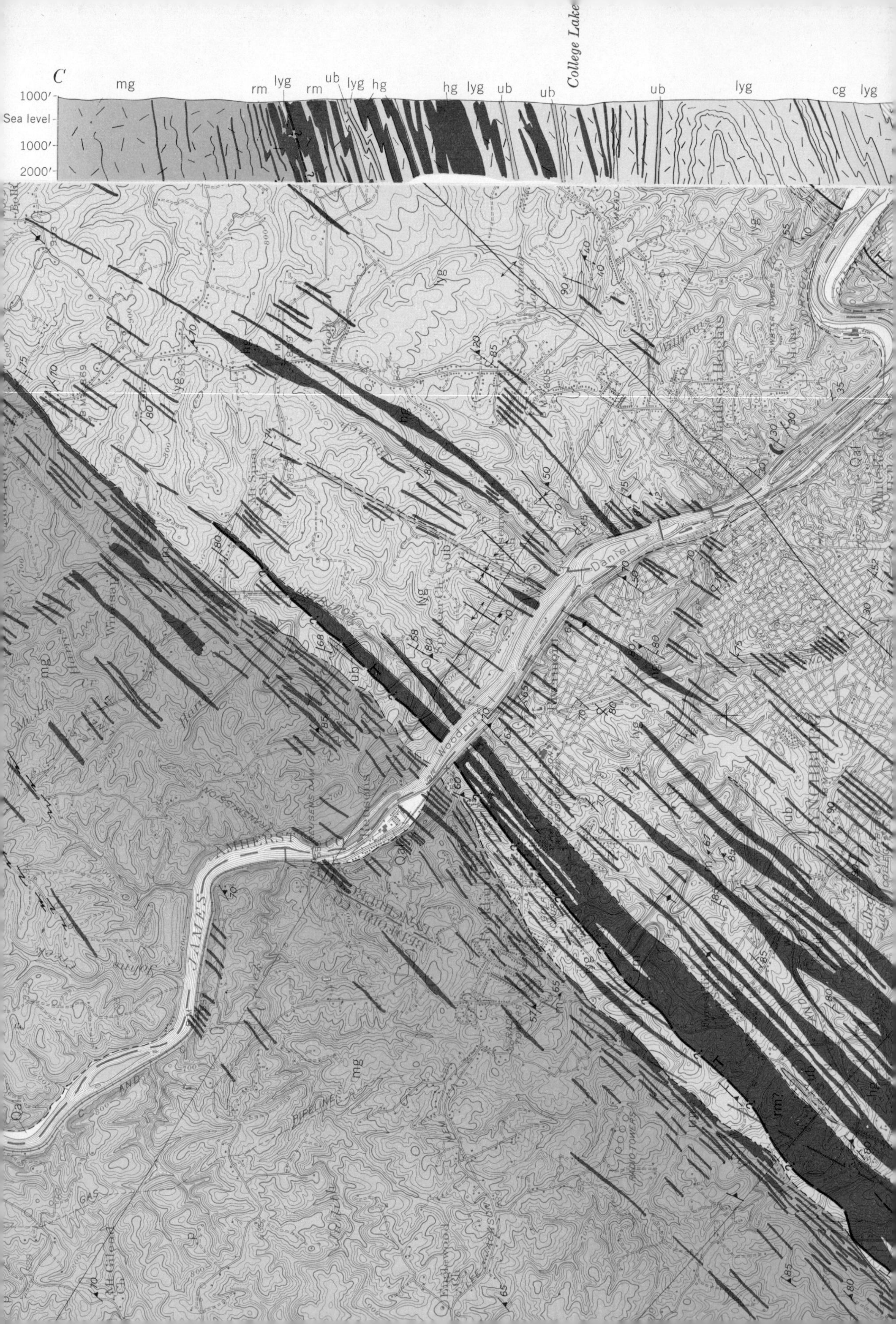
C
1000′
Sea level
1000′
2000′
mg
rm
lyg
rm
ub
lyg
hg
hg
lyg
ub
ub
College Lake
ub
lyg
cg
lyg
hg
lyg
mg
ub
Daniel
Woodruff
AMHERST
JAMES
PIPELINE
GAS
Qal
mg
RADIO TOWERS
rm?
hg
ub

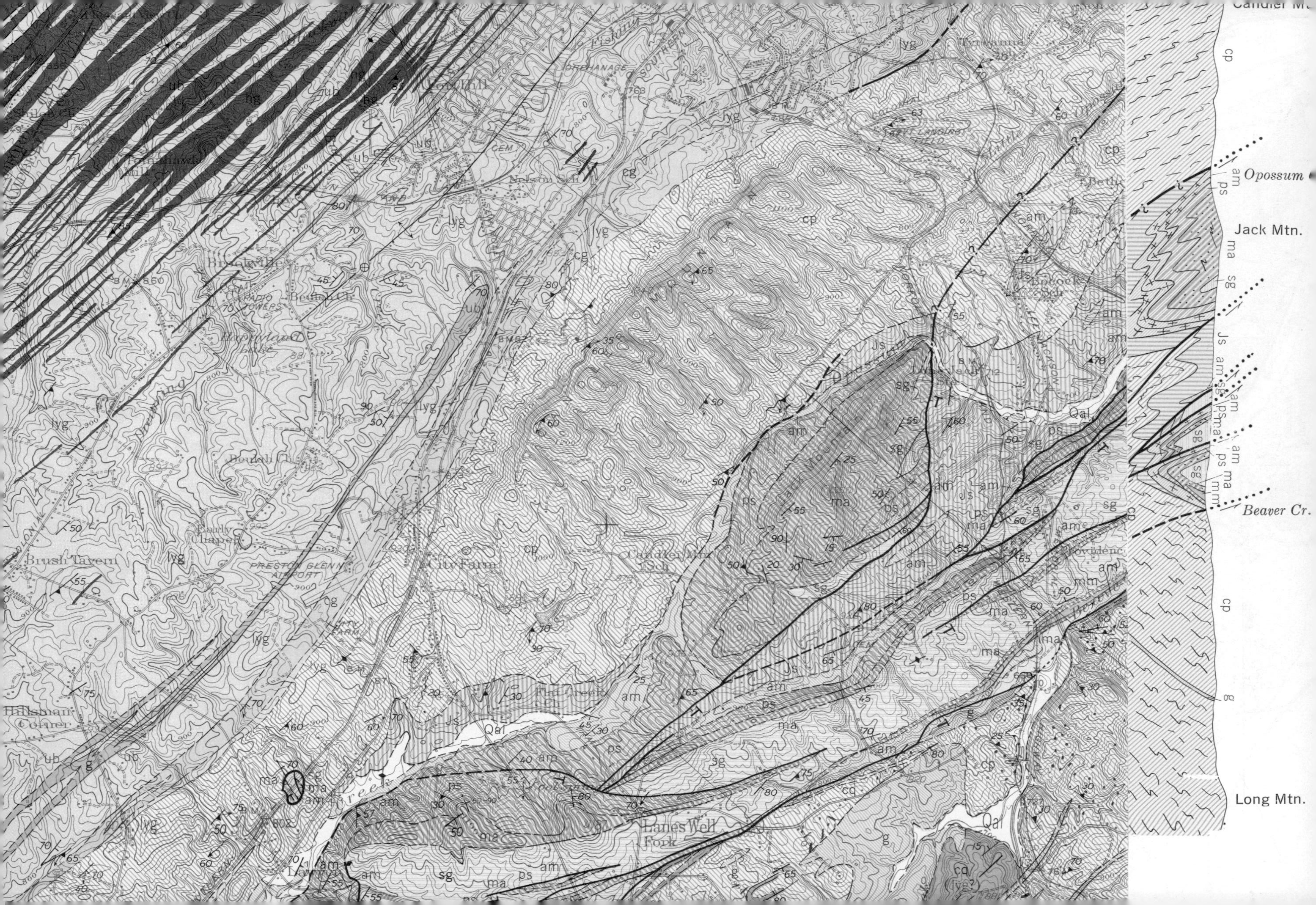
Opossum
Jack Mtn.
Beaver Cr.
Long Mtn.
Brush Tavern
Lanes Well Fork

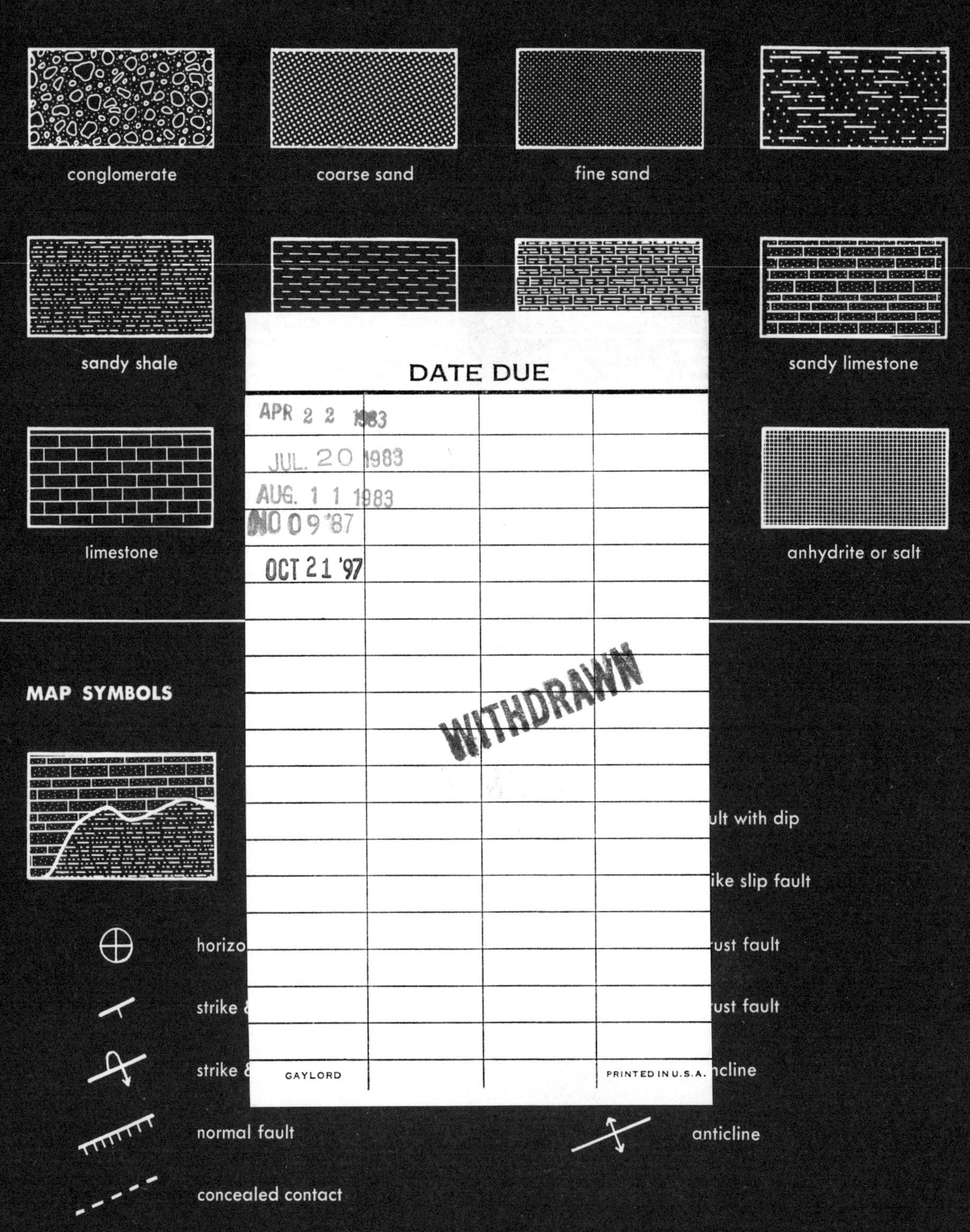
SEDIMENTARY ROCKS
conglomerate
coarse sand
fine sand
sandy shale
sandy limestone
limestone
anhydrite or salt
DATE DUE
APR 22 1983
JUL. 20 1983
AUG. 11 1983
NO 09 '87
OCT 21 '97
WITHDRAWN
GAYLORD
PRINTED IN U.S.A.
MAP SYMBOLS
ult with dip
ike slip fault
horizo
ust fault
strike
ust fault
strike
ncline
normal fault
anticline
concealed contact